Open the door to the fascinating world of physics

Physics, the most fundamental of all natural sciences, will reveal to you the basic principles of the Universe. And while physics can seem challenging, its true beauty lies in the sheer simplicity of fundamental physical theories—theories and concepts that can alter and expand your view of the world around you. Other courses that follow will use the same principles, so it is important that you understand and are able to apply the various concepts and theories discussed in the text. **Physics for Scientists and Engineers, Sixth Edition** is your guide to this fascinating science.

THOMSON
BROOKS/COLE

Your quick start for studying smart

Achieve success in your physics course by making the most of what **Physics for Scientists and Engineers, Sixth Edition** has to offer you. From a host of in-text features to a range of Web resources, you'll have everything you need to understand the natural forces and principles of physics:

▶ **Dynamic built-in study aids.** Throughout every chapter the authors have built in a wide range of examples, exercises, and illustrations that will help you understand and appreciate the laws of physics. *See pages 2 and 3 for more information.*

▶ **A powerful Web-based learning system.** The text is fully integrated with **PhysicsNow**, an interactive learning system that tailors  itself to your needs in the course. It's like having a personal tutor available whenever you need it! *See pages 4–7 to explore* **PhysicsNow**.

Your *Quick Start for Studying Smart* begins with this special tour through the book. On the following pages you'll discover how **Physics for Scientists and Engineers, Sixth Edition** and **PhysicsNow** not only enhance your experience in this course, but help you to succeed!

Quick Start for Studying Smart!

1

Everything you need to succeed in your course is available to you in **Physics for Scientists and Engineers, Sixth Edition.** Authors Serway and Jewett have filled their text with learning tools and study aids that will clarify concepts and help you build a solid base of knowledge. The end result: confidence in the classroom, in your study sessions, and in your exams.

THE RIGHT APPROACH

Start out right! Early on in the text the authors outline a general problem-solving strategy that will enable you to increase your accuracy in solving problems, enhance your understanding of physical concepts, eliminate initial worry or lack of direction in approaching a problem, and organize your work. The problem-solving strategy is integrated into the *Coached Problems* found on **PhysicsNow** to reinforce this key skill. (See pages 4–7 for more information about the **PhysicsNow** Web-based and student-centered learning system.)

PROBLEM-SOLVING HINTS

Problem-Solving Hints help you approach homework assignments with greater confidence. General strategies and suggestions are included for solving the types of problems featured in the worked examples, end-of-chapter problems, and **PhysicsNow**. This feature helps you identify the essential steps in solving problems and increases your skills as a problem solver.

WORKED EXAMPLES

Reinforce your understanding of essential problem-solving techniques using a large number of realistic *Worked Examples*. In many cases, these examples serve as models for solving the end-of-chapter problems. Numerous *Worked Examples* include specific references to the general problem-solving strategy to illustrate the underlying concepts and methodology used in arriving at a correct solution. This will help you understand the logic behind the solution and the advantage of using a particular approach to solve the problem. **PhysicsNow** also features a number of worked examples to further enhance your understanding of problem solving and to give you even more practice solving problems.

GENERAL PROBLEM-SOLVING STRATEGY

Conceptualize

- The first thing to do when approaching a problem is to *think about* and *understand* the situation. Study carefully any diagrams, graphs, tables, or photographs that accompany the problem. Imagine a movie, running in your mind, of what happens in the problem.
- If a diagram is not provided, you should almost always make a quick drawing of the situation. Indicate any known values, perhaps in a table or directly on your sketch.
- Now focus on what algebraic or numerical information is given in the problem. Carefully read the problem statement, looking for key phrases such as "starts from at rest" ($v_i = 0$), "stops" ($v_f = 0$), or "freely falls" ($a_y = -g = -9.80 \text{ m/s}^2$).
- Now focus on the expected result of solving the problem. Exactly what is the question asking? Will the final result be numerical or algebraic? Do you know what units to expect?
- Don't forget to incorporate information from your own experiences and common sense. What should a reasonable answer look like? You wouldn't expect to calculate the speed of an automobile to be

Analyze

- Now you must analyze the problem and strive for a mathematical solution. Because you have already categorized the problem, it should not be too difficult to select relevant equations that apply to the type of situation in the problem. For example, if the problem involves a particle moving under constant acceleration, Equations 2.9 to 2.13 are relevant.
- Use algebra (and calculus, if necessary) to solve symbolically for the unknown variable in terms of what is given. Substitute in the appropriate numbers, calculate the result, and round it to the proper number of significant figures.

Finalize

- This is the most important part. Examine your numerical answer. Does it have the correct units? Does it meet your expectations from your conceptualization of the problem? What about the algebraic form of the result — before you substituted numerical values? Does it make sense? Examine the variables in the problem to see whether the answer would change in a physically meaningful way if they were drastically increased or decreased or even became zero. Looking at limiting cases to see whether they yield expected values is a very useful way to make sure that you are obtaining reasonable results.

Think about how this problem compares with others you have done. How was it similar? In what critical ways did it differ? Why was this problem assigned? You should have learned something by doing it. Can you figure out what? If it is a new category of problem, be sure you understand it so that you can use it as a model for solving future problems in the same category.

When solving complex problems, you may need to identify a series of sub-problems and apply the problem-solv-

---

PROBLEM-SOLVING HINTS

Applying Newton's Laws

The following procedure is recommended when dealing with problems involving Newton's laws:

- Draw a simple, neat diagram of the system to help *conceptualize* the problem.
- *Categorize* the problem: if any acceleration component is zero, the particle is in equilibrium in this direction and $\Sigma F = 0$. If not, the particle is undergoing an acceleration, the problem is one of nonequilibrium in this direction, and $\Sigma F = ma$.
- *Analyze* the problem by isolating the object whose motion is being analyzed. Draw a free-body diagram for this object. For systems containing more than one object, draw *separate* free-body diagrams for each object. *Do not* include in the free-body diagram forces exerted by the object on its surroundings.
- Establish convenient coordinate axes for each object and find the components of the forces along these axes. Apply Newton's second law, $\Sigma \mathbf{F} = m\mathbf{a}$, in component form. Check your dimensions to make sure that all terms have units of force.
- Solve the comp[...] have as many i[...] complete soluti[...]
- *Finalize* by maki[...] Also check the [...] variables. By do[...]

Example 4.3   The Long Jump

A long-jumper (Fig. 4.12) leaves the ground at an angle of 20.0° above the horizontal and at a speed of 11.0 m/s.

(A) How far does he jump in the horizontal direction? (Assume his motion is equivalent to that of a particle.)

Solution We *conceptualize* the motion of the long-jumper as equivalent to that of a simple projectile such as the ball in Example 4.2, and *categorize* this problem as a projectile motion problem. Because the initial speed and launch angle are given, and because the final height is the same as the initial height, we further categorize this problem as satisfying the conditions for which Equations 4.13 and 4.14 can be used. This is the most direct way to *analyze* this problem, although, in general, the motion of the long-jumper can be described by Equations 4.8 through 4.11. We use the gen[...]

provides a graphical representation of the flight of the long-jumper. As before, we set our origin of coordinates at the takeoff point and label the peak as Ⓐ and the landing point as Ⓑ. The horizontal motion is described by Equation 4.11:

$$x_f = x_B = (v_i \cos \theta_i)t_B = (11.0 \text{ m/s})(\cos 20.0°)t_B$$

The value of x_B can be found if the time of landing t_B is known. We can find t_B by remembering that $a_y = -g$ and by using the y part of Equation 4.8a. We also note that at the top of the jump the vertical component of velocity v_{yA} is zero:

$$v_{yf} = v_{yA} = v_i \sin \theta_i - gt_A$$

This is the time at which the long-jumper is at the *top* of the jump. Because of the symmetry of the vertical motion,

another 0.384 s passes before the jumper returns to the ground. Therefore, the time at which the jumper lands is $t_B = 2t_A = 0.768$ s. Substituting this value into the above expression for x_f gives

$$x_f = x_B = (11.0 \text{ m/s})(\cos 20.0°)(0.768 \text{ s}) = \boxed{7.94 \text{ m}}$$

This is a reasonable distance for a world-class athlete.

(B) What is the maximum height reached?

Solution We find the maximum height reached by using Equation 4.12:

$$y_{max} = y_A = (v_i \sin \theta_i)t_A - \tfrac{1}{2}gt_A^2$$
$$= (11.0 \text{ m/s})(\sin 20.0°)(0.384 \text{ s})$$
$$- \tfrac{1}{2}(9.80 \text{ m/s}^2)(0.384 \text{ s})^2 = \boxed{0.722 \text{ m}}$$

To *finalize* this problem, find the answers to parts (a) and (b) using Equations 4.13 and 4.14. The results should agree. Treating the long-jumper as a particle is an oversimplification. Nevertheless, the values obtained are consistent with experience in sports. We learn that we can model a complicated system such as a long-jumper as a particle and still obtain results that are reasonable.

Figure 4.12 (Example 4.3) Mike Powell, current holder of the world long jump record of 8.95 m.

where k is a dimensionless constant of proportionality. Knowing the dimensions of a, r, and v, we see that the dimensional equation must be

$$\frac{L}{T^2} = L^n \left(\frac{L}{T}\right)^m = \frac{L^{n+m}}{T^m}$$

... $n = -1$, and we can write the acceleration expression as

$$a = kr^{-1}v^2 = k\frac{v^2}{r}$$

When we discuss uniform circular motion later, we shall see that $k = 1$ if a consistent set of units is used. The constant k would not equal 1 if, for example, v were in km/h and you wanted a in m/s².

▲ **PITFALL PREVENTION**

1.5 Always Include Units

When performing calculations, include the units for every quantity and carry the units through the entire calculation. Avoid the temptation to drop the units early and then attach the expected units once you have an answer. By including the units in every step, you can detect errors if the units for the answer turn out to be incorrect.

1.5 Conversion of Units

Sometimes it is necessary to convert units from one measurement system to another, or to convert within a system, for example, from kilometers to meters. Equalities between SI and U.S. customary units of length are as follows:

$$1 \text{ mile} = 1\ 609 \text{ m} = 1.609 \text{ km} \qquad 1 \text{ ft} = 0.304\ 8 \text{ m} = 30.48 \text{ cm}$$

$$1 \text{ m} = 39.37 \text{ in.} = 3.281 \text{ ft} \qquad 1 \text{ in.} = 0.025\ 4 \text{ m} = 2.54 \text{ cm (exactly)}$$

A more complete list of conversion factors can be found in Appendix A.

Units can be treated as algebraic quantities that can cancel each other. For example, suppose we wish to convert 15.0 in. to centimeters. Because 1 in. is defined as exactly 2.54 cm, we find that

---

PITFALL PREVENTIONS

An easy way to make sure you avoid common mistakes—while studying *and* while taking exams! These helpful notes, found in the margins, allow you to correct misconceptions before applying them to new material.

WHAT IF?

What if you could get even more out of the text's worked examples? You can with this feature. The authors change some of the data or assumptions in about one-third of the *Worked Examples* and then explore the consequences. This allows you to apply concepts and problem-solving skills to new situations as well as test the final result to see if it's realistic.

Example 4.5 That's Quite an Arm!

A stone is thrown from the top of a building upward at an angle of 30.0° to the horizontal with an initial speed of 20.0 m/s, as shown in Figure 4.14. If the height of the building is 45.0 m,

(A) how long before the stone hits the ground?

Solution We *conceptualize* the problem by studying Figure 4.14, in which we have indicated the various parameters. By now, it should be natural to *categorize* this as a projectile motion problem.

To *analyze* the problem, let us once again separate motion into two components. The initial x and y components of the stone's velocity are

$$v_{xi} = v_i \cos\theta_i = (20.0 \text{ m/s})\cos 30.0° = 17.3 \text{ m/s}$$

$$v_{yi} = v_i \sin\theta_i = (20.0 \text{ m/s})\sin 30.0° = 10.0 \text{ m/s}$$

To find t, we can use $y_f = y_i + v_{yi}t + \frac{1}{2}a_y t^2$ (Eq. 4.9a) with $y_i = 0$, $y_f = -45.0$ m, $a_y = -g$, and $v_{yi} = 10.0$ m/s (there is a negative sign on the numerical value of y_f because we have chosen the top of the building as the origin):

$$-45.0 \text{ m} = (10.0 \text{ m/s})t - \frac{1}{2}(9.80 \text{ m/s}^2)t^2$$

Solving the quadratic equation for t gives, for the positive root, $t = 4.22$ s . To *finalize* this part, think: Does the negative root have any physical meaning?

(B) What is the speed of the stone just before it strikes the ground?

Solution We can use Equation 4.8a, $v_{yf} = v_{yi} + a_y t$, with $t = 4.22$ s to obtain the y component of the velocity just before the stone strikes the ground:

$$v_{yf} = 10.0 \text{ m/s} - (9.80 \text{ m/s}^2)(4.22 \text{ s}) = -31.4 \text{ m/s}$$

Because $v_{xf} = v_{xi} = 17.3$ m/s, the required speed is

$$v_f = \sqrt{v_{xf}^2 + v_{yf}^2} = \sqrt{(17.3)^2 + (-31.4)^2} \text{ m/s} = 35.9 \text{ m/s}$$

What If? What if a horizontal wind is blowing in the same direction as the ball is thrown and it causes the ball to have a horizontal acceleration component $a_x = 0.500$ m/s². Which part of this example, (a) or (b), will have a different answer?

Answer Recall that the motions in the x and y directions are independent. Thus, the horizontal wind cannot affect the vertical motion. The vertical motion determines the time of the projectile in the air, so the answer to (a) does not change. The wind will cause the horizontal velocity component to increase with time, so that the final speed will change in part (b).

We can find the new final horizontal velocity component by using Equation 4.8a:

$$v_{xf} = v_{xi} + a_x t = 17.3 \text{ m/s} + (0.500 \text{ m/s}^2)(4.22 \text{ s})$$
$$= 19.4 \text{ m/s}$$

and the new final speed:

$$v_f = \sqrt{v_{xf}^2 + v_{yf}^2} = \sqrt{(19.4)^2 + (-31.4)^2} \text{ m/s} = 36.9 \text{ m/s}$$

Figure 4.14 (Example 4.5) A stone is thrown from the top of a building.

... ample link at http://www.pse6.com.

Quick Quiz 5.2 An object experiences no acceleration. Which of the following *cannot* be true for the object? (a) A single force acts on the object. (b) No forces act on the object. (c) Forces act on the object, but the forces cancel.

Quick Quiz 5.3 An object experiences a net force and exhibits an acceleration in response. Which of the following statements is *always* true? (a) The object moves in the direction of the force. (b) The acceleration is in the same ... velocity. (c) The acceleration is in the same ... the object increases.

Quick Quiz 5.4 You push an object ... with a constant force for a time interval Δ... object. You repeat the experiment, but with ... terval is now required to reach the same fina... (e) Δt/4.

Answers to Quick Quizzes

5.1 (d). Choice (a) is true. Newton's first law tells us that motion requires no force: an object in motion continues to move at constant velocity in the absence of external forces. Choice (b) is also true. A stationary object can have several forces acting on it, but if the vector sum of all these external forces is zero, there is no net force and the object remains stationary.

5.2 (a). If a single force acts, this force constitutes the net force and there is an acceleration according to Newton's second law.

5.3 (c). Newton's second law relates only the force and the acceleration. Direction of motion is part of an object's *velocity*, and force determines the direction of acceleration, not that of velocity.

5.4 (d). With twice the force, the object will experience twice the acceleration. Because the force is constant, the acceler-

---

QUICK QUIZZES

Test your understanding of the concepts before investigating the worked examples. Found throughout each chapter, these quizzes give you an opportunity to test your conceptual understanding while also making the material more interactive. Comprehensive answers are found at the end of each chapter. A supplementary set of *Quick Quizzes* is available on the text's Web site, accessible through **www.pse6.com**.

"You do not know anything until you have practiced."

R. P. Feynman, Nobel Laureate in Physics

Quick Start for Studying Smart!

3

Take a practice test for this chapter by clicking on the Practice Test link at http://www.pse6.com.

SUMMARY

Scalar quantities are those that have only magnitude and no associated direction. **Vector quantities** have both magnitude and direction and obey the laws of vector addition. The magnitude of a vector is *always* a positive number.

When two or more vectors are added together, all of them must have the same units and all of them must be the same type of quantity. We can add two vectors **A** and **B** graphically. In this method (Fig. 3.6), the resultant vector $\mathbf{R} = \mathbf{A} + \mathbf{B}$ runs from the tail of **A** to the tip of **B**.

A second method of adding vectors involves **components** of the vectors. The x component A_x of the vector **A** is equal to the projection of **A** along the x axis of a coordinate system, as shown in Figure 3.13, where $A_x = A\cos\theta$. The y component A_y of **A** is the projection of **A** along the y axis, where $A_y = A\sin\theta$. Be sure you can determine which trigonometric functions you should use in all situations, especially when θ is defined as something other than the counterclockwise angle from the positive x axis.

If a vector **A** has an x component A_x and a y component A_y, the vector can be expressed in unit–vector form as $\mathbf{A} = A_x\hat{\mathbf{i}} + A_y\hat{\mathbf{j}}$. In this notation, $\hat{\mathbf{i}}$ is a unit vector pointing in the positive x direction, and $\hat{\mathbf{j}}$ is a unit vector pointing in the positive y direction. Because $\hat{\mathbf{i}}$ and $\hat{\mathbf{j}}$ are unit vectors, $|\hat{\mathbf{i}}| = |\hat{\mathbf{j}}| = 1$.

We can find the resultant of two or more vectors by resolving all vectors into their x and y components, adding their resultant x and y components, and then using the Pythagorean theorem to find the magnitude of the resultant vector. We can find the angle that the resultant vector makes with respect to the x axis by using a suitable trigonometric function.

QUESTIONS

1. Two vectors have unequal magnitudes. Can their sum be zero? Explain.

2. Can the magnitude of a particle's displacement be greater

4. Which of the following are vectors and which are not: force, temperature, the volume of water in a can, the ratings of a TV show, the height of a building, the velocity of ___ the Universe?

___ y plane. For what orientations of **A** ___ nts be negative? For what orienta- ___ s have opposite signs?

Example 4.5   That's Quite an Arm!

A stone is thrown from the top of a building upward at an angle of 30.0° to the horizontal with an initial speed of 20.0 m/s, as shown in Figure 4.14. If the height of the building is 45.0 m,

(A) how long before the stone hits the ground?

Solution We *conceptualize* the problem by studying Figure 4.14, in which we have indicated the various parameters. By now, it should be natural to *categorize* this as a projectile motion problem.

To *analyze* the problem, let us once again separate motion into two components. The initial x and y components of the stone's velocity are

$$v_{xi} = v_i\cos\theta_i = (20.0 \text{ m/s})\cos 30.0° = 17.3 \text{ m/s}$$

$$v_{yi} = v_i\sin\theta_i = (20.0 \text{ m/s})\sin 30.0° = 10.0 \text{ m/s}$$

To find t, we can use $y_f = y_i + v_{yi}t + \frac{1}{2}a_yt^2$ (Eq. 4.9a) with $y_i = 0$, $y_f = -45.0$ m, $a_y = -g$, and $v_{yi} = 10.0$ m/s (there is a negative sign on the numerical value of y_f because we have chosen the top of the building as the origin):

$$-45.0 \text{ m} = (10.0 \text{ m/s})t - \frac{1}{2}(9.80 \text{ m/s}^2)t^2$$

Solving the quadratic equation for t gives, for the positive root, $t = 4.22$ s. To *finalize* this part, think: Does the negative root have any physical meaning?

(B) What is the speed of the stone just before it strikes the ground?

Solution We can use Equation 4.8a, $v_{yf} = v_{yi} + a_yt$, with $t = 4.22$ s to obtain the y component of the velocity just before the stone strikes the ground:

$$v_{yf} = 10.0 \text{ m/s} - (9.80 \text{ m/s}^2)(4.22 \text{ s}) = -31.4 \text{ m/s}$$

Because $v_{xf} = v_{xi} = 17.3$ m/s, the required speed is

$$v_f = \sqrt{v_{xf}^2 + v_{yf}^2} = \sqrt{(17.3)^2 + (-31.4)^2} \text{ m/s} = 35.9 \text{ m/s}$$

To *finalize* this part, is it reasonable that the y component of the final velocity is negative? Is it reasonable that the final speed is larger than the initial speed of 20.0 m/s?

What If? What if a horizontal wind is blowing in the same direction as the ball is thrown and it causes the ball to have a horizontal acceleration component $a_x = 0.500$ m/s². Which part of this example, (a) or (b), will have a different answer?

Answer Recall that the motions in the x and y directions are independent. Thus, the horizontal wind cannot affect the vertical motion. The vertical motion determines the time of the projectile in the air, so the answer to (a) does not change. The wind will cause the horizontal velocity component to increase with time, so that the final speed will change in part (b).

We can find the new final horizontal velocity component by using Equation 4.8a:

$$v_{xf} = v_{xi} + a_xt = 17.3 \text{ m/s} + (0.500 \text{ m/s}^2)(4.22 \text{ s})$$
$$= 19.4 \text{ m/s}$$

and the new final speed:

$$v_f = \sqrt{v_{xf}^2 + v_{yf}^2} = \sqrt{(19.4)^2 + (-31.4)^2} \text{ m/s} = 36.9 \text{ m/s}$$

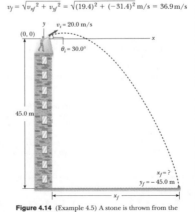

Figure 4.14 (Example 4.5) A stone is thrown from the top of a building.

Investigate this situation at the Interactive Worked Example link at http://www.pse6.com.

GO ONLINE AT www.pse6.com

Log on to **PhysicsNow** at **www.pse6.com** by using the free pincode packaged with this text.* You'll immediately notice the system's easy-to-use, browser-based format. Getting to where you need to go is as easy as a click of the mouse. The **PhysicsNow** system is made up of three interrelated parts:

▶ **How Much Do I Know?**

▶ **What Do I Need to Learn?**

▶ **What Have I Learned?**

These three interrelated elements work together, but are distinct enough to allow you the freedom to explore only those assets that meet your personal needs. You can use **PhysicsNow** like a traditional Web site, accessing all assets of a particular chapter and exploring on your own. The best way to maximize the system and *your* time is to start by taking the *Pre-Test*.

* Free PIN codes are only available with new copies of
Physics for Scientists and Engineers, Sixth Edition.

HOW MUCH DO I KNOW?

The Pre-Test is the first step in creating your *Personalized Learning Plan*. Each *Pre-Test* is based on the end-of-chapter homework problems and includes approximately 15 questions.

Once you've completed the *Pre-Test* you'll be presented with a detailed *Learning Plan* that outlines the elements you need to review to master the chapter's most essential concepts.

At each stage, the text is referenced to reinforce its value as a learning tool.

Turn the page to view problems from a sample *Personalized Learning Plan.*

WHAT DO I NEED TO LEARN?

Once you've completed the *Pre-Test* you're ready to work the problems in your *Personalized Learning Plan*—problems that will help you master concepts essential to your success in this course.

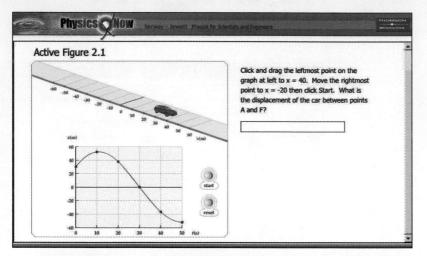

More than 200 *Active Figures* are taken from the text and animated to help you visualize physics in action. Each figure is paired with a question to help you focus on physics at work, and a brief quiz ensures that you understand the concept played out in the animations.

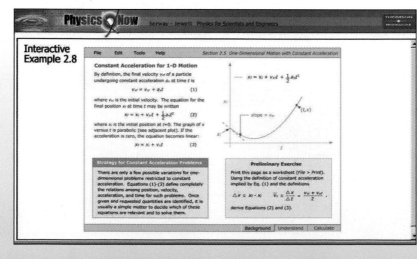

You'll continue to master the concepts though *Coached Problems.* These engaging problems reinforce the lessons in the text by taking a step-by-step approach to problem-solving methodology. Each *Coached Problem* gives you the option of working a question and receiving feedback, or seeing a solution worked for you. You'll find approximately five *Coached Problems* per chapter.

You'll strengthen your problem-solving and visualization skills by working through the *Interactive Examples.* Each step in the examples uses the authors' problem-solving methodology that is introduced in the text (see page 2 of this Visual Preface). You'll find *Interactive Examples* for each chapter of the text.

WHAT HAVE I LEARNED?

After working through the problems highlighted in your personal *Learning Plan* you'll move on to a *Chapter Quiz*. These multiple-choice quizzes present you with questions that are similar to those you might find in an exam. You can even e-mail your quiz results to your instructor.

Once you've completed the quiz you'll receive your results in the form of a percentage. If you need to improve your score, **PhysicsNow** will take you back through the system, beginning with *What Do I Know?*, and work with you as you continue to build your knowledge and skills and master concepts.

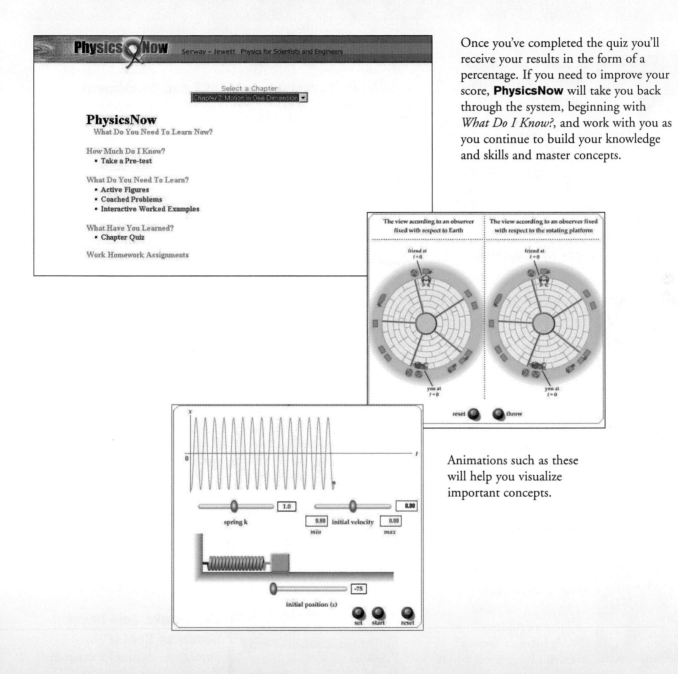

Animations such as these will help you visualize important concepts.

Chart your own course for success . . .

Log on to **www.pse6.com** to take advantage of **PhysicsNow!**

Quick Start for Studying Smart!

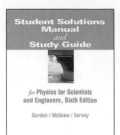

Student Solutions Manual with Study Guide

Volume I ISBN: 0-534-40855-9
Volume II ISBN: 0-534-40856-7

by John R. Gordon, Ralph McGrew, and Raymond Serway
This two-volume manual features detailed solutions to 20% of the end-of-chapter problems from the text. The manual also features a list of important equations, concepts, and answers to selected end-of-chapter questions.

Essential Study Skills for Science Students

ISBN: 0-534-37595-2

by Daniel D. Chiras
Written specifically for science students, this book discusses how to develop good study habits, sharpen memory, learn more quickly, get the most out of lectures, prepare for tests, produce excellent term papers, and improve critical-thinking skills.

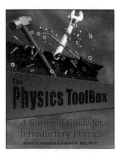

The Physics Toolbox: A Survival Guide for Introductory Physics

ISBN: 0-03-034652-5

by Kirsten A. Hubbard and Debora M. Katz
This "paperback mentor" gives you the material critical for success in physics, including an introduction to the nature of physics and science, a look at what to expect and how to succeed, a verbal overview of the concepts you'll encounter, and an extensive review of the math you'll need to solve the problems.

WebTUTOR Advantage

WebTutor™ Advantage on WebCT and Blackboard

WebCT ISBN: 0-534-40859-1
Blackboard ISBN: 0-534-40950-4

WebTutor Advantage offers real-time access to a full array of study tools, including chapter outlines, summaries, learning objectives, glossary flashcards (with audio), practice quizzes, **InfoTrac® College Edition** exercises, and Web links. **WebTutor Advantage** also provides robust communication tools, such as a course calendar, asynchronous discussion, real-time chat, a whiteboard, and an integrated e-mail system. Also new to **WebTutor Advantage** is access to *NewsEdge,* an online news service that brings the latest news to the **WebTutor Advantage** site daily.

Contact your instructor for more information.

Additional Web resources . . .

available FREE to you with each new copy of this text:

InfoTrac® College Edition

When you purchase a new copy of **Physics for Scientists and Engineers, Sixth Edition**, you automatically receive a FREE four-month subscription to **InfoTrac College Edition!** Newly improved, this extensive online library opens the door to the full text (not just abstracts) of countless articles from thousands of publications including *American Scientist, Physical Review, Science, Science Weekly*, and more! Use the passcode included with the new copy of this text and log on to **www.infotrac-college.com** to explore the wealth of resources available to you—24 hours a day and seven days a week!

Available only to college and university students. Journals subject to change.

The Brooks/Cole Physics Resource Center

http://physics.brookscole.com
Here you'll find even more opportunities to hone your skills and expand your knowledge. **The Brooks/Cole Physics Resource Center** is filled with helpful content that will engage you while you master the material. You'll find additional online quizzes, Web links, animations, and *NewEdge*—an online news service that brings the latest news to this site daily.

We dedicate this book to the courageous astronauts
who died on the space shuttle Columbia *on February 1, 2003.*
The women and men of the international team lost their lives
not in a contest between countries or a struggle for
necessities but in advancing one of humankind's noblest
creations—science.

6th Edition

PHYSICS

for Scientists and Engineers

Chapters 23 – 34

Raymond A. Serway

John W. Jewett, Jr.

California State Polytechnic University–Pomona

THOMSON

BROOKS/COLE

Australia • Canada • Mexico • Singapore • Spain
United Kingdom • United States

THOMSON
™
BROOKS/COLE

Editor-in-Chief: Michelle Julet
Publisher: David Harris
Physics Editor: Chris Hall
Development Editor: Susan Dust Pashos
Assistant Editor: Rebecca Heider, Alyssa White
Editorial Assistant: Seth Dobrin, Jessica Howard
Technology Project Manager: Sam Subity
Marketing Manager: Kelley McAllister
Marketing Assistant: Sandra Perin
Advertising Project Manager: Stacey Purviance
Project Manager, Editorial Production: Teri Hyde
Print/Media Buyer: Barbara Britton
Permissions Editor: Joohee Lee

Production Service: Sparkpoint Communications,
a division of J. B. Woolsey Associates
Text Designer: Lisa Devenish
Photo Researcher: Terri Wright
Copy Editor: Andrew Potter
Illustrator: Rolin Graphics
Cover Designer: Lisa Devenish
Cover Image: Water Displaced by Oil Tanker, © Stuart
Westmorland/CORBIS
Compositor: Progressive Information Technologies
Cover Printer: Quebecor World, Versailles
Printer: Quebecor World, Versailles

For more information about our products, contact us at:
Thomson Learning Academic Resource Center
1-800-423-0563

For permission to use material from this text, contact us by:
Phone: 1-800-730-2214
Fax: 1-800-730-2215
Web: http://www.thomsonrights.com

Library of Congress Control Number: 2003100126

PHYSICS FOR SCIENTISTS AND ENGINEERS, Sixth Edition
0-534-40848-6, Volume 1 (Chapters 1–14)
0-534-40849-4, Volume 2 (Chapters 15–22)
0-534-40850-8, Volume 3 (Chapters 23–34)
0-534-40853-2, Volume 4 (Chapters 35–39)

Brooks/Cole—Thomson Learning
10 Davis Drive
Belmont, CA 94002
USA

Asia
Thomson Learning
5 Shenton Way #01-01
UIC Building
Singapore 068808

Australia
Nelson Thomson Learning
102 Dodds Street
South Melbourne, Victoria 3205
Australia

Canada
Nelson Thomson Learning
1120 Birchmount Road
Toronto, Ontario M1K 5G4
Canada

Europe/Middle East/Africa
Thomson Learning
High Holborn House
50/51 Bedford Row
London WC1R 4LR
United Kingdom

Latin America
Thomson Learning
Seneca, 53
Colonia Polanco
11560 Mexico D.F.
Mexico

Spain
Paraninfo Thomson Learning
Calle/Magallanes, 25
28015 Madrid, Spain

Contents Overview

Steve Niedorf/Getty Images

v

Table of Contents

elektraVision/Index Stock Imagery

Courtesy Tourism Malaysia

Don Bonsey/Getty Images

© 1973 Kim Vandiver & Harold E. Edgerton/Courtesy of Palm Press, Inc.

Lowell Georgia/CORBIS

Richard Megna/Fundamental Photographs

About the Authors

Raymond A. Serway received his doctorate at Illinois Institute of Technology and is Professor Emeritus at James Madison University. Dr. Serway began his teaching career at Clarkson University, where he conducted research and taught from 1967 to 1980. His second academic appointment was at James Madison University as Professor of Physics and Head of the Physics Department from 1980 to 1986. He remained at James Madison University until his retirement in 1997. He was the recipient of the Madison Scholar Award at James Madison University in 1990, the Distinguished Teaching Award at Clarkson University in 1977, and the Alumni Achievement Award from Utica College in 1985. As Guest Scientist at the IBM Research Laboratory in Zurich, Switzerland, he worked with K. Alex Müller, 1987 Nobel Prize recipient. Dr. Serway also held research appointments at Rome Air Development Center from 1961 to 1963, at IIT Research Institute from 1963 to 1967, and as a visiting scientist at Argonne National Laboratory, where he collaborated with his mentor and friend, Sam Marshall. In addition to earlier editions of this textbook, Dr. Serway is the co-author of the high-school textbook *Physics* with Jerry Faughn, published by Holt, Rinehart, & Winston and co-author of the third edition of *Principles of Physics* with John Jewett, the sixth edition of *College Physics* with Jerry Faughn, and the second edition of *Modern Physics* with Clem Moses and Curt Moyer. In addition, Dr. Serway has published more than 40 research papers in the field of condensed matter physics and has given more than 70 presentations at professional meetings. Dr. Serway and his wife Elizabeth enjoy traveling, golfing, gardening, and spending quality time with their four children and five grandchildren.

John W. Jewett, Jr. earned his doctorate at Ohio State University, specializing in optical and magnetic properties of condensed matter. Dr. Jewett began his academic career at Richard Stockton College of New Jersey, where he taught from 1974 to 1984. He is currently Professor of Physics at California State Polytechnic University, Pomona. Throughout his teaching career, Dr. Jewett has been active in promoting science education. In addition to receiving four National Science Foundation grants, he helped found and direct the Southern California Area Modern Physics Institute (SCAMPI). He also directed Science IMPACT (Institute for Modern Pedagogy and Creative Teaching), which works with teachers and schools to develop effective science curricula. Dr. Jewett's honors include the Stockton Merit Award at Richard Stockton College, the Outstanding Professor Award at California State Polytechnic University for 1991–1992, and the Excellence in Undergraduate Physics Teaching Award from the American Association of Physics Teachers (AAPT) in 1998. He has given over 80 presentations at professional meetings, including presentations at international conferences in China and Japan. In addition to his work on this textbook, he is co-author of the third edition of *Principles of Physics* with Ray Serway and author of *The World of Physics . . . Mysteries, Magic, and Myth.* Dr. Jewett enjoys playing piano, traveling, and collecting antiques that can be used as demonstration apparatus in physics lectures, as well as spending time with his wife Lisa and their children and grandchildren.

Preface

Mark Cooper/Corbis Stock Market

In writing this sixth edition of *Physics for Scientists and Engineers,* we continue our ongoing efforts to improve the clarity of presentation and we again include new pedagogical features that help support the learning and teaching processes. Drawing on positive feedback from users of the fifth edition and reviewers' suggestions, we have refined the text in order to better meet the needs of students and teachers. We have for the first time integrated a powerful collection of media resources into many of the illustrations, examples, and end-of-chapter problems in the text. These resources compose the Web-based learning system *PhysicsNow* and are flagged by the media icon. Further details are described below.

This textbook is intended for a course in introductory physics for students majoring in science or engineering. The entire contents of the text in its extended version could be covered in a three-semester course, but it is possible to use the material in shorter sequences with the omission of selected chapters and sections. The mathematical background of the student taking this course should ideally include one semester of calculus. If that is not possible, the student should be enrolled in a concurrent course in introductory calculus.

Objectives

This introductory physics textbook has two main objectives: to provide the student with a clear and logical presentation of the basic concepts and principles of physics, and to strengthen an understanding of the concepts and principles through a broad range of interesting applications to the real world. To meet these objectives, we have placed emphasis on sound physical arguments and problem-solving methodology. At the same time, we have attempted to motivate the student through practical examples that demonstrate the role of physics in other disciplines, including engineering, chemistry, and medicine.

Changes in the Sixth Edition

A large number of changes and improvements have been made in preparing the sixth edition of this text. Some of the new features are based on our experiences and on current trends in science education. Other changes have been incorporated in response to comments and suggestions offered by users of the fifth edition and by reviewers of the manuscript. The following represent the major changes in the sixth edition:

Active Figures Many diagrams from the text have been animated to form **Active Figures,** part of the *PhysicsNow* integrated Web-based learning system. By visualizing phenomena and processes that cannot be fully represented on a static page, students greatly increase their conceptual understanding. **Active Figures** are identified with the media icon. An addition to the figure caption in blue type describes briefly the nature and contents of the animation.

Interactive Worked Examples Approximately 76 of the worked examples in the text have been identified as interactive, labeled with the media icon. As part of the *PhysicsNow* Web-based learning system, students can engage in an extension of the problem solved in the example. This often includes elements of both visualization and calculation, and may also involve prediction and intuition building. Often the interactivity is inspired by the **"What If?"** question we posed in the example text.

What If? Approximately one-third of the worked examples in the text contain this new feature. At the completion of the example solution, a **What If?** question offers a variation on the situation posed in the text of the example. For instance, this feature might explore the effects of changing the conditions of the situation, determine what happens when a quantity is taken to a particular limiting value, or question whether additional information can be determined about the problem situation. The answer to the question generally includes both a conceptual response and a mathematical response. This feature encourages students to think about the results of the example and assists in conceptual understanding of the principles. It also prepares students to encounter novel problems featured on exams. Some of the end-of-chapter problems also carry the **"What If?"** feature.

Quick Quizzes The number of Quick Quiz questions in each chapter has been increased. Quick Quizzes provide students with opportunities to test their understanding of the physical concepts presented. The questions require students to make decisions on the basis of sound reasoning, and some of them have been written to help students overcome common misconceptions. Quick Quizzes have been cast in an objective format, including multiple choice, true–false, and ranking. Answers to all Quick Quiz questions are found at the end of each chapter. Additional Quick Quizzes that can be used in classroom teaching are available on the instructor's companion Web site. Many instructors choose to use such questions in a "peer instruction" teaching style, but they can be used in standard quiz format as well.

Pitfall Preventions These new features are placed in the margins of the text and address common student misconceptions and situations in which students often follow unproductive paths. Over 200 Pitfall Preventions are provided to help students avoid common mistakes and misunderstandings.

General Problem-Solving Strategy A general strategy to be followed by the student is outlined at the end of Chapter 2 and provides students with a structured process for solving problems. In Chapters 3 through 5, the strategy is employed explicitly in every example so that students learn how it is applied. In the remaining chapters, the strategy appears explicitly in one example per chapter so that students are encouraged throughout the course to follow the procedure.

Line-by-Line Revision The entire text has been carefully edited to improve clarity of presentation and precision of language. We hope that the result is a book that is both accurate and enjoyable to read.

Problems A substantial revision of the end-of-chapter problems was made in an effort to improve their variety and interest, while maintaining their clarity and quality. Approximately 17% of the problems (about 550) are new. All problems have been carefully edited. Solutions to approximately 20% of the end-of-chapter problems are included in the *Student Solutions Manual and Study Guide*. These problems are identified by boxes around their numbers. A smaller subset of solutions, identified by the media icon 🌐, are available on the World Wide Web (**http://www.pse6.com**) as coached solutions with hints. Targeted feedback is provided for students whose instructors adopt *Physics for Scientists and Engineers,* sixth edition. See the next section for a complete description of other features of the problem set.

Content Changes The content and organization of the textbook is essentially the same as that of the fifth edition. An exception is that Chapter 13 (Oscillatory Motion) in the fifth edition has been moved to the Chapter 15 position in the sixth edition, in order to form a cohesive four-chapter Part 2 on oscillations and waves. Many sections in various chapters have been streamlined, deleted, or combined with other sections to allow for a more balanced presentation. The chapters on Modern Physics, Chapters 39–46, have been extensively rewritten to provide more up-to-date material as well as modern applications. A more detailed list of content changes can be found on the instructor's companion Web site.

Content

The material in this book covers fundamental topics in classical physics and provides an introduction to modern physics. The book is divided into six parts. Part 1 (Chapters 1 to 14) deals with the fundamentals of Newtonian mechanics and the physics of fluids, Part 2 (Chapters 15 to 18) covers oscillations, mechanical waves, and sound, Part 3 (Chapters 19 to 22) addresses heat and thermodynamics, Part 4 (Chapters 23 to 34) treats electricity and magnetism, Part 5 (Chapters 35 to 38) covers light and optics, and Part 6 (Chapters 39 to 46) deals with relativity and modern physics. Each part opener includes an overview of the subject matter covered in that part, as well as some historical perspectives.

Text Features

Most instructors would agree that the textbook selected for a course should be the student's primary guide for understanding and learning the subject matter. Furthermore, the textbook should be easily accessible and should be styled and written to facilitate instruction and learning. With these points in mind, we have included many pedagogical features in the textbook that are intended to enhance its usefulness to both students and instructors. These features are as follows:

Style To facilitate rapid comprehension, we have attempted to write the book in a style that is clear, logical, and engaging. We have chosen a writing style that is somewhat informal and relaxed so that students will find the text appealing and enjoyable to read. New terms are carefully defined, and we have avoided the use of jargon.

Previews All chapters begin with a brief preview that includes a discussion of the chapter's objectives and content.

Important Statements and Equations Most important statements and definitions are set in **boldface** type or are highlighted with a background screen for added emphasis and ease of review. Similarly, important equations are highlighted with a background screen to facilitate location.

Problem-Solving Hints In several chapters, we have included general strategies for solving the types of problems featured both in the examples and in the end-of-chapter problems. This feature helps students to identify necessary steps in problem solving and to eliminate any uncertainty they might have. Problem-solving strategies are highlighted with a light red background screen for emphasis and ease of location.

Bruce Ayers/Getty Images

Marginal Notes Comments and notes appearing in blue type in the margin can be used to locate important statements, equations, and concepts in the text.

Pedagogical Use of Color Readers should consult the **pedagogical color chart** (second page inside the front cover) for a listing of the color-coded symbols used in the text diagrams, Web-based **Active Figures,** and diagrams within **Interactive Worked Examples.** This system is followed consistently whenever possible, with slight variations made necessary by the complexity of physical situations depicted in Part 4.

Mathematical Level We have introduced calculus gradually, keeping in mind that students often take introductory courses in calculus and physics concurrently. Most steps are shown when basic equations are developed, and reference is often made to mathematical appendices at the end of the textbook. Vector products are introduced later in the text, where they are needed in physical applications. The dot product is introduced in Chapter 7, which addresses energy and energy transfer; the cross product is introduced in Chapter 11, which deals with angular momentum.

Worked Examples A large number of worked examples of varying difficulty are presented to promote students' understanding of concepts. In many cases, the examples serve as models for solving the end-of-chapter problems. Because of the increased emphasis on understanding physical concepts, many examples are conceptual in nature and are labeled as such. The examples are set off in boxes, and the answers to examples with numerical solutions are highlighted with a background screen. We have already mentioned that a number of examples are designated as interactive and are part of the *PhysicsNow* Web-based learning system.

Questions   Questions of a conceptual nature requiring verbal or written responses are provided at the end of each chapter. Over 1000 questions are included in this edition. Some questions provide the student with a means of self-testing the concepts presented in the chapter. Others could serve as a basis for initiating classroom discussions. Answers to selected questions are included in the *Student Solutions Manual and Study Guide,* and answers to all questions are found in the *Instructor's Solutions Manual.*

Significant Figures   Significant figures in both worked examples and end-of-chapter problems have been handled with care. Most numerical examples are worked out to either two or three significant figures, depending on the precision of the data provided. End-of-chapter problems regularly state data and answers to three-digit precision.

Problems   An extensive set of problems is included at the end of each chapter; in all, over 3000 problems are given throughout the text. Answers to odd-numbered problems are provided at the end of the book in a section whose pages have colored edges for ease of location. For the convenience of both the student and the instructor, about two thirds of the problems are keyed to specific sections of the chapter. The remaining problems, labeled "Additional Problems," are not keyed to specific sections.

Usually, the problems within a given section are presented so that the straightforward problems (those with black problem numbers) appear first. For ease of identification, the numbers of intermediate-level problems are printed in blue, and those of challenging problems are printed in magenta.

- **Review Problems**   Many chapters include review problems requiring the student to combine concepts covered in the chapter with those discussed in previous chapters. These problems reflect the cohesive nature of the principles in the text and verify that physics is not a scattered set of ideas. When facing real-world issues such as global warming or nuclear weapons, it may be necessary to call on ideas in physics from several parts of a textbook such as this one.

- **Paired Problems**   To allow focused practice in solving problems stated in symbolic terms, some end-of-chapter numerical problems are paired with the same problems in symbolic form. Paired problems are identified by a common light red background screen.

- **Computer- and Calculator-Based Problems**   Many chapters include one or more problems whose solution requires the use of a computer or graphing calculator. Computer modeling of physical phenomena enables students to obtain graphical representations of variables and to perform numerical analyses.

- **Coached Problems with Hints**   These have been described above as part of the *PhysicsNow* Web-based learning system. These problems are identified by the media icon  and targeted feedback is provided to students of instructors adopting the sixth edition.

Units   The international system of units (SI) is used throughout the text. The U.S. customary system of units is used only to a limited extent in the chapters on mechanics, heat, and thermodynamics.

Summaries   Each chapter contains a summary that reviews the important concepts and equations discussed in that chapter. A marginal note in blue type next to each chapter summary directs students to a practice test (Post-Test) for the chapter.

Appendices and Endpapers   Several appendices are provided at the end of the textbook. Most of the appendix material represents a review of mathematical concepts and techniques used in the text, including scientific notation, algebra, geometry, trigonometry, differential calculus, and integral calculus. Reference to these appendices is made

Courtesy NASA

throughout the text. Most mathematical review sections in the appendices include worked examples and exercises with answers. In addition to the mathematical reviews, the appendices contain tables of physical data, conversion factors, atomic masses, and the SI units of physical quantities, as well as a periodic table of the elements. Other useful information, including fundamental constants and physical data, planetary data, a list of standard prefixes, mathematical symbols, the Greek alphabet, and standard abbreviations of units of measure, appears on the endpapers.

Student Ancillaries

Student Solutions Manual and Study Guide by John R. Gordon, Ralph McGrew, and Raymond Serway. This two-volume manual features detailed solutions to 20% of the end-of-chapter problems from the text. The manual also features a list of important equations, concepts, and notes from key sections of the text, in addition to answers to selected end-of-chapter questions. Volume 1 contains Chapters 1 through 22 and Volume 2 contains Chapters 23 through 46.

WebTutor™ on WebCT and Blackboard   WebTutor offers students real-time access to a full array of study tools, including chapter outlines, summaries, learning objectives, glossary flashcards (with audio), practice quizzes, **InfoTrac® College Edition** exercises, and Web links.

InfoTrac® College Edition   Adopters and their students automatically receive a four-month subscription to **InfoTrac® College Edition** with every new copy of this book. Newly improved, this extensive online library opens the door to the full text (not just abstracts) of countless articles from thousands of publications including *American Scientist, Physical Review, Science, Science Weekly,* and more! Available only to college and university students. Journals subject to change.

The Brooks/Cole Physics Resource Center   You will find additional online quizzes, Web links and animations at **http://physics.brookscole.com.**

Ancillaries for Instructors

The first four ancillaries below are available to qualified adopters. Please consult your local sales representative for details.

Instructor's Solutions Manual by Ralph McGrew and James A. Currie. This two-volume manual contains complete worked solutions to all of the end-of-chapter problems in the textbook as well as answers to even-numbered problems. The solutions to problems new to the sixth edition are marked for easy identification by the instructor. New to this edition are complete answers to the conceptual questions in the main text. Volume 1 contains Chapters 1 through 22 and Volume 2 contains Chapters 23 through 46.

Printed Test Bank by Edward Adelson. This two-volume test bank contains approximately 2 300 multiple-choice questions. These questions are also available in electronic format with complete answers and solutions in the Brooks/Cole Assessment test program. Volume 1 contains Chapters 1 through 22 and Volume 2 contains Chapters 23 through 46.

Multimedia Manager   This easy-to-use multimedia lecture tool allows you to quickly assemble art and database files with notes to create fluid lectures. The CD-ROM set (Volume 1, Chapters 1–22; Volume 2, Chapters 23–46) includes a database of animations, video clips, and digital art from the text as well as electronic files of the *Instructor's Solutions Manual and Test Bank*. The simple interface makes it easy for you to incorporate graphics, digital video, animations, and audio clips into your lectures.

Transparency Acetates   Each volume contains approximately 100 acetates featuring art from the text. Volume 1 contains Chapters 1 through 22 and Volume 2 contains Chapters 23 through 46.

Brooks/Cole Assessment   With a balance of efficiency, high performance, simplicity and versatility, **Brooks/Cole Assessment (BCA)** gives you the power to transform the learning and teaching experience. **BCA** is fully integrated testing, tutorial, and course management software accessible by instructors and students anytime, anywhere. Delivered for FREE in a browser-based format without the need for any proprietary software or plug-ins, **BCA** uses correct scientific notation to provide the drill of basic skills that students need, enabling the instructor to focus more time in higher-level learning activities (i.e., concepts and applications). Students can have unlimited practice in questions and problems, building their own confidence and skills. Results flow automatically to a grade book for tracking so that instructors will be better able to assess student understanding of the material, even prior to class or an actual test.

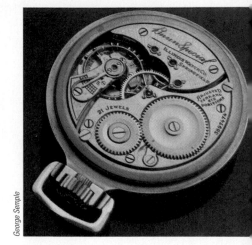

George Semple

WebTutor™ on WebCT and Blackboard   With **WebTutor's** text-specific, preformatted content and total flexibility, instructors can easily create and manage their own personal Web site. **WebTutor's** course management tool gives instructors the ability to provide virtual office hours, post syllabi, set up threaded discussions, track student progress with the quizzing material, and much more. **WebTutor** also provides robust communication tools, such as a course calendar, asynchronous discussion, real-time chat, a whiteboard, and an integrated e-mail system.

Additional Options for Online Homework   For detailed information and demonstrations, contact your Thomson•Brooks/Cole representative or visit the following:

- WebAssign: A Web-based Homework System
  http://www.webassign.net or contact WebAssign at *webassign@ncsu.edu*
- Homework Service
  http://hw.ph.utexas.edu/hw.html or contact *moore@physics.utexas.edu*
- CAPA: A Computer-Assisted Personalized Approach
  http://capa4.lite.msu.edu/homepage/

Instructor's Companion Web Site   Consult the instructor's site at *http://www.pse6.com* for additional Quick Quiz questions, a detailed list of content changes since the fifth edition, a problem correlation guide, images from the text, and sample PowerPoint lectures. Instructors adopting the sixth edition of *Physics for Scientists and Engineers* may download these materials after securing the appropriate password from their local Thomson•Brooks/Cole sales representative.

Teaching Options

The topics in this textbook are presented in the following sequence: classical mechanics, oscillations and mechanical waves, and heat and thermodynamics followed by electricity and magnetism, electromagnetic waves, optics, relativity, and modern physics. This presentation represents a traditional sequence, with the subject of mechanical waves being presented before electricity and magnetism. Some instructors may prefer to cover this material after completing electricity and magnetism (i.e., after Chapter 34). The chapter on relativity is placed near the end of the text because this topic often is treated as an introduction to the era of "modern physics." If time permits, instructors may choose to cover Chapter 39 after completing Chapter 13, as it concludes the material on Newtonian mechanics.

For those instructors teaching a two-semester sequence, some sections and chapters could be deleted without any loss of continuity. The following sections can be considered optional for this purpose:

2.7	Kinematic Equations Derived from Calculus	6.4	Motion in the Presence of Resistive Forces
4.6	Relative Velocity and Relative Acceleration	6.5	Numerical Modeling in Particle Dynamics
6.3	Motion in Accelerated Frames	7.9	Energy and the Automobile

Topham Picturepoint/The Image Works

Acknowledgments

The sixth edition of this textbook was prepared with the guidance and assistance of many professors who reviewed selections of the manuscript, the pre-revision text, or both. We wish to acknowledge the following scholars and express our sincere appreciation for their suggestions, criticisms, and encouragement:

Edward Adelson, *Ohio State University*

Michael R. Cohen, *Shippensburg University*

Jerry D. Cook, *Eastern Kentucky University*

J. William Dawicke, *Milwaukee School of Engineering*

N. John DiNardo, *Drexel University*

Andrew Duffy, *Boston University*

Robert J. Endorf, *University of Cincinnati*

F. Paul Esposito, *University of Cincinnati*

Joe L. Ferguson, *Mississippi State University*

Perry Ganas, *California State University, Los Angeles*

John C. Hardy, *Texas A&M University*

Michael Hayes, *University of Pretoria (South Africa)*

John T. Ho, *The State University of New York, Buffalo*

Joseph W. Howard, *Salisbury University*

Robert Hunt, *Johnson County Community College*

Walter S. Jaronski, *Radford University*

Sangyong Jeon, *McGill University, Quebec*

Stan Jones, *University of Alabama*

L. R. Jordan, *Palm Beach Community College*

Teruki Kamon, *Texas A & M University*

Louis E. Keiner, *Coastal Carolina University*

Mario Klaric̀, *Midlands Technical College*

Laird Kramer, *Florida International University*

Edwin H. Lo, *American University*

James G. McLean, *The State University of New York, Geneseo*

Richard E. Miers, *Indiana University–Purdue University, Fort Wayne*

Oscar Romulo Ochoa, *The College of New Jersey*

Paul S. Ormsby, *Moraine Valley Community College*

Didarul I. Qadir, *Central Michigan University*

Judith D. Redling, *New Jersey Institute of Technology*

Richard W. Robinett, *Pennsylvania State University*

Om P. Rustgi, *SUNY College at Buffalo*

Mesgun Sebhatu, *Winthrop University*

Natalia Semushkina, *Shippensburg University*

Daniel Stump, *Michigan State University*

Uwe C. Täuber, *Virginia Polytechnic Institute*

Perry A. Tompkins, *Samford University*

Doug Welch, *McMaster University, Ontario*

Augden Windelborn, *Northern Illinois University*

Jerzy M. Wrobel, *University of Missouri, Kansas City*

Jianshi Wu, *Fayetteville State University*

Michael Zincani, *University of Dallas*

Frank Oberle/Getty Images

This title was carefully checked for accuracy by Michael Kotlarchyk *(Rochester Institute of Technology)*, Chris Vuille *(Embry-Riddle Aeronautical University)*, Laurencin Dunbar *(St. Louis Community College)*, William Dawicke *(Milwaukee School of Engineering)*, Ioan Kosztin *(University of Missouri)*, Tom Barrett *(Ohio State University)*, Z. M. Stadnik *(University of Ottawa)*, Ronald E. Jodoin *(Rochester Institute of Technology)*, Brian A. Raue *(Florida International University)*, Peter Moeck *(Portland State University)*, and Grant Hart *(Brigham Young University)*. We thank them for their diligent efforts under schedule pressure!

We are grateful to Ralph McGrew for organizing the end-of-chapter problems, writing many new problems, and his excellent suggestions for improving the content of the textbook. Problems new to this edition were written by Edward Adelson, Ronald Bieniek, Michael Browne, Andrew Duffy, Robert Forsythe, Perry Ganas, Michael Hones, John Jewett, Boris Korsunsky, Edwin Lo, Ralph McGrew, Raymond Serway, and Jerzy Wrobel, with the help of Bennett Simpson and JoAnne Maniago. Students Alexander Coto, Karl Payne, and Eric Peterman made corrections to problems taken from previous editions, as did teachers David Aspnes, Robert Beichner, Joseph Biegen, Tom Devlin, Vasili Haralambous, Frank Hayes, Erika Hermon, Ken Menningen, Henry Nebel, and Charles Teague. We are grateful to authors John R. Gordon and Ralph McGrew and compositor Michael Rudmin for preparing the *Student Solutions Manual and Study Guide.* Authors Ralph McGrew and James Currie and compositor Mary Toscano have prepared an excellent *Instructor's Solutions Manual,* and we thank them. Edward Adelson has carefully edited and improved the Test Bank for the sixth edition. Kurt Vandervoort prepared extra Quick Quiz questions for the instructor's companion Web site.

Special thanks and recognition go to the professional staff at the Brooks/Cole Publishing Company—in particular Susan Pashos, Rebecca Heider and Alyssa White (who managed the ancillary program and so much more), Jessica Howard, Seth Dobrin, Peter McGahey, Teri Hyde, Michelle Julet, David Harris, and Chris Hall—for their fine work during the development and production of this textbook. We are most appreciative of Sam Subity's masterful management of the *PhysicsNow* media program. Kelley McAllister is our energetic Marketing Manager, and Stacey Purviance coordinates our marketing communications. We recognize the skilled production service provided by the staff at Sparkpoint Communications, the excellent artwork produced by Rolin Graphics, and the dedicated photo research efforts of Terri Wright.

Finally, we are deeply indebted to our wives and children for their love, support, and long-term sacrifices.

Raymond A. Serway
Leesburg, Virginia

John W. Jewett, Jr.
Pomona, California

To the Student

t is appropriate to offer some words of advice that should be of benefit to you, the student. Before doing so, we assume that you have read the Preface, which describes the various features of the text that will help you through the course.

How to Study

Very often instructors are asked, "How should I study physics and prepare for examinations?" There is no simple answer to this question, but we would like to offer some suggestions that are based on our own experiences in learning and teaching over the years.

First and foremost, maintain a positive attitude toward the subject matter, keeping in mind that physics is the most fundamental of all natural sciences. Other science courses that follow will use the same physical principles, so it is important that you understand and are able to apply the various concepts and theories discussed in the text.

Concepts and Principles

It is essential that you understand the basic concepts and principles before attempting to solve assigned problems. You can best accomplish this goal by carefully reading the textbook before you attend your lecture on the covered material. When reading the text, you should jot down those points that are not clear to you. We've purposely left wide margins in the text to give you space for making notes. Also be sure to make a diligent attempt at answering the questions in the Quick Quizzes as you come to them in your reading. We have worked hard to prepare questions that help you judge for yourself how well you understand the material. Study carefully the **What If?** features that appear with many of the worked examples. These will help you to extend your understanding beyond the simple act of arriving at a numerical result. The Pitfall Preventions will also help guide you away from common misunderstandings about physics. During class, take careful notes and ask questions about those ideas that are unclear to you. Keep in mind that few people are able to absorb the full meaning of scientific material after only one reading. Several readings of the text and your notes may be necessary. Your lectures and laboratory work supplement reading of the textbook and should clarify some of the more difficult material. You should minimize your memorization of material. Successful memorization of passages from the text, equations, and derivations does not necessarily indicate that you understand the material. Your understanding of the material will be enhanced through a combination of efficient study habits, discussions with other students and with instructors, and your ability to solve the problems presented in the textbook. Ask questions whenever you feel clarification of a concept is necessary.

Study Schedule

It is important that you set up a regular study schedule, preferably a daily one. Make sure that you read the syllabus for the course and adhere to the schedule set by your instructor. The lectures will make much more sense if you read the corresponding text material before attending them. As a general rule, you should devote about two hours of study time for every hour you are in class. If you are having trouble with the course, seek the advice of the instructor or other students who have taken the course. You may find it necessary to seek further instruction from experienced students. Very often, instructors offer review sessions in addition to regular class periods. It is important that you avoid the practice of delaying study until a day or two before an exam. More often than not, this approach has disastrous results. Rather than undertake an all-night study session, briefly review the basic concepts and equations, and get a good night's rest. If you feel you need additional help in understanding the concepts, in preparing for exams, or in problem solving, we suggest that you acquire a copy of the *Student Solutions Manual and Study Guide* that accompanies this textbook; this manual should be available at your college bookstore.

George Semple

Use the Features

You should make full use of the various features of the text discussed in the Preface. For example, marginal notes are useful for locating and describing important equations and concepts, and **boldfaced** type indicates important statements and definitions. Many useful tables are contained in the Appendices, but most are incorporated in the text where they are most often referenced. Appendix B is a convenient review of mathematical techniques.

Answers to odd-numbered problems are given at the end of the textbook, answers to Quick Quizzes are located at the end of each chapter, and answers to selected end-of-chapter questions are provided in the *Student Solutions Manual and Study Guide.* Problem-Solving Strategies and Hints are included in selected chapters throughout the text and give you additional information about how you should solve problems. The Table of Contents provides an overview of the entire text, while the Index enables you to locate specific material quickly. Footnotes sometimes are used to supplement the text or to cite other references on the subject discussed.

After reading a chapter, you should be able to define any new quantities introduced in that chapter and to discuss the principles and assumptions that were used to arrive at certain key relations. The chapter summaries and the review sections of the *Student Solutions Manual and Study Guide* should help you in this regard. In some cases, it may be necessary for you to refer to the index of the text to locate certain topics. You should be able to associate with each physical quantity the correct symbol used to represent that quantity and the unit in which the quantity is specified. Furthermore, you should be able to express each important equation in a concise and accurate prose statement.

Problem Solving

R. P. Feynman, Nobel laureate in physics, once said, "You do not know anything until you have practiced." In keeping with this statement, we strongly advise that you develop the skills necessary to solve a wide range of problems. Your ability to solve problems will be one of the main tests of your knowledge of physics, and therefore you should try to solve as many problems as possible. It is essential that you understand basic concepts and principles before attempting to solve problems. It is good practice to try to find alternate solutions to the same problem. For example, you can solve problems in mechanics using Newton's laws, but very often an alternative method that draws on energy considerations is more direct. You should not deceive yourself into thinking that you understand a problem merely because you have seen it solved in class. You must be able to solve the problem and similar problems on your own.

The approach to solving problems should be carefully planned. A systematic plan is especially important when a problem involves several concepts. First, read the problem several times until you are confident you understand what is being asked. Look for any key words that will help you interpret the problem and perhaps allow you to make certain assumptions. Your ability to interpret a question properly is an integral part of problem solving. Second, you should acquire the habit of writing down the information given in a problem and those quantities that need to be found; for example, you might construct a table listing both the quantities given and the quantities to be found. This procedure is sometimes used in the worked examples of the textbook. Finally, after you have decided on the method you feel is appropriate for a given problem, proceed with your solution. Specific problem-solving strategies (Hints) of this type are included in the text and are highlighted with a light red screen. We have also developed a General Problem-Solving Strategy to help guide you through complex problems. If you follow the steps of this procedure *(Conceptualize, Categorize, Analyze, Finalize)*, you will not only find it easier to come up with a solution, but you will also gain more from your efforts. This Strategy is located at the end of Chapter 2 (page 47) and is used in all worked examples in Chapters 3 through 5 so that you can learn how to apply it. In the remaining chapters, the Strategy is used in one example per chapter as a reminder of its usefulness.

Often, students fail to recognize the limitations of certain equations or physical laws in a particular situation. It is very important that you understand and remember the assumptions that underlie a particular theory or formalism. For example, certain equations in kinematics apply only to a particle moving with constant acceleration. These equations are not valid for describing motion whose acceleration is not constant, such as the motion of an object connected to a spring or the motion of an object through a fluid.

Experiments

© Phil Degginger/Stone/Getty

Physics is a science based on experimental observations. In view of this fact, we recommend that you try to supplement the text by performing various types of "hands-on" experiments, either at home or in the laboratory. These can be used to test ideas and models discussed in class or in the textbook. For example, the common Slinky™ toy is excellent for studying traveling waves; a ball swinging on the end of a long string can be used to investigate pendulum motion; various masses attached to the end of a vertical spring or rubber band can be used to determine their elastic nature; an old pair of Polaroid sunglasses and some discarded lenses and a magnifying glass are the components of various experiments in optics; and an approximate measure of the free-fall acceleration can be determined simply by measuring with a stopwatch the time it takes for a ball to drop from a known height. The list of such experiments is endless. When physical models are not available, be imaginative and try to develop models of your own.

New Media

We strongly encourage you to use the *PhysicsNow* Web-based learning system that accompanies this textbook. It is far easier to understand physics if you see it in action, and these new materials will enable you to become a part of that action. *PhysicsNow* media described in the Preface are accessed at the URL *http://www.pse6.com,* and feature a three-step learning process consisting of a Pre-Test, a personalized learning plan, and a Post-Test.

In addition to other elements, *PhysicsNow* includes the following Active Figures and Interactive Worked Examples:

Chapter 2
Active Figures 2.1, 2.3, 2.9, 2.10, 2.11, and 2.13
Examples 2.8 and 2.12

Chapter 3
Active Figures 3.2, 3.3, 3.6, and 3.16
Example 3.5

Chapter 4
Active Figures 4.5, 4.7, and 4.11
Examples 4.4, 4.5, and 4.18

Chapter 5
Active Figure 5.16
Examples 5.9, 5.10, 5.12, and 5.14

Chapter 6
Active Figures 6.2, 6.8, 6.12, and 6.15
Examples 6.4, 6.5, and 6.7

Chapter 7
Active Figure 7.10
Examples 7.9 and 7.11

Chapter 8
Active Figures 8.3, 8.4, and 8.16
Examples 8.2 and 8.4

Chapter 9
Active Figures 9.8, 9.9, 9.13, 9.16, and 9.17
Examples 9.1, 9.5, and 9.8

Chapter 10
Active Figures 10.4, 10.14, and 10.30
Examples 10.12, 10.13, and 10.14

Chapter 11
Active Figures 11.1, 11.3, and 11.4
Examples 11.6 and 11.10

An Invitation to Physics

It is our sincere hope that you too will find physics an exciting and enjoyable experience and that you will profit from this experience, regardless of your chosen profession. Welcome to the exciting world of physics!

The scientist does not study nature because it is useful; he studies it because he delights in it, and he delights in it because it is beautiful. If nature were not beautiful, it would not be worth knowing, and if nature were not worth knowing, life would not be worth living.

—**Henri Poincaré**

PART 4

Electricity and Magnetism

We now study the branch of physics concerned with electric and magnetic phenomena. The laws of electricity and magnetism have a central role in the operation of such devices as radios, televisions, electric motors, computers, high-energy accelerators, and other electronic devices. More fundamentally, the interatomic and intermolecular forces responsible for the formation of solids and liquids are electric in origin. Furthermore, such forces as the pushes and pulls between objects and the elastic force in a spring arise from electric forces at the atomic level.

Evidence in Chinese documents suggests that magnetism was observed as early as 2000 B.C. The ancient Greeks observed electric and magnetic phenomena possibly as early as 700 B.C. They found that a piece of amber, when rubbed, becomes electrified and attracts pieces of straw or feathers. The Greeks knew about magnetic forces from observations that the naturally occurring stone *magnetite* (Fe_3O_4) is attracted to iron. (The word *electric* comes from *elecktron*, the Greek word for "amber." The word *magnetic* comes from *Magnesia*, the name of the district of Greece where magnetite was first found.) In 1600, the Englishman William Gilbert discovered that electrification is not limited to amber but rather is a general phenomenon. In the years following this discovery, scientists electrified a variety of objects. Experiments by Charles Coulomb in 1785 confirmed the inverse-square law for electric forces.

It was not until the early part of the nineteenth century that scientists established that electricity and magnetism are related phenomena. In 1819, Hans Oersted discovered that a compass needle is deflected when placed near a circuit carrying an electric current. In 1831, Michael Faraday and, almost simultaneously, Joseph Henry showed that when a wire is moved near a magnet (or, equivalently, when a magnet is moved near a wire), an electric current is established in the wire. In 1873, James Clerk Maxwell used these observations and other experimental facts as a basis for formulating the laws of electromagnetism as we know them today. (*Electromagnetism* is a name given to the combined study of electricity and magnetism.) Shortly thereafter (around 1888), Heinrich Hertz verified Maxwell's predictions by producing electromagnetic waves in the laboratory. This achievement led to such practical developments as radio and television.

Maxwell's contributions to the field of electromagnetism were especially significant because the laws he formulated are basic to *all* forms of electromagnetic phenomena. His work is as important as Newton's work on the laws of motion and the theory of gravitation.

◀ *Lightning is a dramatic example of electrical phenomena occurring in nature. While we are most familiar with lightning originating from thunderclouds, it can occur in other situations, such as in a volcanic eruption (here, the Sakurajima volcano, Japan). (M. Zhilin/ M. Newman/Photo Researchers, Inc.)*

Chapter 23

Electric Fields

▲ *Mother and daughter are both enjoying the effects of electrically charging their bodies. Each individual hair on their heads becomes charged and exerts a repulsive force on the other hairs, resulting in the "stand-up" hairdos that you see here. (Courtesy of Resonance Research Corporation)*

The electromagnetic force between charged particles is one of the fundamental forces of nature. We begin this chapter by describing some of the basic properties of one manifestation of the electromagnetic force, the electric force. We then discuss Coulomb's law, which is the fundamental law governing the electric force between any two charged particles. Next, we introduce the concept of an electric field associated with a charge distribution and describe its effect on other charged particles. We then show how to use Coulomb's law to calculate the electric field for a given charge distribution. We conclude the chapter with a discussion of the motion of a charged particle in a uniform electric field.

23.1   Properties of Electric Charges

A number of simple experiments demonstrate the existence of electric forces and charges. For example, after running a comb through your hair on a dry day, you will find that the comb attracts bits of paper. The attractive force is often strong enough to suspend the paper. The same effect occurs when certain materials are rubbed together, such as glass rubbed with silk or rubber with fur.

Another simple experiment is to rub an inflated balloon with wool. The balloon then adheres to a wall, often for hours. When materials behave in this way, they are said to be *electrified,* or to have become **electrically charged.** You can easily electrify your body by vigorously rubbing your shoes on a wool rug. Evidence of the electric charge on your body can be detected by lightly touching (and startling) a friend. Under the right conditions, you will see a spark when you touch, and both of you will feel a slight tingle. (Experiments such as these work best on a dry day because an excessive amount of moisture in the air can cause any charge you build up to "leak" from your body to the Earth.)

In a series of simple experiments, it was found that there are two kinds of electric charges, which were given the names **positive** and **negative** by Benjamin Franklin (1706–1790). We identify negative charge as that type possessed by electrons and positive charge as that possessed by protons. To verify that there are two types of charge, suppose a hard rubber rod that has been rubbed with fur is suspended by a sewing thread, as shown in Figure 23.1. When a glass rod that has been rubbed with silk is brought near the rubber rod, the two attract each other (Fig. 23.1a). On the other hand, if two charged rubber rods (or two charged glass rods) are brought near each other, as shown in Figure 23.1b, the two repel each other. This observation shows that the rubber and glass have two different types of charge on them. On the basis of these observations, we conclude that **charges of the same sign repel one another and charges with opposite signs attract one another.**

Using the convention suggested by Franklin, the electric charge on the glass rod is called positive and that on the rubber rod is called negative. Therefore, any charged object attracted to a charged rubber rod (or repelled by a charged glass rod) must

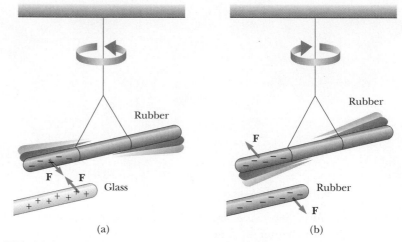

(a)   (b)

Figure 23.1 (a) A negatively charged rubber rod suspended by a thread is attracted to a positively charged glass rod. (b) A negatively charged rubber rod is repelled by another negatively charged rubber rod.

have a positive charge, and any charged object repelled by a charged rubber rod (or attracted to a charged glass rod) must have a negative charge.

Attractive electric forces are responsible for the behavior of a wide variety of commercial products. For example, the plastic in many contact lenses, *etafilcon*, is made up of molecules that electrically attract the protein molecules in human tears. These protein molecules are absorbed and held by the plastic so that the lens ends up being primarily composed of the wearer's tears. Because of this, the lens does not behave as a foreign object to the wearer's eye, and it can be worn comfortably. Many cosmetics also take advantage of electric forces by incorporating materials that are electrically attracted to skin or hair, causing the pigments or other chemicals to stay put once they are applied.

Another important aspect of electricity that arises from experimental observations is that **electric charge is always conserved** in an isolated system. That is, when one object is rubbed against another, charge is not created in the process. The electrified state is due to a *transfer* of charge from one object to the other. One object gains some amount of negative charge while the other gains an equal amount of positive charge. For example, when a glass rod is rubbed with silk, as in Figure 23.2, the silk obtains a negative charge that is equal in magnitude to the positive charge on the glass rod. We now know from our understanding of atomic structure that electrons are transferred from the glass to the silk in the rubbing process. Similarly, when rubber is rubbed with fur, electrons are transferred from the fur to the rubber, giving the rubber a net negative charge and the fur a net positive charge. This process is consistent with the fact that neutral, uncharged matter contains as many positive charges (protons within atomic nuclei) as negative charges (electrons).

In 1909, Robert Millikan (1868–1953) discovered that electric charge always occurs as some integral multiple of a fundamental amount of charge e (see Section 25.7). In modern terms, the electric charge q is said to be **quantized,** where q is the standard symbol used for charge as a variable. That is, electric charge exists as discrete "packets," and we can write $q = Ne$, where N is some integer. Other experiments in the same period showed that the electron has a charge $-e$ and the proton has a charge of equal magnitude but opposite sign $+e$. Some particles, such as the neutron, have no charge.

From our discussion thus far, we conclude that electric charge has the following important properties:

Electric charge is conserved

Figure 23.2 When a glass rod is rubbed with silk, electrons are transferred from the glass to the silk. Because of conservation of charge, each electron adds negative charge to the silk, and an equal positive charge is left behind on the rod. Also, because the charges are transferred in discrete bundles, the charges on the two objects are $\pm e$, or $\pm 2e$, or $\pm 3e$, and so on.

- There are two kinds of charges in nature; charges of opposite sign attract one another and charges of the same sign repel one another.
- Total charge in an isolated system is conserved.
- Charge is quantized.

Properties of electric charge

Quick Quiz 23.1 If you rub an inflated balloon against your hair, the two materials attract each other, as shown in Figure 23.3. Is the amount of charge present in the system of the balloon and your hair after rubbing (a) less than, (b) the same as, or (c) more than the amount of charge present before rubbing?

Quick Quiz 23.2 Three objects are brought close to each other, two at a time. When objects A and B are brought together, they repel. When objects B and C are brought together, they also repel. Which of the following are true? (a) Objects A and C possess charges of the same sign. (b) Objects A and C possess charges of oppo-site sign. (c) All three of the objects possess charges of the same sign. (d) One of the objects is neutral. (e) We would need to perform additional experiments to determine the signs of the charges.

Charles D. Winters

Figure 23.3 (Quick Quiz 23.1) Rubbing a balloon against your hair on a dry day causes the balloon and your hair to become charged.

23.2 Charging Objects By Induction

It is convenient to classify materials in terms of the ability of electrons to move through the material:

Electrical **conductors** are materials in which some of the electrons are free electrons[1] that are not bound to atoms and can move relatively freely through the material; electrical **insulators** are materials in which all electrons are bound to atoms and cannot move freely through the material.

Materials such as glass, rubber, and wood fall into the category of electrical insulators. When such materials are charged by rubbing, only the area rubbed becomes charged, and the charged particles are unable to move to other regions of the material.

In contrast, materials such as copper, aluminum, and silver are good electrical con-ductors. When such materials are charged in some small region, the charge readily dis-tributes itself over the entire surface of the material. If you hold a copper rod in your hand and rub it with wool or fur, it will not attract a small piece of paper. This might suggest that a metal cannot be charged. However, if you attach a wooden handle to the rod and then hold it by that handle as you rub the rod, the rod will remain charged and attract the piece of paper. The explanation for this is as follows: without the insu-lating wood, the electric charges produced by rubbing readily move from the copper through your body, which is also a conductor, and into the Earth. The insulating wooden handle prevents the flow of charge into your hand.

Semiconductors are a third class of materials, and their electrical properties are somewhere between those of insulators and those of conductors. Silicon and

---

[1]   A metal atom contains one or more outer electrons, which are weakly bound to the nucleus. When many atoms combine to form a metal, the so-called *free electrons* are these outer electrons, which are not bound to any one atom. These electrons move about the metal in a manner similar to that of gas mole-cules moving in a container.

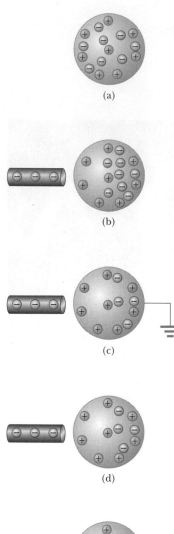

Figure 23.4 Charging a metallic object by *induction* (that is, the two objects never touch each other). (a) A neutral metallic sphere, with equal numbers of positive and negative charges. (b) The electrons on the neutral sphere are redistributed when a charged rubber rod is placed near the sphere. (c) When the sphere is grounded, some of its electrons leave through the ground wire. (d) When the ground connection is removed, the sphere has excess positive charge that is nonuniformly distributed. (e) When the rod is removed, the remaining electrons redistribute uniformly and there is a net uniform distribution of positive charge on the sphere.

germanium are well-known examples of semiconductors commonly used in the fabrication of a variety of electronic chips used in computers, cellular telephones, and stereo systems. The electrical properties of semiconductors can be changed over many orders of magnitude by the addition of controlled amounts of certain atoms to the materials.

To understand how to charge a conductor by a process known as **induction,** consider a neutral (uncharged) conducting sphere insulated from the ground, as shown in Figure 23.4a. There are an equal number of electrons and protons in the sphere if the charge on the sphere is exactly zero. When a negatively charged rubber rod is brought near the sphere, electrons in the region nearest the rod experience a repulsive force and migrate to the opposite side of the sphere. This leaves the side of the sphere near the rod with an effective positive charge because of the diminished number of electrons, as in Figure 23.4b. (The left side of the sphere in Figure 23.4b is positively charged *as if* positive charges moved into this region, but remember that it is only electrons that are free to move.) This occurs even if the rod never actually touches the sphere. If the same experiment is performed with a conducting wire connected from the sphere to the Earth (Fig. 23.4c), some of the electrons in the conductor are so strongly repelled by the presence of the negative charge in the rod that they move out of the sphere through the wire and into the Earth. The symbol ⏚ at the end of the wire in Figure 23.4c indicates that the wire is connected to **ground,** which means a reservoir, such as the Earth, that can accept or provide electrons freely with negligible effect on its electrical characteristics. If the wire to ground is then removed (Fig. 23.4d), the conducting sphere contains an excess of *induced* positive charge because it has fewer electrons than it needs to cancel out the positive charge of the protons. When the rubber rod is removed from the vicinity of the sphere (Fig. 23.4e), this induced positive charge remains on the ungrounded sphere. Note that the rubber rod loses none of its negative charge during this process.

Charging an object by induction requires no contact with the object inducing the charge. This is in contrast to charging an object by rubbing (that is, by *conduction*), which does require contact between the two objects.

A process similar to induction in conductors takes place in insulators. In most neutral molecules, the center of positive charge coincides with the center of negative charge. However, in the presence of a charged object, these centers inside each molecule in an insulator may shift slightly, resulting in more positive charge on one side of the molecule than on the other. This realignment of charge within individual molecules produces a layer of charge on the surface of the insulator, as shown in Figure 23.5a. Knowing about induction in insulators, you should be able to explain why a comb that has been rubbed through hair attracts bits of electrically neutral paper and why a balloon that has been rubbed against your clothing is able to stick to an electrically neutral wall.

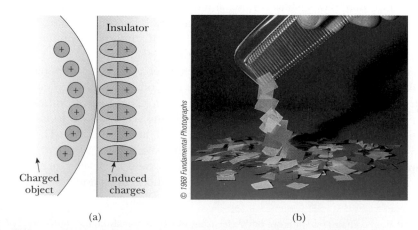

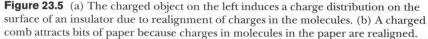

Figure 23.5 (a) The charged object on the left induces a charge distribution on the surface of an insulator due to realignment of charges in the molecules. (b) A charged comb attracts bits of paper because charges in molecules in the paper are realigned.

Quick Quiz 23.3 Three objects are brought close to each other, two at a time. When objects A and B are brought together, they attract. When objects B and C are brought together, they repel. From this, we conclude that (a) objects A and C possess charges of the same sign. (b) objects A and C possess charges of opposite sign. (c) all three of the objects possess charges of the same sign. (d) one of the objects is neutral. (e) we need to perform additional experiments to determine information about the charges on the objects.

23.3 Coulomb's Law

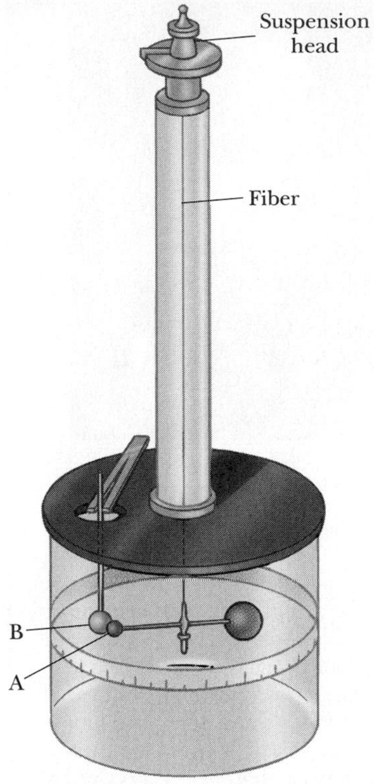

Charles Coulomb (1736–1806) measured the magnitudes of the electric forces between charged objects using the torsion balance, which he invented (Fig. 23.6). Coulomb confirmed that the electric force between two small charged spheres is proportional to the inverse square of their separation distance r—that is, $F_e \propto 1/r^2$. The operating principle of the torsion balance is the same as that of the apparatus used by Cavendish to measure the gravitational constant (see Section 13.2), with the electrically neutral spheres replaced by charged ones. The electric force between charged spheres A and B in Figure 23.6 causes the spheres to either attract or repel each other, and the resulting motion causes the suspended fiber to twist. Because the restoring torque of the twisted fiber is proportional to the angle through which the fiber rotates, a measurement of this angle provides a quantitative measure of the electric force of attraction or repulsion. Once the spheres are charged by rubbing, the electric force between them is very large compared with the gravitational attraction, and so the gravitational force can be neglected.

Figure 23.6 Coulomb's torsion balance, used to establish the inverse-square law for the electric force between two charges.

From Coulomb's experiments, we can generalize the following properties of the **electric force** between two stationary charged particles. The electric force

- is inversely proportional to the square of the separation r between the particles and directed along the line joining them;
- is proportional to the product of the charges q_1 and q_2 on the two particles;
- is attractive if the charges are of opposite sign and repulsive if the charges have the same sign;
- is a conservative force.

We will use the term **point charge** to mean a particle of zero size that carries an electric charge. The electrical behavior of electrons and protons is very well described by modeling them as point charges. From experimental observations on the electric force, we can express **Coulomb's law** as an equation giving the magnitude of the electric force (sometimes called the *Coulomb force*) between two point charges:

$$F_e = k_e \frac{|q_1||q_2|}{r^2} \qquad (23.1)$$

Coulomb's law

where k_e is a constant called the **Coulomb constant.** In his experiments, Coulomb was able to show that the value of the exponent of r was 2 to within an uncertainty of a few percent. Modern experiments have shown that the exponent is 2 to within an uncertainty of a few parts in 10^{16}.

The value of the Coulomb constant depends on the choice of units. The SI unit of charge is the **coulomb** (C). The Coulomb constant k_e in SI units has the value

$$k_e = 8.9875 \times 10^9 \text{ N} \cdot \text{m}^2/\text{C}^2 \qquad (23.2)$$

Coulomb constant

This constant is also written in the form

$$k_e = \frac{1}{4\pi\epsilon_0} \qquad (23.3)$$

Charles Coulomb

French physicist (1736–1806)

Coulomb's major contributions to science were in the areas of electrostatics and magnetism. During his lifetime, he also investigated the strengths of materials and determined the forces that affect objects on beams, thereby contributing to the field of structural mechanics. In the field of ergonomics, his research provided a fundamental understanding of the ways in which people and animals can best do work. *(Photo courtesy of AIP Niels Bohr Library/E. Scott Barr Collection)*

Table 23.1

Charge and Mass of the Electron, Proton, and Neutron		
Particle	Charge (C)	Mass (kg)
Electron (e)	$-1.602\ 191\ 7 \times 10^{-19}$	$9.109\ 5 \times 10^{-31}$
Proton (p)	$+1.602\ 191\ 7 \times 10^{-19}$	$1.672\ 61 \times 10^{-27}$
Neutron (n)	0	$1.674\ 92 \times 10^{-27}$

where the constant ϵ_0 (lowercase Greek epsilon) is known as the **permittivity of free space** and has the value

$$\epsilon_0 = 8.854\ 2 \times 10^{-12}\ \text{C}^2/\text{N}\cdot\text{m}^2 \tag{23.4}$$

The smallest unit of charge e known in nature[2] is the charge on an electron $(-e)$ or a proton $(+e)$ and has a magnitude

$$e = 1.602\ 19 \times 10^{-19}\ \text{C} \tag{23.5}$$

Therefore, 1 C of charge is approximately equal to the charge of 6.24×10^{18} electrons or protons. This number is very small when compared with the number of free electrons in 1 cm^3 of copper, which is on the order of 10^{23}. Still, 1 C is a substantial amount of charge. In typical experiments in which a rubber or glass rod is charged by friction, a net charge on the order of 10^{-6} C is obtained. In other words, only a very small fraction of the total available charge is transferred between the rod and the rubbing material.

The charges and masses of the electron, proton, and neutron are given in Table 23.1.

Quick Quiz 23.4 Object A has a charge of $+2\ \mu\text{C}$, and object B has a charge of $+6\ \mu\text{C}$. Which statement is true about the electric forces on the objects? (a) $F_{AB} = -3F_{BA}$ (b) $F_{AB} = -F_{BA}$ (c) $3F_{AB} = -F_{BA}$ (d) $F_{AB} = 3F_{BA}$ (e) $F_{AB} = F_{BA}$ (f) $3F_{AB} = F_{BA}$

Example 23.1   The Hydrogen Atom

The electron and proton of a hydrogen atom are separated (on the average) by a distance of approximately 5.3×10^{-11} m. Find the magnitudes of the electric force and the gravitational force between the two particles.

Solution From Coulomb's law, we find that the magnitude of the electric force is

$$F_e = k_e \frac{|e||-e|}{r^2} = (8.99 \times 10^9\ \text{N}\cdot\text{m}^2/\text{C}^2)\ \frac{(1.60 \times 10^{-19}\ \text{C})^2}{(5.3 \times 10^{-11}\ \text{m})^2}$$

$$= \boxed{8.2 \times 10^{-8}\ \text{N}}$$

Using Newton's law of universal gravitation and Table 23.1 for the particle masses, we find that the magnitude of the

gravitational force is

$$F_g = G \frac{m_e m_p}{r^2}$$

$$= (6.67 \times 10^{-11}\ \text{N}\cdot\text{m}^2/\text{kg}^2)$$

$$\times \frac{(9.11 \times 10^{-31}\ \text{kg})(1.67 \times 10^{-27}\ \text{kg})}{(5.3 \times 10^{-11}\ \text{m})^2}$$

$$= \boxed{3.6 \times 10^{-47}\ \text{N}}$$

The ratio $F_e/F_g \approx 2 \times 10^{39}$. Thus, the gravitational force between charged atomic particles is negligible when compared with the electric force. Note the similarity of form of Newton's law of universal gravitation and Coulomb's law of electric forces. Other than magnitude, what is a fundamental difference between the two forces?

---

[2]   No unit of charge smaller than e has been detected on a free particle; however, current theories propose the existence of particles called *quarks* having charges $-e/3$ and $2e/3$. Although there is considerable experimental evidence for such particles inside nuclear matter, *free* quarks have never been detected. We discuss other properties of quarks in Chapter 46 of the extended version of this text.

When dealing with Coulomb's law, you must remember that force is a vector quantity and must be treated accordingly. The law expressed in vector form for the electric force exerted by a charge q_1 on a second charge q_2, written $\mathbf{F}_{12}$, is

$$\mathbf{F}_{12} = k_e \frac{q_1 q_2}{r^2} \hat{\mathbf{r}} \qquad (23.6)$$

where $\hat{\mathbf{r}}$ is a unit vector directed from q_1 toward q_2, as shown in Figure 23.7a. Because the electric force obeys Newton's third law, the electric force exerted by q_2 on q_1 is equal in magnitude to the force exerted by q_1 on q_2 and in the opposite direction; that is, $\mathbf{F}_{21} = -\mathbf{F}_{12}$. Finally, from Equation 23.6, we see that if q_1 and q_2 have the same sign, as in Figure 23.7a, the product $q_1 q_2$ is positive. If q_1 and q_2 are of opposite sign, as shown in Figure 23.7b, the product $q_1 q_2$ is negative. These signs describe the *relative* direction of the force but not the *absolute* direction. A negative product indicates an attractive force, so that the charges each experience a force toward the other—thus, the force on one charge is in a direction *relative* to the other. A positive product indicates a repulsive force such that each charge experiences a force away from the other. The *absolute* direction of the force in space is not determined solely by the sign of $q_1 q_2$—whether the force on an individual charge is in the positive or negative direction on a coordinate axis depends on the location of the other charge. For example, if an x axis lies along the two charges in Figure 23.7a, the product $q_1 q_2$ is positive, but $\mathbf{F}_{12}$ points in the $+x$ direction and $\mathbf{F}_{21}$ points in the $-x$ direction.

Vector form of Coulomb's law

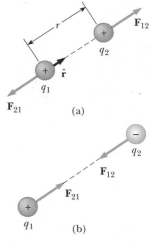

Active Figure 23.7 Two point charges separated by a distance r exert a force on each other that is given by Coulomb's law. The force $\mathbf{F}_{21}$ exerted by q_2 on q_1 is equal in magnitude and opposite in direction to the force $\mathbf{F}_{12}$ exerted by q_1 on q_2. (a) When the charges are of the same sign, the force is repulsive. (b) When the charges are of opposite signs, the force is attractive.

At the Active Figures link at http://www.pse6.com, you can move the charges to any position in two-dimensional space and observe the electric forces on them.

Quick Quiz 23.5 Object A has a charge of $+2\ \mu\text{C}$, and object B has a charge of $+6\ \mu\text{C}$. Which statement is true about the electric forces on the objects? (a) $\mathbf{F}_{AB} = -3\mathbf{F}_{BA}$ (b) $\mathbf{F}_{AB} = -\mathbf{F}_{BA}$ (c) $3\mathbf{F}_{AB} = -\mathbf{F}_{BA}$ (d) $\mathbf{F}_{AB} = 3\mathbf{F}_{BA}$ (e) $\mathbf{F}_{AB} = \mathbf{F}_{BA}$ (f) $3\mathbf{F}_{AB} = \mathbf{F}_{BA}$

When more than two charges are present, the force between any pair of them is given by Equation 23.6. Therefore, the resultant force on any one of them equals the vector sum of the forces exerted by the various individual charges. For example, if four charges are present, then the resultant force exerted by particles 2, 3, and 4 on particle 1 is

$$\mathbf{F}_1 = \mathbf{F}_{21} + \mathbf{F}_{31} + \mathbf{F}_{41}$$

Example 23.2 Find the Resultant Force

Consider three point charges located at the corners of a right triangle as shown in Figure 23.8, where $q_1 = q_3 = 5.0\ \mu\text{C}$,

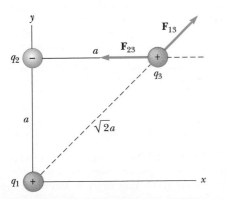

Figure 23.8 (Example 23.2) The force exerted by q_1 on q_3 is $\mathbf{F}_{13}$. The force exerted by q_2 on q_3 is $\mathbf{F}_{23}$. The resultant force $\mathbf{F}_3$ exerted on q_3 is the vector sum $\mathbf{F}_{13} + \mathbf{F}_{23}$.

$q_2 = -2.0\ \mu\text{C}$, and $a = 0.10$ m. Find the resultant force exerted on q_3.

Solution First, note the direction of the individual forces exerted by q_1 and q_2 on q_3. The force $\mathbf{F}_{23}$ exerted by q_2 on q_3 is attractive because q_2 and q_3 have opposite signs. The force $\mathbf{F}_{13}$ exerted by q_1 on q_3 is repulsive because both charges are positive.

The magnitude of $\mathbf{F}_{23}$ is

$$F_{23} = k_e \frac{|q_2||q_3|}{a^2}$$

$$= (8.99 \times 10^9\ \text{N}\cdot\text{m}^2/\text{C}^2) \frac{(2.0 \times 10^{-6}\ \text{C})(5.0 \times 10^{-6}\ \text{C})}{(0.10\ \text{m})^2}$$

$$= 9.0\ \text{N}$$

In the coordinate system shown in Figure 23.8, the attractive force $\mathbf{F}_{23}$ is to the left (in the negative x direction).

The magnitude of the force $\mathbf{F}_{13}$ exerted by q_1 on q_3 is

$$F_{13} = k_e \frac{|q_1||q_3|}{(\sqrt{2}a)^2}$$

$$= (8.99 \times 10^9 \text{ N} \cdot \text{m}^2/\text{C}^2) \frac{(5.0 \times 10^{-6} \text{ C})(5.0 \times 10^{-6} \text{ C})}{2(0.10 \text{ m})^2}$$

$$= 11 \text{ N}$$

The repulsive force $\mathbf{F}_{13}$ makes an angle of 45° with the x axis. Therefore, the x and y components of $\mathbf{F}_{13}$ are equal, with magnitude given by $F_{13} \cos 45° = 7.9$ N.

Combining $\mathbf{F}_{13}$ with $\mathbf{F}_{23}$ by the rules of vector addition, we arrive at the x and y components of the resultant force acting on q_3:

$$F_{3x} = F_{13x} + F_{23x} = 7.9 \text{ N} + (-9.0 \text{ N}) = -1.1 \text{ N}$$

$$F_{3y} = F_{13y} + F_{23y} = 7.9 \text{ N} + 0 = 7.9 \text{ N}$$

We can also express the resultant force acting on q_3 in unit-vector form as

$$\mathbf{F}_3 = \boxed{(-1.1\hat{\mathbf{i}} + 7.9\hat{\mathbf{j}}) \text{ N}}$$

What If? What if the signs of all three charges were changed to the opposite signs? How would this affect the result for $\mathbf{F}_3$?

Answer The charge q_3 would still be attracted toward q_2 and repelled from q_1 with forces of the same magnitude. Thus, the final result for $\mathbf{F}_3$ would be exactly the same.

Example 23.3 Where Is the Resultant Force Zero? `Interactive`

Three point charges lie along the x axis as shown in Figure 23.9. The positive charge $q_1 = 15.0$ μC is at $x = 2.00$ m, the positive charge $q_2 = 6.00$ μC is at the origin, and the resultant force acting on q_3 is zero. What is the x coordinate of q_3?

Solution Because q_3 is negative and q_1 and q_2 are positive, the forces $\mathbf{F}_{13}$ and $\mathbf{F}_{23}$ are both attractive, as indicated in Figure 23.9. From Coulomb's law, $\mathbf{F}_{13}$ and $\mathbf{F}_{23}$ have magnitudes

$$F_{13} = k_e \frac{|q_1||q_3|}{(2.00 - x)^2} \qquad F_{23} = k_e \frac{|q_2||q_3|}{x^2}$$

For the resultant force on q_3 to be zero, $\mathbf{F}_{23}$ must be equal in magnitude and opposite in direction to $\mathbf{F}_{13}$. Setting the magnitudes of the two forces equal, we have

$$k_e \frac{|q_2||q_3|}{x^2} = k_e \frac{|q_1||q_3|}{(2.00 - x)^2}$$

Noting that k_e and $|q_3|$ are common to both sides and so can be dropped, we solve for x and find that

$$(2.00 - x)^2|q_2| = x^2|q_1|$$

$$(4.00 - 4.00x + x^2)(6.00 \times 10^{-6} \text{ C}) = x^2(15.0 \times 10^{-6} \text{ C})$$

This can be reduced to the following quadratic equation:

$$3.00x^2 + 8.00x - 8.00 = 0$$

Solving this quadratic equation for x, we find that the positive root is $x = \boxed{0.775 \text{ m}}$. There is also a second root, $x = -3.44$ m. This is another location at which the magnitudes

of the forces on q_3 are equal, but both forces are in the same direction at this location.

What If? Suppose charge q_3 is constrained to move only along the x axis. From its initial position at $x = 0.775$ m, it is pulled a very small distance along the x axis. When released, will it return to equilibrium or be pulled further from equilibrium? That is, is the equilibrium stable or unstable?

Answer If the charge is moved to the right, $\mathbf{F}_{13}$ becomes larger and $\mathbf{F}_{23}$ becomes smaller. This results in a net force to the right, in the same direction as the displacement. Thus, the equilibrium is *unstable*.

Note that if the charge is constrained to stay at a *fixed x* coordinate but allowed to move up and down in Figure 23.9, the equilibrium is stable. In this case, if the charge is pulled upward (or downward) and released, it will move back toward the equilibrium position and undergo oscillation.

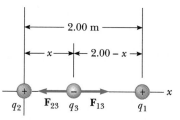

Figure 23.9 (Example 23.3) Three point charges are placed along the x axis. If the resultant force acting on q_3 is zero, then the force $\mathbf{F}_{13}$ exerted by q_1 on q_3 must be equal in magnitude and opposite in direction to the force $\mathbf{F}_{23}$ exerted by q_2 on q_3.

🖱 At the *Interactive Worked Example* link at **http://www.pse6.com,** you can predict where on the x axis the electric force is zero for random values of q_1 and q_2.

Example 23.4 Find the Charge on the Spheres

Two identical small charged spheres, each having a mass of 3.0×10^{-2} kg, hang in equilibrium as shown in Figure 23.10a. The length of each string is 0.15 m, and the angle θ is 5.0°. Find the magnitude of the charge on each sphere.

Solution Figure 23.10a helps us conceptualize this problem—the two spheres exert repulsive forces on each other. If they are held close to each other and released, they will move outward from the center and settle into the configuration in Figure 23.10a after the damped oscillations

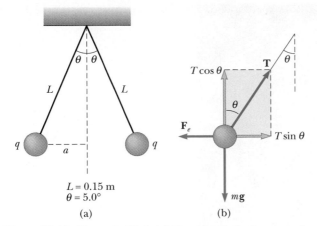

(a)   **(b)**

Figure 23.10 (Example 23.4) (a) Two identical spheres, each carrying the same charge q, suspended in equilibrium. (b) The free-body diagram for the sphere on the left.

due to air resistance have vanished. The key phrase "in equilibrium" helps us categorize this as an equilibrium problem, which we approach as we did equilibrium problems in Chapter 5 with the added feature that one of the forces on a sphere is an electric force. We analyze this problem by drawing the free-body diagram for the left-hand sphere in Figure 23.10b. The sphere is in equilibrium under the application of the forces **T** from the string, the electric force **F**$_e$ from the other sphere, and the gravitational force m**g**.

Because the sphere is in equilibrium, the forces in the horizontal and vertical directions must separately add up to zero:

$$(1) \qquad \sum F_x = T \sin \theta - F_e = 0$$

$$(2) \qquad \sum F_y = T \cos \theta - mg = 0$$

From Equation (2), we see that $T = mg/\cos \theta$; thus, T can be eliminated from Equation (1) if we make this substitution. This gives a value for the magnitude of the electric force F_e:

$$F_e = mg \tan \theta = (3.0 \times 10^{-2} \text{ kg})(9.80 \text{ m/s}^2) \tan(5.0°)$$

$$= 2.6 \times 10^{-2} \text{ N}$$

Considering the geometry of the right triangle in Figure 23.10a, we see that $\sin \theta = a/L$. Therefore,

$$a = L \sin \theta = (0.15 \text{ m}) \sin(5.0°) = 0.013 \text{ m}$$

The separation of the spheres is $2a = 0.026$ m.

From Coulomb's law (Eq. 23.1), the magnitude of the electric force is

$$F_e = k_e \frac{|q|^2}{r^2}$$

where $r = 2a = 0.026$ m and $|q|$ is the magnitude of the charge on each sphere. (Note that the term $|q|^2$ arises here because the charge is the same on both spheres.) This equation can be solved for $|q|^2$ to give

$$|q|^2 = \frac{F_e r^2}{k_e} = \frac{(2.6 \times 10^{-2} \text{ N})(0.026 \text{ m})^2}{8.99 \times 10^9 \text{ N} \cdot \text{m}^2/\text{C}^2} = 1.96 \times 10^{-15} \text{ C}^2$$

$$|q| = \quad 4.4 \times 10^{-8} \text{ C}$$

To finalize the problem, note that we found only the magnitude of the charge $|q|$ on the spheres. There is no way we could find the sign of the charge from the information given. In fact, the sign of the charge is not important. The situation will be exactly the same whether both spheres are positively charged or negatively charged.

What If? Suppose your roommate proposes solving this problem without the assumption that the charges are of equal magnitude. She claims that the symmetry of the problem is destroyed if the charges are not equal, so that the strings would make two different angles with the vertical, and the problem would be much more complicated. How would you respond?

Answer You should argue that the symmetry is not destroyed and the angles remain the same. Newton's third law requires that the electric forces on the two charges be the same, regardless of the equality or nonequality of the charges. The solution to the example remains the same through the calculation of $|q|^2$. In this situation, the value of 1.96×10^{-15} C^2 corresponds to the product $q_1 q_2$, where q_1 and q_2 are the values of the charges on the two spheres. The symmetry of the problem would be destroyed if the *masses* of the spheres were not the same. In this case, the strings would make different angles with the vertical and the problem would be more complicated.

23.4 The Electric Field

Two field forces have been introduced into our discussions so far—the gravitational force in Chapter 13 and the electric force here. As pointed out earlier, field forces can act through space, producing an effect even when no physical contact occurs between interacting objects. The gravitational field **g** at a point in space was defined in Section 13.5 to be equal to the gravitational force **F**$_g$ acting on a test particle of mass m divided by that mass: $\mathbf{g} \equiv \mathbf{F}_g/m$. The concept of a field was developed by Michael Faraday (1791–1867) in the context of electric forces and is of such practical value that we shall devote much attention to it in the next several chapters. In this approach, an **electric field** is said to exist in the region of space around a charged object—the **source charge.** When another charged object—the **test charge**—enters this electric field, an

This dramatic photograph captures a lightning bolt striking a tree near some rural homes. Lightning is associated with very strong electric fields in the atmosphere.

©Johnny Autery

Figure 23.11 A small positive test charge q_0 placed near an object carrying a much larger positive charge Q experiences an electric field $\mathbf{E}$ directed as shown.

Definition of electric field

electric force acts on it. As an example, consider Figure 23.11, which shows a small positive test charge q_0 placed near a second object carrying a much greater positive charge Q. We define the electric field due to the source charge at the location of the test charge to be the electric force on the test charge *per unit charge*, or to be more specific

> **the electric field vector E** at a point in space is defined as the electric force $\mathbf{F}_e$ acting on a positive test charge q_0 placed at that point divided by the test charge:
>
> $$\mathbf{E} \equiv \frac{\mathbf{F}_e}{q_0} \qquad (23.7)$$

▲ **PITFALL PREVENTION**

23.1 Particles Only

Equation 23.8 is only valid for a charged *particle*—an object of zero size. For a charged object of finite size in an electric field, the field may vary in magnitude and direction over the size of the object, so the corresponding force equation may be more complicated.

Note that $\mathbf{E}$ is the field produced by some charge or charge distribution *separate from* the test charge—it is not the field produced by the test charge itself. Also, note that the existence of an electric field is a property of its source—the presence of the test charge is not necessary for the field to exist. The test charge serves as a *detector* of the electric field.

Equation 23.7 can be rearranged as

$$\mathbf{F}_e = q\mathbf{E} \qquad (23.8)$$

where we have used the general symbol q for a charge. This equation gives us the force on a charged particle placed in an electric field. If q is positive, the force is in the same

Table 23.2

Typical Electric Field Values	
Source	$E\,(\text{N/C})$
Fluorescent lighting tube	10
Atmosphere (fair weather)	100
Balloon rubbed on hair	1 000
Atmosphere (under thundercloud)	10 000
Photocopier	100 000
Spark in air	>3 000 000
Near electron in hydrogen atom	5×10^{11}

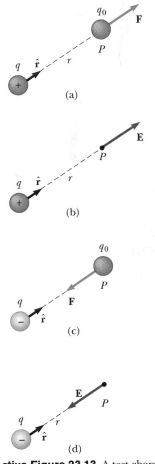

Figure 23.12 (a) For a small enough test charge q_0, the charge distribution on the sphere is undisturbed. (b) When the test charge q'_0 is greater, the charge distribution on the sphere is disturbed as the result of the proximity of q'_0.

Active Figure 23.13 A test charge q_0 at point P is a distance r from a point charge q. (a) If q is positive, then the force on the test charge is directed away from q. (b) For the positive source charge, the electric field at P points radially outward from q. (c) If q is negative, then the force on the test charge is directed toward q. (d) For the negative source charge, the electric field at P points radially inward toward q.

At the Active Figures link at http://www.pse6.com, you can move point P to any position in two-dimensional space and observe the electric field due to q.

direction as the field. If q is negative, the force and the field are in opposite directions. Notice the similarity between Equation 23.8 and the corresponding equation for a particle with mass placed in a gravitational field, $\mathbf{F}_g = m\mathbf{g}$ (Eq. 5.6).

The vector $\mathbf{E}$ has the SI units of newtons per coulomb (N/C). The direction of $\mathbf{E}$, as shown in Figure 23.11, is the direction of the force a positive test charge experiences when placed in the field. We say that **an electric field exists at a point if a test charge at that point experiences an electric force.** Once the magnitude and direction of the electric field are known at some point, the electric force exerted on *any* charged particle placed at that point can be calculated from Equation 23.8. The electric field magnitudes for various field sources are given in Table 23.2.

When using Equation 23.7, we must assume that the test charge q_0 is small enough that it does not disturb the charge distribution responsible for the electric field. If a vanishingly small test charge q_0 is placed near a uniformly charged metallic sphere, as in Figure 23.12a, the charge on the metallic sphere, which produces the electric field, remains uniformly distributed. If the test charge is great enough ($q'_0 \gg q_0$), as in Figure 23.12b, the charge on the metallic sphere is redistributed and the ratio of the force to the test charge is different: $(F'_e/q'_0 \neq F_e/q_0)$. That is, because of this redistribution of charge on the metallic sphere, the electric field it sets up is different from the field it sets up in the presence of the much smaller test charge q_0.

To determine the direction of an electric field, consider a point charge q as a source charge. This charge creates an electric field at all points in space surrounding it. A test charge q_0 is placed at point P, a distance r from the source charge, as in Figure 23.13a. We imagine using the test charge to determine the direction of the electric force and therefore that of the electric field. However, the electric field does not depend on the existence of the test charge—it is established solely by the source charge. According to Coulomb's law, the force exerted by q on the test charge is

$$\mathbf{F}_e = k_e \frac{qq_0}{r^2}\,\hat{\mathbf{r}}$$

where $\hat{\mathbf{r}}$ is a unit vector directed from q toward q_0. This force in Figure 23.13a is directed away from the source charge q. Because the electric field at P, the position of the test charge, is defined by $\mathbf{E} = \mathbf{F}_e/q_0$, we find that at P, the electric field created by q is

$$\mathbf{E} = k_e \frac{q}{r^2}\,\hat{\mathbf{r}} \tag{23.9}$$

If the source charge q is positive, Figure 23.13b shows the situation with the test charge removed—the source charge sets up an electric field at point P, directed away from q. If q is negative, as in Figure 23.13c, the force on the test charge is toward the source charge, so the electric field at P is directed toward the source charge, as in Figure 23.13d.

To calculate the electric field at a point P due to a group of point charges, we first calculate the electric field vectors at P individually using Equation 23.9 and then add them vectorially. In other words,

> at any point P, the total electric field due to a group of source charges equals the vector sum of the electric fields of all the charges.

This superposition principle applied to fields follows directly from the superposition property of electric forces, which, in turn, follows from the fact that we know that forces add as vectors from Chapter 5. Thus, the electric field at point P due to a group of source charges can be expressed as the vector sum

Electric field due to a finite number of point charges

$$\mathbf{E} = k_e \sum_i \frac{q_i}{r_i^2} \hat{\mathbf{r}}_i \qquad (23.10)$$

where r_i is the distance from the ith source charge q_i to the point P and $\hat{\mathbf{r}}_i$ is a unit vector directed from q_i toward P.

Quick Quiz 23.6 A test charge of $+3 \ \mu C$ is at a point P where an external electric field is directed to the right and has a magnitude of 4×10^6 N/C. If the test charge is replaced with another test charge of $-3 \ \mu C$, the external electric field at P (a) is unaffected (b) reverses direction (c) changes in a way that cannot be determined

Example 23.5 Electric Field Due to Two Charges

A charge $q_1 = 7.0 \ \mu C$ is located at the origin, and a second charge $q_2 = -5.0 \ \mu C$ is located on the x axis, 0.30 m from the origin (Fig. 23.14). Find the electric field at the point P, which has coordinates (0, 0.40) m.

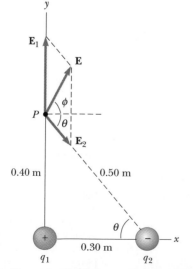

Figure 23.14 (Example 23.5) The total electric field $\mathbf{E}$ at P equals the vector sum $\mathbf{E}_1 + \mathbf{E}_2$, where $\mathbf{E}_1$ is the field due to the positive charge q_1 and $\mathbf{E}_2$ is the field due to the negative charge q_2.

Solution First, let us find the magnitude of the electric field at P due to each charge. The fields $\mathbf{E}_1$ due to the 7.0-μC charge and $\mathbf{E}_2$ due to the -5.0-μC charge are shown in Figure 23.14. Their magnitudes are

$$E_1 = k_e \frac{|q_1|}{r_1^2} = (8.99 \times 10^9 \ \text{N} \cdot \text{m}^2/\text{C}^2) \frac{(7.0 \times 10^{-6} \ \text{C})}{(0.40 \ \text{m})^2}$$
$$= 3.9 \times 10^5 \ \text{N/C}$$

$$E_2 = k_e \frac{|q_2|}{r_2^2} = (8.99 \times 10^9 \ \text{N} \cdot \text{m}^2/\text{C}^2) \frac{(5.0 \times 10^{-6} \ \text{C})}{(0.50 \ \text{m})^2}$$
$$= 1.8 \times 10^5 \ \text{N/C}$$

The vector $\mathbf{E}_1$ has only a y component. The vector $\mathbf{E}_2$ has an x component given by $E_2 \cos \theta = \frac{3}{5} E_2$ and a negative y component given by $-E_2 \sin \theta = -\frac{4}{5} E_2$. Hence, we can express the vectors as

$$\mathbf{E}_1 = 3.9 \times 10^5 \hat{\mathbf{j}} \ \text{N/C}$$
$$\mathbf{E}_2 = (1.1 \times 10^5 \hat{\mathbf{i}} - 1.4 \times 10^5 \hat{\mathbf{j}}) \ \text{N/C}$$

The resultant field $\mathbf{E}$ at P is the superposition of $\mathbf{E}_1$ and $\mathbf{E}_2$:

$$\mathbf{E} = \mathbf{E}_1 + \mathbf{E}_2 = (1.1 \times 10^5 \hat{\mathbf{i}} + 2.5 \times 10^5 \hat{\mathbf{j}}) \ \text{N/C}$$

From this result, we find that $\mathbf{E}$ makes an angle ϕ of 66° with the positive x axis and has a magnitude of 2.7×10^5 N/C.

Example 23.6   Electric Field of a Dipole

An **electric dipole** is defined as a positive charge q and a negative charge $-q$ separated by a distance $2a$. For the dipole shown in Figure 23.15, find the electric field $\mathbf{E}$ at P due to the dipole, where P is a distance $y \gg a$ from the origin.

Solution At P, the fields $\mathbf{E}_1$ and $\mathbf{E}_2$ due to the two charges are equal in magnitude because P is equidistant from the charges. The total field is $\mathbf{E} = \mathbf{E}_1 + \mathbf{E}_2$, where

$$E_1 = E_2 = k_e \frac{q}{r^2} = k_e \frac{q}{y^2 + a^2}$$

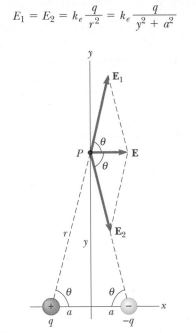

Figure 23.15 (Example 23.6) The total electric field $\mathbf{E}$ at P due to two charges of equal magnitude and opposite sign (an electric dipole) equals the vector sum $\mathbf{E}_1 + \mathbf{E}_2$. The field $\mathbf{E}_1$ is due to the positive charge q, and $\mathbf{E}_2$ is the field due to the negative charge $-q$.

The y components of $\mathbf{E}_1$ and $\mathbf{E}_2$ cancel each other, and the x components are both in the positive x direction and have the same magnitude. Therefore, $\mathbf{E}$ is parallel to the x axis and has a magnitude equal to $2E_1 \cos \theta$. From Figure 23.15 we see that $\cos \theta = a/r = a/(y^2 + a^2)^{1/2}$. Therefore,

$$E = 2E_1 \cos \theta = 2k_e \frac{q}{(y^2 + a^2)} \frac{a}{(y^2 + a^2)^{1/2}}$$

$$= k_e \frac{2qa}{(y^2 + a^2)^{3/2}}$$

Because $y \gg a$, we can neglect a^2 compared to y^2 and write

$$E \approx k_e \frac{2qa}{y^3}$$

Thus, we see that, at distances far from a dipole but along the perpendicular bisector of the line joining the two charges, the magnitude of the electric field created by the dipole varies as $1/r^3$, whereas the more slowly varying field of a point charge varies as $1/r^2$ (see Eq. 23.9). This is because at distant points, the fields of the two charges of equal magnitude and opposite sign almost cancel each other. The $1/r^3$ variation in E for the dipole also is obtained for a distant point along the x axis (see Problem 22) and for any general distant point.

The electric dipole is a good model of many molecules, such as hydrochloric acid (HCl). Neutral atoms and molecules behave as dipoles when placed in an external electric field. Furthermore, many molecules, such as HCl, are permanent dipoles. The effect of such dipoles on the behavior of materials subjected to electric fields is discussed in Chapter 26.

23.5 Electric Field of a Continuous Charge Distribution

Very often the distances between charges in a group of charges are much smaller than the distance from the group to some point of interest (for example, a point where the electric field is to be calculated). In such situations, the system of charges can be modeled as continuous. That is, the system of closely spaced charges is equivalent to a total charge that is continuously distributed along some line, over some surface, or throughout some volume.

To evaluate the electric field created by a continuous charge distribution, we use the following procedure: first, we divide the charge distribution into small elements, each of which contains a small charge Δq, as shown in Figure 23.16. Next, we use Equation 23.9 to calculate the electric field due to one of these elements at a point P. Finally, we evaluate the total electric field at P due to the charge distribution by summing the contributions of all the charge elements (that is, by applying the superposition principle).

The electric field at P due to one charge element carrying charge Δq is

$$\Delta \mathbf{E} = k_e \frac{\Delta q}{r^2} \hat{\mathbf{r}}$$

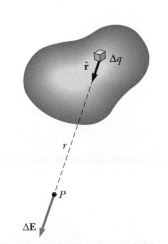

Figure 23.16 The electric field at P due to a continuous charge distribution is the vector sum of the fields $\Delta \mathbf{E}$ due to all the elements Δq of the charge distribution.

where r is the distance from the charge element to point P and $\hat{\mathbf{r}}$ is a unit vector directed from the element toward P. The total electric field at P due to all elements in the charge distribution is approximately

$$\mathbf{E} \approx k_e \sum_i \frac{\Delta q_i}{r_i{}^2} \hat{\mathbf{r}}_i$$

where the index i refers to the ith element in the distribution. Because the charge distribution is modeled as continuous, the total field at P in the limit $\Delta q_i \rightarrow 0$ is

$$\mathbf{E} = k_e \lim_{\Delta q_i \rightarrow 0} \sum_i \frac{\Delta q_i}{r_i{}^2} \hat{\mathbf{r}}_i = k_e \int \frac{dq}{r^2} \hat{\mathbf{r}} \qquad (23.11)$$

where the integration is over the entire charge distribution. This is a vector operation and must be treated appropriately.

We illustrate this type of calculation with several examples, in which we assume the charge is uniformly distributed on a line, on a surface, or throughout a volume. When performing such calculations, it is convenient to use the concept of a *charge density* along with the following notations:

- If a charge Q is uniformly distributed throughout a volume V, the **volume charge density** ρ is defined by

$$\rho \equiv \frac{Q}{V}$$

where ρ has units of coulombs per cubic meter (C/m^3).

- If a charge Q is uniformly distributed on a surface of area A, the **surface charge density** σ (lowercase Greek sigma) is defined by

$$\sigma \equiv \frac{Q}{A}$$

where σ has units of coulombs per square meter (C/m^2).

- If a charge Q is uniformly distributed along a line of length ℓ, the **linear charge density** λ is defined by

$$\lambda \equiv \frac{Q}{\ell}$$

where λ has units of coulombs per meter (C/m).

- If the charge is nonuniformly distributed over a volume, surface, or line, the amounts of charge dq in a small volume, surface, or length element are

$$dq = \rho \, dV \qquad dq = \sigma \, dA \qquad dq = \lambda \, d\ell$$

PROBLEM-SOLVING HINTS

Finding the Electric Field

- **Units:** in calculations using the Coulomb constant k_e $(= 1/4\pi\epsilon_0)$, charges must be expressed in coulombs and distances in meters.

- **Calculating the electric field of point charges:** to find the total electric field at a given point, first calculate the electric field at the point due to each individual charge. The resultant field at the point is the vector sum of the fields due to the individual charges.

- **Continuous charge distributions:** when you are confronted with problems that involve a continuous distribution of charge, the vector sums for evaluating the total electric field at some point must be replaced by vector integrals. Divide the charge distribution into infinitesimal pieces, and calculate the vector sum by integrating over the entire charge distribution. Examples 23.7 through 23.9 demonstrate this technique.

● **Symmetry:** with both distributions of point charges and continuous charge distributions, take advantage of any symmetry in the system to simplify your calculations.

Example 23.7   The Electric Field Due to a Charged Rod

A rod of length ℓ has a uniform positive charge per unit length λ and a total charge Q. Calculate the electric field at a point P that is located along the long axis of the rod and a distance a from one end (Fig. 23.17).

Solution Let us assume that the rod is lying along the x axis, that dx is the length of one small segment, and that dq is the charge on that segment. Because the rod has a charge per unit length λ, the charge dq on the small segment is $dq = \lambda \, dx$.

The field $d\mathbf{E}$ at P due to this segment is in the negative x direction (because the source of the field carries a positive charge), and its magnitude is

$$dE = k_e \frac{dq}{x^2} = k_e \frac{\lambda \, dx}{x^2}$$

Because every other element also produces a field in the negative x direction, the problem of summing their contributions

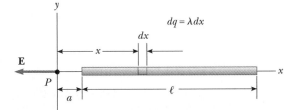

Figure 23.17 (Example 23.7) The electric field at P due to a uniformly charged rod lying along the x axis. The magnitude of the field at P due to the segment of charge dq is $k_e dq/x^2$. The total field at P is the vector sum over all segments of the rod.

is particularly simple in this case. The total field at P due to all segments of the rod, which are at different distances from P, is given by Equation 23.11, which in this case becomes[3]

$$E = \int_a^{\ell+a} k_e \lambda \frac{dx}{x^2}$$

where the limits on the integral extend from one end of the rod ($x = a$) to the other ($x = \ell + a$). The constants k_e and λ can be removed from the integral to yield

$$E = k_e \lambda \int_a^{\ell+a} \frac{dx}{x^2} = k_e \lambda \left[-\frac{1}{x} \right]_a^{\ell+a}$$

$$= k_e \lambda \left(\frac{1}{a} - \frac{1}{\ell + a} \right) = \boxed{\frac{k_e Q}{a(\ell + a)}}$$

where we have used the fact that the total charge $Q = \lambda \ell$.

What If? Suppose we move to a point P very far away from the rod. What is the nature of the electric field at such a point?

Answer If P is far from the rod ($a \gg \ell$), then ℓ in the denominator of the final expression for E can be neglected, and $E \approx k_e Q/a^2$. This is just the form you would expect for a point charge. Therefore, at large values of a/ℓ, the charge distribution appears to be a point charge of magnitude Q—we are so far away from the rod that we cannot distinguish that it has a size. The use of the limiting technique ($a/\ell \to \infty$) often is a good method for checking a mathematical expression.

Example 23.8   The Electric Field of a Uniform Ring of Charge

A ring of radius a carries a uniformly distributed positive total charge Q. Calculate the electric field due to the ring at a point P lying a distance x from its center along the central axis perpendicular to the plane of the ring (Fig. 23.18a).

Solution The magnitude of the electric field at P due to the segment of charge dq is

$$dE = k_e \frac{dq}{r^2}$$

This field has an x component $dE_x = dE \cos \theta$ along the x axis and a component $dE_\perp$ perpendicular to the x axis. As we see in Figure 23.18b, however, the resultant field at P must lie along the x axis because the perpendicular com-

---

[3]   It is important that you understand how to carry out integrations such as this. First, express the charge element dq in terms of the other variables in the integral. (In this example, there is one variable, x, and so we made the change $dq = \lambda \, dx$.) The integral must be over scalar quantities; therefore, you must express the electric field in terms of components, if necessary. (In this example the field has only an x component, so we do not bother with this detail.) Then, reduce your expression to an integral over a single variable (or to multiple integrals, each over a single variable). In examples that have spherical or cylindrical symmetry, the single variable will be a radial coordinate.

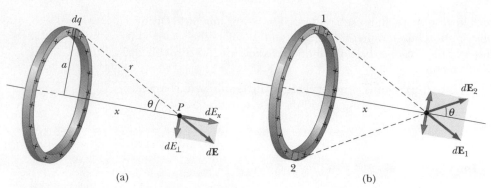

Figure 23.18 (Example 23.8) A uniformly charged ring of radius a. (a) The field at P on the x axis due to an element of charge dq. (b) The total electric field at P is along the x axis. The perpendicular component of the field at P due to segment 1 is canceled by the perpendicular component due to segment 2.

ponents of all the various charge segments sum to zero. That is, the perpendicular component of the field created by any charge element is canceled by the perpendicular component created by an element on the opposite side of the ring. Because $r = (x^2 + a^2)^{1/2}$ and $\cos \theta = x/r$, we find that

$$dE_x = dE \cos \theta = \left(k_e \frac{dq}{r^2} \right) \frac{x}{r} = \frac{k_e x}{(x^2 + a^2)^{3/2}} \, dq$$

All segments of the ring make the same contribution to the field at P because they are all equidistant from this point. Thus, we can integrate to obtain the total field at P:

$$E_x = \int \frac{k_e x}{(x^2 + a^2)^{3/2}} \, dq = \frac{k_e x}{(x^2 + a^2)^{3/2}} \int dq$$

$$= \frac{k_e x}{(x^2 + a^2)^{3/2}} \, Q$$

This result shows that the field is zero at $x = 0$. Does this finding surprise you?

What If? Suppose a negative charge is placed at the center of the ring in Figure 23.18 and displaced slightly by a distance $x \ll a$ along the x axis. When released, what type of motion does it exhibit?

Answer In the expression for the field due to a ring of charge, we let $x \ll a$, which results in

$$E_x = \frac{k_e Q}{a^3} \, x$$

Thus, from Equation 23.8, the force on a charge $-q$ placed near the center of the ring is

$$F_x = -\frac{k_e q Q}{a^3} \, x$$

Because this force has the form of Hooke's law (Eq. 15.1), the motion will be *simple harmonic*!

Example 23.9   The Electric Field of a Uniformly Charged Disk

A disk of radius R has a uniform surface charge density σ. Calculate the electric field at a point P that lies along the central perpendicular axis of the disk and a distance x from the center of the disk (Fig. 23.19).

Solution If we consider the disk as a set of concentric rings, we can use our result from Example 23.8—which gives the field created by a ring of radius a—and sum the contributions of all rings making up the disk. By symmetry, the field at an axial point must be along the central axis.

The ring of radius r and width dr shown in Figure 23.19 has a surface area equal to $2\pi r \, dr$. The charge dq on this ring is equal to the area of the ring multiplied by the surface charge density: $dq = 2\pi \sigma r \, dr$. Using this result in the equation given for E_x in Example 23.8 (with a replaced by r), we have for the field due to the ring

$$dE_x = \frac{k_e x}{(x^2 + r^2)^{3/2}} (2\pi \sigma r \, dr)$$

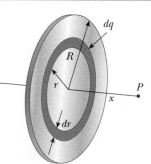

Figure 23.19 (Example 23.9) A uniformly charged disk of radius R. The electric field at an axial point P is directed along the central axis, perpendicular to the plane of the disk.

To obtain the total field at P, we integrate this expression over the limits $r = 0$ to $r = R$, noting that x is a constant.

This gives

$$E_x = k_e x \pi \sigma \int_0^R \frac{2r\,dr}{(x^2 + r^2)^{3/2}}$$

$$= k_e x \pi \sigma \int_0^R (x^2 + r^2)^{-3/2}\,d(r^2)$$

$$= k_e x \pi \sigma \left[\frac{(x^2 + r^2)^{-1/2}}{-1/2} \right]_0^R$$

$$= 2\pi k_e \sigma \left(1 - \frac{x}{(x^2 + R^2)^{1/2}} \right)$$

This result is valid for all values of $x > 0$. We can calculate the field close to the disk along the axis by assuming that $R \gg x$; thus, the expression in parentheses reduces to unity to give us the near-field approximation:

$$E_x = 2\pi k_e \sigma = \frac{\sigma}{2\epsilon_0}$$

where ϵ_0 is the permittivity of free space. In the next chapter we shall obtain the same result for the field created by a uniformly charged infinite sheet.

23.6 Electric Field Lines

We have defined the electric field mathematically through Equation 23.7. We now explore a means of representing the electric field pictorially. A convenient way of visualizing electric field patterns is to draw curved lines that are parallel to the electric field vector at any point in space. These lines, called *electric field lines* and first introduced by Faraday, are related to the electric field in a region of space in the following manner:

- The electric field vector **E** is tangent to the electric field line at each point. The line has a direction, indicated by an arrowhead, that is the same as that of the electric field vector.

- The number of lines per unit area through a surface perpendicular to the lines is proportional to the magnitude of the electric field in that region. Thus, the field lines are close together where the electric field is strong and far apart where the field is weak.

These properties are illustrated in Figure 23.20. The density of lines through surface A is greater than the density of lines through surface B. Therefore, the magnitude of the electric field is larger on surface A than on surface B. Furthermore, the fact that the lines at different locations point in different directions indicates that the field is nonuniform.

Is this relationship between strength of the electric field and the density of field lines consistent with Equation 23.9, the expression we obtained for E using Coulomb's law? To answer this question, consider an imaginary spherical surface of radius r concentric with a point charge. From symmetry, we see that the magnitude of the electric field is the same everywhere on the surface of the sphere. The number of lines N that emerge from the charge is equal to the number that penetrate the spherical surface. Hence, the number of lines per unit area on the sphere is $N/4\pi r^2$ (where the surface area of the sphere is $4\pi r^2$). Because E is proportional to the number of lines per unit area, we see that E varies as $1/r^2$; this finding is consistent with Equation 23.9.

Representative electric field lines for the field due to a single positive point charge are shown in Figure 23.21a. This two-dimensional drawing shows only the field lines that lie in the plane containing the point charge. The lines are actually directed radially outward from the charge in all directions; thus, instead of the flat "wheel" of lines shown, you should picture an entire spherical distribution of lines. Because a positive test charge placed in this field would be repelled by the positive source charge, the lines are directed radially away from the source charge. The electric field lines representing the field due to a single negative point charge are directed toward the charge (Fig. 23.21b). In either case, the lines are along the radial direction and extend all the way to infinity. Note that the lines become closer together as they approach the charge; this indicates that the strength of the field increases as we move toward the source charge.

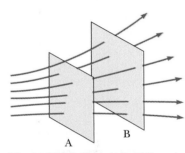

Figure 23.20 Electric field lines penetrating two surfaces. The magnitude of the field is greater on surface A than on surface B.

⚠ **PITFALL PREVENTION**

23.2 Electric Field Lines are not Paths of Particles!

Electric field lines represent the field at various locations. Except in very special cases, they *do not* represent the path of a charged particle moving in an electric field.

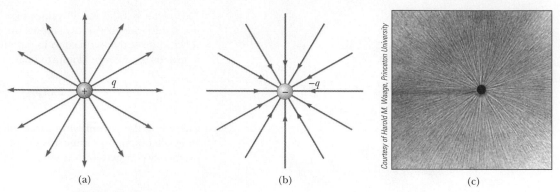

(a)   (b)   (c)

Figure 23.21 The electric field lines for a point charge. (a) For a positive point charge, the lines are directed radially outward. (b) For a negative point charge, the lines are directed radially inward. Note that the figures show only those field lines that lie in the plane of the page. (c) The dark areas are small pieces of thread suspended in oil, which align with the electric field produced by a small charged conductor at the center.

The rules for drawing electric field lines are as follows:

- The lines must begin on a positive charge and terminate on a negative charge. In the case of an excess of one type of charge, some lines will begin or end infinitely far away.
- The number of lines drawn leaving a positive charge or approaching a negative charge is proportional to the magnitude of the charge.
- No two field lines can cross.

We choose the number of field lines starting from any positively charged object to be Cq and the number of lines ending on any negatively charged object to be $C|q|$, where C is an arbitrary proportionality constant. Once C is chosen, the number of lines is fixed. For example, if object 1 has charge Q_1 and object 2 has charge Q_2, then the ratio of number of lines is $N_2/N_1 = Q_2/Q_1$. The electric field lines for two point charges of equal magnitude but opposite signs (an electric dipole) are shown in Figure 23.22. Because the charges are of equal magnitude, the number of lines that begin at the positive charge must equal the number that terminate at the negative charge. At points very near the charges, the lines are nearly radial. The high density of lines between the charges indicates a region of strong electric field.

PITFALL PREVENTION

23.3 Electric Field Lines are not Real

Electric field lines are not material objects. They are used only as a pictorial representation to provide a qualitative description of the electric field. Only a finite number of lines from each charge can be drawn, which makes it appear as if the field were quantized and exists only in certain parts of space. The field, in fact, is continuous—existing at every point. You should avoid obtaining the wrong impression from a two-dimensional drawing of field lines used to describe a three-dimensional situation.

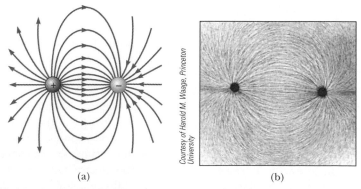

(a)   (b)

Figure 23.22 (a) The electric field lines for two point charges of equal magnitude and opposite sign (an electric dipole). The number of lines leaving the positive charge equals the number terminating at the negative charge. (b) The dark lines are small pieces of thread suspended in oil, which align with the electric field of a dipole.

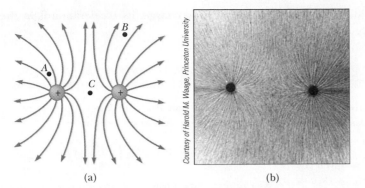

Courtesy of Harold M. Waage, Princeton University

(a)   (b)

Figure 23.23 (a) The electric field lines for two positive point charges. (The locations A, B, and C are discussed in Quick Quiz 23.7.) (b) Pieces of thread suspended in oil, which align with the electric field created by two equal-magnitude positive charges.

Figure 23.23 shows the electric field lines in the vicinity of two equal positive point charges. Again, the lines are nearly radial at points close to either charge, and the same number of lines emerge from each charge because the charges are equal in magnitude. At great distances from the charges, the field is approximately equal to that of a single point charge of magnitude $2q$.

Finally, in Figure 23.24 we sketch the electric field lines associated with a positive charge $+2q$ and a negative charge $-q$. In this case, the number of lines leaving $+2q$ is twice the number terminating at $-q$. Hence, only half of the lines that leave the positive charge reach the negative charge. The remaining half terminate on a negative charge we assume to be at infinity. At distances that are much greater than the charge separation, the electric field lines are equivalent to those of a single charge $+q$.

> **Quick Quiz 23.7** Rank the magnitudes of the electric field at points A, B, and C shown in Figure 23.23a (greatest magnitude first).

> **Quick Quiz 23.8** Which of the following statements about electric field lines associated with electric charges is false? (a) Electric field lines can be either straight or curved. (b) Electric field lines can form closed loops. (c) Electric field lines begin on positive charges and end on negative charges. (d) Electric field lines can never intersect with one another.

23.7 Motion of Charged Particles in a Uniform Electric Field

When a particle of charge q and mass m is placed in an electric field $\mathbf{E}$, the electric force exerted on the charge is $q\mathbf{E}$ according to Equation 23.8. If this is the only force exerted on the particle, it must be the net force and causes the particle to accelerate according to Newton's second law. Thus,

$$\mathbf{F}_e = q\mathbf{E} = m\mathbf{a}$$

The acceleration of the particle is therefore

$$\mathbf{a} = \frac{q\mathbf{E}}{m} \qquad (23.12)$$

If $\mathbf{E}$ is uniform (that is, constant in magnitude and direction), then the acceleration is constant. If the particle has a positive charge, its acceleration is in the direction of the

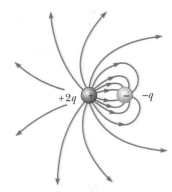

$+2q$ $-q$

Active Figure 23.24 The electric field lines for a point charge $+2q$ and a second point charge $-q$. Note that two lines leave $+2q$ for every one that terminates on $-q$.

At the Active Figures link at http://www.pse6.com, you can choose the values and signs for the two charges and observe the electric field lines for the configuration that you have chosen.

electric field. If the particle has a negative charge, its acceleration is in the direction opposite the electric field.

Example 23.10   An Accelerating Positive Charge

A positive point charge q of mass m is released from rest in a uniform electric field $\mathbf{E}$ directed along the x axis, as shown in Figure 23.25. Describe its motion.

Solution The acceleration is constant and is given by $q\mathbf{E}/m$. The motion is simple linear motion along the x axis. Therefore, we can apply the equations of kinematics in one dimension (see Chapter 2):

$$x_f = x_i + v_i t + \tfrac{1}{2}at^2$$

$$v_f = v_i + at$$

$$v_f{}^2 = v_i{}^2 + 2a(x_f - x_i)$$

Choosing the initial position of the charge as $x_i = 0$ and assigning $v_i = 0$ because the particle starts from rest, the position of the particle as a function of time is

$$x_f = \tfrac{1}{2}at^2 = \frac{qE}{2m}t^2$$

The speed of the particle is given by

$$v_f = at = \frac{qE}{m}t$$

The third kinematic equation gives us

$$v_f{}^2 = 2ax_f = \left(\frac{2qE}{m}\right)x_f$$

from which we can find the kinetic energy of the charge after it has moved a distance $\Delta x = x_f - x_i$:

$$K = \tfrac{1}{2}mv_f{}^2 = \tfrac{1}{2}m\left(\frac{2qE}{m}\right)\Delta x = qE\Delta x$$

We can also obtain this result from the work–kinetic energy theorem because the work done by the electric force is $F_e\Delta x = qE\Delta x$ and $W = \Delta K$.

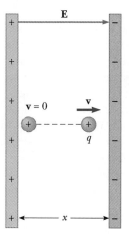

Figure 23.25 (Example 23.10) A positive point charge q in a uniform electric field $\mathbf{E}$ undergoes constant acceleration in the direction of the field.

The electric field in the region between two oppositely charged flat metallic plates is approximately uniform (Fig. 23.26). Suppose an electron of charge $-e$ is projected horizontally into this field from the origin with an initial velocity $v_i\hat{\mathbf{i}}$ at time $t = 0$. Because the electric field $\mathbf{E}$ in Figure 23.26 is in the positive y direction, the acceleration of the electron is in the negative y direction. That is,

$$\mathbf{a} = -\frac{eE}{m_e}\hat{\mathbf{j}} \tag{23.13}$$

Because the acceleration is constant, we can apply the equations of kinematics in two dimensions (see Chapter 4) with $v_{xi} = v_i$ and $v_{yi} = 0$. After the electron has been in the

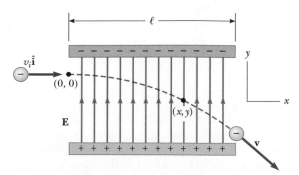

At the Active Figures link at http://www.pse6.com, you can choose the strength of the electric field and the mass and charge of the projected particle.

Active Figure 23.26 An electron is projected horizontally into a uniform electric field produced by two charged plates. The electron undergoes a downward acceleration (opposite $\mathbf{E}$), and its motion is parabolic while it is between the plates.

electric field for a time interval, the components of its velocity at time t are

$$v_x = v_i = \text{constant} \qquad (23.14)$$

$$v_y = a_y t = -\frac{eE}{m_e} t \qquad (23.15)$$

Its position coordinates at time t are

$$x_f = v_i t \qquad (23.16)$$

$$y_f = \tfrac{1}{2} a_y t^2 = -\tfrac{1}{2} \frac{eE}{m_e} t^2 \qquad (23.17)$$

Substituting the value $t = x_f/v_i$ from Equation 23.16 into Equation 23.17, we see that y_f is proportional to $x_f{}^2$. Hence, the trajectory is a parabola. This should not be a surprise—consider the analogous situation of throwing a ball horizontally in a uniform gravitational field (Chapter 4). After the electron leaves the field, the electric force vanishes and the electron continues to move in a straight line in the direction of **v** in Figure 23.26 with a speed $v > v_i$.

Note that we have neglected the gravitational force acting on the electron. This is a good approximation when we are dealing with atomic particles. For an electric field of 10^4 N/C, the ratio of the magnitude of the electric force eE to the magnitude of the gravitational force mg is on the order of 10^{14} for an electron and on the order of 10^{11} for a proton.

> ▲ **PITFALL PREVENTION**
>
> **23.4 Just Another Force**
>
> Electric forces and fields may seem abstract to you. However, once $\mathbf{F}_e$ is evaluated, it causes a particle to move according to our well-established understanding of forces and motion from Chapters 5 and 6. Keeping this link with the past in mind will help you solve problems in this chapter.

Example 23.11   An Accelerated Electron   `Interactive`

An electron enters the region of a uniform electric field as shown in Figure 23.26, with $v_i = 3.00 \times 10^6$ m/s and $E = 200$ N/C. The horizontal length of the plates is $\ell = 0.100$ m.

(A) Find the acceleration of the electron while it is in the electric field.

Solution The charge on the electron has an absolute value of 1.60×10^{-19} C, and $m_e = 9.11 \times 10^{-31}$ kg. Therefore, Equation 23.13 gives

$$\mathbf{a} = -\frac{eE}{m_e}\,\hat{\mathbf{j}} = -\frac{(1.60 \times 10^{-19}\text{ C})(200\text{ N/C})}{9.11 \times 10^{-31}\text{ kg}}\,\hat{\mathbf{j}}$$

$$= \boxed{-3.51 \times 10^{13}\,\hat{\mathbf{j}}\text{ m/s}^2}$$

(B) If the electron enters the field at time $t = 0$, find the time at which it leaves the field.

Solution The horizontal distance across the field is $\ell = 0.100$ m. Using Equation 23.16 with $x_f = \ell$, we find that the time at which the electron exits the electric field is

$$t = \frac{\ell}{v_i} = \frac{0.100\text{ m}}{3.00 \times 10^6\text{ m/s}} = \boxed{3.33 \times 10^{-8}\text{ s}}$$

(C) If the vertical position of the electron as it enters the field is $y_i = 0$, what is its vertical position when it leaves the field?

Solution Using Equation 23.17 and the results from parts (A) and (B), we find that

$$y_f = \tfrac{1}{2} a_y t^2 = -\tfrac{1}{2}(3.51 \times 10^{13}\text{ m/s}^2)(3.33 \times 10^{-8}\text{ s})^2$$

$$= -0.019\ 5\text{ m} = \boxed{-1.95\text{ cm}}$$

If the electron enters just below the negative plate in Figure 23.26 and the separation between the plates is less than the value we have just calculated, the electron will strike the positive plate.

At the Interactive Worked Example link at **http://www.pse6.com,** *you can predict the required initial velocity for the exiting electron to just miss the right edge of the lower plate, for random values of the electric field.*

The Cathode Ray Tube

The example we just worked describes a portion of a cathode ray tube (CRT). This tube, illustrated in Figure 23.27, is commonly used to obtain a visual display of electronic information in oscilloscopes, radar systems, television receivers, and computer monitors. The CRT is a vacuum tube in which a beam of electrons is accelerated and deflected under the influence of electric or magnetic fields. The electron beam is

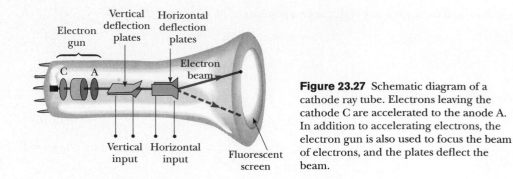

Figure 23.27 Schematic diagram of a cathode ray tube. Electrons leaving the cathode C are accelerated to the anode A. In addition to accelerating electrons, the electron gun is also used to focus the beam of electrons, and the plates deflect the beam.

produced by an assembly called an *electron gun* located in the neck of the tube. These electrons, if left undisturbed, travel in a straight-line path until they strike the front of the CRT, the "screen," which is coated with a material that emits visible light when bombarded with electrons.

In an oscilloscope, the electrons are deflected in various directions by two sets of plates placed at right angles to each other in the neck of the tube. (A television CRT steers the beam with a magnetic field, as discussed in Chapter 29.) An external electric circuit is used to control the amount of charge present on the plates. The placing of positive charge on one horizontal plate and negative charge on the other creates an electric field between the plates and allows the beam to be steered from side to side. The vertical deflection plates act in the same way, except that changing the charge on them deflects the beam vertically.

SUMMARY

Take a practice test for this chapter by clicking on the Practice Test link at http://www.pse6.com.

Electric charges have the following important properties:

* Charges of opposite sign attract one another and charges of the same sign repel one another.
* Total charge in an isolated system is conserved.
* Charge is quantized.

Conductors are materials in which electrons move freely. **Insulators** are materials in which electrons do not move freely.

Coulomb's law states that the electric force exerted by a charge q_1 on a second charge q_2 is

$$\mathbf{F}_{12} = k_e \frac{q_1 q_2}{r^2} \hat{\mathbf{r}} \qquad (23.6)$$

where r is the distance between the two charges and $\hat{\mathbf{r}}$ is a unit vector directed from q_1 toward q_2. The constant k_e, which is called the Coulomb constant, has the value $k_e = 8.99 \times 10^9 \ \text{N} \cdot \text{m}^2/\text{C}^2$.

The smallest unit of free charge e known to exist in nature is the charge on an electron $(-e)$ or proton $(+e)$, where $e = 1.602\ 19 \times 10^{-19}$ C.

The electric field **E** at some point in space is defined as the electric force $\mathbf{F}_e$ that acts on a small positive test charge placed at that point divided by the magnitude q_0 of the test charge:

$$\mathbf{E} \equiv \frac{\mathbf{F}_e}{q_0} \qquad (23.7)$$

Thus, the electric force on a charge q placed in an electric field **E** is given by

$$\mathbf{F}_e = q\mathbf{E} \qquad (23.8)$$

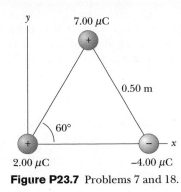

Figure P23.7 Problems 7 and 18.

8. Suppose that 1.00 g of hydrogen is separated into electrons and protons. Suppose also that the protons are placed at the Earth's north pole and the electrons are placed at the south pole. What is the resulting compressional force on the Earth?

9. Two identical conducting small spheres are placed with their centers 0.300 m apart. One is given a charge of 12.0 nC and the other a charge of − 18.0 nC. (a) Find the electric force exerted by one sphere on the other. (b) **What If?** The spheres are connected by a conducting wire. Find the electric force between the two after they have come to equilibrium.

10. Two small beads having positive charges $3q$ and q are fixed at the opposite ends of a horizontal, insulating rod, extending from the origin to the point $x = d$. As shown in Figure P23.10, a third small charged bead is free to slide on the rod. At what position is the third bead in equilibrium? Can it be in stable equilibrium?

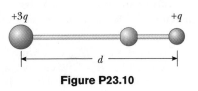

Figure P23.10

11. Review problem. In the Bohr theory of the hydrogen atom, an electron moves in a circular orbit about a proton, where the radius of the orbit is 0.529×10^{-10} m. (a) Find the electric force between the two. (b) If this force causes the centripetal acceleration of the electron, what is the speed of the electron?

12. Review problem. Two identical particles, each having charge $+ q$, are fixed in space and separated by a distance d. A third point charge $- Q$ is free to move and lies initially at rest on the perpendicular bisector of the two fixed charges a distance x from the midpoint between the two fixed charges (Fig. P23.12). (a) Show that if x is small compared with d, the motion of $- Q$ will be simple harmonic along the perpendicular bisector. Determine the period of that motion. (b) How fast will the charge $- Q$ be moving when it is at the midpoint between the two fixed charges, if initially it is released at a distance $a \ll d$ from the midpoint?

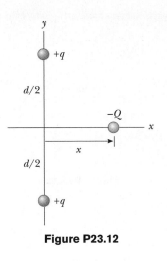

Figure P23.12

Section 23.4   The Electric Field

13. What are the magnitude and direction of the electric field that will balance the weight of (a) an electron and (b) a proton? (Use the data in Table 23.1.)

14. An object having a net charge of 24.0 μC is placed in a uniform electric field of 610 N/C directed vertically. What is the mass of this object if it "floats" in the field?

15. In Figure P23.15, determine the point (other than infinity) at which the electric field is zero.

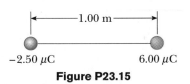

Figure P23.15

16. An airplane is flying through a thundercloud at a height of 2 000 m. (This is a very dangerous thing to do because of updrafts, turbulence, and the possibility of electric discharge.) If a charge concentration of + 40.0 C is above the plane at a height of 3 000 m within the cloud and a charge concentration of − 40.0 C is at height 1 000 m, what is the electric field at the aircraft?

17. Two point charges are located on the x axis. The first is a charge $+ Q$ at $x = - a$. The second is an unknown charge located at $x = + 3a$. The net electric field these charges produce at the origin has a magnitude of $2k_e Q/a^2$. What are the two possible values of the unknown charge?

18. Three charges are at the corners of an equilateral triangle as shown in Figure P23.7. (a) Calculate the electric field at the position of the 2.00-μC charge due to the 7.00-μC and − 4.00-μC charges. (b) Use your answer to part (a) to determine the force on the 2.00-μC charge.

19. Three point charges are arranged as shown in Figure P23.19. (a) Find the vector electric field that the 6.00-nC and − 3.00-nC charges together create at the origin. (b) Find the vector force on the 5.00-nC charge.

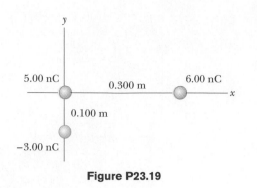

Figure P23.19

20. Two 2.00-μC point charges are located on the x axis. One is at $x = 1.00$ m, and the other is at $x = -1.00$ m. (a) Determine the electric field on the y axis at $y = 0.500$ m. (b) Calculate the electric force on a -3.00-μC charge placed on the y axis at $y = 0.500$ m.

21. Four point charges are at the corners of a square of side a as shown in Figure P23.21. (a) Determine the magnitude and direction of the electric field at the location of charge q. (b) What is the resultant force on q?

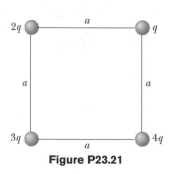

Figure P23.21

22. Consider the electric dipole shown in Figure P23.22. Show that the electric field at a *distant* point on the $+ x$ axis is $E_x \approx 4k_e qa/x^3$.

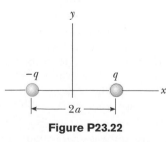

Figure P23.22

23. Consider n equal positive point charges each of magnitude Q/n placed symmetrically around a circle of radius R. (a) Calculate the magnitude of the electric field at a point a distance x on the line passing through the center of the circle and perpendicular to the plane of the circle. (b) Explain why this result is identical to that of the calculation done in Example 23.8.

24. Consider an infinite number of identical charges (each of charge q) placed along the x axis at distances a, $2a$, $3a$, $4a$, . . . , from the origin. What is the electric field at the origin due to this distribution? *Suggestion:* Use the fact that

$$1 + \frac{1}{2^2} + \frac{1}{3^2} + \frac{1}{4^2} + \cdots = \frac{\pi^2}{6}$$

Section 23.5 Electric Field of a Continuous Charge Distribution

25. A rod 14.0 cm long is uniformly charged and has a total charge of -22.0 μC. Determine the magnitude and direction of the electric field along the axis of the rod at a point 36.0 cm from its center.

26. A continuous line of charge lies along the x axis, extending from $x = +x_0$ to positive infinity. The line carries charge with a uniform linear charge density λ_0. What are the magnitude and direction of the electric field at the origin?

27. A uniformly charged ring of radius 10.0 cm has a total charge of 75.0 μC. Find the electric field on the axis of the ring at (a) 1.00 cm, (b) 5.00 cm, (c) 30.0 cm, and (d) 100 cm from the center of the ring.

28. A line of charge starts at $x = + x_0$ and extends to positive infinity. The linear charge density is $\lambda = \lambda_0 x_0/x$. Determine the electric field at the origin.

29. Show that the maximum magnitude E_{max} of the electric field along the axis of a uniformly charged ring occurs at $x = a/\sqrt{2}$ (see Fig. 23.18) and has the value $Q/(6\sqrt{3}\pi\epsilon_0 a^2)$.

30. A uniformly charged disk of radius 35.0 cm carries charge with a density of 7.90×10^{-3} C/m^2. Calculate the electric field on the axis of the disk at (a) 5.00 cm, (b) 10.0 cm, (c) 50.0 cm, and (d) 200 cm from the center of the disk.

31. Example 23.9 derives the exact expression for the electric field at a point on the axis of a uniformly charged disk. Consider a disk, of radius $R = 3.00$ cm, having a uniformly distributed charge of $+5.20$ μC. (a) Using the result of Example 23.9, compute the electric field at a point on the axis and 3.00 mm from the center. **What If?** Compare this answer with the field computed from the near-field approximation $E = \sigma/2\epsilon_0$. (b) Using the result of Example 23.9, compute the electric field at a point on the axis and 30.0 cm from the center of the disk. **What If?** Compare this with the electric field obtained by treating the disk as a $+5.20$-μC point charge at a distance of 30.0 cm.

32. The electric field along the axis of a uniformly charged disk of radius R and total charge Q was calculated in Example 23.9. Show that the electric field at distances x that are large compared with R approaches that of a point charge $Q = \sigma\pi R^2$. (*Suggestion:* First show that $x/(x^2 + R^2)^{1/2} = (1 + R^2/x^2)^{-1/2}$ and use the binomial expansion $(1 + \delta)^n \approx 1 + n\delta$ when $\delta \ll 1$.)

33. A uniformly charged insulating rod of length 14.0 cm is bent into the shape of a semicircle as shown in Figure P23.33. The rod has a total charge of -7.50 μC. Find the magnitude and direction of the electric field at O, the center of the semicircle.

Figure P23.33

34. (a) Consider a uniformly charged thin-walled right circular cylindrical shell having total charge Q, radius R, and height h. Determine the electric field at a point a distance d from the right side of the cylinder as shown in Figure P23.34. (*Suggestion:* Use the result of Example 23.8 and treat the cylinder as a collection of ring charges.) (b) **What If?** Consider now a solid cylinder with the same dimensions and carrying the same charge, uniformly distributed through its volume. Use the result of Example 23.9 to find the field it creates at the same point.

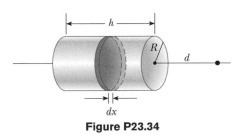

Figure P23.34

35. A thin rod of length ℓ and uniform charge per unit length λ lies along the x axis, as shown in Figure P23.35. (a) Show that the electric field at P, a distance y from the rod along its perpendicular bisector, has no x component and is given by $E = 2k_e\lambda \sin \theta_0/y$. (b) **What If?** Using your result to part (a), show that the field of a rod of infinite length is $E = 2k_e\lambda/y$. (*Suggestion:* First calculate the field at P due to an element of length dx, which has a charge $\lambda\,dx$. Then change variables from x to θ, using the relationships $x = y \tan \theta$ and $dx = y \sec^2 \theta\,d\theta$, and integrate over θ.)

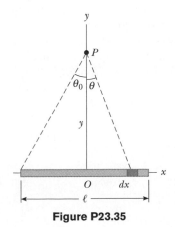

Figure P23.35

36. Three solid plastic cylinders all have radius 2.50 cm and length 6.00 cm. One (a) carries charge with uniform density 15.0 nC/m² everywhere on its surface. Another (b) carries charge with the same uniform density on its curved lateral surface only. The third (c) carries charge with uniform density 500 nC/m³ throughout the plastic. Find the charge of each cylinder.

37. Eight solid plastic cubes, each 3.00 cm on each edge, are glued together to form each one of the objects (i, ii, iii, and iv) shown in Figure P23.37. (a) Assuming each object carries charge with uniform density 400 nC/m³ throughout its volume, find the charge of each object. (b) Assuming each object carries charge with uniform density 15.0 nC/m² everywhere on its exposed surface, find the charge on each object. (c) Assuming charge is placed only on the edges where perpendicular surfaces meet, with uniform density 80.0 pC/m, find the charge of each object.

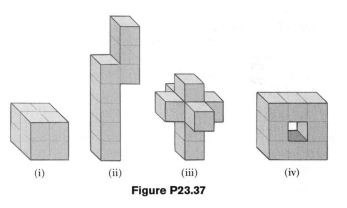

(i)   (ii)   (iii)   (iv)

Figure P23.37

Section 23.6 Electric Field Lines

38. A positively charged disk has a uniform charge per unit area as described in Example 23.9. Sketch the electric field lines in a plane perpendicular to the plane of the disk passing through its center.

39. A negatively charged rod of finite length carries charge with a uniform charge per unit length. Sketch the electric field lines in a plane containing the rod.

40. Figure P23.40 shows the electric field lines for two point charges separated by a small distance. (a) Determine the ratio q_1/q_2. (b) What are the signs of q_1 and q_2?

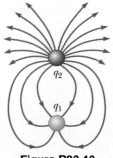

Figure P23.40

41. 🪐 Three equal positive charges q are at the corners of an equilateral triangle of side a as shown in Figure P23.41. (a) Assume that the three charges together create an electric field. Sketch the field lines in the plane of the charges. Find the location of a point (other than ∞) where the electric field is zero. (b) What are the magnitude and direction of the electric field at P due to the two charges at the base?

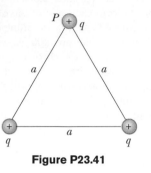

Figure P23.41

Section 23.7 Motion of Charged Particles in a Uniform Electric Field

42. An electron and a proton are each placed at rest in an electric field of 520 N/C. Calculate the speed of each particle 48.0 ns after being released.

43. A proton accelerates from rest in a uniform electric field of 640 N/C. At some later time, its speed is 1.20×10^6 m/s (nonrelativistic, because v is much less than the speed of light). (a) Find the acceleration of the proton. (b) How long does it take the proton to reach this speed? (c) How far has it moved in this time? (d) What is its kinetic energy at this time?

44. A proton is projected in the positive x direction into a region of a uniform electric field $\mathbf{E} = -6.00 \times 10^5 \hat{\mathbf{i}}$ N/C at $t = 0$. The proton travels 7.00 cm before coming to rest. Determine (a) the acceleration of the proton, (b) its initial speed, and (c) the time at which the proton comes to rest.

45. 🪐 The electrons in a particle beam each have a kinetic energy K. What are the magnitude and direction of the electric field that will stop these electrons in a distance d?

46. A positively charged bead having a mass of 1.00 g falls from rest in a vacuum from a height of 5.00 m in a uniform vertical electric field with a magnitude of 1.00×10^4 N/C. The bead hits the ground at a speed of 21.0 m/s. Determine (a) the direction of the electric field (up or down), and (b) the charge on the bead.

47. A proton moves at 4.50×10^5 m/s in the horizontal direction. It enters a uniform vertical electric field with a magnitude of 9.60×10^3 N/C. Ignoring any gravitational effects, find (a) the time interval required for the proton to travel 5.00 cm horizontally, (b) its vertical displacement during the time interval in which it travels 5.00 cm horizontally, and (c) the horizontal and vertical components of its velocity after it has traveled 5.00 cm horizontally.

48. Two horizontal metal plates, each 100 mm square, are aligned 10.0 mm apart, with one above the other. They are given equal-magnitude charges of opposite sign so that a uniform downward electric field of 2 000 N/C exists in the region between them. A particle of mass 2.00×10^{-16} kg

and with a positive charge of 1.00×10^{-6} C leaves the center of the bottom negative plate with an initial speed of 1.00×10^5 m/s at an angle of 37.0° above the horizontal. Describe the trajectory of the particle. Which plate does it strike? Where does it strike, relative to its starting point?

49. Protons are projected with an initial speed $v_i = 9.55 \times 10^3$ m/s into a region where a uniform electric field $\mathbf{E} = -720\hat{\mathbf{j}}$ N/C is present, as shown in Figure P23.49. The protons are to hit a target that lies at a horizontal distance of 1.27 mm from the point where the protons cross the plane and enter the electric field in Figure P23.49. Find (a) the two projection angles θ that will result in a hit and (b) the total time of flight (the time interval during which the proton is above the plane in Figure P23.49) for each trajectory.

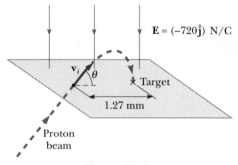

Figure P23.49

Additional Problems

50. Two known charges, -12.0 μC and 45.0 μC, and an unknown charge are located on the x axis. The charge -12.0 μC is at the origin, and the charge 45.0 μC is at $x = 15.0$ cm. The unknown charge is to be placed so that each charge is in equilibrium under the action of the electric forces exerted by the other two charges. Is this situation possible? Is it possible in more than one way? Find the required location, magnitude, and sign of the unknown charge.

51. A uniform electric field of magnitude 640 N/C exists between two parallel plates that are 4.00 cm apart. A proton is released from the positive plate at the same instant that an electron is released from the negative plate. (a) Determine the distance from the positive plate at which the two pass each other. (Ignore the electrical attraction between the proton and electron.) (b) **What If?** Repeat part (a) for a sodium ion (Na^+) and a chloride ion (Cl^-).

52. Three point charges are aligned along the x axis as shown in Figure P23.52. Find the electric field at (a) the position (2.00, 0) and (b) the position (0, 2.00).

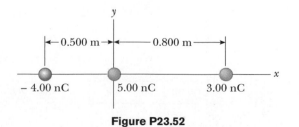

Figure P23.52

53. A researcher studying the properties of ions in the upper atmosphere wishes to construct an apparatus with the following characteristics: Using an electric field, a beam of ions, each having charge q, mass m, and initial velocity $v\hat{\mathbf{i}}$, is turned through an angle of 90° as each ion undergoes displacement $R\hat{\mathbf{i}} + R\hat{\mathbf{j}}$. The ions enter a chamber as shown in Figure P23.53, and leave through the exit port with the same speed they had when they entered the chamber. The electric field acting on the ions is to have constant magnitude. (a) Suppose the electric field is produced by two concentric cylindrical electrodes not shown in the diagram, and hence is radial. What magnitude should the field have? **What If?** (b) If the field is produced by two flat plates and is uniform in direction, what value should the field have in this case?

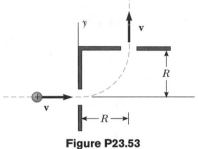

Figure P23.53

54. A small, 2.00-g plastic ball is suspended by a 20.0-cm-long string in a uniform electric field as shown in Figure P23.54. If the ball is in equilibrium when the string makes a 15.0° angle with the vertical, what is the net charge on the ball?

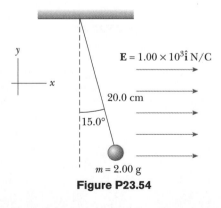

Figure P23.54

55. [www] A charged cork ball of mass 1.00 g is suspended on a light string in the presence of a uniform electric field as shown in Figure P23.55. When $\mathbf{E} = (3.00\hat{\mathbf{i}} + 5.00\hat{\mathbf{j}}) \times 10^5$ N/C, the ball is in equilibrium at $\theta = 37.0°$. Find (a) the charge on the ball and (b) the tension in the string.

56. A charged cork ball of mass m is suspended on a light string in the presence of a uniform electric field as shown in Figure P23.55. When $\mathbf{E} = (A\hat{\mathbf{i}} + B\hat{\mathbf{j}})$ N/C, where A and B are positive numbers, the ball is in equilibrium at

the angle θ. Find (a) the charge on the ball and (b) the tension in the string.

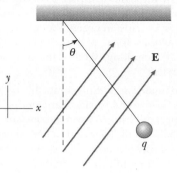

Figure P23.55 Problems 55 and 56.

57. Four identical point charges ($q = +10.0\ \mu$C) are located on the corners of a rectangle as shown in Figure P23.57. The dimensions of the rectangle are $L = 60.0$ cm and $W = 15.0$ cm. Calculate the magnitude and direction of the resultant electric force exerted on the charge at the lower left corner by the other three charges.

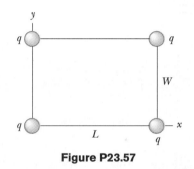

Figure P23.57

58. Inez is putting up decorations for her sister's quinceañera (fifteenth birthday party). She ties three light silk ribbons together to the top of a gateway and hangs a rubber balloon from each ribbon (Fig. P23.58). To include the

Figure P23.58

effects of the gravitational and buoyant forces on it, each balloon can be modeled as a particle of mass 2.00 g, with its center 50.0 cm from the point of support. To show off the colors of the balloons, Inez rubs the whole surface of each balloon with her woolen scarf, to make them hang separately with gaps between them. The centers of the hanging balloons form a horizontal equilateral triangle with sides 30.0 cm long. What is the common charge each balloon carries?

59. **Review problem.** Two identical metallic blocks resting on a frictionless horizontal surface are connected by a light metallic spring having a spring constant k as shown in Figure P23.59a and an unstretched length L_i. A total charge Q is slowly placed on the system, causing the spring to stretch to an equilibrium length L, as shown in Figure P23.59b. Determine the value of Q, assuming that all the charge resides on the blocks and modeling the blocks as point charges.

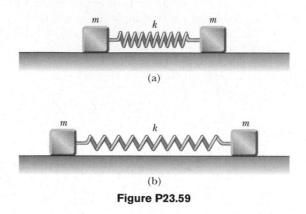

(a)

(b)

Figure P23.59

60. Consider a regular polygon with 29 sides. The distance from the center to each vertex is a. Identical charges q are placed at 28 vertices of the polygon. A single charge Q is placed at the center of the polygon. What is the magnitude and direction of the force experienced by the charge Q? (*Suggestion:* You may use the result of Problem 63 in Chapter 3.)

61. Identical thin rods of length $2a$ carry equal charges $+Q$ uniformly distributed along their lengths. The rods lie along the x axis with their centers separated by a distance $b > 2a$ (Fig. P23.61). Show that the magnitude of the force exerted by the left rod on the right one is given by

$$F = \left(\frac{k_e Q^2}{4a^2} \right) \ln \left(\frac{b^2}{b^2 - 4a^2} \right)$$

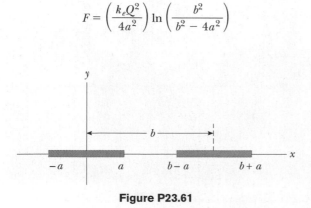

Figure P23.61

62. Two small spheres, each of mass 2.00 g, are suspended by light strings 10.0 cm in length (Fig. P23.62). A uniform electric field is applied in the x direction. The spheres have charges equal to -5.00×10^{-8} C and $+5.00 \times 10^{-8}$ C. Determine the electric field that enables the spheres to be in equilibrium at an angle $\theta = 10.0°$.

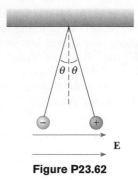

Figure P23.62

63. A line of positive charge is formed into a semicircle of radius $R = 60.0$ cm as shown in Figure P23.63. The charge per unit length along the semicircle is described by the expression $\lambda = \lambda_0 \cos \theta$. The total charge on the semicircle is 12.0 μC. Calculate the total force on a charge of 3.00 μC placed at the center of curvature.

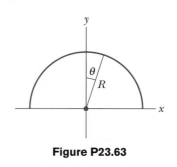

Figure P23.63

64. ⌨ Three charges of equal magnitude q are fixed in position at the vertices of an equilateral triangle (Fig. P23.64). A fourth charge Q is free to move along the positive x axis

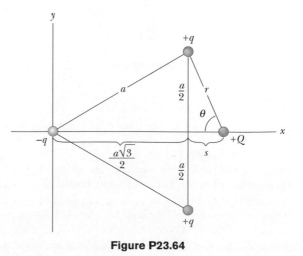

Figure P23.64

under the influence of the forces exerted by the three fixed charges. Find a value for s for which Q is in equilibrium. You will need to solve a transcendental equation.

65. Two small spheres of mass m are suspended from strings of length ℓ that are connected at a common point. One sphere has charge Q; the other has charge $2Q$. The strings make angles θ_1 and θ_2 with the vertical. (a) How are θ_1 and θ_2 related? (b) Assume θ_1 and θ_2 are small. Show that the distance r between the spheres is given by

$$r \approx \left(\frac{4k_e Q^2 \ell}{mg} \right)^{1/3}$$

66. Review problem. Four identical particles, each having charge $+q$, are fixed at the corners of a square of side L. A fifth point charge $-Q$ lies a distance z along the line perpendicular to the plane of the square and passing through the center of the square (Fig. P23.66). (a) Show that the force exerted by the other four charges on $-Q$ is

$$\mathbf{F} = -\frac{4k_e q Q z}{[z^2 + (L^2/2)]^{3/2}}\, \hat{\mathbf{k}}$$

Note that this force is directed toward the center of the square whether z is positive ($-Q$ above the square) or negative ($-Q$ below the square). (b) If z is small compared with L, the above expression reduces to $\mathbf{F} \approx -(\text{constant})z\hat{\mathbf{k}}$. Why does this imply that the motion of the charge $-Q$ is simple harmonic, and what is the period of this motion if the mass of $-Q$ is m?

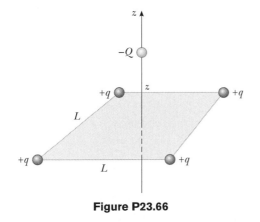

Figure P23.66

67. Review problem. A 1.00-g cork ball with charge 2.00 μC is suspended vertically on a 0.500-m-long light string in the presence of a uniform, downward-directed electric field of magnitude $E = 1.00 \times 10^5$ N/C. If the ball is displaced slightly from the vertical, it oscillates like a simple pendulum. (a) Determine the period of this oscillation. (b) Should gravity be included in the calculation for part (a)? Explain.

68. Two identical beads each have a mass m and charge q. When placed in a hemispherical bowl of radius R with frictionless, nonconducting walls, the beads move, and at equilibrium they are a distance R apart (Fig. P23.68). Determine the charge on each bead.

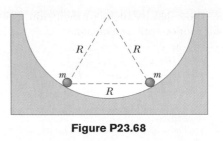

Figure P23.68

69. Eight point charges, each of magnitude q, are located on the corners of a cube of edge s, as shown in Figure P23.69. (a) Determine the x, y, and z components of the resultant force exerted by the other charges on the charge located at point A. (b) What are the magnitude and direction of this resultant force?

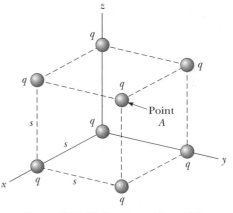

Figure P23.69 Problems 69 and 70.

70. Consider the charge distribution shown in Figure P23.69. (a) Show that the magnitude of the electric field at the center of any face of the cube has a value of $2.18k_e q/s^2$. (b) What is the direction of the electric field at the center of the top face of the cube?

71. Review problem. A negatively charged particle $-q$ is placed at the center of a uniformly charged ring, where the ring has a total positive charge Q as shown in Example 23.8. The particle, confined to move along the x axis, is displaced a small distance x along the axis (where $x \ll a$) and released. Show that the particle oscillates in simple harmonic motion with a frequency given by

$$f = \frac{1}{2\pi} \left(\frac{k_e q Q}{ma^3} \right)^{1/2}$$

72. A line of charge with uniform density 35.0 nC/m lies along the line $y = -15.0$ cm, between the points with coordinates $x = 0$ and $x = 40.0$ cm. Find the electric field it creates at the origin.

73. Review problem. An electric dipole in a uniform electric field is displaced slightly from its equilibrium position, as shown in Figure P23.73, where θ is small. The separation of the charges is $2a$, and the moment of inertia of the dipole is I. Assuming the dipole is released from this position, show that its angular orientation exhibits simple harmonic motion with a frequency

$$f = \frac{1}{2\pi} \sqrt{\frac{2qaE}{I}}$$

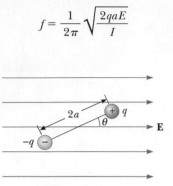

Figure P23.73

Answers to Quick Quizzes

23.1 (b). The amount of charge present in the isolated system after rubbing is the same as that before because charge is conserved; it is just distributed differently.

23.2 (a), (c), and (e). The experiment shows that A and B have charges of the same sign, as do objects B and C. Thus, all three objects have charges of the same sign. We cannot determine from this information, however, whether the charges are positive or negative.

23.3 (e). In the first experiment, objects A and B may have charges with opposite signs, or one of the objects may be neutral. The second experiment shows that B and C have charges with the same signs, so that B must be charged. But we still do not know if A is charged or neutral.

23.4 (e). From Newton's third law, the electric force exerted by object B on object A is equal in magnitude to the force exerted by object A on object B.

23.5 (b). From Newton's third law, the electric force exerted by object B on object A is equal in magnitude to the force exerted by object A on object B and in the opposite direction.

23.6 (a). There is no effect on the electric field if we assume that the source charge producing the field is not disturbed by our actions. Remember that the electric field is created by source charge(s) (unseen in this case), not the test charge(s).

23.7 A, B, C. The field is greatest at point A because this is where the field lines are closest together. The absence of lines near point C indicates that the electric field there is zero.

23.8 (b). Electric field lines begin and end on charges and cannot close on themselves to form loops.

Chapter 24

Gauss's Law

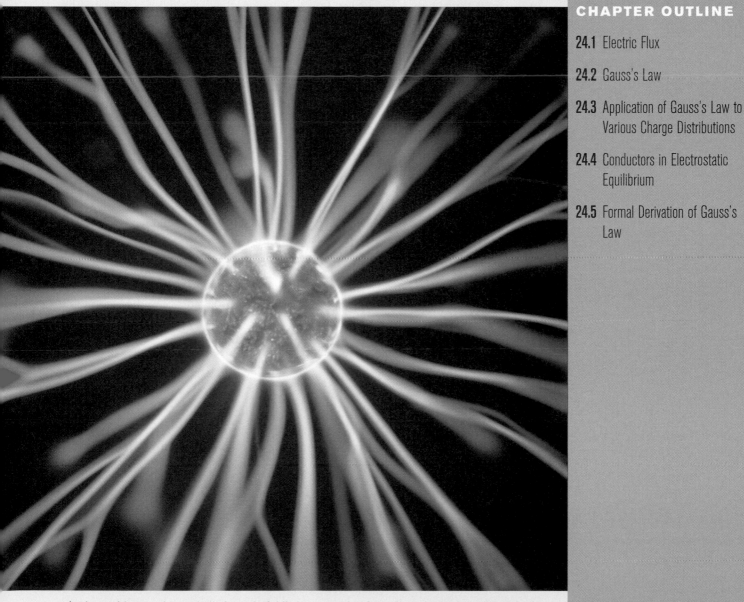

▲ In a table-top plasma ball, the colorful lines emanating from the sphere give evidence of strong electric fields. Using Gauss's law, we show in this chapter that the electric field surrounding a charged sphere is identical to that of a point charge. (Getty Images)

In the preceding chapter we showed how to calculate the electric field generated by a given charge distribution. In this chapter, we describe *Gauss's law* and an alternative procedure for calculating electric fields. The law is based on the fact that the fundamental electrostatic force between point charges exhibits an inverse-square behavior. Although a consequence of Coulomb's law, Gauss's law is more convenient for calculating the electric fields of highly symmetric charge distributions and makes possible useful qualitative reasoning when dealing with complicated problems.

24.1 Electric Flux

The concept of electric field lines was described qualitatively in Chapter 23. We now treat electric field lines in a more quantitative way.

Consider an electric field that is uniform in both magnitude and direction, as shown in Figure 24.1. The field lines penetrate a rectangular surface of area A, whose plane is oriented perpendicular to the field. Recall from Section 23.6 that the number of lines per unit area (in other words, the *line density*) is proportional to the magnitude of the electric field. Therefore, the total number of lines penetrating the surface is proportional to the product EA. This product of the magnitude of the electric field E and surface area A perpendicular to the field is called the **electric flux** Φ_E (uppercase Greek phi):

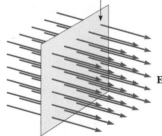

Figure 24.1 Field lines representing a uniform electric field penetrating a plane of area A perpendicular to the field. The electric flux Φ_E through this area is equal to EA.

$$\Phi_E = EA \tag{24.1}$$

From the SI units of E and A, we see that Φ_E has units of newton-meters squared per coulomb (N·m²/C.) **Electric flux is proportional to the number of electric field lines penetrating some surface.**

Example 24.1 Electric Flux Through a Sphere

What is the electric flux through a sphere that has a radius of 1.00 m and carries a charge of $+1.00\ \mu C$ at its center?

Solution The magnitude of the electric field 1.00 m from this charge is found using Equation 23.9:

$$E = k_e\ \frac{q}{r^2} = (8.99 \times 10^9\ \text{N·m}^2/\text{C}^2)\ \frac{1.00 \times 10^{-6}\ \text{C}}{(1.00\ \text{m})^2}$$

$$= 8.99 \times 10^3\ \text{N/C}$$

The field points radially outward and is therefore everywhere perpendicular to the surface of the sphere. The flux through the sphere (whose surface area $A = 4\pi r^2 = 12.6\ \text{m}^2$) is thus

$$\Phi_E = EA = (8.99 \times 10^3\ \text{N/C})(12.6\ \text{m}^2)$$

$$= 1.13 \times 10^5\ \text{N·m}^2/\text{C}$$

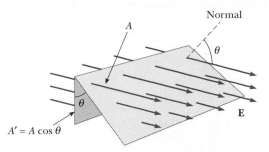

Figure 24.2 Field lines representing a uniform electric field penetrating an area A that is at an angle θ to the field. Because the number of lines that go through the area A' is the same as the number that go through A, the flux through A' is equal to the flux through A and is given by $\Phi_E = EA\cos\theta$.

If the surface under consideration is not perpendicular to the field, the flux through it must be less than that given by Equation 24.1. We can understand this by considering Figure 24.2, where the normal to the surface of area A is at an angle θ to the uniform electric field. Note that the number of lines that cross this area A is equal to the number that cross the area A', which is a projection of area A onto a plane oriented perpendicular to the field. From Figure 24.2 we see that the two areas are related by $A' = A\cos\theta$. Because the flux through A equals the flux through A', we conclude that the flux through A is

$$\Phi_E = EA' = EA\cos\theta \tag{24.2}$$

From this result, we see that the flux through a surface of fixed area A has a maximum value EA when the surface is perpendicular to the field (when the normal to the surface is parallel to the field, that is, $\theta = 0°$ in Figure 24.2); the flux is zero when the surface is parallel to the field (when the normal to the surface is perpendicular to the field, that is, $\theta = 90°$).

We assumed a uniform electric field in the preceding discussion. In more general situations, the electric field may vary over a surface. Therefore, our definition of flux given by Equation 24.2 has meaning only over a small element of area. Consider a general surface divided up into a large number of small elements, each of area ΔA. The variation in the electric field over one element can be neglected if the element is sufficiently small. It is convenient to define a vector $\Delta\mathbf{A}_i$ whose magnitude represents the area of the ith element of the surface and whose direction is defined to be *perpendicular* to the surface element, as shown in Figure 24.3. The electric field $\mathbf{E}_i$ at the location of this element makes an angle θ_i with the vector $\Delta\mathbf{A}_i$. The electric flux $\Delta\Phi_E$ through this element is

$$\Delta\Phi_E = E_i\,\Delta A_i\cos\theta_i = \mathbf{E}_i\cdot\Delta\mathbf{A}_i$$

where we have used the definition of the scalar product (or dot product; see Chapter 7) of two vectors ($\mathbf{A}\cdot\mathbf{B} = AB\cos\theta$). By summing the contributions of all elements, we obtain the total flux through the surface. If we let the area of each element approach zero, then the number of elements approaches infinity and the sum is replaced by an integral. Therefore, the general definition of electric flux is[1]

$$\Phi_E = \lim_{\Delta A_i\to 0}\sum \mathbf{E}_i\cdot\Delta\mathbf{A}_i = \int_{\text{surface}} \mathbf{E}\cdot d\mathbf{A} \tag{24.3}$$

Equation 24.3 is a *surface integral,* which means it must be evaluated over the surface in question. In general, the value of Φ_E depends both on the field pattern and on the surface.

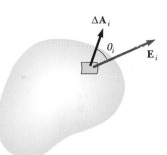

Figure 24.3 A small element of surface area ΔA_i. The electric field makes an angle θ_i with the vector $\Delta\mathbf{A}_i$, defined as being normal to the surface element, and the flux through the element is equal to $E_i\,\Delta A_i\cos\theta_i$.

Definition of electric flux

[1] Drawings with field lines have their inaccuracies because a limited number of field lines are typically drawn in a diagram. Consequently, a small area element drawn on a diagram (depending on its location) may happen to have too few field lines penetrating it to represent the flux accurately. We stress that the basic definition of electric flux is Equation 24.3. The use of lines is only an aid for visualizing the concept.

At the Active Figures link at http://www.pse6.com, you can select any segment on the surface and see the relationship between the electric field vector E and the area vector $\Delta \mathbf{A}_i$.

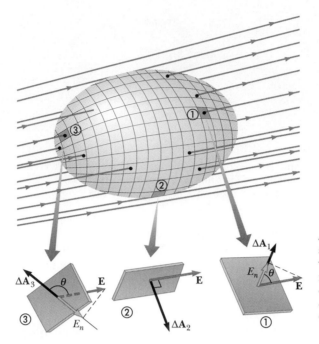

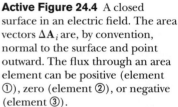

Active Figure 24.4 A closed surface in an electric field. The area vectors $\Delta \mathbf{A}_i$ are, by convention, normal to the surface and point outward. The flux through an area element can be positive (element ①), zero (element ②), or negative (element ③).

Karl Friedrich Gauss

German mathematician and astronomer (1777–1855)

Gauss received a doctoral degree in mathematics from the University of Helmstedt in 1799. In addition to his work in electromagnetism, he made contributions to mathematics and science in number theory, statistics, non-Euclidean geometry, and cometary orbital mechanics. He was a founder of the German Magnetic Union, which studies the Earth's magnetic field on a continual basis.

We are often interested in evaluating the flux through a *closed surface*, which is defined as one that divides space into an inside and an outside region, so that one cannot move from one region to the other without crossing the surface. The surface of a sphere, for example, is a closed surface.

Consider the closed surface in Figure 24.4. The vectors $\Delta \mathbf{A}_i$ point in different directions for the various surface elements, but at each point they are normal to the surface and, by convention, always point outward. At the element labeled ①, the field lines are crossing the surface from the inside to the outside and $\theta < 90°$; hence, the flux $\Delta \Phi_E = \mathbf{E} \cdot \Delta \mathbf{A}_1$ through this element is positive. For element ②, the field lines graze the surface (perpendicular to the vector $\Delta \mathbf{A}_2$); thus, $\theta = 90°$ and the flux is zero. For elements such as ③, where the field lines are crossing the surface from outside to inside, $180° > \theta > 90°$ and the flux is negative because $\cos \theta$ is negative. The *net* flux through the surface is proportional to the net number of lines leaving the surface, where the net number means *the number leaving the surface minus the number entering the surface.* If more lines are leaving than entering, the net flux is positive. If more lines are entering than leaving, the net flux is negative. Using the symbol $\oint$ to represent an integral over a closed surface, we can write the net flux Φ_E through a closed surface as

$$\Phi_E = \oint \mathbf{E} \cdot d\mathbf{A} = \oint E_n \, dA \qquad (24.4)$$

where E_n represents the component of the electric field normal to the surface. If the field is normal to the surface at each point and constant in magnitude, the calculation is straightforward, as it was in Example 24.1. Example 24.2 also illustrates this point.

Quick Quiz 24.1 Suppose the radius of the sphere in Example 24.1 is changed to 0.500 m. What happens to the flux through the sphere and the magnitude of the electric field at the surface of the sphere? (a) The flux and field both increase. (b) The flux and field both decrease. (c) The flux increases and the field decreases. (d) The flux decreases and the field increases. (e) The flux remains the same and the field increases. (f) The flux decreases and the field remains the same.

Example 24.2   Flux Through a Cube

Consider a uniform electric field $\mathbf{E}$ oriented in the x direction. Find the net electric flux through the surface of a cube of edge length ℓ, oriented as shown in Figure 24.5.

Solution The net flux is the sum of the fluxes through all faces of the cube. First, note that the flux through four of

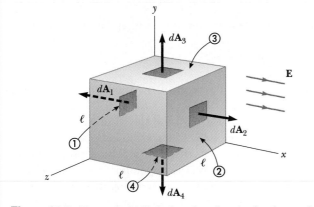

Figure 24.5 (Example 24.2) A closed surface in the shape of a cube in a uniform electric field oriented parallel to the x axis. Side ④ is the bottom of the cube, and side ① is opposite side ②.

the faces (③, ④, and the unnumbered ones) is zero because $\mathbf{E}$ is perpendicular to $d\mathbf{A}$ on these faces.

The net flux through faces ① and ② is

$$\Phi_E = \int_1 \mathbf{E} \cdot d\mathbf{A} + \int_2 \mathbf{E} \cdot d\mathbf{A}$$

For face ①, $\mathbf{E}$ is constant and directed inward but $d\mathbf{A}_1$ is directed outward ($\theta = 180°$); thus, the flux through this face is

$$\int_1 \mathbf{E} \cdot d\mathbf{A} = \int_1 E(\cos 180°) \, dA = -E \int_1 dA = -EA = -E\ell^2$$

because the area of each face is $A = \ell^2$.

For face ②, $\mathbf{E}$ is constant and outward and in the same direction as $d\mathbf{A}_2$ ($\theta = 0°$); hence, the flux through this face is

$$\int_2 \mathbf{E} \cdot d\mathbf{A} = \int_2 E(\cos 0°) \, dA = E \int_2 dA = +EA = E\ell^2$$

Therefore, the net flux over all six faces is

$$\Phi_E = -E\ell^2 + E\ell^2 + 0 + 0 + 0 + 0 = \boxed{0}$$

24.2 Gauss's Law

In this section we describe a general relationship between the net electric flux through a closed surface (often called a *gaussian surface*) and the charge enclosed by the surface. This relationship, known as *Gauss's law*, is of fundamental importance in the study of electric fields.

Let us again consider a positive point charge q located at the center of a sphere of radius r, as shown in Figure 24.6. From Equation 23.9 we know that the magnitude of the electric field everywhere on the surface of the sphere is $E = k_e q/r^2$. As noted in Example 24.1, the field lines are directed radially outward and hence are perpendicular to the surface at every point on the surface. That is, at each surface point, $\mathbf{E}$ is parallel to the vector $\Delta \mathbf{A}_i$ representing a local element of area ΔA_i surrounding the surface point. Therefore,

$$\mathbf{E} \cdot \Delta \mathbf{A}_i = E \, \Delta A_i$$

and from Equation 24.4 we find that the net flux through the gaussian surface is

$$\Phi_E = \oint \mathbf{E} \cdot d\mathbf{A} = \oint E \, dA = E \oint dA$$

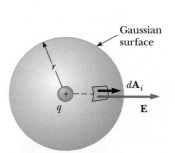

Figure 24.6 A spherical gaussian surface of radius r surrounding a point charge q. When the charge is at the center of the sphere, the electric field is everywhere normal to the surface and constant in magnitude.

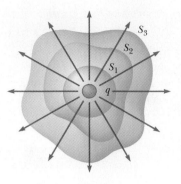

Figure 24.7 Closed surfaces of various shapes surrounding a charge q. The net electric flux is the same through all surfaces.

where we have moved E outside of the integral because, by symmetry, E is constant over the surface and given by $E = k_e q/r^2$. Furthermore, because the surface is spherical, $\oint dA = A = 4\pi r^2$. Hence, the net flux through the gaussian surface is

$$\Phi_E = \frac{k_e q}{r^2}(4\pi r^2) = 4\pi k_e q$$

Recalling from Section 23.3 that $k_e = 1/4\pi\epsilon_0$, we can write this equation in the form

$$\Phi_E = \frac{q}{\epsilon_0} \qquad (24.5)$$

We can verify that this expression for the net flux gives the same result as Example 24.1: $\Phi_E = (1.00 \times 10^{-6}\ \text{C})/(8.85 \times 10^{-12}\ \text{C}^2/\text{N}\cdot\text{m}^2) = 1.13 \times 10^5\ \text{N}\cdot\text{m}^2/\text{C}$.

Note from Equation 24.5 that the net flux through the spherical surface is proportional to the charge inside. The flux is independent of the radius r because the area of the spherical surface is proportional to r^2, whereas the electric field is proportional to $1/r^2$. Thus, in the product of area and electric field, the dependence on r cancels.

Now consider several closed surfaces surrounding a charge q, as shown in Figure 24.7. Surface S_1 is spherical, but surfaces S_2 and S_3 are not. From Equation 24.5, the flux that passes through S_1 has the value q/ϵ_0. As we discussed in the preceding section, flux is proportional to the number of electric field lines passing through a surface. The construction shown in Figure 24.7 shows that the number of lines through S_1 is equal to the number of lines through the nonspherical surfaces S_2 and S_3. Therefore, we conclude that **the net flux through *any* closed surface surrounding a point charge q is given by q/ϵ_0 and is independent of the shape of that surface.**

Now consider a point charge located *outside* a closed surface of arbitrary shape, as shown in Figure 24.8. As you can see from this construction, any electric field line that enters the surface leaves the surface at another point. The number of electric field lines entering the surface equals the number leaving the surface. Therefore, we conclude that **the net electric flux through a closed surface that surrounds no charge is zero.** If we apply this result to Example 24.2, we can easily see that the net flux through the cube is zero because there is no charge inside the cube.

Let us extend these arguments to two generalized cases: (1) that of many point charges and (2) that of a continuous distribution of charge. We once again use the superposition principle, which states that **the electric field due to many charges is the vector sum of the electric fields produced by the individual charges.** Therefore, we can express the flux through any closed surface as

$$\oint \mathbf{E}\cdot d\mathbf{A} = \oint (\mathbf{E}_1 + \mathbf{E}_2 + \cdots)\cdot d\mathbf{A}$$

where $\mathbf{E}$ is the total electric field at any point on the surface produced by the vector addition of the electric fields at that point due to the individual charges. Consider the system of charges shown in Figure 24.9. The surface S surrounds only one charge, q_1; hence, the net flux through S is q_1/ϵ_0. The flux through S due to charges q_2, q_3, and q_4 outside it is zero because each electric field line that enters S at one point leaves it at

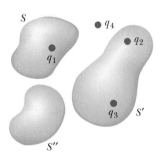

Figure 24.8 A point charge located *outside* a closed surface. The number of lines entering the surface equals the number leaving the surface.

Active Figure 24.9 The net electric flux through any closed surface depends only on the charge *inside* that surface. The net flux through surface S is q_1/ϵ_0, the net flux through surface S' is $(q_2 + q_3)/\epsilon_0$, and the net flux through surface S'' is zero. Charge q_4 does not contribute to the flux through any surface because it is outside all surfaces.

At the Active Figures link at http://www.pse6.com, you can change the size and shape of a closed surface and see the effect on the electric flux of surrounding combinations of charge with that surface.

another. The surface S' surrounds charges q_2 and q_3; hence, the net flux through it is $(q_2 + q_3)/\epsilon_0$. Finally, the net flux through surface S'' is zero because there is no charge inside this surface. That is, *all* the electric field lines that enter S'' at one point leave at another. Notice that charge q_4 does not contribute to the net flux through any of the surfaces because it is outside all of the surfaces.

Gauss's law, which is a generalization of what we have just described, states that the net flux through *any* closed surface is

$$\Phi_E = \oint \mathbf{E} \cdot d\mathbf{A} = \frac{q_{\text{in}}}{\epsilon_0} \qquad (24.6)$$

Gauss's law

where q_{in} represents the net charge inside the surface and $\mathbf{E}$ represents the electric field at any point on the surface.

A formal proof of Gauss's law is presented in Section 24.5. When using Equation 24.6, you should note that although the charge q_{in} is the net charge inside the gaussian surface, $\mathbf{E}$ represents the *total electric field*, which includes contributions from charges both inside and outside the surface.

In principle, Gauss's law can be solved for $\mathbf{E}$ to determine the electric field due to a system of charges or a continuous distribution of charge. In practice, however, this type of solution is applicable only in a limited number of highly symmetric situations. In the next section we use Gauss's law to evaluate the electric field for charge distributions that have spherical, cylindrical, or planar symmetry. If one chooses the gaussian surface surrounding the charge distribution carefully, the integral in Equation 24.6 can be simplified.

Quick Quiz 24.3 If the net flux through a gaussian surface is *zero*, the following four statements *could be true*. Which of the statements *must be true*? (a) There are no charges inside the surface. (b) The net charge inside the surface is zero. (c) The electric field is zero everywhere on the surface. (d) The number of electric field lines entering the surface equals the number leaving the surface.

Quick Quiz 24.4 Consider the charge distribution shown in Figure 24.9. The charges contributing to the total electric *flux* through surface S' are (a) q_1 only (b) q_4 only (c) q_2 and q_3 (d) all four charges (e) none of the charges.

Quick Quiz 24.5 Again consider the charge distribution shown in Figure 24.9. The charges contributing to the total electric *field* at a chosen point on the surface S' are (a) q_1 only (b) q_4 only (c) q_2 and q_3 (d) all four charges (e) none of the charges.

▲ **PITFALL PREVENTION**

24.1 Zero Flux is not Zero Field

We see two situations in which there is zero flux through a closed surface—either there are no charged particles enclosed by the surface or there are charged particles enclosed, but the net charge inside the surface is zero. For either situation, it is *incorrect* to conclude that the electric field on the surface is zero. Gauss's law states that the electric *flux* is proportional to the enclosed charge, not the electric *field*.

Conceptual Example 24.3   Flux Due to a Point Charge

A spherical gaussian surface surrounds a point charge q. Describe what happens to the total flux through the surface if

(A) the charge is tripled,

(B) the radius of the sphere is doubled,

(C) the surface is changed to a cube, and

(D) the charge is moved to another location inside the surface.

Solution

(A) The flux through the surface is tripled because flux is proportional to the amount of charge inside the surface.

(B) The flux does not change because all electric field lines from the charge pass through the sphere, regardless of its radius.

(C) The flux does not change when the shape of the gaussian surface changes because all electric field lines from the charge pass through the surface, regardless of its shape.

(D) The flux does not change when the charge is moved to another location inside that surface because Gauss's law refers to the total charge enclosed, regardless of where the charge is located inside the surface.

24.3 Application of Gauss's Law to Various Charge Distributions

As mentioned earlier, Gauss's law is useful in determining electric fields when the charge distribution is characterized by a high degree of symmetry. The following examples demonstrate ways of choosing the gaussian surface over which the surface integral given by Equation 24.6 can be simplified and the electric field determined. In choosing the surface, we should always take advantage of the symmetry of the charge distribution so that we can remove E from the integral and solve for it. The goal in this type of calculation is to determine a surface that satisfies one or more of the following conditions:

1. The value of the electric field can be argued by symmetry to be constant over the surface.

2. The dot product in Equation 24.6 can be expressed as a simple algebraic product $E\,dA$ because $\mathbf{E}$ and $d\mathbf{A}$ are parallel.

3. The dot product in Equation 24.6 is zero because $\mathbf{E}$ and $d\mathbf{A}$ are perpendicular.

4. The field can be argued to be zero over the surface.

All four of these conditions are used in examples throughout the remainder of this chapter.

▲ **PITFALL PREVENTION**

24.2 Gaussian Surfaces are not Real

A gaussian surface is an imaginary surface that you choose to satisfy the conditions listed here. It does not have to coincide with a physical surface in the situation.

Example 24.4 The Electric Field Due to a Point Charge

Starting with Gauss's law, calculate the electric field due to an isolated point charge q.

Solution A single charge represents the simplest possible charge distribution, and we use this familiar case to show how to solve for the electric field with Gauss's law. Figure 24.10 and our discussion of the electric field due to a point charge in Chapter 23 help us to conceptualize the physical situation. Because the space around the single charge has spherical symmetry, we categorize this problem as one in which there is enough symmetry to apply Gauss's law. To analyze any Gauss's law problem, we consider the details of the electric field and choose a gaussian surface that satisfies some or all of the conditions that we have listed above. We choose a spherical gaussian surface of radius r centered on the point charge, as shown in Figure 24.10. The electric field due to a positive point charge is directed radially outward by

symmetry and is therefore normal to the surface at every point. Thus, as in condition (2), $\mathbf{E}$ is parallel to $d\mathbf{A}$ at each point. Therefore, $\mathbf{E} \cdot d\mathbf{A} = E\,dA$ and Gauss's law gives

$$\Phi_E = \oint \mathbf{E} \cdot d\mathbf{A} = \oint E\,dA = \frac{q}{\epsilon_0}$$

By symmetry, E is constant everywhere on the surface, which satisfies condition (1), so it can be removed from the integral. Therefore,

$$\oint E\,dA = E \oint dA = E(4\pi r^2) = \frac{q}{\epsilon_0}$$

where we have used the fact that the surface area of a sphere is $4\pi r^2$. Now, we solve for the electric field:

$$E = \frac{q}{4\pi\epsilon_0 r^2} = k_e \frac{q}{r^2}$$

To finalize this problem, note that this is the familiar electric field due to a point charge that we developed from Coulomb's law in Chapter 23.

What If? What if the charge in Figure 24.10 were not at the center of the spherical gaussian surface?

Answer In this case, while Gauss's law would still be valid, the situation would not possess enough symmetry to evaluate the electric field. Because the charge is not at the center, the magnitude of $\mathbf{E}$ would vary over the surface of the sphere and the vector $\mathbf{E}$ would not be everywhere perpendicular to the surface.

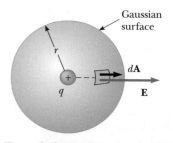
Gaussian surface

Figure 24.10 (Example 24.4) The point charge q is at the center of the spherical gaussian surface, and $\mathbf{E}$ is parallel to $d\mathbf{A}$ at every point on the surface.

Example 24.5   A Spherically Symmetric Charge Distribution

An insulating solid sphere of radius a has a uniform volume charge density ρ and carries a total positive charge Q (Fig. 24.11).

(A) Calculate the magnitude of the electric field at a point outside the sphere.

Solution Because the charge distribution is spherically symmetric, we again select a spherical gaussian surface of radius r, concentric with the sphere, as shown in Figure 24.11a. For this choice, conditions (1) and (2) are satisfied, as they were for the point charge in Example 24.4. Following the line of reasoning given in Example 24.4, we find that

$$(1) \qquad E = k_e \frac{Q}{r^2} \qquad (\text{for } r > a)$$

Note that this result is identical to the one we obtained for a point charge. Therefore, we conclude that, **for a uniformly charged sphere, the field in the region external to the sphere is** *equivalent* **to that of a point charge located at the center of the sphere.**

(B) Find the magnitude of the electric field at a point inside the sphere.

Solution In this case we select a spherical gaussian surface having radius $r < a$, concentric with the insulating sphere (Fig. 24.11b). Let us denote the volume of this smaller sphere by V'. To apply Gauss's law in this situation, it is important to recognize that the charge q_{in} within the gaussian surface of volume V' is less than Q. To calculate q_{in}, we use the fact that $q_{in} = \rho V'$:

$$q_{in} = \rho V' = \rho \left(\tfrac{4}{3} \pi r^3\right)$$

By symmetry, the magnitude of the electric field is constant everywhere on the spherical gaussian surface and is normal to the surface at each point—both conditions

(1) and (2) are satisfied. Therefore, Gauss's law in the region $r < a$ gives

$$\oint E \, dA = E \oint dA = E \,(4\pi r^2) = \frac{q_{in}}{\epsilon_0}$$

Solving for E gives

$$E = \frac{q_{in}}{4\pi\epsilon_0 r^2} = \frac{\rho(\tfrac{4}{3}\pi r^3)}{4\pi\epsilon_0 r^2} = \frac{\rho}{3\epsilon_0} \, r$$

Because $\rho = Q/\tfrac{4}{3}\pi a^3$ by definition and because $k_e = 1/4\pi\epsilon_0$, this expression for E can be written as

$$(2) \qquad E = \frac{Qr}{4\pi\epsilon_0 a^3} = k_e \frac{Q}{a^3} \, r \qquad (\text{for } r < a)$$

Note that this result for E differs from the one we obtained in part (A). It shows that $E \rightarrow 0$ as $r \rightarrow 0$. Therefore, the result eliminates the problem that would exist at $r = 0$ if E varied as $1/r^2$ inside the sphere as it does outside the sphere. That is, if $E \propto 1/r^2$ for $r < a$, the field would be infinite at $r = 0$, which is physically impossible.

What If? Suppose we approach the radial position $r = a$ from inside the sphere and from outside. Do we measure the same value of the electric field from both directions?

Answer From Equation (1), we see that the field approaches a value from the outside given by

$$E = \lim_{r \rightarrow a} \left(k_e \frac{Q}{r^2} \right) = k_e \frac{Q}{a^2}$$

From the inside, Equation (2) gives us

$$E = \lim_{r \rightarrow a} \left(k_e \frac{Q}{a^3} \, r \right) = k_e \frac{Q}{a^3} \, a = k_e \frac{Q}{a^2}$$

Thus, the value of the field is the same as we approach the surface from both directions. A plot of E versus r is shown in Figure 24.12. Note that the magnitude of the field is continuous, but the derivative of the field magnitude is not.

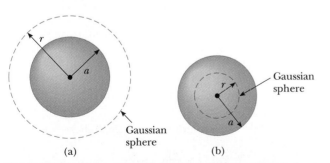

(a)   (b)

Figure 24.11 (Example 24.5) A uniformly charged insulating sphere of radius a and total charge Q. (a) For points outside the sphere, a large spherical gaussian surface is drawn concentric with the sphere. In diagrams such as this, the dotted line represents the intersection of the gaussian surface with the plane of the page. (b) For points inside the sphere, a spherical gaussian surface smaller than the sphere is drawn.

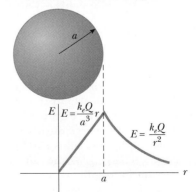

Figure 24.12 (Example 24.5) A plot of E versus r for a uniformly charged insulating sphere. The electric field inside the sphere $(r < a)$ varies linearly with r. The field outside the sphere $(r > a)$ is the same as that of a point charge Q located at $r = 0$.

At the Interactive Worked Example link at **http://www.pse6.com,** *you can investigate the electric field inside and outside the sphere.*

Example 24.6   The Electric Field Due to a Thin Spherical Shell

A thin spherical shell of radius a has a total charge Q distributed uniformly over its surface (Fig. 24.13a). Find the electric field at points

(A) outside and

(B) inside the shell.

Solution

(A) The calculation for the field outside the shell is identical to that for the solid sphere shown in Example 24.5a. If we construct a spherical gaussian surface of radius $r > a$ concentric with the shell (Fig. 24.13b), the charge inside this surface is Q. Therefore, the field at a point outside the shell is equivalent to that due to a point charge Q located at the center:

$$E = k_e \frac{Q}{r^2} \qquad \text{(for } r > a\text{)}$$

(B) The electric field inside the spherical shell is zero. This follows from Gauss's law applied to a spherical surface of radius $r < a$ concentric with the shell (Fig. 24.13c). Because of the spherical symmetry of the charge distribution and because the net charge inside the surface is zero—satisfaction of conditions (1) and (2) again—application of Gauss's law shows that $E = 0$ in the region $r < a$. We obtain the same results using Equation 23.11 and integrating over the charge distribution. This calculation is rather complicated. Gauss's law allows us to determine these results in a much simpler way.

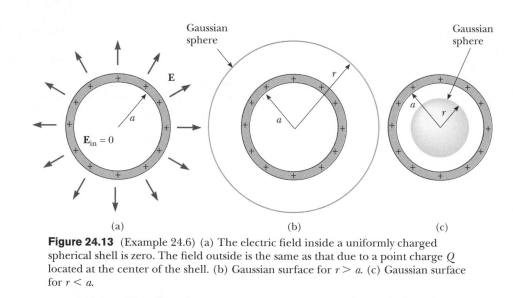

Figure 24.13   (Example 24.6) (a) The electric field inside a uniformly charged spherical shell is zero. The field outside is the same as that due to a point charge Q located at the center of the shell. (b) Gaussian surface for $r > a$. (c) Gaussian surface for $r < a$.

Example 24.7   A Cylindrically Symmetric Charge Distribution

Find the electric field a distance r from a line of positive charge of infinite length and constant charge per unit length λ (Fig. 24.14a).

Solution The symmetry of the charge distribution requires that **E** be perpendicular to the line charge and directed outward, as shown in Figure 24.14a and b. To reflect the symmetry of the charge distribution, we select a cylindrical gaussian surface of radius r and length ℓ that is coaxial with the line charge. For the curved part of this surface, **E** is constant in magnitude and perpendicular to the surface at each point—satisfaction of conditions (1) and (2). Furthermore, the flux through the ends of the gaussian cylinder is zero because **E** is parallel to these surfaces—the first application we have seen of condition (3).

We take the surface integral in Gauss's law over the entire gaussian surface. Because of the zero value of $\mathbf{E} \cdot d\mathbf{A}$ for the ends of the cylinder, however, we can restrict our attention to only the curved surface of the cylinder.

The total charge inside our gaussian surface is $\lambda\ell$. Applying Gauss's law and conditions (1) and (2), we find that for the curved surface

$$\Phi_E = \oint \mathbf{E} \cdot d\mathbf{A} = E \oint dA = EA = \frac{q_{\text{in}}}{\epsilon_0} = \frac{\lambda\ell}{\epsilon_0}$$

The area of the curved surface is $A = 2\pi r\ell$; therefore,

$$E(2\pi r\ell) = \frac{\lambda\ell}{\epsilon_0}$$

$$E = \frac{\lambda}{2\pi\epsilon_0 r} = 2k_e \frac{\lambda}{r} \qquad (24.7)$$

Thus, we see that the electric field due to a cylindrically symmetric charge distribution varies as $1/r$, whereas the field external to a spherically symmetric charge distribution varies as $1/r^2$. Equation 24.7 was also derived by integration of the field of a point charge. (See Problem 35 in Chapter 23.)

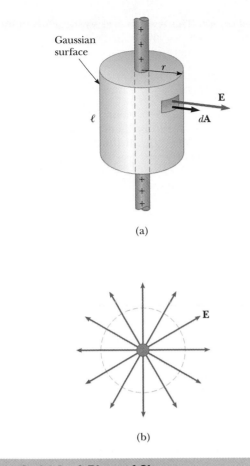

(a)

(b)

Figure 24.14 (Example 24.7) (a) An infinite line of charge surrounded by a cylindrical gaussian surface concentric with the line. (b) An end view shows that the electric field at the cylindrical surface is constant in magnitude and perpendicular to the surface.

What If? What if the line segment in this example were not infinitely long?

Answer If the line charge in this example were of finite length, the result for E would not be that given by Equation 24.7. A finite line charge does not possess sufficient symmetry for us to make use of Gauss's law. This is because the magnitude of the electric field is no longer constant over the surface of the gaussian cylinder—the field near the ends of the line would be different from that far from the ends. Thus, condition (1) would not be satisfied in this situation. Furthermore, **E** is not perpendicular to the cylindrical surface at all points—the field vectors near the ends would have a component parallel to the line. Thus, condition (2) would not be satisfied. For points close to a finite line charge and far from the ends, Equation 24.7 gives a good approximation of the value of the field.

It is left for you to show (see Problem 29) that the electric field inside a uniformly charged rod of finite radius and infinite length is proportional to r.

Example 24.8   A Plane of Charge

Find the electric field due to an infinite plane of positive charge with uniform surface charge density σ.

Solution By symmetry, **E** must be perpendicular to the plane and must have the same magnitude at all points equidistant from the plane. The fact that the direction of **E** is away from positive charges indicates that the direction of **E** on one side of the plane must be opposite its direction on the other side, as shown in Figure 24.15. A gaussian surface that reflects the symmetry is a small cylinder whose axis is perpendicular to the plane and whose ends

each have an area A and are equidistant from the plane. Because **E** is parallel to the curved surface—and, therefore, perpendicular to $d\mathbf{A}$ everywhere on the surface—condition (3) is satisfied and there is no contribution to the surface integral from this surface. For the flat ends of the cylinder, conditions (1) and (2) are satisfied. The flux through each end of the cylinder is EA; hence, the total flux through the entire gaussian surface is just that through the ends, $\Phi_E = 2EA$.

Noting that the total charge inside the surface is $q_{in} = \sigma A$, we use Gauss's law and find that the total flux through the gaussian surface is

$$\Phi_E = 2EA = \frac{q_{in}}{\epsilon_0} = \frac{\sigma A}{\epsilon_0}$$

leading to

$$E = \frac{\sigma}{2\epsilon_0} \qquad (24.8)$$

Because the distance from each flat end of the cylinder to the plane does not appear in Equation 24.8, we conclude that $E = \sigma/2\epsilon_0$ at *any* distance from the plane. That is, the field is uniform everywhere.

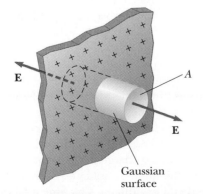

Figure 24.15 (Example 24.8) A cylindrical gaussian surface penetrating an infinite plane of charge. The flux is EA through each end of the gaussian surface and zero through its curved surface.

What If? Suppose we place two infinite planes of charge parallel to each other, one positively charged and the other negatively charged. Both planes have the same surface charge density. What does the electric field look like now?

Answer In this situation, the electric fields due to the two planes add in the region between the planes, resulting in a uniform field of magnitude σ/ϵ_0, and cancel elsewhere to give a field of zero. This is a practical way to achieve uniform electric fields, such as those needed in the CRT tube discussed in Section 23.7.

Conceptual Example 24.9   Don't Use Gauss's Law Here!

Explain why Gauss's law cannot be used to calculate the electric field near an electric dipole, a charged disk, or a triangle with a point charge at each corner.

Solution The charge distributions of all these configurations do not have sufficient symmetry to make the use of Gauss's law practical. We cannot find a closed surface surrounding any of these distributions that satisfies one or more of conditions (1) through (4) listed at the beginning of this section.

24.4   Conductors in Electrostatic Equilibrium

As we learned in Section 23.2, a good electrical conductor contains charges (electrons) that are not bound to any atom and therefore are free to move about within the material. When there is no net motion of charge within a conductor, the conductor is in **electrostatic equilibrium.** A conductor in electrostatic equilibrium has the following properties:

Properties of a conductor in electrostatic equilibrium

1. The electric field is zero everywhere inside the conductor.

2. If an isolated conductor carries a charge, the charge resides on its surface.

3. The electric field just outside a charged conductor is perpendicular to the surface of the conductor and has a magnitude σ/ϵ_0, where σ is the surface charge density at that point.

4. On an irregularly shaped conductor, the surface charge density is greatest at locations where the radius of curvature of the surface is smallest.

We verify the first three properties in the discussion that follows. The fourth property is presented here so that we have a complete list of properties for conductors in electrostatic equilibrium, but cannot be verified until Chapter 25.

We can understand the first property by considering a conducting slab placed in an external field **E** (Fig. 24.16). The electric field inside the conductor *must* be zero under the assumption that we have electrostatic equilibrium. If the field were not zero, free electrons in the conductor would experience an electric force (**F** = q**E**) and would accelerate due to this force. This motion of electrons, however, would mean that the conductor is not in electrostatic equilibrium. Thus, the existence of electrostatic equilibrium is consistent only with a zero field in the conductor.

Let us investigate how this zero field is accomplished. Before the external field is applied, free electrons are uniformly distributed throughout the conductor. When the external field is applied, the free electrons accelerate to the left in Figure 24.16, causing a plane of negative charge to be present on the left surface. The movement of electrons to the left results in a plane of positive charge on the right surface. These planes of charge create an additional electric field inside the conductor that opposes the external field. As the electrons move, the surface charge densities on the left and right surfaces increase until the magnitude of the internal field equals that of the external field, resulting in a net field of zero inside the conductor. The time it takes a good conductor to reach equilibrium is on the order of 10^{-16} s, which for most purposes can be considered instantaneous.

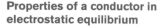

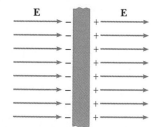

Figure 24.16 A conducting slab in an external electric field **E**. The charges induced on the two surfaces of the slab produce an electric field that opposes the external field, giving a resultant field of zero inside the slab.

We can use Gauss's law to verify the second property of a conductor in electrostatic equilibrium. Figure 24.17 shows an arbitrarily shaped conductor. A gaussian surface is drawn inside the conductor and can be as close to the conductor's surface as we wish. As we have just shown, the electric field everywhere inside the conductor is zero when it is in electrostatic equilibrium. Therefore, the electric field must be zero at every point on the gaussian surface, in accordance with condition (4) in Section 24.3. Thus, the net flux through this gaussian surface is zero. From this result and Gauss's law, we conclude that the net charge inside the gaussian surface is zero. Because there can be no net charge inside the gaussian surface (which is arbitrarily close to the conductor's surface), **any net charge on the conductor must reside on its surface.** Gauss's law does not indicate how this excess charge is distributed on the conductor's surface, only that it resides exclusively on the surface.

We can also use Gauss's law to verify the third property. First, note that if the field vector **E** had a component parallel to the conductor's surface, free electrons would experience an electric force and move along the surface; in such a case, the conductor would not be in equilibrium. Thus, the field vector must be perpendicular to the surface. To determine the magnitude of the electric field, we draw a gaussian surface in the shape of a small cylinder whose end faces are parallel to the surface of the conductor (Fig. 24.18). Part of the cylinder is just outside the conductor, and part is inside. The field is perpendicular to the conductor's surface from the condition of electrostatic equilibrium. Thus, we satisfy condition (3) in Section 24.3 for the curved part of the cylindrical gaussian surface—there is no flux through this part of the gaussian surface because **E** is parallel to the surface. There is no flux through the flat face of the cylinder inside the conductor because here **E** = 0; this satisfies condition (4). Hence, the net flux through the gaussian surface is that through only the flat face outside the conductor, where the field is perpendicular to the gaussian surface. Using conditions (1) and (2) for this face, the flux is EA, where E is the electric field just outside the conductor and A is the area of the cylinder's face. Applying Gauss's law to this surface, we obtain

$$\Phi_E = \oint E \, dA = EA = \frac{q_{\text{in}}}{\epsilon_0} = \frac{\sigma A}{\epsilon_0}$$

where we have used the fact that $q_{\text{in}} = \sigma A$. Solving for E gives for the electric field just outside a charged conductor

$$E = \frac{\sigma}{\epsilon_0} \qquad (24.9)$$

Figure 24.19 shows electric field lines made visible by pieces of thread floating in oil. Notice that the field lines are perpendicular to both the cylindrical conducting surface and the straight conducting surface.

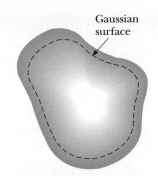

Figure 24.17 A conductor of arbitrary shape. The broken line represents a gaussian surface that can be as close to the surface of the conductor as we wish.

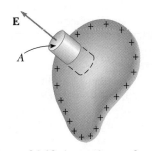

Figure 24.18 A gaussian surface in the shape of a small cylinder is used to calculate the electric field just outside a charged conductor. The flux through the gaussian surface is EA. Remember that **E** is zero inside the conductor.

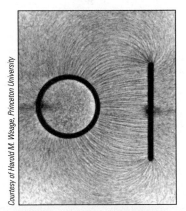

Courtesy of Harold M. Waage, Princeton University

Figure 24.19 Electric field pattern surrounding a charged conducting plate placed near an oppositely charged conducting cylinder. Small pieces of thread suspended in oil align with the electric field lines. Note that (1) the field lines are perpendicular to both conductors and (2) there are no lines inside the cylinder ($E = 0$).

Quick Quiz 24.6 Your little brother likes to rub his feet on the carpet and then touch you to give you a shock. While you are trying to escape the shock treatment, you discover a hollow metal cylinder in your basement, large enough to climb inside. In which of the following cases will you *not* be shocked? (a) You climb inside the cylinder, making contact with the inner surface, and your charged brother touches the outer metal surface. (b) Your charged brother is inside touching the inner metal surface and you are outside, touching the outer metal surface. (c) Both of you are outside the cylinder, touching its outer metal surface but not touching each other directly.

Example 24.10 **A Sphere Inside a Spherical Shell**

A solid conducting sphere of radius a carries a net positive charge $2Q$. A conducting spherical shell of inner radius b and outer radius c is concentric with the solid sphere and carries a net charge $-Q$. Using Gauss's law, find the electric field in the regions labeled ①, ②, ③, and ④ in Figure 24.20 and the charge distribution on the shell when the entire system is in electrostatic equilibrium.

Solution First note that the charge distributions on both the sphere and the shell are characterized by spherical symmetry around their common center. To determine the electric field at various distances r from this center, we construct a spherical gaussian surface for each of the four regions of interest. Such a surface for region ② is shown in Figure 24.20.

To find E inside the solid sphere (region ①), consider a gaussian surface of radius $r < a$. Because there can be no charge inside a conductor in electrostatic equilibrium, we see that $q_{in} = 0$; thus, on the basis of Gauss's law and symmetry, $E_1 = 0$ for $r < a$.

In region ②—between the surface of the solid sphere and the inner surface of the shell—we construct a spherical gaussian surface of radius r where $a < r < b$ and note that the charge inside this surface is $+2Q$ (the charge on the solid sphere). Because of the spherical symmetry, the electric field lines must be directed radially outward and be constant in magnitude on the gaussian surface. Following Example 24.4 and using Gauss's law, we find that

$$E_2 A = E_2(4\pi r^2) = \frac{q_{in}}{\epsilon_0} = \frac{2Q}{\epsilon_0}$$

$$E_2 = \frac{2Q}{4\pi\epsilon_0 r^2} = \boxed{\frac{2k_e Q}{r^2}} \qquad (\text{for } a < r < b)$$

In region ④, where $r > c$, the spherical gaussian surface we construct surrounds a total charge of $q_{in} = 2Q + (-Q) = Q$. Therefore, application of Gauss's law to this surface gives

$$E_4 = \boxed{\frac{k_e Q}{r^2}} \qquad (\text{for } r > c)$$

In region ③, the electric field must be zero because the spherical shell is also a conductor in equilibrium. Figure 24.21 shows a graphical representation of the variation of electric field with r.

If we construct a gaussian surface of radius r where $b < r < c$, we see that q_{in} must be zero because $E_3 = 0$. From this argument, we conclude that the charge on the inner surface of the spherical shell must be $-2Q$ to cancel the charge $+2Q$ on the solid sphere. Because the net charge on the shell is $-Q$, we conclude that its outer surface must carry a charge $+Q$.

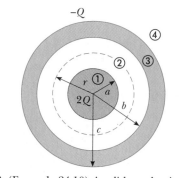

Figure 24.20 (Example 24.10) A solid conducting sphere of radius a and carrying a charge $2Q$ surrounded by a conducting spherical shell carrying a charge $-Q$.

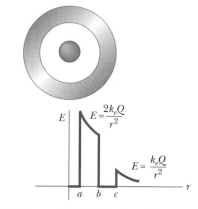

Figure 24.21 (Example 24.10) A plot of E versus r for the two-conductor system shown in Figure 24.20.

Explore the electric field of the system in Figure 24.20 at the Interactive Worked Example link at **http://www.pse6.com.**

24.5 Formal Derivation of Gauss's Law

One way of deriving Gauss's law involves *solid angles*. Consider a spherical surface of radius r containing an area element ΔA. The solid angle $\Delta\Omega$ (Ω: uppercase Greek omega) subtended at the center of the sphere by this element is defined to be

$$\Delta\Omega \equiv \frac{\Delta A}{r^2}$$

From this equation, we see that $\Delta\Omega$ has no dimensions because ΔA and r^2 both have dimensions L^2. The dimensionless unit of a solid angle is the **steradian.** (You may want to compare this equation to Equation 10.1b, the definition of the radian.) Because the

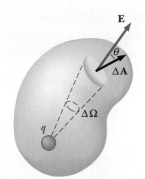

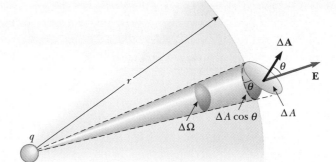

Figure 24.22 A closed surface of arbitrary shape surrounds a point charge q. The net electric flux through the surface is independent of the shape of the surface.

Figure 24.23 The area element ΔA subtends a solid angle $\Delta\Omega = (\Delta A \cos \theta)/r^2$ at the charge q.

surface area of a sphere is $4\pi r^2$, the total solid angle subtended by the sphere is

$$\Omega = \frac{4\pi r^2}{r^2} = 4\pi \text{ steradians}$$

Now consider a point charge q surrounded by a closed surface of arbitrary shape (Fig. 24.22). The total electric flux through this surface can be obtained by evaluating $\mathbf{E} \cdot \Delta\mathbf{A}$ for each small area element ΔA and summing over all elements. The flux through each element is

$$\Delta\Phi_E = \mathbf{E} \cdot \Delta\mathbf{A} = (E \cos \theta)\Delta A = k_e q \frac{\Delta A \cos \theta}{r^2}$$

where r is the distance from the charge to the area element, θ is the angle between the electric field $\mathbf{E}$ and $\Delta\mathbf{A}$ for the element, and $E = k_e q/r^2$ for a point charge. In Figure 24.23, we see that the projection of the area element perpendicular to the radius vector is $\Delta A \cos \theta$. Thus, the quantity $(\Delta A \cos \theta)/r^2$ is equal to the solid angle $\Delta\Omega$ that the surface element ΔA subtends at the charge q. We also see that $\Delta\Omega$ is equal to the solid angle subtended by the area element of a spherical surface of radius r. Because the total solid angle at a point is 4π steradians, the total flux through the closed surface is

$$\Phi_E = k_e q \oint \frac{dA \cos \theta}{r^2} = k_e q \oint d\Omega = 4\pi k_e q = \frac{q}{\epsilon_0}$$

Thus we have derived Gauss's law, Equation 24.6. Note that this result is independent of the shape of the closed surface and independent of the position of the charge within the surface.

SUMMARY

Electric flux is proportional to the number of electric field lines that penetrate a surface. If the electric field is uniform and makes an angle θ with the normal to a surface of area A, the electric flux through the surface is

$$\Phi_E = EA \cos \theta \tag{24.2}$$

In general, the electric flux through a surface is

$$\Phi_E = \int_{\text{surface}} \mathbf{E} \cdot d\mathbf{A} \tag{24.3}$$

Take a practice test for this chapter by clicking on the Practice Test link at http://www.pse6.com.

Table 24.1

Typical Electric Field Calculations Using Gauss's Law		
Charge Distribution	**Electric Field**	**Location**
Insulating sphere of radius R, uniform charge density, and total charge Q	$k_e \dfrac{Q}{r^2}$	$r > R$
	$k_e \dfrac{Q}{R^2} r$	$r < R$
Thin spherical shell of radius R and total charge Q	$k_e \dfrac{Q}{r^2}$	$r > R$
	0	$r < R$
Line charge of infinite length and charge per unit length λ	$2k_e \dfrac{\lambda}{r}$	Outside the line
Infinite charged plane having surface charge density σ	$\dfrac{\sigma}{2\epsilon_0}$	Everywhere outside the plane
Conductor having surface charge density σ	$\dfrac{\sigma}{\epsilon_0}$	Just outside the conductor
	0	Inside the conductor

You should be able to apply Equations 24.2 and 24.3 in a variety of situations, particularly those in which symmetry simplifies the calculation.

Gauss's law says that the net electric flux Φ_E through any closed gaussian surface is equal to the *net* charge q_{in} inside the surface divided by ϵ_0:

$$\Phi_E = \oint \mathbf{E} \cdot d\mathbf{A} = \frac{q_{in}}{\epsilon_0} \tag{24.6}$$

Using Gauss's law, you can calculate the electric field due to various symmetric charge distributions. Table 24.1 lists some typical results.

A conductor in **electrostatic equilibrium** has the following properties:

1. The electric field is zero everywhere inside the conductor.
2. Any net charge on the conductor resides entirely on its surface.
3. The electric field just outside the conductor is perpendicular to its surface and has a magnitude σ/ϵ_0, where σ is the surface charge density at that point.
4. On an irregularly shaped conductor, the surface charge density is greatest where the radius of curvature of the surface is the smallest.

QUESTIONS

1. The Sun is lower in the sky during the winter months than it is in the summer. How does this change the flux of sunlight hitting a given area on the surface of the Earth? How does this affect the weather?

2. If the electric field in a region of space is zero, can you conclude that no electric charges are in that region? Explain.

3. If more electric field lines leave a gaussian surface than enter it, what can you conclude about the net charge enclosed by that surface?

4. A uniform electric field exists in a region of space in which there are no charges. What can you conclude about the net electric flux through a gaussian surface placed in this region of space?

5. If the total charge inside a closed surface is known but the distribution of the charge is unspecified, can you use Gauss's law to find the electric field? Explain.

6. Explain why the electric flux through a closed surface with a given enclosed charge is independent of the size or shape of the surface.

7. Consider the electric field due to a nonconducting infinite plane having a uniform charge density. Explain why the electric field does not depend on the distance from the plane, in terms of the spacing of the electric field lines.

8. Use Gauss's law to explain why electric field lines must begin or end on electric charges. (*Suggestion:* Change the size of the gaussian surface.)

9. On the basis of the repulsive nature of the force between like charges and the freedom of motion of charge within a conductor, explain why excess charge on an isolated conductor must reside on its surface.

10. A person is placed in a large hollow metallic sphere that is insulated from ground. If a large charge is placed on the sphere, will the person be harmed upon touching the inside of the sphere? Explain what will happen if the person also has an initial charge whose sign is opposite that of the charge on the sphere.

11. Two solid spheres, both of radius R, carry identical total charges, Q. One sphere is a good conductor while the other is an insulator. If the charge on the insulating sphere is uniformly distributed throughout its interior volume, how do the electric fields outside these two spheres compare? Are the fields identical inside the two spheres?

12. A common demonstration involves charging a rubber balloon, which is an insulator, by rubbing it on your hair, and touching the balloon to a ceiling or wall, which is also an insulator. The electrical attraction between the charged balloon and the neutral wall results in the balloon sticking to the wall. Imagine now that we have two infinitely large flat sheets of insulating material. One is charged and the other is neutral. If these are brought into contact, will an attractive force exist between them, as there was for the balloon and the wall?

13. You may have heard that one of the safer places to be during a lightning storm is inside a car. Why would this be the case?

PROBLEMS

1, 2, 3 = straightforward, intermediate, challenging ☐ = full solution available in the *Student Solutions Manual and Study Guide*

🌐 = coached solution with hints available at http://www.pse6.com   💻 = computer useful in solving problem

▨ = paired numerical and symbolic problems

Section 24.1 Electric Flux

1. An electric field with a magnitude of 3.50 kN/C is applied along the x axis. Calculate the electric flux through a rectangular plane 0.350 m wide and 0.700 m long assuming that (a) the plane is parallel to the yz plane; (b) the plane is parallel to the xy plane; (c) the plane contains the y axis, and its normal makes an angle of 40.0° with the x axis.

2. A vertical electric field of magnitude 2.00×10^4 N/C exists above the Earth's surface on a day when a thunderstorm is brewing. A car with a rectangular size of 6.00 m by 3.00 m is traveling along a roadway sloping downward at 10.0°. Determine the electric flux through the bottom of the car.

3. A 40.0-cm-diameter loop is rotated in a uniform electric field until the position of maximum electric flux is found. The flux in this position is measured to be 5.20×10^5 N·m²/C. What is the magnitude of the electric field?

4. Consider a closed triangular box resting within a horizontal electric field of magnitude $E = 7.80 \times 10^4$ N/C as shown in Figure P24.4. Calculate the electric flux through (a) the vertical rectangular surface, (b) the slanted surface, and (c) the entire surface of the box.

6. A point charge q is located at the center of a uniform ring having linear charge density λ and radius a, as shown in Figure P24.6. Determine the total electric flux through a sphere centered at the point charge and having radius R, where $R < a$.

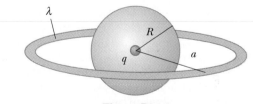

Figure P24.6

7. A pyramid with horizontal square base, 6.00 m on each side, and a height of 4.00 m is placed in a vertical electric field of 52.0 N/C. Calculate the total electric flux through the pyramid's four slanted surfaces.

8. A cone with base radius R and height h is located on a horizontal table. A horizontal uniform field E penetrates the cone, as shown in Figure P24.8. Determine the electric flux that enters the left-hand side of the cone.

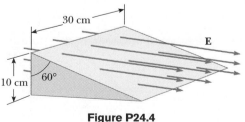

Figure P24.4

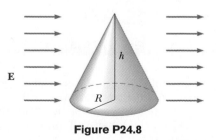

Figure P24.8

Section 24.2 Gauss's Law

9. The following charges are located inside a submarine: 5.00 μC, − 9.00 μC, 27.0 μC, and − 84.0 μC. (a) Calculate

5. A uniform electric field $a\hat{\mathbf{i}} + b\hat{\mathbf{j}}$ intersects a surface of area A. What is the flux through this area if the surface lies (a) in the yz plane? (b) in the xz plane? (c) in the xy plane?

the net electric flux through the hull of the submarine. (b) Is the number of electric field lines leaving the submarine greater than, equal to, or less than the number entering it?

10. The electric field everywhere on the surface of a thin spherical shell of radius 0.750 m is measured to be 890 N/C and points radially toward the center of the sphere. (a) What is the net charge within the sphere's surface? (b) What can you conclude about the nature and distribution of the charge inside the spherical shell?

11. Four closed surfaces, S_1 through S_4, together with the charges $-2Q$, Q, and $-Q$ are sketched in Figure P24.11. (The colored lines are the intersections of the surfaces with the page.) Find the electric flux through each surface.

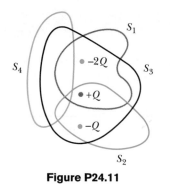

Figure P24.11

12. (a) A point charge q is located a distance d from an infinite plane. Determine the electric flux through the plane due to the point charge. (b) **What If?** A point charge q is located a *very small* distance from the center of a *very large* square on the line perpendicular to the square and going through its center. Determine the approximate electric flux through the square due to the point charge. (c) Explain why the answers to parts (a) and (b) are identical.

13. Calculate the total electric flux through the paraboloidal surface due to a uniform electric field of magnitude E_0 in the direction shown in Figure P24.13.

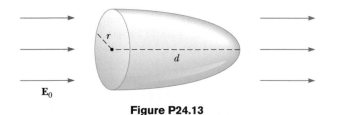

Figure P24.13

14. A point charge of 12.0 μC is placed at the center of a spherical shell of radius 22.0 cm. What is the total electric flux through (a) the surface of the shell and (b) any hemispherical surface of the shell? (c) Do the results depend on the radius? Explain.

15. [www] A point charge Q is located just above the center of the flat face of a hemisphere of radius R as shown in Figure P24.15. What is the electric flux (a) through the curved surface and (b) through the flat face?

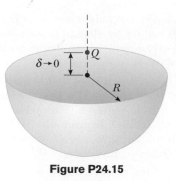

Figure P24.15

16. In the air over a particular region at an altitude of 500 m above the ground the electric field is 120 N/C directed downward. At 600 m above the ground the electric field is 100 N/C downward. What is the average volume charge density in the layer of air between these two elevations? Is it positive or negative?

17. A point charge $Q = 5.00$ μC is located at the center of a cube of edge $L = 0.100$ m. In addition, six other identical point charges having $q = -1.00$ μC are positioned symmetrically around Q as shown in Figure P24.17. Determine the electric flux through one face of the cube.

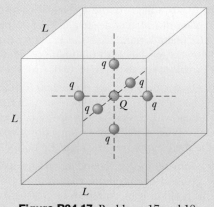

Figure P24.17 Problems 17 and 18.

18. A positive point charge Q is located at the center of a cube of edge L. In addition, six other identical negative point charges q are positioned symmetrically around Q as shown in Figure P24.17. Determine the electric flux through one face of the cube.

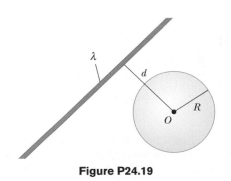

Figure P24.19

19. An infinitely long line charge having a uniform charge per unit length λ lies a distance d from point O as shown in Figure P24.19. Determine the total electric flux through the surface of a sphere of radius R centered at O resulting from this line charge. Consider both cases, where $R < d$ and $R > d$.

20. An uncharged nonconducting hollow sphere of radius 10.0 cm surrounds a 10.0-μC charge located at the origin of a cartesian coordinate system. A drill with a radius of 1.00 mm is aligned along the z axis, and a hole is drilled in the sphere. Calculate the electric flux through the hole.

21. A charge of 170 μC is at the center of a cube of edge 80.0 cm. (a) Find the total flux through each face of the cube. (b) Find the flux through the whole surface of the cube. (c) **What If?** Would your answers to parts (a) or (b) change if the charge were not at the center? Explain.

22. The line ag in Figure P24.22 is a diagonal of a cube. A point charge q is located on the extension of line ag, very close to vertex a of the cube. Determine the electric flux through each of the sides of the cube which meet at the point a.

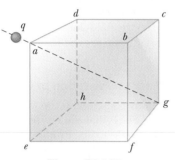

Figure P24.22

Section 24.3 Application of Gauss's Law to Various Charge Distributions

23. Determine the magnitude of the electric field at the surface of a lead-208 nucleus, which contains 82 protons and 126 neutrons. Assume the lead nucleus has a volume 208 times that of one proton, and consider a proton to be a sphere of radius 1.20×10^{-15} m.

24. A solid sphere of radius 40.0 cm has a total positive charge of 26.0 μC uniformly distributed throughout its volume. Calculate the magnitude of the electric field at (a) 0 cm, (b) 10.0 cm, (c) 40.0 cm, and (d) 60.0 cm from the center of the sphere.

25. A 10.0-g piece of Styrofoam carries a net charge of -0.700 μC and floats above the center of a large horizontal sheet of plastic that has a uniform charge density on its surface. What is the charge per unit area on the plastic sheet?

26. A cylindrical shell of radius 7.00 cm and length 240 cm has its charge uniformly distributed on its curved surface. The magnitude of the electric field at a point 19.0 cm radially outward from its axis (measured from the midpoint of the shell) is 36.0 kN/C. Find (a) the net charge on the shell and (b) the electric field at a point 4.00 cm from the axis, measured radially outward from the midpoint of the shell.

27. A particle with a charge of -60.0 nC is placed at the center of a nonconducting spherical shell of inner radius 20.0 cm and outer radius 25.0 cm. The spherical shell carries charge with a uniform density of -1.33 μC/m^3. A proton moves in a circular orbit just outside the spherical shell. Calculate the speed of the proton.

28. A nonconducting wall carries a uniform charge density of 8.60 μC/cm^2. What is the electric field 7.00 cm in front of the wall? Does your result change as the distance from the wall is varied?

29. Consider a long cylindrical charge distribution of radius R with a uniform charge density ρ. Find the electric field at distance r from the axis where $r < R$.

30. A solid plastic sphere of radius 10.0 cm has charge with uniform density throughout its volume. The electric field 5.00 cm from the center is 86.0 kN/C radially inward. Find the magnitude of the electric field 15.0 cm from the center.

31. Consider a thin spherical shell of radius 14.0 cm with a total charge of 32.0 μC distributed uniformly on its surface. Find the electric field (a) 10.0 cm and (b) 20.0 cm from the center of the charge distribution.

32. In nuclear fission, a nucleus of uranium-238, which contains 92 protons, can divide into two smaller spheres, each having 46 protons and a radius of 5.90×10^{-15} m. What is the magnitude of the repulsive electric force pushing the two spheres apart?

33. Fill two rubber balloons with air. Suspend both of them from the same point and let them hang down on strings of equal length. Rub each with wool or on your hair, so that they hang apart with a noticeable separation from each other. Make order-of-magnitude estimates of (a) the force on each, (b) the charge on each, (c) the field each creates at the center of the other, and (d) the total flux of electric field created by each balloon. In your solution state the quantities you take as data and the values you measure or estimate for them.

34. An insulating solid sphere of radius a has a uniform volume charge density and carries a total positive charge Q. A spherical gaussian surface of radius r, which shares a common center with the insulating sphere, is inflated starting from $r = 0$. (a) Find an expression for the electric flux passing through the surface of the gaussian sphere as a function of r for $r < a$. (b) Find an expression for the electric flux for $r > a$. (c) Plot the flux versus r.

35. A uniformly charged, straight filament 7.00 m in length has a total positive charge of 2.00 μC. An uncharged cardboard cylinder 2.00 cm in length and 10.0 cm in radius surrounds the filament at its center, with the filament as the axis of the cylinder. Using reasonable approximations, find (a) the electric field at the surface of the cylinder and (b) the total electric flux through the cylinder.

36. An insulating sphere is 8.00 cm in diameter and carries a 5.70-μC charge uniformly distributed throughout its interior volume. Calculate the charge enclosed by a concentric spherical surface with radius (a) $r = 2.00$ cm and (b) $r = 6.00$ cm.

37. A large flat horizontal sheet of charge has a charge per unit area of 9.00 μC/m^2. Find the electric field just above the middle of the sheet.

38. The charge per unit length on a long, straight filament is $-90.0\ \mu C/m$. Find the electric field (a) 10.0 cm, (b) 20.0 cm, and (c) 100 cm from the filament, where distances are measured perpendicular to the length of the filament.

Section 24.4   Conductors in Electrostatic Equilibrium

39. A long, straight metal rod has a radius of 5.00 cm and a charge per unit length of 30.0 nC/m. Find the electric field (a) 3.00 cm, (b) 10.0 cm, and (c) 100 cm from the axis of the rod, where distances are measured perpendicular to the rod.

40. On a clear, sunny day, a vertical electric field of about 130 N/C points down over flat ground. What is the surface charge density on the ground for these conditions?

41. A very large, thin, flat plate of aluminum of area A has a total charge Q uniformly distributed over its surfaces. Assuming the same charge is spread uniformly over the *upper* surface of an otherwise identical glass plate, compare the electric fields just above the center of the upper surface of each plate.

42. A solid copper sphere of radius 15.0 cm carries a charge of 40.0 nC. Find the electric field (a) 12.0 cm, (b) 17.0 cm, and (c) 75.0 cm from the center of the sphere. (d) **What If?** How would your answers change if the sphere were hollow?

43. A square plate of copper with 50.0-cm sides has no net charge and is placed in a region of uniform electric field of 80.0 kN/C directed perpendicularly to the plate. Find (a) the charge density of each face of the plate and (b) the total charge on each face.

44. A solid conducting sphere of radius 2.00 cm has a charge of 8.00 μC. A conducting spherical shell of inner radius 4.00 cm and outer radius 5.00 cm is concentric with the solid sphere and has a total charge of $-4.00\ \mu C$. Find the electric field at (a) $r = 1.00$ cm, (b) $r = 3.00$ cm, (c) $r = 4.50$ cm, and (d) $r = 7.00$ cm from the center of this charge configuration.

45. Two identical conducting spheres each having a radius of 0.500 cm are connected by a light 2.00-m-long conducting wire. A charge of 60.0 μC is placed on one of the conductors. Assume that the surface distribution of charge on each sphere is uniform. Determine the tension in the wire.

46. The electric field on the surface of an irregularly shaped conductor varies from 56.0 kN/C to 28.0 kN/C. Calculate the local surface charge density at the point on the surface where the radius of curvature of the surface is (a) greatest and (b) smallest.

47. A long, straight wire is surrounded by a hollow metal cylinder whose axis coincides with that of the wire. The wire has a charge per unit length of λ, and the cylinder has a net charge per unit length of 2λ. From this information, use Gauss's law to find (a) the charge per unit length on the inner and outer surfaces of the cylinder and (b) the electric field outside the cylinder, a distance r from the axis.

48. A conducting spherical shell of radius 15.0 cm carries a net charge of $-6.40\ \mu C$ uniformly distributed on its surface. Find the electric field at points (a) just outside the shell and (b) inside the shell.

49. A thin square conducting plate 50.0 cm on a side lies in the xy plane. A total charge of 4.00×10^{-8} C is placed on the plate. Find (a) the charge density on the plate, (b) the electric field just above the plate, and (c) the electric field just below the plate. You may assume that the charge density is uniform.

50. A conducting spherical shell of inner radius a and outer radius b carries a net charge Q. A point charge q is placed at the center of this shell. Determine the surface charge density on (a) the inner surface of the shell and (b) the outer surface of the shell.

51. A hollow conducting sphere is surrounded by a larger concentric spherical conducting shell. The inner sphere has charge $-Q$, and the outer shell has net charge $+3Q$. The charges are in electrostatic equilibrium. Using Gauss's law, find the charges and the electric fields everywhere.

52. A positive point charge is at a distance $R/2$ from the center of an uncharged thin conducting spherical shell of radius R. Sketch the electric field lines set up by this arrangement both inside and outside the shell.

Section 24.5   Formal Derivation of Gauss's Law

53. A sphere of radius R surrounds a point charge Q, located at its center. (a) Show that the electric flux through a circular cap of half-angle θ (Fig. P24.53) is

$$\Phi_E = \frac{Q}{2\epsilon_0}\ (1 - \cos\theta)$$

What is the flux for (b) $\theta = 90°$ and (c) $\theta = 180°$?

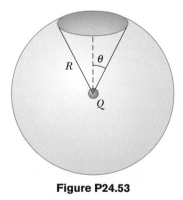

Figure P24.53

Additional Problems

54. A nonuniform electric field is given by the expression $\mathbf{E} = ay\hat{\mathbf{i}} + bz\hat{\mathbf{j}} + cx\hat{\mathbf{k}}$, where a, b, and c are constants. Determine the electric flux through a rectangular surface in the xy plane, extending from $x = 0$ to $x = w$ and from $y = 0$ to $y = h$.

55. A solid insulating sphere of radius a carries a net positive charge $3Q$, uniformly distributed throughout its volume. Concentric with this sphere is a conducting spherical shell with inner radius b and outer radius c, and having a net charge $-Q$, as shown in Figure P24.55. (a) Construct a spherical gaussian surface of radius $r > c$ and find the net charge enclosed by this surface. (b) What is the direction of the electric field at $r > c$? (c) Find the electric field at $r > c$. (d) Find the electric field in the region with radius r where $c > r > b$. (e) Construct a spherical gaussian surface of radius r, where $c > r > b$, and find the net charge enclosed by this surface. (f) Construct a spherical gaussian surface of radius r, where $b > r > a$, and find the net charge enclosed by this surface. (g) Find the electric field in the region $b > r > a$. (h) Construct a spherical gaussian surface of radius $r < a$, and find an expression for the net charge enclosed by this surface, as a function of r. Note that the charge inside this surface is less than $3Q$. (i) Find the electric field in the region $r < a$. (j) Determine the charge on the inner surface of the conducting shell. (k) Determine the charge on the outer surface of the conducting shell. (l) Make a plot of the magnitude of the electric field versus r.

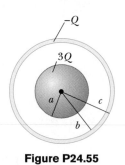

Figure P24.55

56. Consider two identical conducting spheres whose surfaces are separated by a small distance. One sphere is given a large net positive charge while the other is given a small net positive charge. It is found that the force between them is attractive even though both spheres have net charges of the same sign. Explain how this is possible.

57. A solid, insulating sphere of radius a has a uniform charge density ρ and a total charge Q. Concentric with this sphere is an uncharged, conducting hollow sphere whose inner and outer radii are b and c, as shown in Figure P24.57. (a) Find the magnitude of the electric field in the regions $r < a$, $a < r < b$, $b < r < c$, and $r > c$. (b) Determine the induced charge per unit area on the inner and outer surfaces of the hollow sphere.

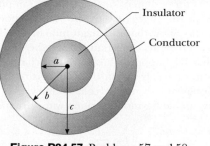

Figure P24.57 Problems 57 and 58.

58. For the configuration shown in Figure P24.57, suppose that $a = 5.00$ cm, $b = 20.0$ cm, and $c = 25.0$ cm. Furthermore, suppose that the electric field at a point 10.0 cm from the center is measured to be 3.60×10^3 N/C radially inward while the electric field at a point 50.0 cm from the center is 2.00×10^2 N/C radially outward. From this information, find (a) the charge on the insulating sphere, (b) the net charge on the hollow conducting sphere, and (c) the charges on the inner and outer surfaces of the hollow conducting sphere.

59. A particle of mass m and charge q moves at high speed along the x axis. It is initially near $x = -\infty$, and it ends up near $x = +\infty$. A second charge Q is fixed at the point $x = 0$, $y = -d$. As the moving charge passes the stationary charge, its x component of velocity does not change appreciably, but it acquires a small velocity in the y direction. Determine the angle through which the moving charge is deflected. *Suggestion:* The integral you encounter in determining v_y can be evaluated by applying Gauss's law to a long cylinder of radius d, centered on the stationary charge.

60. **Review problem.** An early (incorrect) model of the hydrogen atom, suggested by J. J. Thomson, proposed that a positive cloud of charge $+e$ was uniformly distributed throughout the volume of a sphere of radius R, with the electron an equal-magnitude negative point charge $-e$ at the center. (a) Using Gauss's law, show that the electron would be in equilibrium at the center and, if displaced from the center a distance $r < R$, would experience a restoring force of the form $F = -Kr$, where K is a constant. (b) Show that $K = k_e e^2/R^3$. (c) Find an expression for the frequency f of simple harmonic oscillations that an electron of mass m_e would undergo if displaced a small distance ($<R$) from the center and released. (d) Calculate a numerical value for R that would result in a frequency of 2.47×10^{15} Hz, the frequency of the light radiated in the most intense line in the hydrogen spectrum.

61. An infinitely long cylindrical insulating shell of inner radius a and outer radius b has a uniform volume charge density ρ. A line of uniform linear charge density λ is placed along the axis of the shell. Determine the electric field everywhere.

62. Two infinite, nonconducting sheets of charge are parallel to each other, as shown in Figure P24.62. The sheet on the left has a uniform surface charge density σ, and the one

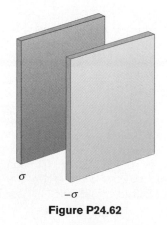

Figure P24.62

on the right has a uniform charge density $-\sigma$. Calculate the electric field at points (a) to the left of, (b) in between, and (c) to the right of the two sheets.

63. **What If?** Repeat the calculations for Problem 62 when both sheets have *positive* uniform surface charge densities of value σ.

64. A sphere of radius $2a$ is made of a nonconducting material that has a uniform volume charge density ρ. (Assume that the material does not affect the electric field.) A spherical cavity of radius a is now removed from the sphere, as shown in Figure P24.64. Show that the electric field within the cavity is uniform and is given by $E_x = 0$ and $E_y = \rho a/3\epsilon_0$. (*Suggestion:* The field within the cavity is the superposition of the field due to the original uncut sphere, plus the field due to a sphere the size of the cavity with a uniform negative charge density $-\rho$.)

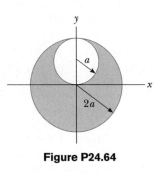

Figure P24.64

65. A uniformly charged spherical shell with surface charge density σ contains a circular hole in its surface. The radius of the hole is small compared with the radius of the sphere. What is the electric field at the center of the hole? (*Suggestion:* This problem, like Problem 64, can be solved by using the idea of superposition.)

66. A closed surface with dimensions $a = b = 0.400$ m and $c = 0.600$ m is located as in Figure P24.66. The left edge of the closed surface is located at position $x = a$. The electric field throughout the region is nonuniform and given by $\mathbf{E} = (3.0 + 2.0x^2)\hat{\mathbf{i}}$ N/C, where x is in meters. Calculate the net electric flux leaving the closed surface. What net charge is enclosed by the surface?

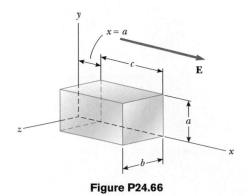

Figure P24.66

67. A solid insulating sphere of radius R has a nonuniform charge density that varies with r according to the expression $\rho = Ar^2$, where A is a constant and $r < R$ is measured from the center of the sphere. (a) Show that the magnitude of the electric field outside $(r > R)$ the sphere is $E = AR^5/5\epsilon_0 r^2$. (b) Show that the magnitude of the electric field inside $(r < R)$ the sphere is $E = Ar^3/5\epsilon_0$. (*Suggestion:* The total charge Q on the sphere is equal to the integral of $\rho \, dV$, where r extends from 0 to R; also, the charge q within a radius $r < R$ is less than Q. To evaluate the integrals, note that the volume element dV for a spherical shell of radius r and thickness dr is equal to $4\pi r^2 dr$.)

68. A point charge Q is located on the axis of a disk of radius R at a distance b from the plane of the disk (Fig. P24.68). Show that if one fourth of the electric flux from the charge passes through the disk, then $R = \sqrt{3}b$.

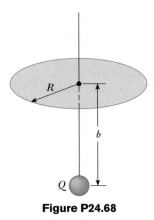

Figure P24.68

69. A spherically symmetric charge distribution has a charge density given by $\rho = a/r$, where a is constant. Find the electric field as a function of r. (*Suggestion:* The charge within a sphere of radius R is equal to the integral of $\rho \, dV$, where r extends from 0 to R. To evaluate the integral, note that the volume element dV for a spherical shell of radius r and thickness dr is equal to $4\pi r^2 dr$.)

70. An infinitely long insulating cylinder of radius R has a volume charge density that varies with the radius as

$$\rho = \rho_0 \left(a - \frac{r}{b} \right)$$

where ρ_0, a, and b are positive constants and r is the distance from the axis of the cylinder. Use Gauss's law to determine the magnitude of the electric field at radial distances (a) $r < R$ and (b) $r > R$.

71. **Review problem.** A slab of insulating material (infinite in two of its three dimensions) has a uniform positive charge density ρ. An edge view of the slab is shown in Figure P24.71. (a) Show that the magnitude of the electric field a distance x from its center and inside the slab is $E = \rho x/\epsilon_0$. (b) **What If?** Suppose an electron of charge $-e$ and mass m_e can move freely within the slab. It is released from rest at a distance x from the center. Show that the electron exhibits simple harmonic motion with a frequency

$$f = \frac{1}{2\pi} \sqrt{\frac{\rho e}{m_e \epsilon_0}}$$

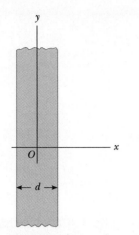

Figure P24.71 Problems 71 and 72.

72. A slab of insulating material has a nonuniform positive charge density $\rho = Cx^2$, where x is measured from the center of the slab as shown in Figure P24.71, and C is a constant. The slab is infinite in the y and z directions. Derive expressions for the electric field in (a) the exterior regions and (b) the interior region of the slab $(-d/2 < x < d/2)$.

73. (a) Using the mathematical similarity between Coulomb's law and Newton's law of universal gravitation, show that Gauss's law for gravitation can be written as

$$\oint \mathbf{g} \cdot d\mathbf{A} = -4\pi G m_{in}$$

where m_{in} is the net mass inside the gaussian surface and $\mathbf{g} = \mathbf{F}_g / m$ represents the gravitational field at any point on the gaussian surface. (b) Determine the gravitational field at a distance r from the center of the Earth where $r < R_E$, assuming that the Earth's mass density is uniform.

Answers to Quick Quizzes

24.1 (e). The same number of field lines pass through a sphere of any size. Because points on the surface of the sphere are closer to the charge, the field is stronger.

24.2 (d). All field lines that enter the container also leave the container so that the total flux is zero, regardless of the nature of the field or the container.

24.3 (b) and (d). Statement (a) is not necessarily true because an equal number of positive and negative charges could be present inside the surface. Statement (c) is not necessarily true, as can be seen from Figure 24.8: a nonzero electric field exists everywhere on the surface, but the charge is not enclosed within the surface; thus, the net flux is zero.

24.4 (c). The charges q_1 and q_4 are outside the surface and contribute zero net flux through S'.

24.5 (d). We don't need the surfaces to realize that any given point in space will experience an electric field due to all local source charges.

24.6 (a). Charges added to the metal cylinder by your brother will reside on the outer surface of the conducting cylinder. If you are on the inside, these charges cannot transfer to you from the inner surface. For this same reason, you are safe in a metal automobile during a lightning storm.

Chapter 25

Electric Potential

▲ *Processes occurring during thunderstorms cause large differences in electric potential between a thundercloud and the ground. The result of this potential difference is an electrical discharge that we call lightning, such as this display over Tucson, Arizona. (© Keith Kent/ Photo Researchers, Inc.)*

The concept of potential energy was introduced in Chapter 8 in connection with such conservative forces as the gravitational force and the elastic force exerted by a spring. By using the law of conservation of energy, we were able to avoid working directly with forces when solving various problems in mechanics. The concept of potential energy is also of great value in the study of electricity. Because the electrostatic force is conservative, electrostatic phenomena can be conveniently described in terms of an electric potential energy. This idea enables us to define a scalar quantity known as *electric potential*. Because the electric potential at any point in an electric field is a scalar quantity, we can use it to describe electrostatic phenomena more simply than if we were to rely only on the electric field and electric forces. The concept of electric potential is of great practical value in the operation of electric circuits and devices we will study in later chapters.

25.1 Potential Difference and Electric Potential

When a test charge q_0 is placed in an electric field $\mathbf{E}$ created by some source charge distribution, the electric force acting on the test charge is $q_0\mathbf{E}$. The force $q_0\mathbf{E}$ is conservative because the force between charges described by Coulomb's law is conservative. When the test charge is moved in the field by some external agent, the work done by the field on the charge is equal to the negative of the work done by the external agent causing the displacement. This is analogous to the situation of lifting an object with mass in a gravitational field—the work done by the external agent is mgh and the work done by the gravitational force is $-mgh$.

When analyzing electric and magnetic fields, it is common practice to use the notation $d\mathbf{s}$ to represent an infinitesimal displacement vector that is oriented tangent to a path through space. This path may be straight or curved, and an integral performed along this path is called either a *path integral* or a *line integral* (the two terms are synonymous).

For an infinitesimal displacement $d\mathbf{s}$ of a charge, the work done by the electric field on the charge is $\mathbf{F} \cdot d\mathbf{s} = q_0\mathbf{E} \cdot d\mathbf{s}$. As this amount of work is done by the field, the potential energy of the charge–field system is changed by an amount $dU = -q_0\mathbf{E} \cdot d\mathbf{s}$. For a finite displacement of the charge from point A to point B, the change in potential energy of the system $\Delta U = U_B - U_A$ is

$$\Delta U = -q_0 \int_A^B \mathbf{E} \cdot d\mathbf{s} \qquad (25.1)$$

◀ Change in electric potential energy of a system

The integration is performed along the path that q_0 follows as it moves from A to B. Because the force $q_0\mathbf{E}$ is conservative, **this line integral does not depend on the path taken from A to B.**

For a given position of the test charge in the field, the charge–field system has a potential energy U relative to the configuration of the system that is defined as $U = 0$. Dividing the potential energy by the test charge gives a physical quantity that depends only on the source charge distribution. The potential energy per unit charge U/q_0 is

25.1 Potential and Potential Energy

The *potential is characteristic of the field only*, independent of a charged test particle that may be placed in the field. *Potential energy is characteristic of the charge–field system* due to an interaction between the field and a charged particle placed in the field.

Potential difference between two points

independent of the value of q_0 and has a value at every point in an electric field. This quantity U/q_0 is called the **electric potential** (or simply the **potential**) V. Thus, the electric potential at any point in an electric field is

$$V = \frac{U}{q_0} \qquad (25.2)$$

The fact that potential energy is a scalar quantity means that electric potential also is a scalar quantity.

As described by Equation 25.1, if the test charge is moved between two positions A and B in an electric field, the charge–field system experiences a change in potential energy. The **potential difference** $\Delta V = V_B - V_A$ between two points A and B in an electric field is defined as the change in potential energy of the system when a test charge is moved between the points divided by the test charge q_0:

$$\Delta V \equiv \frac{\Delta U}{q_0} = -\int_A^B \mathbf{E} \cdot d\mathbf{s} \qquad (25.3)$$

Just as with potential energy, only *differences* in electric potential are meaningful. To avoid having to work with potential differences, however, we often take the value of the electric potential to be zero at some convenient point in an electric field.

Potential difference should not be confused with difference in potential energy. The potential difference between A and B depends only on the source charge distribution (consider points A and B *without* the presence of the test charge), while the difference in potential energy exists only if a test charge is moved between the points. **Electric potential is a scalar characteristic of an electric field, independent of any charges that may be placed in the field.**

If an external agent moves a test charge from A to B without changing the kinetic energy of the test charge, the agent performs work which changes the potential energy of the system: $W = \Delta U$. The test charge q_0 is used as a mental device to define the electric potential. Imagine an arbitrary charge q located in an electric field. From Equation 25.3, the work done by an external agent in moving a charge q through an electric field at constant velocity is

$$W = q \, \Delta V \qquad (25.4)$$

25.2 Voltage

A variety of phrases are used to describe the potential difference between two points, the most common being **voltage,** arising from the unit for potential. A voltage *applied* to a device, such as a television, or *across* a device is the same as the potential difference across the device. If we say that the voltage applied to a lightbulb is 120 volts, we mean that the potential difference between the two electrical contacts on the lightbulb is 120 volts.

The electron volt

Because electric potential is a measure of potential energy per unit charge, the SI unit of both electric potential and potential difference is joules per coulomb, which is defined as a **volt** (V):

$$1 \text{ V} \equiv 1 \, \frac{\text{J}}{\text{C}}$$

That is, 1 J of work must be done to move a 1-C charge through a potential difference of 1 V.

Equation 25.3 shows that potential difference also has units of electric field times distance. From this, it follows that the SI unit of electric field (N/C) can also be expressed in volts per meter:

$$1 \, \frac{\text{N}}{\text{C}} = 1 \, \frac{\text{V}}{\text{m}}$$

Therefore, **we can interpret the electric field as a measure of the rate of change with position of the electric potential.**

A unit of energy commonly used in atomic and nuclear physics is the **electron volt** (eV), which is defined as **the energy a charge–field system gains or loses when a charge of magnitude e (that is, an electron or a proton) is moved through a potential difference of 1 V.** Because $1 \text{ V} = 1 \text{ J/C}$ and because the fundamental charge is 1.60×10^{-19} C, the electron volt is related to the joule as follows:

$$1 \text{ eV} = 1.60 \times 10^{-19} \text{ C} \cdot \text{V} = 1.60 \times 10^{-19} \text{ J} \qquad (25.5)$$

For instance, an electron in the beam of a typical television picture tube may have a speed of 3.0×10^7 m/s. This corresponds to a kinetic energy of 4.1×10^{-16} J, which is equivalent to 2.6×10^3 eV. Such an electron has to be accelerated from rest through a potential difference of 2.6 kV to reach this speed.

> **Quick Quiz 25.1** In Figure 25.1, two points A and B are located within a region in which there is an electric field. The potential difference $\Delta V = V_B - V_A$ is (a) positive (b) negative (c) zero.
>
> **Quick Quiz 25.2** In Figure 25.1, a negative charge is placed at A and then moved to B. The change in potential energy of the charge–field system for this process is (a) positive (b) negative (c) zero.

25.2 Potential Differences in a Uniform Electric Field

Equations 25.1 and 25.3 hold in all electric fields, whether uniform or varying, but they can be simplified for a uniform field. First, consider a uniform electric field directed along the negative y axis, as shown in Figure 25.2a. Let us calculate the potential difference between two points A and B separated by a distance $|\mathbf{s}| = d$, where $\mathbf{s}$ is parallel to the field lines. Equation 25.3 gives

$$V_B - V_A = \Delta V = -\int_A^B \mathbf{E} \cdot d\mathbf{s} = -\int_A^B (E \cos 0^\circ)\, ds = -\int_A^B E\, ds$$

Because E is constant, we can remove it from the integral sign; this gives

$$\Delta V = -E \int_A^B ds = -Ed \qquad (25.6)$$

The negative sign indicates that the electric potential at point B is lower than at point A; that is, $V_B < V_A$. **Electric field lines always point in the direction of decreasing electric potential,** as shown in Figure 25.2a.

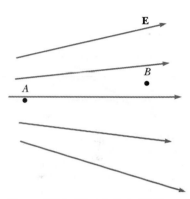

► **PITFALL PREVENTION**

25.3 The Electron Volt
The electron volt is a unit of *energy,* NOT of potential. The energy of any system may be expressed in eV, but this unit is most convenient for describing the emission and absorption of visible light from atoms. Energies of nuclear processes are often expressed in MeV.

Figure 25.1 (Quick Quiz 25.1) Two points in an electric field.

Potential difference between two points in a uniform electric field

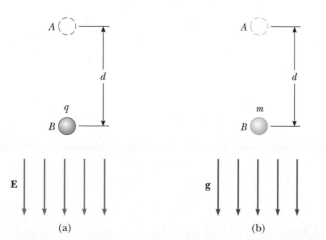

Figure 25.2 (a) When the electric field $\mathbf{E}$ is directed downward, point B is at a lower electric potential than point A. When a positive test charge moves from point A to point B, the charge–field system loses electric potential energy. (b) When an object of mass m moves downward in the direction of the gravitational field $\mathbf{g}$, the object–field system loses gravitational potential energy.

Now suppose that a test charge q_0 moves from A to B. We can calculate the change in the potential energy of the charge–field system from Equations 25.3 and 25.6:

$$\Delta U = q_0 \, \Delta V = -q_0 Ed \tag{25.7}$$

From this result, we see that if q_0 is positive, then ΔU is negative. We conclude that **a system consisting of a positive charge and an electric field loses electric potential energy when the charge moves in the direction of the field.** This means that an electric field does work on a positive charge when the charge moves in the direction of the electric field. (This is analogous to the work done by the gravitational field on a falling object, as shown in Figure 25.2b.) If a positive test charge is released from rest in this electric field, it experiences an electric force $q_0 \mathbf{E}$ in the direction of $\mathbf{E}$ (downward in Fig. 25.2a). Therefore, it accelerates downward, gaining kinetic energy. **As the charged particle gains kinetic energy, the charge–field system loses an equal amount of potential energy.** This should not be surprising—it is simply conservation of energy in an isolated system as introduced in Chapter 8.

If q_0 is negative, then ΔU in Equation 25.7 is positive and the situation is reversed: **A system consisting of a negative charge and an electric field gains electric potential energy when the charge moves in the direction of the field.** If a negative charge is released from rest in an electric field, it accelerates in a direction opposite the direction of the field. In order for the negative charge to move in the direction of the field, an external agent must apply a force and do positive work on the charge.

Now consider the more general case of a charged particle that moves between A and B in a uniform electric field such that the vector $\mathbf{s}$ is not parallel to the field lines, as shown in Figure 25.3. In this case, Equation 25.3 gives

$$\Delta V = -\int_A^B \mathbf{E} \cdot d\mathbf{s} = -\mathbf{E} \cdot \int_A^B d\mathbf{s} = -\mathbf{E} \cdot \mathbf{s} \tag{25.8}$$

where again we are able to remove $\mathbf{E}$ from the integral because it is constant. The change in potential energy of the charge–field system is

$$\Delta U = q_0 \, \Delta V = -q_0 \mathbf{E} \cdot \mathbf{s} \tag{25.9}$$

Finally, we conclude from Equation 25.8 that all points in a plane perpendicular to a uniform electric field are at the same electric potential. We can see this in Figure 25.3, where the potential difference $V_B - V_A$ is equal to the potential difference $V_C - V_A$. (Prove this to yourself by working out the dot product $\mathbf{E} \cdot \mathbf{s}$ for $\mathbf{s}_{A \to B}$, where the angle θ between $\mathbf{E}$ and $\mathbf{s}$ is arbitrary as shown in Figure 25.3, and the dot product for $\mathbf{s}_{A \to C}$, where $\theta = 0$.) Therefore, $V_B = V_C$. **The name equipotential surface is given to any surface consisting of a continuous distribution of points having the same electric potential.**

The equipotential surfaces of a uniform electric field consist of a family of parallel planes that are all perpendicular to the field. Equipotential surfaces for fields with other symmetries are described in later sections.

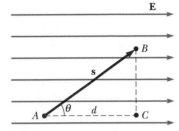

Figure 25.3 A uniform electric field directed along the positive x axis. Point B is at a lower electric potential than point A. Points B and C are at the *same* electric potential.

Change in potential energy when a charged particle is moved in a uniform electric field

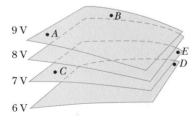

Figure 25.4 (Quick Quiz 25.3) Four equipotential surfaces.

Quick Quiz 25.3 The labeled points in Figure 25.4 are on a series of equipotential surfaces associated with an electric field. Rank (from greatest to least) the work done by the electric field on a positively charged particle that moves from A to B; from B to C; from C to D; from D to E.

Quick Quiz 25.4 For the equipotential surfaces in Figure 25.4, what is the *approximate* direction of the electric field? (a) Out of the page (b) Into the page (c) Toward the right edge of the page (d) Toward the left edge of the page (e) Toward the top of the page (f) Toward the bottom of the page.

Example 25.1   The Electric Field Between Two Parallel Plates of Opposite Charge

A battery produces a specified potential difference ΔV between conductors attached to the battery terminals. A 12-V battery is connected between two parallel plates, as shown in Figure 25.5. The separation between the plates is $d = 0.30$ cm, and we assume the electric field between the plates to be

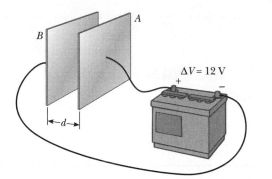

Figure 25.5 (Example 25.1) A 12-V battery connected to two parallel plates. The electric field between the plates has a magnitude given by the potential difference ΔV divided by the plate separation d.

uniform. (This assumption is reasonable if the plate separation is small relative to the plate dimensions and if we do not consider locations near the plate edges.) Find the magnitude of the electric field between the plates.

Solution The electric field is directed from the positive plate (A) to the negative one (B), and the positive plate is at a higher electric potential than the negative plate is. The potential difference between the plates must equal the potential difference between the battery terminals. We can understand this by noting that all points on a conductor in equilibrium are at the same electric potential[1]; no potential difference exists between a terminal and any portion of the plate to which it is connected. Therefore, the magnitude of the electric field between the plates is, from Equation 25.6,

$$E = \frac{|V_B - V_A|}{d} = \frac{12 \text{ V}}{0.30 \times 10^{-2} \text{ m}} = \boxed{4.0 \times 10^3 \text{ V/m}}$$

The configuration of plates in Figure 25.5 is called a *parallel-plate capacitor*, and is examined in greater detail in Chapter 26.

Example 25.2   Motion of a Proton in a Uniform Electric Field

A proton is released from rest in a uniform electric field that has a magnitude of 8.0×10^4 V/m (Fig. 25.6). The proton undergoes a displacement of 0.50 m in the direction of **E**.

(A) Find the change in electric potential between points A and B.

Solution Because the positively charged proton moves in the direction of the field, we expect it to move to a position of lower electric potential. From Equation 25.6, we have

$$\Delta V = -Ed = -(8.0 \times 10^4 \text{ V/m})(0.50 \text{ m}) = \boxed{-4.0 \times 10^4 \text{ V}}$$

(B) Find the change in potential energy of the proton–field system for this displacement.

Solution Using Equation 25.3,

$$\Delta U = q_0 \, \Delta V = e \, \Delta V$$
$$= (1.6 \times 10^{-19} \text{ C})(-4.0 \times 10^4 \text{ V})$$
$$= \boxed{-6.4 \times 10^{-15} \text{ J}}$$

The negative sign means the potential energy of the system decreases as the proton moves in the direction of the electric field. As the proton accelerates in the direction of the field, it gains kinetic energy and at the same time the system loses electric potential energy.

(C) Find the speed of the proton after completing the 0.50 m displacement in the electric field.

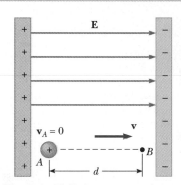

Figure 25.6 (Example 25.2) A proton accelerates from A to B in the direction of the electric field.

Solution The charge–field system is isolated, so the mechanical energy of the system is conserved:

$$\Delta K + \Delta U = 0$$
$$(\tfrac{1}{2}mv^2 - 0) + e \, \Delta V = 0$$
$$v = \sqrt{\frac{-(2e\,\Delta V)}{m}}$$
$$= \sqrt{\frac{-2(1.6 \times 10^{-19} \text{ C})(-4.0 \times 10^4 \text{ V})}{1.67 \times 10^{-27} \text{ kg}}}$$
$$= \boxed{2.8 \times 10^6 \text{ m/s}}$$

What If? What if the situation is exactly the same as that shown in Figure 25.6, but no proton is present? Could both parts (A) and (B) of this example still be answered?

---

[1] The electric field vanishes within a conductor in electrostatic equilibrium; thus, the path integral between any two points in the conductor must be zero. A more complete discussion of this point is given in Section 25.6.

Answer Part (A) of the example would remain exactly the same because the potential difference between points A and B is established by the source charges in the parallel plates. The potential difference does not depend on the presence of the proton, which plays the role of a test charge. Part (B) of the example would be meaningless if the proton is not present. A change in potential energy is related to a change in the charge–field system. In the absence of the proton, the system of the electric field alone does not change.

> **At the Interactive Worked Example link at http://www.pse6.com, you can predict and observe the speed of the proton as it arrives at the negative plate for random values of the electric field.**

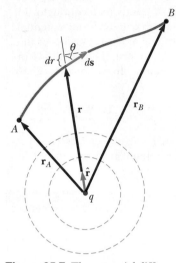

Figure 25.7 The potential difference between points A and B due to a point charge q depends *only* on the initial and final radial coordinates r_A and r_B. The two dashed circles represent intersections of spherical equipotential surfaces with the page.

▲ **PITFALL PREVENTION**

25.4 Similar Equation Warning

Do not confuse Equation 25.11 for the electric potential of a point charge with Equation 23.9 for the electric field of a point charge. Potential is proportional to $1/r$, while the field is proportional to $1/r^2$. The effect of a charge on the space surrounding it can be described in two ways. The charge sets up a vector electric field $\mathbf{E}$, which is related to the force experienced by a test charge placed in the field. It also sets up a scalar potential V, which is related to the potential energy of the two-charge system when a test charge is placed in the field.

25.3 Electric Potential and Potential Energy Due to Point Charges

In Section 23.4 we discussed the fact that an isolated positive point charge q produces an electric field that is directed radially outward from the charge. To find the electric potential at a point located a distance r from the charge, we begin with the general expression for potential difference:

$$V_B - V_A = -\int_A^B \mathbf{E} \cdot d\mathbf{s}$$

where A and B are the two arbitrary points shown in Figure 25.7. At any point in space, the electric field due to the point charge is $\mathbf{E} = k_e q \hat{\mathbf{r}}/r^2$ (Eq. 23.9), where $\hat{\mathbf{r}}$ is a unit vector directed from the charge toward the point. The quantity $\mathbf{E} \cdot d\mathbf{s}$ can be expressed as

$$\mathbf{E} \cdot d\mathbf{s} = k_e \frac{q}{r^2} \hat{\mathbf{r}} \cdot d\mathbf{s}$$

Because the magnitude of $\hat{\mathbf{r}}$ is 1, the dot product $\hat{\mathbf{r}} \cdot d\mathbf{s} = ds \cos\theta$, where θ is the angle between $\hat{\mathbf{r}}$ and $d\mathbf{s}$. Furthermore, $ds \cos\theta$ is the projection of $d\mathbf{s}$ onto $\mathbf{r}$; thus, $ds \cos\theta = dr$. That is, any displacement $d\mathbf{s}$ along the path from point A to point B produces a change dr in the magnitude of $\mathbf{r}$, the position vector of the point relative to the charge creating the field. Making these substitutions, we find that $\mathbf{E} \cdot d\mathbf{s} = (k_e q/r^2)\,dr$; hence, the expression for the potential difference becomes

$$V_B - V_A = -k_e q \int_{r_A}^{r_B} \frac{dr}{r^2} = \left. \frac{k_e q}{r} \right]_{r_A}^{r_B}$$

$$V_B - V_A = k_e q \left[\frac{1}{r_B} - \frac{1}{r_A} \right] \qquad (25.10)$$

This equation shows us that the integral of $\mathbf{E} \cdot d\mathbf{s}$ is *independent* of the path between points A and B. Multiplying by a charge q_0 that moves between points A and B, we see that the integral of $q_0 \mathbf{E} \cdot d\mathbf{s}$ is also independent of path. This latter integral is the work done by the electric force, which tells us that the electric force is conservative (see Section 8.3). We define a field that is related to a conservative force as a **conservative field.** Thus, Equation 25.10 tells us that the electric field of a fixed point charge is conservative. Furthermore, Equation 25.10 expresses the important result that the potential difference between any two points A and B in a field created by a point charge depends only on the radial coordinates r_A and r_B. It is customary to choose the reference of electric potential for a point charge to be $V = 0$ at $r_A = \infty$. With this reference choice, the electric potential created by a point charge at any distance r from the charge is

$$V = k_e \frac{q}{r} \qquad (25.11)$$

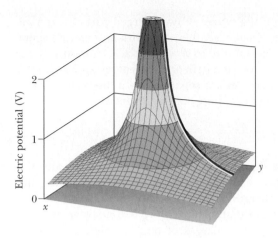

Figure 25.8 The electric potential in the plane around a single positive charge is plotted on the vertical axis. (The electric potential function for a negative charge would look like a hole instead of a hill.) The red line shows the $1/r$ nature of the electric potential, as given by Equation 25.11.

Figure 25.8 shows a plot of the electric potential on the vertical axis for a positive charge located in the xy plane. Consider the following analogy to gravitational potential: imagine trying to roll a marble toward the top of a hill shaped like the surface in Figure 25.8. Pushing the marble up the hill is analogous to pushing one positively charged object toward another positively charged object. Similarly, the electric potential graph of the region surrounding a negative charge is analogous to a "hole" with respect to any approaching positively charged objects. A charged object must be infinitely distant from another charge before the surface in Figure 25.8 is "flat" and has an electric potential of zero.

We obtain the electric potential resulting from two or more point charges by applying the superposition principle. That is, the total electric potential at some point P due to several point charges is the sum of the potentials due to the individual charges. For a group of point charges, we can write the total electric potential at P in the form

$$V = k_e \sum_i \frac{q_i}{r_i} \qquad (25.12)$$

◀ **Electric potential due to several point charges**

where the potential is again taken to be zero at infinity and r_i is the distance from the point P to the charge q_i. Note that the sum in Equation 25.12 is an algebraic sum of scalars rather than a vector sum (which we use to calculate the electric field of a group of charges). Thus, it is often much easier to evaluate V than to evaluate $\mathbf{E}$. The electric potential around a dipole is illustrated in Figure 25.9. Notice the steep slope of the potential between the charges, representing a region of strong electric field.

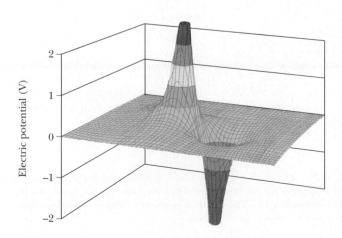

Figure 25.9 The electric potential in the plane containing a dipole.

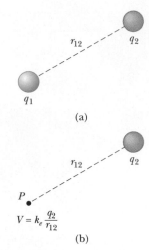

(a)

(b)

$$V = k_e \frac{q_2}{r_{12}}$$

Active Figure 25.10 (a) If two point charges are separated by a distance r_{12}, the potential energy of the pair of charges is given by $k_e q_1 q_2 / r_{12}$. (b) If charge q_1 is removed, a potential $k_e q_2 / r_{12}$ exists at point P due to charge q_2.

At the Active Figures link at http://www.pse6.com, you can move charge q_1 or point P and see the result on the electric potential energy of the system for part (a) and the electric potential due to charge q₂ for part (b).

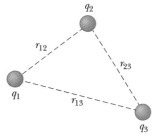

Figure 25.11 Three point charges are fixed at the positions shown. The potential energy of this system of charges is given by Equation 25.14.

▲ **PITFALL PREVENTION**

25.5 Which Work?

There is a difference between work done *by one member of a system on another member* and work done *on a system by an external agent*. In the present discussion, we are considering the group of charges to be the system and an external agent is doing work on the system to move the charges from an infinite separation to a small separation.

We now consider the potential energy of a system of two charged particles. If V_2 is the electric potential at a point P due to charge q_2, then the work an external agent must do to bring a second charge q_1 from infinity to P without acceleration is $q_1 V_2$. This work represents a transfer of energy into the system and the energy appears in the system as potential energy U when the particles are separated by a distance r_{12} (Fig. 25.10a). Therefore, we can express the potential energy of the system as[2]

$$U = k_e \frac{q_1 q_2}{r_{12}} \qquad (25.13)$$

Note that if the charges are of the same sign, U is positive. This is consistent with the fact that positive work must be done by an external agent on the system to bring the two charges near one another (because charges of the same sign repel). If the charges are of opposite sign, U is negative; this means that negative work is done by an external agent against the attractive force between the charges of opposite sign as they are brought near each other—a force must be applied opposite to the displacement to prevent q_1 from accelerating toward q_2.

In Figure 25.10b, we have removed the charge q_1. At the position that this charge previously occupied, point P, we can use Equations 25.2 and 25.13 to define a potential due to charge q_2 as $V = U/q_1 = k_e q_2 / r_{12}$. This expression is consistent with Equation 25.11.

If the system consists of more than two charged particles, we can obtain the total potential energy by calculating U for every pair of charges and summing the terms algebraically. As an example, the total potential energy of the system of three charges shown in Figure 25.11 is

$$U = k_e \left(\frac{q_1 q_2}{r_{12}} + \frac{q_1 q_3}{r_{13}} + \frac{q_2 q_3}{r_{23}} \right) \qquad (25.14)$$

Physically, we can interpret this as follows: imagine that q_1 is fixed at the position shown in Figure 25.11 but that q_2 and q_3 are at infinity. The work an external agent must do to bring q_2 from infinity to its position near q_1 is $k_e q_1 q_2 / r_{12}$, which is the first term in Equation 25.14. The last two terms represent the work required to bring q_3 from infinity to its position near q_1 and q_2. (The result is independent of the order in which the charges are transported.)

Quick Quiz 25.5 A spherical balloon contains a positively charged object at its center. As the balloon is inflated to a greater volume while the charged object remains at the center, does the electric potential at the surface of the balloon (a) increase, (b) decrease, or (c) remain the same? Does the electric flux through the surface of the balloon (d) increase, (e) decrease, or (f) remain the same?

Quick Quiz 25.6 In Figure 25.10a, take q_1 to be a negative source charge and q_2 to be the test charge. If q_2 is initially positive and is changed to a charge of the same magnitude but negative, the potential at the position of q_2 due to q_1 (a) increases (b) decreases (c) remains the same.

Quick Quiz 25.7 Consider the situation in Quick Quiz 25.6 again. When q_2 is changed from positive to negative, the potential energy of the two-charge system (a) increases (b) decreases (c) remains the same.

---

[2]   The expression for the electric potential energy of a system made up of two point charges, Equation 25.13, is of the *same* form as the equation for the gravitational potential energy of a system made up of two point masses, $-Gm_1 m_2 / r$ (see Chapter 13). The similarity is not surprising in view of the fact that both expressions are derived from an inverse-square force law.

Example 25.3 The Electric Potential Due to Two Point Charges Interactive

A charge $q_1 = 2.00\ \mu C$ is located at the origin, and a charge $q_2 = -6.00\ \mu C$ is located at $(0, 3.00)$ m, as shown in Figure 25.12a.

(A) Find the total electric potential due to these charges at the point P, whose coordinates are $(4.00, 0)$ m.

Solution For two charges, the sum in Equation 25.12 gives

$$V_P = k_e\left(\frac{q_1}{r_1} + \frac{q_2}{r_2}\right)$$

$$V_P = (8.99 \times 10^9\ \text{N}\cdot\text{m}^2/\text{C}^2)$$

$$\times \left(\frac{2.00 \times 10^{-6}\ \text{C}}{4.00\ \text{m}} - \frac{6.00 \times 10^{-6}\ \text{C}}{5.00\ \text{m}}\right)$$

$$= \boxed{-6.29 \times 10^3\ \text{V}}$$

(B) Find the change in potential energy of the system of two charges plus a charge $q_3 = 3.00\ \mu C$ as the latter charge moves from infinity to point P (Fig. 25.12b).

Solution When the charge q_3 is at infinity, let us define $U_i = 0$ for the system, and when the charge is at P, $U_f = q_3 V_P$; therefore,

$$\Delta U = q_3 V_P - 0 = (3.00 \times 10^{-6}\ \text{C})(-6.29 \times 10^3\ \text{V})$$

$$= \boxed{-1.89 \times 10^{-2}\ \text{J}}$$

Therefore, because the potential energy of the system has decreased, positive work would have to be done by an external agent to remove the charge from point P back to infinity.

What If? You are working through this example with a classmate and she says, "Wait a minute! In part (B), we ignored the potential energy associated with the pair of charges q_1 and q_2!" How would you respond?

Answer Given the statement of the problem, it is not necessary to include this potential energy, because part (B) asks for the *change* in potential energy of the system as q_3 is brought in from infinity. Because the configuration of charges q_1 and q_2 does not change in the process, there is no ΔU associated with these charges. However, if part (B) had asked to find the change in potential energy when *all three* charges start out infinitely far apart and are then brought to the positions in Figure 25.12b, we would need to calculate the change as follows, using Equation 25.14:

$$U = k_e\left(\frac{q_1 q_2}{r_{12}} + \frac{q_1 q_3}{r_{13}} + \frac{q_2 q_3}{r_{23}}\right)$$

$$= (8.99 \times 10^9\ \text{N}\cdot\text{m}^2/\text{C}^2)$$

$$\times \left(\frac{(2.00 \times 10^{-6}\ \text{C})(-6.00 \times 10^{-6}\ \text{C})}{3.00\ \text{m}}\right.$$

$$+ \frac{(2.00 \times 10^{-6}\ \text{C})(3.00 \times 10^{-6}\ \text{C})}{4.00\ \text{m}}$$

$$\left.+ \frac{(3.00 \times 10^{-6}\ \text{C})(-6.00 \times 10^{-6}\ \text{C})}{5.00\ \text{m}}\right)$$

$$= -5.48 \times 10^{-2}\ \text{J}$$

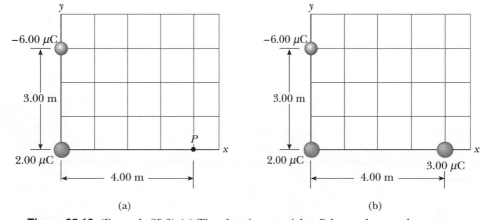

(a)　　　　　　　　　(b)

Figure 25.12 (Example 25.3) (a) The electric potential at P due to the two charges q_1 and q_2 is the algebraic sum of the potentials due to the individual charges. (b) A third charge $q_3 = 3.00\ \mu C$ is brought from infinity to a position near the other charges.

Explore the value of the electric potential at point P and the electric potential energy of the system in Figure 25.12b at the Interactive Worked Example link at http://www.pse6.com.

25.4 Obtaining the Value of the Electric Field from the Electric Potential

The electric field **E** and the electric potential V are related as shown in Equation 25.3. We now show how to calculate the value of the electric field if the electric potential is known in a certain region.

From Equation 25.3 we can express the potential difference dV between two points a distance ds apart as

$$dV = -\mathbf{E} \cdot d\mathbf{s} \tag{25.15}$$

If the electric field has only one component E_x, then $\mathbf{E} \cdot d\mathbf{s} = E_x\,dx$. Therefore, Equation 25.15 becomes $dV = -E_x\,dx$, or

$$E_x = -\frac{dV}{dx} \tag{25.16}$$

That is, the x component of the electric field is equal to the negative of the derivative of the electric potential with respect to x. Similar statements can be made about the y and z components. Equation 25.16 is the mathematical statement of the fact that the electric field is a measure of the rate of change with position of the electric potential, as mentioned in Section 25.1.

Experimentally, electric potential and position can be measured easily with a voltmeter (see Section 28.5) and a meter stick. Consequently, an electric field can be determined by measuring the electric potential at several positions in the field and making a graph of the results. According to Equation 25.16, the slope of a graph of V versus x at a given point provides the magnitude of the electric field at that point.

When a test charge undergoes a displacement $d\mathbf{s}$ along an equipotential surface, then $dV = 0$ because the potential is constant along an equipotential surface. From Equation 25.15, we see that $dV = -\mathbf{E} \cdot d\mathbf{s} = 0$; thus, **E** must be perpendicular to the displacement along the equipotential surface. This shows that the **equipotential surfaces must always be perpendicular to the electric field lines passing through them.**

As mentioned at the end of Section 25.2, the equipotential surfaces for a uniform electric field consist of a family of planes perpendicular to the field lines. Figure 25.13a shows some representative equipotential surfaces for this situation.

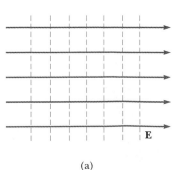

(a)

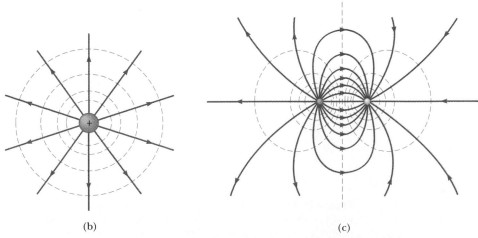

(b)   (c)

Figure 25.13 Equipotential surfaces (the dashed blue lines are intersections of these surfaces with the page) and electric field lines (red-brown lines) for (a) a uniform electric field produced by an infinite sheet of charge, (b) a point charge, and (c) an electric dipole. In all cases, the equipotential surfaces are *perpendicular* to the electric field lines at every point.

If the charge distribution creating an electric field has spherical symmetry such that the volume charge density depends only on the radial distance r, then the electric field is radial. In this case, $\mathbf{E} \cdot d\mathbf{s} = E_r\, dr$, and we can express dV in the form $dV = -E_r\, dr$. Therefore,

$$E_r = -\frac{dV}{dr} \tag{25.17}$$

For example, the electric potential of a point charge is $V = k_e q/r$. Because V is a function of r only, the potential function has spherical symmetry. Applying Equation 25.17, we find that the electric field due to the point charge is $E_r = k_e q/r^2$, a familiar result. Note that the potential changes only in the radial direction, not in any direction perpendicular to r. Thus, V (like E_r) is a function only of r. Again, this is consistent with the idea that **equipotential surfaces are perpendicular to field lines.** In this case the equipotential surfaces are a family of spheres concentric with the spherically symmetric charge distribution (Fig. 25.13b).

The equipotential surfaces for an electric dipole are sketched in Figure 25.13c.

In general, the electric potential is a function of all three spatial coordinates. If $V(r)$ is given in terms of the Cartesian coordinates, the electric field components E_x, E_y, and E_z can readily be found from $V(x, y, z)$ as the partial derivatives[3]

$$E_x = -\frac{\partial V}{\partial x} \qquad E_y = -\frac{\partial V}{\partial y} \qquad E_z = -\frac{\partial V}{\partial z} \tag{25.18}$$

Finding the electric field from the potential

For example, if $V = 3x^2 y + y^2 + yz$, then

$$\frac{\partial V}{\partial x} = \frac{\partial}{\partial x}(3x^2 y + y^2 + yz) = \frac{\partial}{\partial x}(3x^2 y) = 3y\frac{d}{dx}(x^2) = 6xy$$

Quick Quiz 25.8 In a certain region of space, the electric potential is zero everywhere along the x axis. From this we can conclude that the x component of the electric field in this region is (a) zero (b) in the $+x$ direction (c) in the $-x$ direction.

Quick Quiz 25.9 In a certain region of space, the electric field is zero. From this we can conclude that the electric potential in this region is (a) zero (b) constant (c) positive (d) negative.

Example 25.4 The Electric Potential Due to a Dipole

An electric dipole consists of two charges of equal magnitude and opposite sign separated by a distance $2a$, as shown in Figure 25.14. The dipole is along the x axis and is centered at the origin.

(A) Calculate the electric potential at point P.

Solution For point P in Figure 25.14,

$$V = k_e \sum \frac{q_i}{r_i} = k_e\left(\frac{q}{x-a} - \frac{q}{x+a}\right) = \boxed{\frac{2k_e qa}{x^2 - a^2}}$$

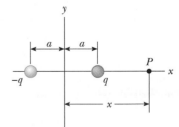

Figure 25.14 (Example 25.4) An electric dipole located on the x axis.

---

[3]   In vector notation, $\mathbf{E}$ is often written in Cartesian coordinate systems as

$$\mathbf{E} = -\nabla V = -\left(\hat{\mathbf{i}}\,\frac{\partial}{\partial x} + \hat{\mathbf{j}}\,\frac{\partial}{\partial y} + \hat{\mathbf{k}}\,\frac{\partial}{\partial z}\right)V$$

where ∇ is called the *gradient operator*.

(B) Calculate V and E_x at a point far from the dipole.

Solution If point P is far from the dipole, such that $x \gg a$, then a^2 can be neglected in the term $x^2 - a^2$ and V becomes

$$V \approx \frac{2k_e qa}{x^2} \qquad (x \gg a)$$

Using Equation 25.16 and this result, we can calculate the magnitude of the electric field at a point far from the dipole:

$$E_x = -\frac{dV}{dx} = \frac{4k_e qa}{x^3} \qquad (x \gg a)$$

(C) Calculate V and E_x if point P is located anywhere between the two charges.

Solution Using Equation 25.12,

$$V = k_e \sum \frac{q_i}{r_i} = k_e \left(\frac{q}{a-x} - \frac{q}{a+x} \right) = \frac{2k_e qx}{a^2 - x^2}$$

and using Equation 25.16,

$$E_x = -\frac{dV}{dx} = -\frac{d}{dx} \left(\frac{2k_e qx}{a^2 - x^2} \right) = -2k_e q \left(\frac{a^2 + x^2}{(a^2 - x^2)^2} \right)$$

We can check these results by considering the situation at the center of the dipole, where $x = 0$, $V = 0$, and $E_x = -2k_e q / a^2$.

What If? What if point P in Figure 25.14 happens to be located to the left of the negative charge? Would the answer to part (A) be the same?

Answer The potential should be negative because a point to the left of the dipole is closer to the negative charge than to the positive charge. If we redo the calculation in part (A) with P on the left side of $-q$, we have

$$V = k_e \sum \frac{q_i}{r_i} = k_e \left(\frac{q}{x+a} - \frac{q}{x-a} \right) = -\frac{2k_e qa}{x^2 - a^2}$$

Thus, the potential has the same value but is negative for points on the left of the dipole.

25.5 Electric Potential Due to Continuous Charge Distributions

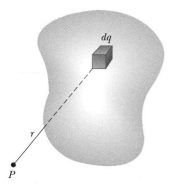

Figure 25.15 The electric potential at the point P due to a continuous charge distribution can be calculated by dividing the charge distribution into elements of charge dq and summing the electric potential contributions over all elements.

Electric potential due to a continuous charge distribution

We can calculate the electric potential due to a continuous charge distribution in two ways. If the charge distribution is known, we can start with Equation 25.11 for the electric potential of a point charge. We then consider the potential due to a small charge element dq, treating this element as a point charge (Fig. 25.15). The electric potential dV at some point P due to the charge element dq is

$$dV = k_e \frac{dq}{r} \tag{25.19}$$

where r is the distance from the charge element to point P. To obtain the total potential at point P, we integrate Equation 25.19 to include contributions from all elements of the charge distribution. Because each element is, in general, a different distance from point P and because k_e is constant, we can express V as

$$V = k_e \int \frac{dq}{r} \tag{25.20}$$

In effect, we have replaced the sum in Equation 25.12 with an integral. Note that this expression for V uses a particular reference: the electric potential is taken to be zero when point P is infinitely far from the charge distribution.

If the electric field is already known from other considerations, such as Gauss's law, we can calculate the electric potential due to a continuous charge distribution using Equation 25.3. If the charge distribution has sufficient symmetry, we first evaluate $\mathbf{E}$ at any point using Gauss's law and then substitute the value obtained into Equation 25.3 to determine the potential difference ΔV between any two points. We then choose the electric potential V to be zero at some convenient point.

PROBLEM-SOLVING HINTS

Calculating Electric Potential

- Remember that electric potential is a scalar quantity, so vector components do not exist. Therefore, when using the superposition principle to evaluate the electric potential at a point due to a system of point charges, simply take the algebraic sum of the potentials due to the various charges. However, you must keep track of signs. The potential is positive for positive charges and negative for negative charges.

- Just as with gravitational potential energy in mechanics, only *changes* in electric potential are significant; hence, the point where you choose the potential to be zero is arbitrary. When dealing with point charges or a charge distribution of finite size, we usually define $V = 0$ to be at a point infinitely far from the charges.

- You can evaluate the electric potential at some point P due to a continuous distribution of charge by dividing the charge distribution into infinitesimal elements of charge dq located at a distance r from P. Then, treat one charge element as a point charge, such that the potential at P due to the element is $dV = k_e dq/r$. Obtain the total potential at P by integrating dV over the entire charge distribution. In performing the integration for most problems, you must express dq and r in terms of a single variable. To simplify the integration, consider the geometry involved in the problem carefully. Study Examples 25.5 through 25.7 below for guidance.

- Another method that you can use to obtain the electric potential due to a finite continuous charge distribution is to start with the definition of potential difference given by Equation 25.3. If you know or can easily obtain **E** (from Gauss's law), then you can evaluate the line integral of $\mathbf{E} \cdot d\mathbf{s}$. This method is demonstrated in Example 25.8.

Example 25.5 Electric Potential Due to a Uniformly Charged Ring

(A) Find an expression for the electric potential at a point P located on the perpendicular central axis of a uniformly charged ring of radius a and total charge Q.

Solution Figure 25.16, in which the ring is oriented so that its plane is perpendicular to the x axis and its center is at the origin, helps us to conceptualize this problem. Because the ring consists of a continuous distribution of charge rather

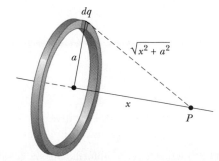

Figure 25.16 (Example 25.5) A uniformly charged ring of radius a lies in a plane perpendicular to the x axis. All elements dq of the ring are the same distance from a point P lying on the x axis.

than a set of discrete charges, we categorize this problem as one in which we need to use the integration technique represented by Equation 25.20. To analyze the problem, we take point P to be at a distance x from the center of the ring, as shown in Figure 25.16. The charge element dq is at a distance $\sqrt{x^2 + a^2}$ from point P. Hence, we can express V as

$$V = k_e \int \frac{dq}{r} = k_e \int \frac{dq}{\sqrt{x^2 + a^2}}$$

Because each element dq is at the same distance from point P, we can bring $\sqrt{x^2 + a^2}$ in front of the integral sign, and V reduces to

$$V = \frac{k_e}{\sqrt{x^2 + a^2}} \int dq = \frac{k_e Q}{\sqrt{x^2 + a^2}} \qquad (25.21)$$

The only variable in this expression for V is x. This is not surprising because our calculation is valid only for points along the x axis, where y and z are both zero.

(B) Find an expression for the magnitude of the electric field at point P.

Solution From symmetry, we see that along the x axis $\mathbf{E}$ can have only an x component. Therefore, we can use Equation 25.16:

$$E_x = -\frac{dV}{dx} = -k_e Q \frac{d}{dx} (x^2 + a^2)^{-1/2}$$

$$= -k_e Q(-\tfrac{1}{2})(x^2 + a^2)^{-3/2}(2x)$$

$$E_x = \frac{k_e Q x}{(x^2 + a^2)^{3/2}} \qquad (25.22)$$

To finalize this problem, we see that this result for the electric field agrees with that obtained by direct integration (see Example 23.8). Note that $E_x = 0$ at $x = 0$ (the center of the ring). Could you have guessed this?

Example 25.6 Electric Potential Due to a Uniformly Charged Disk

A uniformly charged disk has radius a and surface charge density σ. Find

(A) the electric potential and

(B) the magnitude of the electric field along the perpendicular central axis of the disk.

Solution (A) Again, we choose the point P to be at a distance x from the center of the disk and take the plane of the disk to be perpendicular to the x axis. We can simplify the problem by dividing the disk into a series of charged rings of infinitesimal width dr. The electric potential due to each ring is given by Equation 25.21. Consider one such ring of radius r and width dr, as indicated in Figure 25.17. The surface area of the ring is $dA = 2\pi r\, dr$. From the definition of surface charge density (see Section 23.5), we know that the charge on the ring is $dq = \sigma\, dA = \sigma 2\pi r\, dr$. Hence, the potential at the point P due to this ring is

$$dV = \frac{k_e dq}{\sqrt{r^2 + x^2}} = \frac{k_e \sigma 2\pi r\, dr}{\sqrt{r^2 + x^2}}$$

where x is a constant and r is a variable. To find the *total* electric potential at P, we sum over all rings making up the disk. That is, we integrate dV from $r = 0$ to $r = a$:

$$V = \pi k_e \sigma \int_0^a \frac{2r\, dr}{\sqrt{r^2 + x^2}} = \pi k_e \sigma \int_0^a (r^2 + x^2)^{-1/2} 2r\, dr$$

This integral is of the common form $\int u^n\, du$ and has the value $u^{n+1}/(n+1)$, where $n = -\tfrac{1}{2}$ and $u = r^2 + x^2$. This gives

$$V = 2\pi k_e \sigma\,[(x^2 + a^2)^{1/2} - x] \qquad (25.23)$$

(B) As in Example 25.5, we can find the electric field at any axial point using Equation 25.16:

$$E_x = -\frac{dV}{dx} = 2\pi k_e \sigma \left(1 - \frac{x}{\sqrt{x^2 + a^2}}\right) \qquad (25.24)$$

The calculation of V and $\mathbf{E}$ for an arbitrary point off the axis is more difficult to perform, and we do not treat this situation in this text.

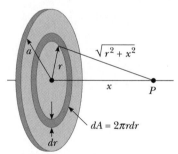
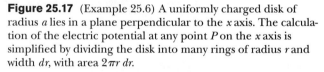

Figure 25.17 (Example 25.6) A uniformly charged disk of radius a lies in a plane perpendicular to the x axis. The calculation of the electric potential at any point P on the x axis is simplified by dividing the disk into many rings of radius r and width dr, with area $2\pi r\, dr$.

Example 25.7 Electric Potential Due to a Finite Line of Charge

A rod of length ℓ located along the x axis has a total charge Q and a uniform linear charge density $\lambda = Q/\ell$. Find the electric potential at a point P located on the y axis a distance a from the origin (Fig. 25.18).

Solution The length element dx has a charge $dq = \lambda\, dx$. Because this element is a distance $r = \sqrt{x^2 + a^2}$ from point P, we can express the potential at point P due to this element as

$$dV = k_e \frac{dq}{r} = k_e \frac{\lambda\, dx}{\sqrt{x^2 + a^2}}$$

To obtain the total potential at P, we integrate this expression over the limits $x = 0$ to $x = \ell$. Noting that k_e and λ are

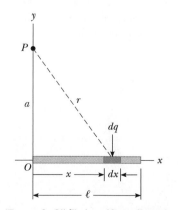

Figure 25.18 (Example 25.7) A uniform line charge of length ℓ located along the x axis. To calculate the electric potential at P, the line charge is divided into segments each of length dx and each carrying a charge $dq = \lambda\, dx$.

constants, we find that

$$V = k_e\lambda \int_0^\ell \frac{dx}{\sqrt{x^2 + a^2}} = k_e\frac{Q}{\ell}\int_0^\ell \frac{dx}{\sqrt{x^2 + a^2}}$$

This integral has the following value (see Appendix B):

$$\int \frac{dx}{\sqrt{x^2 + a^2}} = \ln(x + \sqrt{x^2 + a^2})$$

Evaluating V, we find

$$V = \frac{k_e Q}{\ell}\ln\left(\frac{\ell + \sqrt{\ell^2 + a^2}}{a}\right) \qquad (25.25)$$

What If? What if we were asked to find the electric field at point P? Would this be a simple calculation?

Answer Calculating the electric field by means of Equation 23.11 would be a little messy. There is no symmetry to appeal to, and the integration over the line of charge would represent a vector addition of electric fields at point P. Using Equation 25.18, we could find E_y by replacing a with y in Equation 25.25 and performing the differentiation with respect to y. Because the charged rod in Figure 25.18 lies entirely to the right of $x = 0$, the electric field at point P would have an x component to the left if the rod is charged positively. We cannot use Equation 25.18 to find the x component of the field, however, because we evaluated the potential due to the rod at a specific value of x ($x = 0$) rather than a general value of x. We would need to find the potential as a function of both x and y to be able to find the x and y components of the electric field using Equation 25.25.

Example 25.8   Electric Potential Due to a Uniformly Charged Sphere

An insulating solid sphere of radius R has a uniform positive volume charge density and total charge Q.

(A) Find the electric potential at a point outside the sphere, that is, for $r > R$. Take the potential to be zero at $r = \infty$.

Solution In Example 24.5, we found that the magnitude of the electric field outside a uniformly charged sphere of radius R is

$$E_r = k_e\frac{Q}{r^2} \qquad \text{(for } r > R)$$

where the field is directed radially outward when Q is positive. This is the same as the field due to a point charge, which we studied in Section 23.4. In this case, to obtain the electric potential at an exterior point, such as B in Figure 25.19, we use Equation 25.10, choosing point A as $r = \infty$:

$$V_B - V_A = k_e Q\left[\frac{1}{r_B} - \frac{1}{r_A}\right]$$

$$V_B - 0 = k_e Q\left[\frac{1}{r_B} - 0\right]$$

$$V_B = k_e\frac{Q}{r} \qquad \text{(for } r > R)$$

Because the potential must be continuous at $r = R$, we can use this expression to obtain the potential at the surface of the sphere. That is, the potential at a point such as C shown in Figure 25.19 is

$$V_C = k_e\frac{Q}{R} \qquad \text{(for } r = R)$$

(B) Find the potential at a point inside the sphere, that is, for $r < R$.

Solution In Example 24.5 we found that the electric field inside an insulating uniformly charged sphere is

$$E_r = \frac{k_e Q}{R^3}r \qquad \text{(for } r < R)$$

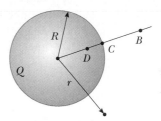

Figure 25.19 (Example 25.8) A uniformly charged insulating sphere of radius R and total charge Q. The electric potentials at points B and C are equivalent to those produced by a point charge Q located at the center of the sphere, but this is not true for point D.

We can use this result and Equation 25.3 to evaluate the potential difference $V_D - V_C$ at some interior point D:

$$V_D - V_C = -\int_R^r E_r\,dr = -\frac{k_e Q}{R^3}\int_R^r r\,dr = \frac{k_e Q}{2R^3}(R^2 - r^2)$$

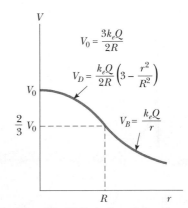

Figure 25.20 (Example 25.8) A plot of electric potential V versus distance r from the center of a uniformly charged insulating sphere of radius R. The curve for V_D inside the sphere is parabolic and joins smoothly with the curve for V_B outside the sphere, which is a hyperbola. The potential has a maximum value V_0 at the center of the sphere. We could make this graph three dimensional (similar to Figures 25.8 and 25.9) by revolving it around the vertical axis.

Substituting $V_C = k_e Q/R$ into this expression and solving for V_D, we obtain

$$V_D = \frac{k_e Q}{2R}\left(3 - \frac{r^2}{R^2}\right) \quad \text{(for } r < R\text{)} \quad (25.26)$$

At $r = R$, this expression gives a result that agrees with that for the potential at the surface, that is, V_C. A plot of V versus r for this charge distribution is given in Figure 25.20.

25.6 Electric Potential Due to a Charged Conductor

In Section 24.4 we found that when a solid conductor in equilibrium carries a net charge, the charge resides on the outer surface of the conductor. Furthermore, we showed that the electric field just outside the conductor is perpendicular to the surface and that the field inside is zero.

We now show that **every point on the surface of a charged conductor in equilibrium is at the same electric potential.** Consider two points A and B on the surface of a charged conductor, as shown in Figure 25.21. Along a surface path connecting these points, **E** is always perpendicular to the displacement $d\mathbf{s}$; therefore $\mathbf{E} \cdot d\mathbf{s} = 0$. Using this result and Equation 25.3, we conclude that the potential difference between A and B is necessarily zero:

$$V_B - V_A = -\int_A^B \mathbf{E} \cdot d\mathbf{s} = 0$$

This result applies to any two points on the surface. Therefore, V is constant everywhere on the surface of a charged conductor in equilibrium. That is,

the surface of any charged conductor in electrostatic equilibrium is an equipotential surface. Furthermore, because the electric field is zero inside the conductor, we conclude that the electric potential is constant everywhere inside the conductor and equal to its value at the surface.

Because this is true, no work is required to move a test charge from the interior of a charged conductor to its surface.

Consider a solid metal conducting sphere of radius R and total positive charge Q, as shown in Figure 25.22a. The electric field outside the sphere is $k_e Q/r^2$ and points radially outward. From Example 25.8, we know that the electric potential at the interior and surface of the sphere must be $k_e Q/R$ relative to infinity. The potential outside the sphere is $k_e Q/r$. Figure 25.22b is a plot of the electric potential as a function of r, and Figure 25.22c shows how the electric field varies with r.

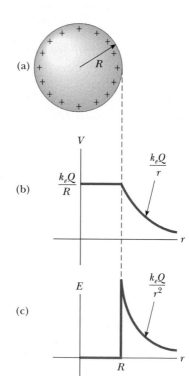

Figure 25.22 (a) The excess charge on a conducting sphere of radius R is uniformly distributed on its surface. (b) Electric potential versus distance r from the center of the charged conducting sphere. (c) Electric field magnitude versus distance r from the center of the charged conducting sphere.

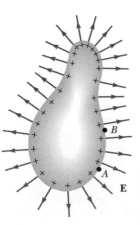

Figure 25.21 An arbitrarily shaped conductor carrying a positive charge. When the conductor is in electrostatic equilibrium, all of the charge resides at the surface, **E** = 0 inside the conductor, and the direction of **E** just outside the conductor is perpendicular to the surface. The electric potential is constant inside the conductor and is equal to the potential at the surface. Note from the spacing of the positive signs that the surface charge density is nonuniform.

When a net charge is placed on a spherical conductor, the surface charge density is uniform, as indicated in Figure 25.22a. However, if the conductor is nonspherical, as in Figure 25.21, the surface charge density is high where the radius of curvature is small (as noted in Section 24.4), and it is low where the radius of curvature is large. Because the electric field just outside the conductor is proportional to the surface charge density, we see that **the electric field is large near convex points having small radii of curvature and reaches very high values at sharp points.** This is demonstrated in Figure 25.23, in which small pieces of thread suspended in oil show the electric field lines. Notice that the density of field lines is highest at the sharp tip of the left-hand conductor and at the highly curved ends of the right-hand conductor. In Example 25.9, the relationship between electric field and radius of curvature is explored mathematically.

Figure 25.24 shows the electric field lines around two spherical conductors: one carrying a net charge Q, and a larger one carrying zero net charge. In this case, the surface charge density is not uniform on either conductor. The sphere having zero net charge has negative charges induced on its side that faces the charged sphere and positive charges induced on its side opposite the charged sphere. The broken blue curves in the figure represent the cross sections of the equipotential surfaces for this charge configuration. As usual, the field lines are perpendicular to the conducting surfaces at all points, and the equipotential surfaces are perpendicular to the field lines everywhere.

Quick Quiz 25.10 Consider starting at the center of the left-hand sphere (sphere 1, of radius a) in Figure 25.24 and moving to the far right of the diagram, passing through the center of the right-hand sphere (sphere 2, of radius c) along the way. The centers of the spheres are a distance b apart. Draw a graph of the electric potential as a function of position relative to the center of the left-hand sphere.

▲ **PITFALL PREVENTION**

25.6 Potential May Not Be Zero

The electric potential inside the conductor is not necessarily zero in Figure 25.22, even though the electric field is zero. From Equation 25.15, we see that a zero value of the field results in no *change* in the potential from one point to another inside the conductor. Thus, the potential everywhere inside the conductor, including the surface, has the same value, which may or may not be zero, depending on where the zero of potential is defined.

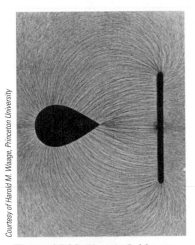

Figure 25.23 Electric field pattern of a charged conducting plate placed near an oppositely charged pointed conductor. Small pieces of thread suspended in oil align with the electric field lines. The field surrounding the pointed conductor is most intense near the pointed end and at other places where the radius of curvature is small.

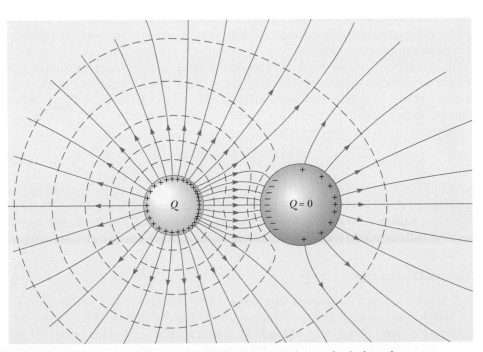

Figure 25.24 The electric field lines (in red-brown) around two spherical conductors. The smaller sphere has a net charge Q, and the larger one has zero net charge. The broken blue curves are intersections of equipotential surfaces with the page.

Example 25.9 Two Connected Charged Spheres

Two spherical conductors of radii r_1 and r_2 are separated by a distance much greater than the radius of either sphere. The spheres are connected by a conducting wire, as shown in Figure 25.25. The charges on the spheres in equilibrium are q_1 and q_2, respectively, and they are uniformly charged. Find the ratio of the magnitudes of the electric fields at the surfaces of the spheres.

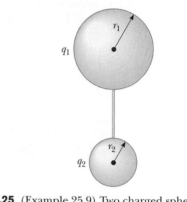

q_1

r_1

r_2

q_2

Figure 25.25 (Example 25.9) Two charged spherical conductors connected by a conducting wire. The spheres are at the *same* electric potential V.

Solution Because the spheres are connected by a conducting wire, they must both be at the same electric potential:

$$V = k_e \frac{q_1}{r_1} = k_e \frac{q_2}{r_2}$$

Therefore, the ratio of charges is

$$(1) \qquad \frac{q_1}{q_2} = \frac{r_1}{r_2}$$

Because the spheres are very far apart and their surfaces uniformly charged, we can express the magnitude of the electric fields at their surfaces as

$$E_1 = k_e \frac{q_1}{r_1^2} \qquad \text{and} \qquad E_2 = k_e \frac{q_2}{r_2^2}$$

Taking the ratio of these two fields and making use of Equation (1), we find that

$$(2) \qquad \frac{E_1}{E_2} = \frac{r_2}{r_1}$$

Hence, the field is more intense in the vicinity of the smaller sphere even though the electric potentials of both spheres are the same.

A Cavity Within a Conductor

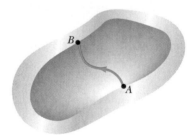

Figure 25.26 A conductor in electrostatic equilibrium containing a cavity. The electric field in the cavity is zero, regardless of the charge on the conductor.

Now suppose a conductor of arbitrary shape contains a cavity as shown in Figure 25.26. Let us assume that no charges are inside the cavity. **In this case, the electric field inside the cavity must be zero** regardless of the charge distribution on the outside surface of the conductor. Furthermore, the field in the cavity is zero even if an electric field exists outside the conductor.

To prove this point, we use the fact that every point on the conductor is at the same electric potential, and therefore any two points A and B on the surface of the cavity must be at the same potential. Now imagine that a field **E** exists in the cavity and evaluate the potential difference $V_B - V_A$ defined by Equation 25.3:

$$V_B - V_A = - \int_A^B \mathbf{E} \cdot d\mathbf{s}$$

Because $V_B - V_A = 0$, the integral of $\mathbf{E} \cdot d\mathbf{s}$ must be zero for all paths between any two points A and B on the conductor. The only way that this can be true for *all* paths is if **E** is zero *everywhere* in the cavity. Thus, we conclude that **a cavity surrounded by conducting walls is a field-free region as long as no charges are inside the cavity.**

Corona Discharge

A phenomenon known as **corona discharge** is often observed near a conductor such as a high-voltage power line. When the electric field in the vicinity of the conductor is sufficiently strong, electrons resulting from random ionizations of air molecules near the conductor accelerate away from their parent molecules. These rapidly moving electrons can ionize additional molecules near the conductor, creating more free electrons. The observed glow (or corona discharge) results from the recombination of these free electrons with the ionized air molecules. If a conductor has an irregular shape, the electric field can be very high near sharp points or edges of the conductor; consequently, the ionization process and corona discharge are most likely to occur around such points.

Corona discharge is used in the electrical transmission industry to locate broken or faulty components. For example, a broken insulator on a transmission tower has sharp edges where corona discharge is likely to occur. Similarly, corona discharge will occur at the sharp end of a broken conductor strand. Observation of these discharges is difficult because the visible radiation emitted is weak and most of the radiation is in the ultraviolet. (We will discuss ultraviolet radiation and other portions of the electromagnetic spectrum in Section 34.6.) Even use of traditional ultraviolet cameras is of little help because the radiation from the corona discharge is overwhelmed by ultraviolet radiation from the Sun. Newly developed dual-spectrum devices combine a narrow-band ultraviolet camera with a visible light camera to show a daylight view of the corona discharge in the actual location on the transmission tower or cable. The ultraviolet part of the camera is designed to operate in a wavelength range in which radiation from the Sun is very weak.

25.7 The Millikan Oil-Drop Experiment

During the period from 1909 to 1913, Robert Millikan performed a brilliant set of experiments in which he measured e, the magnitude of the elementary charge on an electron, and demonstrated the quantized nature of this charge. His apparatus, diagrammed in Figure 25.27, contains two parallel metallic plates. Oil droplets from an atomizer are allowed to pass through a small hole in the upper plate. Millikan used x-rays to ionize the air in the chamber, so that freed electrons would adhere to the oil drops, giving them a negative charge. A horizontally directed light beam is used to illuminate the oil droplets, which are viewed through a telescope whose long axis is perpendicular to the light beam. When the droplets are viewed in this manner, they appear as shining stars against a dark background, and the rate at which individual drops fall can be determined.

Let us assume that a single drop having a mass m and carrying a charge q is being viewed and that its charge is negative. If no electric field is present between the plates,

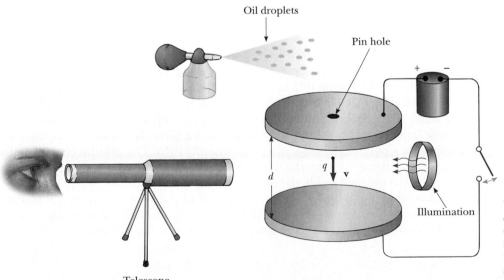

Oil droplets

Pin hole

d

q $\mathbf{v}$

Illumination

Telescope

At the Active Figures link at http://www.pse6.com, *you can do a simplified version of the experiment for yourself. You will be able to take data on a number of oil drops and determine the elementary charge from your data.*

Active Figure 25.27 Schematic drawing of the Millikan oil-drop apparatus.

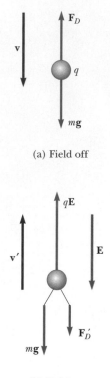

(a) Field off

(b) Field on

Figure 25.28 The forces acting on a negatively charged oil droplet in the Millikan experiment.

the two forces acting on the charge are the gravitational force $m\mathbf{g}$ acting downward[4] and a viscous drag force $\mathbf{F}_D$ acting upward as indicated in Figure 25.28a. The drag force is proportional to the drop's speed. When the drop reaches its terminal speed v, the two forces balance each other ($mg = F_D$).

Now suppose that a battery connected to the plates sets up an electric field between the plates such that the upper plate is at the higher electric potential. In this case, a third force $q\mathbf{E}$ acts on the charged drop. Because q is negative and $\mathbf{E}$ is directed downward, this electric force is directed upward, as shown in Figure 25.28b. If this force is sufficiently great, the drop moves upward and the drag force $\mathbf{F}_D'$ acts downward. When the upward electric force $q\mathbf{E}$ balances the sum of the gravitational force and the downward drag force $\mathbf{F}_D'$, the drop reaches a new terminal speed v' in the upward direction.

With the field turned on, a drop moves slowly upward, typically at rates of hundredths of a centimeter per second. The rate of fall in the absence of a field is comparable. Hence, one can follow a single droplet for hours, alternately rising and falling, by simply turning the electric field on and off.

After recording measurements on thousands of droplets, Millikan and his co-workers found that all droplets, to within about 1% precision, had a charge equal to some integer multiple of the elementary charge e:

$$q = ne \qquad n = 0, -1, -2, -3, \ldots$$

where $e = 1.60 \times 10^{-19}$ C. Millikan's experiment yields conclusive evidence that charge is quantized. For this work, he was awarded the Nobel Prize in Physics in 1923.

25.8   Applications of Electrostatics

The practical application of electrostatics is represented by such devices as lightning rods and electrostatic precipitators and by such processes as xerography and the painting of automobiles. Scientific devices based on the principles of electrostatics include electrostatic generators, the field-ion microscope, and ion-drive rocket engines.

The Van de Graaff Generator

Experimental results show that when a charged conductor is placed in contact with the inside of a hollow conductor, all of the charge on the charged conductor is transferred to the hollow conductor. In principle, the charge on the hollow conductor and its electric potential can be increased without limit by repetition of the process.

In 1929 Robert J. Van de Graaff (1901–1967) used this principle to design and build an electrostatic generator. This type of generator is used extensively in nuclear physics research. A schematic representation of the generator is given in Figure 25.29. Charge is delivered continuously to a high-potential electrode by means of a moving belt of insulating material. The high-voltage electrode is a hollow metal dome mounted on an insulating column. The belt is charged at point A by means of a corona discharge between comb-like metallic needles and a grounded grid. The needles are maintained at a positive electric potential of typically 10^4 V. The positive charge on the moving belt is transferred to the dome by a second comb of needles at point B. Because the electric field inside the dome is negligible, the positive charge on the belt is easily transferred to the conductor regardless of its potential. In practice, it is possible to increase the electric potential of the dome until electrical discharge occurs through the air. Because the "breakdown" electric field in air is about 3×10^6 V/m, a

---

[4]   There is also a buoyant force on the oil drop due to the surrounding air. This force can be incorporated as a correction in the gravitational force $m\mathbf{g}$ on the drop, so we will not consider it in our analysis.

sphere 1 m in radius can be raised to a maximum potential of 3×10^6 V. The potential can be increased further by increasing the radius of the dome and by placing the entire system in a container filled with high-pressure gas.

Van de Graaff generators can produce potential differences as large as 20 million volts. Protons accelerated through such large potential differences receive enough energy to initiate nuclear reactions between themselves and various target nuclei. Smaller generators are often seen in science classrooms and museums. If a person insulated from the ground touches the sphere of a Van de Graaff generator, his or her body can be brought to a high electric potential. The hair acquires a net positive charge, and each strand is repelled by all the others, as in the opening photograph of Chapter 23.

The Electrostatic Precipitator

One important application of electrical discharge in gases is the *electrostatic precipitator.* This device removes particulate matter from combustion gases, thereby reducing air pollution. Precipitators are especially useful in coal-burning power plants and in industrial operations that generate large quantities of smoke. Current systems are able to eliminate more than 99% of the ash from smoke.

Figure 25.30a shows a schematic diagram of an electrostatic precipitator. A high potential difference (typically 40 to 100 kV) is maintained between a wire running down the center of a duct and the walls of the duct, which are grounded. The wire is maintained at a negative electric potential with respect to the walls, so the electric field is directed toward the wire. The values of the field near the wire become high enough to cause a corona discharge around the wire; the air near the wire contains positive ions, electrons, and such negative ions as O_2^-. The air to be cleaned enters the duct and moves near the wire. As the electrons and negative ions created by the discharge are accelerated toward the outer wall by the electric field, the dirt particles in the air become charged by collisions and ion capture. Because most of the charged dirt particles are negative, they too are drawn to the duct walls by the electric field. When the duct is periodically shaken, the particles break loose and are collected at the bottom.

In addition to reducing the level of particulate matter in the atmosphere (compare Figs. 25.30b and c), the electrostatic precipitator recovers valuable materials in the form of metal oxides.

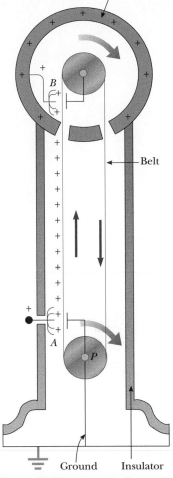

Figure 25.29 Schematic diagram of a Van de Graaff generator. Charge is transferred to the metal dome at the top by means of a moving belt. The charge is deposited on the belt at point *A* and transferred to the hollow conductor at point *B*.

Figure 25.30 (a) Schematic diagram of an electrostatic precipitator. The high negative electric potential maintained on the central coiled wire creates a corona discharge in the vicinity of the wire. Compare the air pollution when the electrostatic precipitator is (b) operating and (c) turned off.

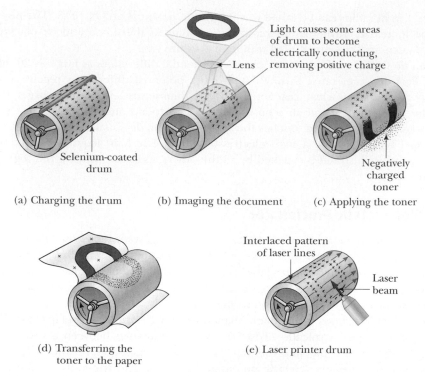

(a) Charging the drum   (b) Imaging the document   (c) Applying the toner

(d) Transferring the toner to the paper   (e) Laser printer drum

Figure 25.31 The xerographic process: (a) The photoconductive surface of the drum is positively charged. (b) Through the use of a light source and lens, an image is formed on the surface in the form of positive charges. (c) The surface containing the image is covered with a negatively charged powder, which adheres only to the image area. (d) A piece of paper is placed over the surface and given a positive charge. This transfers the image to the paper as the negatively charged powder particles migrate to the paper. The paper is then heat-treated to "fix" the powder. (e) A laser printer operates similarly except the image is produced by turning a laser beam on and off as it sweeps across the selenium-coated drum.

Xerography and Laser Printers

The basic idea of xerography[5] was developed by Chester Carlson, who was granted a patent for the xerographic process in 1940. The unique feature of this process is the use of a photoconductive material to form an image. (A *photoconductor* is a material that is a poor electrical conductor in the dark but becomes a good electrical conductor when exposed to light.)

The xerographic process is illustrated in Figure 25.31a to d. First, the surface of a plate or drum that has been coated with a thin film of photoconductive material (usually selenium or some compound of selenium) is given a positive electrostatic charge in the dark. An image of the page to be copied is then focused by a lens onto the charged surface. The photoconducting surface becomes conducting only in areas where light strikes it. In these areas, the light produces charge carriers in the photoconductor that move the positive charge off the drum. However, positive charges remain on those areas of the photoconductor not exposed to light, leaving a latent image of the object in the form of a positive surface charge distribution.

Next, a negatively charged powder called a *toner* is dusted onto the photoconducting surface. The charged powder adheres only to those areas of the surface that contain the positively charged image. At this point, the image becomes visible. The toner (and hence the image) is then transferred to the surface of a sheet of positively charged paper.

Finally, the toner is "fixed" to the surface of the paper as the toner melts while passing through high-temperature rollers. This results in a permanent copy of the original.

A laser printer (Fig. 25.31e) operates by the same principle, with the exception that a computer-directed laser beam is used to illuminate the photoconductor instead of a lens.

[5] The prefix *xero-* is from the Greek word meaning "dry." Note that liquid ink is not used in xerography.

SUMMARY

Take a practice test for this chapter by clicking on the Practice Test link at http://www.pse6.com.

When a positive test charge q_0 is moved between points A and B in an electric field $\mathbf{E}$, the **change in the potential energy of the charge–field system** is

$$\Delta U = -q_0 \int_A^B \mathbf{E} \cdot d\mathbf{s} \qquad (25.1)$$

The **electric potential** $V = U/q_0$ is a scalar quantity and has the units of J/C, where $1\,\text{J/C} \equiv 1\,\text{V}$.

The **potential difference** ΔV between points A and B in an electric field $\mathbf{E}$ is defined as

$$\Delta V \equiv \frac{\Delta U}{q_0} = -\int_A^B \mathbf{E} \cdot d\mathbf{s} \qquad (25.3)$$

The potential difference between two points A and B in a uniform electric field $\mathbf{E}$, where $\mathbf{s}$ is a vector that points from A to B and is parallel to $\mathbf{E}$ is

$$\Delta V = -Ed \qquad (25.6)$$

where $d = |\mathbf{s}|$.

An **equipotential surface** is one on which all points are at the same electric potential. Equipotential surfaces are perpendicular to electric field lines.

If we define $V = 0$ at $r_A = \infty$, the electric potential due to a point charge at any distance r from the charge is

$$V = k_e \frac{q}{r} \qquad (25.11)$$

We can obtain the electric potential associated with a group of point charges by summing the potentials due to the individual charges.

The **potential energy associated with a pair of point charges** separated by a distance r_{12} is

$$U = k_e \frac{q_1 q_2}{r_{12}} \qquad (25.13)$$

This energy represents the work done by an external agent when the charges are brought from an infinite separation to the separation r_{12}. We obtain the potential energy of a distribution of point charges by summing terms like Equation 25.13 over all pairs of particles.

If we know the electric potential as a function of coordinates x, y, z, we can obtain the components of the electric field by taking the negative derivative of the electric potential with respect to the coordinates. For example, the x component of the electric field is

$$E_x = -\frac{dV}{dx} \qquad (25.16)$$

The **electric potential due to a continuous charge distribution** is

$$V = k_e \int \frac{dq}{r} \qquad (25.20)$$

Every point on the surface of a charged conductor in electrostatic equilibrium is at the same electric potential. The potential is constant everywhere inside the conductor and equal to its value at the surface.

Table 25.1 lists electric potentials due to several charge distributions.

Table 25.1

Electric Potential Due to Various Charge Distributions

Charge Distribution	Electric Potential	Location
Uniformly charged ring of radius a	$V = k_e \dfrac{Q}{\sqrt{x^2 + a^2}}$	Along perpendicular central axis of ring, distance x from ring center
Uniformly charged disk of radius a	$V = 2\pi k_e \sigma [(x^2 + a^2)^{1/2} - x]$	Along perpendicular central axis of disk, distance x from disk center
Uniformly charged, *insulating* solid sphere of radius R and total charge Q	$V = k_e \dfrac{Q}{r}$ $V = \dfrac{k_e Q}{2R}\left(3 - \dfrac{r^2}{R^2}\right)$	$r \geq R$ $r < R$
Isolated *conducting* sphere of radius R and total charge Q	$V = k_e \dfrac{Q}{r}$ $V = k_e \dfrac{Q}{R}$	$r > R$ $r \leq R$

QUESTIONS

1. Distinguish between electric potential and electric potential energy.

2. A negative charge moves in the direction of a uniform electric field. Does the potential energy of the charge–field system increase or decrease? Does the charge move to a position of higher or lower potential?

3. Give a physical explanation of the fact that the potential energy of a pair of charges with the same sign is positive whereas the potential energy of a pair of charges with opposite signs is negative.

4. A uniform electric field is parallel to the x axis. In what direction can a charge be displaced in this field without any external work being done on the charge?

5. Explain why equipotential surfaces are always perpendicular to electric field lines.

6. Describe the equipotential surfaces for (a) an infinite line of charge and (b) a uniformly charged sphere.

7. Explain why, under static conditions, all points in a conductor must be at the same electric potential.

8. The electric field inside a hollow, uniformly charged sphere is zero. Does this imply that the potential is zero inside the sphere? Explain.

9. The potential of a point charge is defined to be zero at an infinite distance. Why can we not define the potential of an infinite line of charge to be zero at $r = \infty$?

10. Two charged conducting spheres of different radii are connected by a conducting wire as shown in Figure 25.25. Which sphere has the greater charge density?

11. What determines the maximum potential to which the dome of a Van de Graaff generator can be raised?

12. Explain the origin of the glow sometimes observed around the cables of a high-voltage power line.

13. Why is it important to avoid sharp edges or points on conductors used in high-voltage equipment?

14. How would you shield an electronic circuit or laboratory from stray electric fields? Why does this work?

15. Two concentric spherical conducting shells of radii $a = 0.400$ m and $b = 0.500$ m are connected by a thin wire as shown in Figure Q25.15. If a total charge $Q = 10.0$ μC is placed on the system, how much charge settles on each sphere?

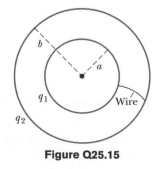

Figure Q25.15

16. Study Figure 23.4 and the accompanying text discussion of charging by induction. You may also compare to Figure

25.24. When the grounding wire is touched to the rightmost point on the sphere in Figure 23.4c, electrons are drained away from the sphere to leave the sphere positively charged. Suppose instead that the grounding wire is touched to the leftmost point on the sphere. Will electrons still drain away, moving closer to the negatively charged rod as they do so? What kind of charge, if any, will remain on the sphere?

PROBLEMS

1, 2, 3 = straightforward, intermediate, challenging ☐ = full solution available in the *Student Solutions Manual and Study Guide*

🌐 = coached solution with hints available at http://www.pse6.com 🖥 = computer useful in solving problem

▨ = paired numerical and symbolic problems

Section 25.1 Potential Difference and Electric Potential

1. How much work is done (by a battery, generator, or some other source of potential difference) in moving Avogadro's number of electrons from an initial point where the electric potential is 9.00 V to a point where the potential is − 5.00 V? (The potential in each case is measured relative to a common reference point.)

2. An ion accelerated through a potential difference of 115 V experiences an increase in kinetic energy of 7.37×10^{-17} J. Calculate the charge on the ion.

3. (a) Calculate the speed of a proton that is accelerated from rest through a potential difference of 120 V. (b) Calculate the speed of an electron that is accelerated through the same potential difference.

4. What potential difference is needed to stop an electron having an initial speed of 4.20×10^5 m/s?

Section 25.2 Potential Differences in a Uniform Electric Field

5. A uniform electric field of magnitude 250 V/m is directed in the positive *x* direction. A +12.0-μC charge moves from the origin to the point $(x, y) = (20.0 \text{ cm}, 50.0 \text{ cm})$. (a) What is the change in the potential energy of the charge–field system? (b) Through what potential difference does the charge move?

6. The difference in potential between the accelerating plates in the electron gun of a TV picture tube is about 25 000 V. If the distance between these plates is 1.50 cm, what is the magnitude of the uniform electric field in this region?

7. 🌐 An electron moving parallel to the *x* axis has an initial speed of 3.70×10^6 m/s at the origin. Its speed is reduced to 1.40×10^5 m/s at the point $x = 2.00$ cm. Calculate the potential difference between the origin and that point. Which point is at the higher potential?

8. Suppose an electron is released from rest in a uniform electric field whose magnitude is 5.90×10^3 V/m. (a) Through what potential difference will it have passed after moving 1.00 cm? (b) How fast will the electron be moving after it has traveled 1.00 cm?

9. A uniform electric field of magnitude 325 V/m is directed in the negative *y* direction in Figure P25.9. The coordinates of point *A* are $(- 0.200, - 0.300)$ m, and those of point *B* are $(0.400, 0.500)$ m. Calculate the potential difference $V_B - V_A$, using the blue path.

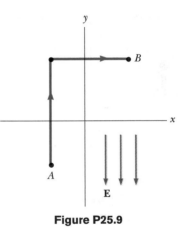

Figure P25.9

10. Starting with the definition of work, prove that at every point on an equipotential surface the surface must be perpendicular to the electric field there.

11. **Review problem.** A block having mass *m* and charge $+ Q$ is connected to a spring having constant *k*. The block lies on a frictionless horizontal track, and the system is immersed in a uniform electric field of magnitude *E*, directed as shown in Figure P25.11. If the block is released from rest when the spring is unstretched (at $x = 0$), (a) by what maximum amount does the spring expand? (b) What is the equilibrium position of the block? (c) Show that the block's motion is simple harmonic, and determine its period. (d) **What If?** Repeat part (a) if the coefficient of kinetic friction between block and surface is μ_k.

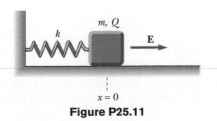

Figure P25.11

12. On planet Tehar, the free-fall acceleration is the same as that on Earth but there is also a strong downward electric field that is uniform close to the planet's surface. A 2.00-kg ball having a charge of 5.00 μC is thrown upward at a speed of 20.1 m/s, and it hits the ground after an interval of 4.10 s. What is the potential difference between the starting point and the top point of the trajectory?

13. An insulating rod having linear charge density $\lambda = 40.0$ μC/m and linear mass density $\mu = 0.100$ kg/m is released from rest in a uniform electric field $E = 100$ V/m directed perpendicular to the rod (Fig. P25.13). (a) Determine the speed of the rod after it has traveled 2.00 m. (b) **What If?** How does your answer to part (a) change if the electric field is not perpendicular to the rod? Explain.

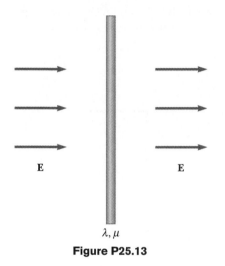

λ, μ

Figure P25.13

14. A particle having charge $q = +2.00$ μC and mass $m = 0.010\,0$ kg is connected to a string that is $L = 1.50$ m long and is tied to the pivot point P in Figure P25.14. The particle, string and pivot point all lie on a frictionless horizontal table. The particle is released from rest when the string makes an angle $\theta = 60.0°$ with a uniform electric field of magnitude $E = 300$ V/m. Determine the speed of the particle when the string is parallel to the electric field (point a in Fig. P25.14).

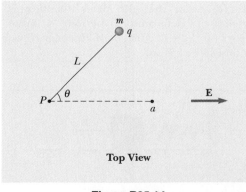

Top View

Figure P25.14

Section 25.3   Electric Potential and Potential Energy Due to Point Charges

Note: Unless stated otherwise, assume the reference level of potential is $V = 0$ at $r = \infty$.

15. (a) Find the potential at a distance of 1.00 cm from a proton. (b) What is the potential difference between two points that are 1.00 cm and 2.00 cm from a proton? (c) **What If?** Repeat parts (a) and (b) for an electron.

16. Given two 2.00-μC charges, as shown in Figure P25.16, and a positive test charge $q = 1.28 \times 10^{-18}$ C at the origin, (a) what is the net force exerted by the two 2.00-μC charges on the test charge q? (b) What is the electric field at the origin due to the two 2.00-μC charges? (c) What is the electric potential at the origin due to the two 2.00-μC charges?

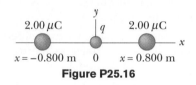

Figure P25.16

17. At a certain distance from a point charge, the magnitude of the electric field is 500 V/m and the electric potential is -3.00 kV. (a) What is the distance to the charge? (b) What is the magnitude of the charge?

18. A charge $+q$ is at the origin. A charge $-2q$ is at $x = 2.00$ m on the x axis. For what finite value(s) of x is (a) the electric field zero? (b) the electric potential zero?

19. The three charges in Figure P25.19 are at the vertices of an isosceles triangle. Calculate the electric potential at the midpoint of the base, taking $q = 7.00$ μC.

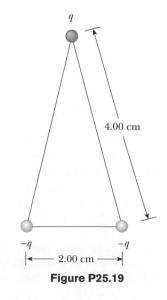

Figure P25.19

20. Two point charges, $Q_1 = +5.00$ nC and $Q_2 = -3.00$ nC, are separated by 35.0 cm. (a) What is the potential energy of the pair? What is the significance of the algebraic sign of your answer? (b) What is the electric potential at a point midway between the charges?

21. *Compare this problem with Problem 57 in Chapter 23.* Four identical point charges ($q = +10.0$ μC) are located on the corners of a rectangle as shown in Figure P23.57. The dimensions of the rectangle are $L = 60.0$ cm and $W = 15.0$ cm. Calculate the change in electric potential energy of the system as the charge at the lower left corner in Figure P23.57 is brought to this position from infinitely far away. Assume that the other three charges in Figure P23.57 remain fixed in position.

22. *Compare this problem with Problem 20 in Chapter 23.* Two point charges each of magnitude 2.00 μC are located on the x axis. One is at $x = 1.00$ m, and the other is at $x = -1.00$ m. (a) Determine the electric potential on the y axis at $y = 0.500$ m. (b) Calculate the change in electric potential energy of the system as a third charge of -3.00 μC is brought from infinitely far away to a position on the y axis at $y = 0.500$ m.

23. Show that the amount of work required to assemble four identical point charges of magnitude Q at the corners of a square of side s is $5.41 k_e Q^2/s$.

24. *Compare this problem with Problem 23 in Chapter 23.* Five equal negative point charges $-q$ are placed symmetrically around a circle of radius R. Calculate the electric potential at the center of the circle.

25. *Compare this problem with Problem 41 in Chapter 23.* Three equal positive charges q are at the corners of an equilateral triangle of side a as shown in Figure P23.41. (a) At what point, if any, in the plane of the charges is the electric potential zero? (b) What is the electric potential at the point P due to the two charges at the base of the triangle?

26. Review problem. Two insulating spheres have radii 0.300 cm and 0.500 cm, masses 0.100 kg and 0.700 kg, and uniformly distributed charges of -2.00 μC and 3.00 μC. They are released from rest when their centers are separated by 1.00 m. (a) How fast will each be moving when they collide? (*Suggestion:* consider conservation of energy and of linear momentum.) (b) **What If?** If the spheres were conductors, would the speeds be greater or less than those calculated in part (a)? Explain.

27. Review problem. Two insulating spheres have radii r_1 and r_2, masses m_1 and m_2, and uniformly distributed charges $-q_1$ and q_2. They are released from rest when their centers are separated by a distance d. (a) How fast is each moving when they collide? (*Suggestion:* consider conservation of energy and conservation of linear momentum.) (b) **What If?** If the spheres were conductors, would their speeds be greater or less than those calculated in part (a)? Explain.

28. Two particles, with charges of 20.0 nC and -20.0 nC, are placed at the points with coordinates (0, 4.00 cm) and (0, -4.00 cm), as shown in Figure P25.28. A particle with charge 10.0 nC is located at the origin. (a) Find the electric potential energy of the configuration of the

three fixed charges. (b) A fourth particle, with a mass of 2.00×10^{-13} kg and a charge of 40.0 nC, is released from rest at the point (3.00 cm, 0). Find its speed after it has moved freely to a very large distance away.

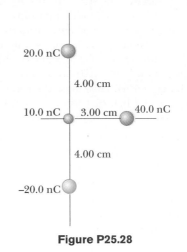

20.0 nC
4.00 cm
10.0 nC   3.00 cm   40.0 nC
4.00 cm
-20.0 nC

Figure P25.28

29. Review problem. A light unstressed spring has length d. Two identical particles, each with charge q, are connected to the opposite ends of the spring. The particles are held stationary a distance d apart and then released at the same time. The system then oscillates on a horizontal frictionless table. The spring has a bit of internal kinetic friction, so the oscillation is damped. The particles eventually stop vibrating when the distance between them is $3d$. Find the increase in internal energy that appears in the spring during the oscillations. Assume that the system of the spring and two charges is isolated.

30. Two point charges of equal magnitude are located along the y axis equal distances above and below the x axis, as shown in Figure P25.30. (a) Plot a graph of the potential at points along the x axis over the interval $-3a < x < 3a$. You should plot the potential in units of $k_e Q/a$. (b) Let the charge located at $-a$ be negative and plot the potential along the y axis over the interval $-4a < y < 4a$.

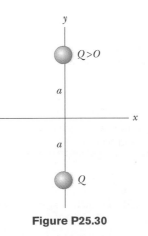

Figure P25.30

31. A small spherical object carries a charge of 8.00 nC. At what distance from the center of the object is the potential equal to 100 V? 50.0 V? 25.0 V? Is the spacing of the equipotentials proportional to the change in potential?

32. In 1911 Ernest Rutherford and his assistants Geiger and Marsden conducted an experiment in which they scattered alpha particles from thin sheets of gold. An alpha particle, having charge $+2e$ and mass 6.64×10^{-27} kg, is a product of certain radioactive decays. The results of the experiment led Rutherford to the idea that most of the mass of an atom is in a very small nucleus, with electrons in orbit around it—his planetary model of the atom. Assume an alpha particle, initially very far from a gold nucleus, is fired with a velocity of 2.00×10^7 m/s directly toward the nucleus (charge $+79e$). How close does the alpha particle get to the nucleus before turning around? Assume the gold nucleus remains stationary.

33. An electron starts from rest 3.00 cm from the center of a uniformly charged insulating sphere of radius 2.00 cm and total charge 1.00 nC. What is the speed of the electron when it reaches the surface of the sphere?

34. Calculate the energy required to assemble the array of charges shown in Figure P25.34, where $a = 0.200$ m, $b = 0.400$ m, and $q = 6.00$ μC.

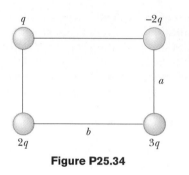

Figure P25.34

35. Four identical particles each have charge q and mass m. They are released from rest at the vertices of a square of side L. How fast is each charge moving when their distance from the center of the square doubles?

36. How much work is required to assemble eight identical point charges, each of magnitude q, at the corners of a cube of side s?

Section 25.4 Obtaining the Value of the Electric Field from the Electric Potential

37. The potential in a region between $x = 0$ and $x = 6.00$ m is $V = a + bx$, where $a = 10.0$ V and $b = -7.00$ V/m. Determine (a) the potential at $x = 0$, 3.00 m, and 6.00 m, and (b) the magnitude and direction of the electric field at $x = 0$, 3.00 m, and 6.00 m.

38. The electric potential inside a charged spherical conductor of radius R is given by $V = k_e Q/R$, and the potential outside is given by $V = k_e Q/r$. Using $E_r = -dV/dr$, derive the electric field (a) inside and (b) outside this charge distribution.

39. Over a certain region of space, the electric potential is $V = 5x - 3x^2y + 2yz^2$. Find the expressions for the x, y, and z components of the electric field over this region. What is the magnitude of the field at the point P that has coordinates $(1, 0, -2)$ m?

40. Figure P25.40 shows several equipotential lines each labeled by its potential in volts. The distance between the lines of the square grid represents 1.00 cm. (a) Is the magnitude of the field larger at A or at B? Why? (b) What is **E** at B? (c) Represent what the field looks like by drawing at least eight field lines.

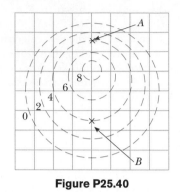

Figure P25.40

41. It is shown in Example 25.7 that the potential at a point P a distance a above one end of a uniformly charged rod of length ℓ lying along the x axis is

$$V = \frac{k_e Q}{\ell} \ln \left(\frac{\ell + \sqrt{\ell^2 + a^2}}{a} \right)$$

Use this result to derive an expression for the y component of the electric field at P. (*Suggestion:* Replace a with y.)

Section 25.5 Electric Potential Due to Continuous Charge Distributions

42. Consider a ring of radius R with the total charge Q spread uniformly over its perimeter. What is the potential difference between the point at the center of the ring and a point on its axis a distance $2R$ from the center?

43. A rod of length L (Fig. P25.43) lies along the x axis with its left end at the origin. It has a nonuniform charge density $\lambda = \alpha x$, where α is a positive constant. (a) What are the units of α? (b) Calculate the electric potential at A.

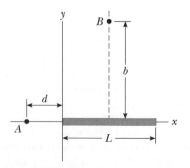

Figure P25.43 Problems 43 and 44.

44. For the arrangement described in the previous problem, calculate the electric potential at point B, which lies on the perpendicular bisector of the rod a distance b above the x axis.

45. *Compare this problem with Problem 33 in Chapter 23.* A uniformly charged insulating rod of length 14.0 cm is bent into the shape of a semicircle as shown in Figure P23.33. The rod has a total charge of $-7.50\ \mu C$. Find the electric potential at O, the center of the semicircle.

46. Calculate the electric potential at point P on the axis of the annulus shown in Figure P25.46, which has a uniform charge density σ.

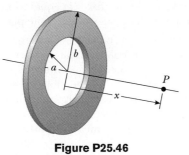

Figure P25.46

47. A wire having a uniform linear charge density λ is bent into the shape shown in Figure P25.47. Find the electric potential at point O.

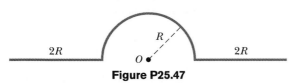

Figure P25.47

Section 25.6   Electric Potential Due to a Charged Conductor

48. How many electrons should be removed from an initially uncharged spherical conductor of radius 0.300 m to produce a potential of 7.50 kV at the surface?

49. A spherical conductor has a radius of 14.0 cm and charge of $26.0\ \mu C$. Calculate the electric field and the electric potential (a) $r = 10.0$ cm, (b) $r = 20.0$ cm, and (c) $r = 14.0$ cm from the center.

50. Electric charge can accumulate on an airplane in flight. You may have observed needle-shaped metal extensions on the wing tips and tail of an airplane. Their purpose is to allow charge to leak off before much of it accumulates. The electric field around the needle is much larger than the field around the body of the airplane, and can become large enough to produce dielectric breakdown of the air, discharging the airplane. To model this process, assume that two charged spherical conductors are connected by a long conducting wire, and a charge of $1.20\ \mu C$ is placed on the combination. One sphere, representing the body of the airplane, has a radius of 6.00 cm, and the other, representing the tip of the needle, has a radius of 2.00 cm. (a) What is the electric potential of each sphere? (b) What is the electric field at the surface of each sphere?

Section 25.8   Applications of Electrostatics

51. Lightning can be studied with a Van de Graaff generator, essentially consisting of a spherical dome on which charge is continuously deposited by a moving belt. Charge can be added until the electric field at the surface of the dome becomes equal to the dielectric strength of air. Any more charge leaks off in sparks, as shown in Figure P25.51. Assume the dome has a diameter of 30.0 cm and is surrounded by dry air with dielectric strength 3.00×10^6 V/m. (a) What is the maximum potential of the dome? (b) What is the maximum charge on the dome?

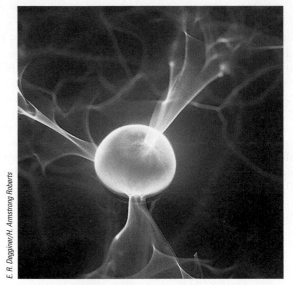

E. R. Degginer/H. Armstrong Roberts

Figure P25.51 Problems 51 and 52.

52. The spherical dome of a Van de Graaff generator can be raised to a maximum potential of 600 kV; then additional charge leaks off in sparks, by producing dielectric breakdown of the surrounding dry air, as shown in Figure P25.51. Determine (a) the charge on the dome and (b) the radius of the dome.

Additional Problems

53. The liquid-drop model of the atomic nucleus suggests that high-energy oscillations of certain nuclei can split the nucleus into two unequal fragments plus a few neutrons. The fission products acquire kinetic energy from their mutual Coulomb repulsion. Calculate the electric potential energy (in electron volts) of two spherical fragments from a uranium nucleus having the following charges and radii: $38e$ and 5.50×10^{-15} m; $54e$ and 6.20×10^{-15} m. Assume that the charge is distributed uniformly throughout the volume of each spherical fragment and that just before separating they are at rest with their surfaces in contact. The electrons surrounding the nucleus can be ignored.

54. On a dry winter day you scuff your leather-soled shoes across a carpet and get a shock when you extend the tip of one finger toward a metal doorknob. In a dark room you see a spark perhaps 5 mm long. Make order-of-magnitude estimates of (a) your electric potential and (b) the charge on your body before you touch the doorknob. Explain your reasoning.

55. The Bohr model of the hydrogen atom states that the single electron can exist only in certain allowed orbits around the proton. The radius of each Bohr orbit is $r = n^2(0.052\ 9\ \text{nm})$ where $n = 1, 2, 3, \ldots$. Calculate the electric potential energy of a hydrogen atom when the electron (a) is in the first allowed orbit, with $n = 1$, (b) is in the second allowed orbit, $n = 2$, and (c) has escaped from the atom, with $r = \infty$. Express your answers in electron volts.

56. An electron is released from rest on the axis of a uniform positively charged ring, 0.100 m from the ring's center. If the linear charge density of the ring is $+0.100\ \mu\text{C/m}$ and the radius of the ring is 0.200 m, how fast will the electron be moving when it reaches the center of the ring?

57. As shown in Figure P25.57, two large parallel vertical conducting plates separated by distance d are charged so that their potentials are $+V_0$ and $-V_0$. A small conducting ball of mass m and radius R (where $R \ll d$) is hung midway between the plates. The thread of length L supporting the ball is a conducting wire connected to ground, so the potential of the ball is fixed at $V = 0$. The ball hangs straight down in stable equilibrium when V_0 is sufficiently small. Show that the equilibrium of the ball is unstable if V_0 exceeds the critical value $k_e d^2 mg/(4RL)$. (*Suggestion:* consider the forces on the ball when it is displaced a distance $x \ll L$.) ·

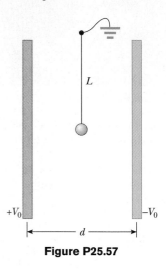

Figure P25.57

58. *Compare this problem with Problem 34 in Chapter 23.* (a) A uniformly charged cylindrical shell has total charge Q, radius R, and height h. Determine the electric potential at a point a distance d from the right end of the cylinder, as shown in Figure P25.58. (*Suggestion:* use the result of Example 25.5 by treating the cylinder as a collection of ring charges.) (b) **What If?** Use the result of Example 25.6 to solve the same problem for a solid cylinder.

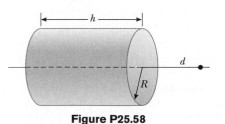

Figure P25.58

59. Calculate the work that must be done to charge a spherical shell of radius R to a total charge Q.

60. Two parallel plates having charges of equal magnitude but opposite sign are separated by 12.0 cm. Each plate has a surface charge density of $36.0\ \text{nC/m}^2$. A proton is released from rest at the positive plate. Determine (a) the potential difference between the plates, (b) the kinetic energy of the proton when it reaches the negative plate, (c) the speed of the proton just before it strikes the negative plate, (d) the acceleration of the proton, and (e) the force on the proton. (f) From the force, find the magnitude of the electric field and show that it is equal to the electric field found from the charge densities on the plates.

61. A Geiger tube is a radiation detector that essentially consists of a closed, hollow metal cylinder (the cathode) of inner radius r_a and a coaxial cylindrical wire (the anode) of radius r_b (Fig. P25.61). The charge per unit length on the anode is λ, while the charge per unit length on the cathode is $-\lambda$. A gas fills the space between the electrodes. When a high-energy elementary particle passes through this space, it can ionize an atom of the gas. The strong electric field makes the resulting ion and electron accelerate in opposite directions. They strike other molecules of the gas to ionize them, producing an avalanche of electrical discharge. The pulse of electric current between the wire and the cylinder is counted by an external circuit. (a) Show that the magnitude of the potential difference between the wire and the cylinder is

$$\Delta V = 2k_e \lambda \ln\left(\frac{r_a}{r_b}\right)$$

(b) Show that the magnitude of the electric field in the space between cathode and anode is given by

$$E = \frac{\Delta V}{\ln(r_a/r_b)}\left(\frac{1}{r}\right)$$

where r is the distance from the axis of the anode to the point where the field is to be calculated.

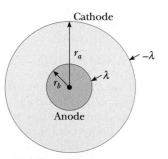

Figure P25.61 Problems 61 and 62.

62. The results of Problem 61 apply also to an electrostatic precipitator (Figures 25.30 and P25.61). An applied voltage $\Delta V = V_a - V_b = 50.0\ \text{kV}$ is to produce an electric field of magnitude 5.50 MV/m at the surface of the central wire. Assume the outer cylindrical wall has uniform radius $r_a = 0.850$ m. (a) What should be the radius r_b of the central wire? You will need to solve a transcendental equation. (b) What is the magnitude of the electric field at the outer wall?

63. From Gauss's law, the electric field set up by a uniform line of charge is

$$\mathbf{E} = \left(\frac{\lambda}{2\pi\epsilon_0 r}\right)\hat{\mathbf{r}}$$

where $\hat{\mathbf{r}}$ is a unit vector pointing radially away from the line and λ is the linear charge density along the line. Derive an expression for the potential difference between $r = r_1$ and $r = r_2$.

64. Four balls, each with mass m, are connected by four nonconducting strings to form a square with side a, as shown in Figure P25.64. The assembly is placed on a horizontal nonconducting frictionless surface. Balls 1 and 2 each have charge q, and balls 3 and 4 are uncharged. Find the maximum speed of balls 3 and 4 after the string connecting balls 1 and 2 is cut.

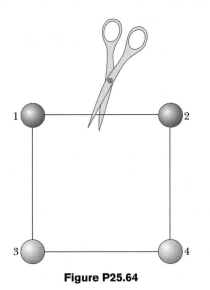

Figure P25.64

65. A point charge q is located at $x = -R$, and a point charge $-2q$ is located at the origin. Prove that the equipotential surface that has zero potential is a sphere centered at $(-4R/3, 0, 0)$ and having a radius $r = 2R/3$.

66. Consider two thin, conducting, spherical shells as shown in Figure P25.66. The inner shell has a radius $r_1 = 15.0$ cm and a charge of 10.0 nC. The outer shell has a radius $r_2 = 30.0$ cm and a charge of -15.0 nC. Find (a) the electric field $\mathbf{E}$ and (b) the electric potential V in regions A, B, and C, with $V = 0$ at $r = \infty$.

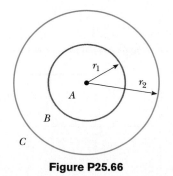

Figure P25.66

67. The x axis is the symmetry axis of a stationary uniformly charged ring of radius R and charge Q (Fig. P25.67).

A point charge Q of mass M is located initially at the center of the ring. When it is displaced slightly, the point charge accelerates along the x axis to infinity. Show that the ultimate speed of the point charge is

$$v = \left(\frac{2k_e Q^2}{MR}\right)^{1/2}$$

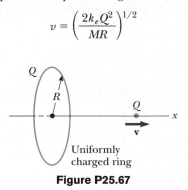

Figure P25.67

68. The thin, uniformly charged rod shown in Figure P25.68 has a linear charge density λ. Find an expression for the electric potential at P.

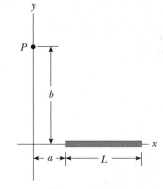

Figure P25.68

69. An electric dipole is located along the y axis as shown in Figure P25.69. The magnitude of its electric dipole moment is defined as $p = 2qa$. (a) At a point P, which is far from the dipole $(r \gg a)$, show that the electric potential is

$$V = \frac{k_e p \cos\theta}{r^2}$$

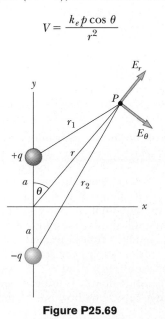

Figure P25.69

(b) Calculate the radial component E_r and the perpendicular component E_θ of the associated electric field. Note that $E_\theta = -(1/r)(\partial V/\partial \theta)$. Do these results seem reasonable for $\theta = 90°$ and $0°$? for $r = 0$? (c) For the dipole arrangement shown, express V in terms of Cartesian coordinates using $r = (x^2 + y^2)^{1/2}$ and

$$\cos \theta = \frac{y}{(x^2 + y^2)^{1/2}}$$

Using these results and again taking $r \gg a$, calculate the field components E_x and E_y.

70. When an uncharged conducting sphere of radius a is placed at the origin of an xyz coordinate system that lies in an initially uniform electric field $\mathbf{E} = E_0\hat{\mathbf{k}}$, the resulting electric potential is $V(x, y, z) = V_0$ for points inside the sphere and

$$V(x,y,z) = V_0 - E_0 z + \frac{E_0 a^3 z}{(x^2 + y^2 + z^2)^{3/2}}$$

for points outside the sphere, where V_0 is the (constant) electric potential on the conductor. Use this equation to determine the x, y, and z components of the resulting electric field.

71. A disk of radius R (Fig. P25.71) has a nonuniform surface charge density $\sigma = Cr$, where C is a constant and r is measured from the center of the disk. Find (by direct integration) the potential at P.

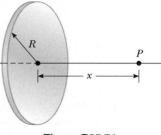

Figure P25.71

72. A solid sphere of radius R has a uniform charge density ρ and total charge Q. Derive an expression for its total electric potential energy. (*Suggestion:* imagine that the sphere is constructed by adding successive layers of concentric shells of charge $dq = (4\pi r^2 dr)\rho$ and use $dU = V dq$.)

73. Charge is uniformly distributed with a density of $100.0 \ \mu C/m^3$ throughout the volume of a cube 10.00 cm on each edge. (a) Find the electric potential at a distance of 5.000 cm from the center of one face of the cube, measured along a perpendicular to the face. Determine the potential to four significant digits. Use a numerical method that divides the cube into a sufficient number of smaller cubes, treated as point charges. Symmetry considerations will reduce the number of actual calculations. (b) **What If?** If the charge on the cube is redistributed into a uniform sphere of charge with the same center, by how much does the potential change?

Answers to Quick Quizzes

25.1 (b). When moving straight from A to B, $\mathbf{E}$ and $d\mathbf{s}$ both point toward the right. Thus, the dot product $\mathbf{E} \cdot d\mathbf{s}$ in Equation 25.3 is positive and ΔV is negative.

25.2 (a). From Equation 25.3, $\Delta U = q_0 \Delta V$, so if a negative test charge is moved through a negative potential difference, the potential energy is positive. Work must be done to move the charge in the direction opposite to the electric force on it.

25.3 $B \rightarrow C$, $C \rightarrow D$, $A \rightarrow B$, $D \rightarrow E$. Moving from B to C decreases the electric potential by 2 V, so the electric field performs 2 J of work on each coulomb of positive charge that moves. Moving from C to D decreases the electric potential by 1 V, so 1 J of work is done by the field. It takes no work to move the charge from A to B because the electric potential does not change. Moving from D to E increases the electric potential by 1 V, and thus the field does -1 J of work per unit of positive charge that moves.

25.4 (f). The electric field points in the direction of decreasing electric potential.

25.5 (b) and (f). The electric potential is inversely proportion to the radius (see Eq. 25.11). Because the same number of field lines passes through a closed surface of any shape or size, the electric flux through the surface remains constant.

25.6 (c). The potential is established only by the source charge and is independent of the test charge.

25.7 (a). The potential energy of the two-charge system is initially negative, due to the products of charges of opposite sign in Equation 25.13. When the sign of q_2 is changed, both charges are negative, and the potential energy of the system is positive.

25.8 (a). If the potential is constant (zero in this case), its derivative along this direction is zero.

25.9 (b). If the electric field is zero, there is no change in the electric potential and it must be constant. This constant value *could be* zero but does not *have to be* zero.

25.10 The graph would look like the sketch below. Notice the flat plateaus at each conductor, representing the constant electric potential inside a conductor.

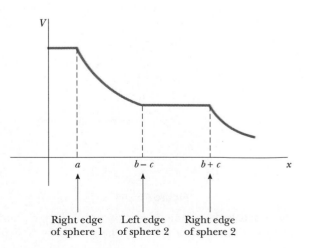

Chapter 26

Capacitance and Dielectrics

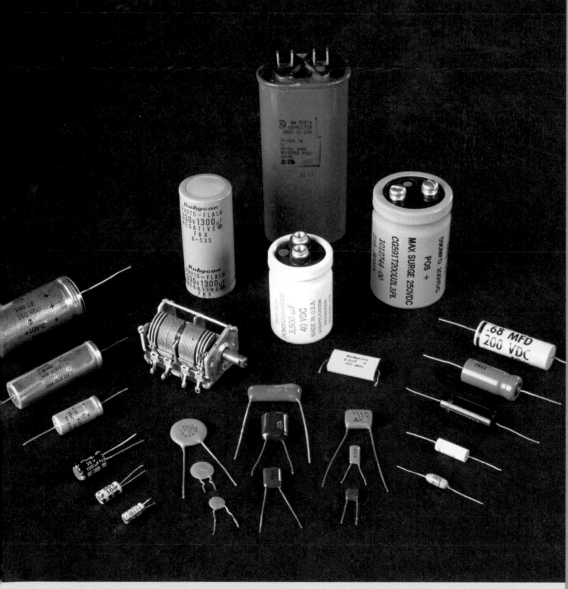

▲ *All of these devices are capacitors, which store electric charge and energy. A capacitor is one type of circuit element that we can combine with others to make electric circuits. (Paul Silverman/Fundamental Photographs)*

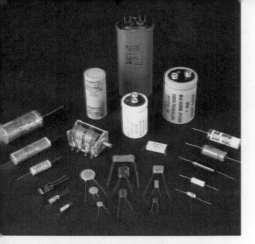

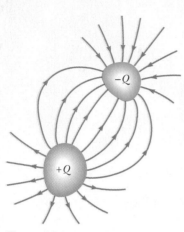

Figure 26.1 A capacitor consists of two conductors. When the capacitor is charged, the conductors carry charges of equal magnitude and opposite sign.

Definition of capacitance

In this chapter, we will introduce the first of three simple *circuit elements* that can be connected with wires to form an electric circuit. Electric circuits are the basis for the vast majority of the devices that we use in current society. We shall discuss *capacitors*—devices that store electric charge. This discussion will be followed by the study of *resistors* in Chapter 27 and *inductors* in Chapter 32. In later chapters, we will study more sophisticated circuit elements such as *diodes* and *transistors*.

Capacitors are commonly used in a variety of electric circuits. For instance, they are used to tune the frequency of radio receivers, as filters in power supplies, to eliminate sparking in automobile ignition systems, and as energy-storing devices in electronic flash units.

A capacitor consists of two conductors separated by an insulator. The capacitance of a given capacitor depends on its geometry and on the material—called a *dielectric*—that separates the conductors.

26.1 Definition of Capacitance

Consider two conductors carrying charges of equal magnitude and opposite sign, as shown in Figure 26.1. Such a combination of two conductors is called a **capacitor.** The conductors are called *plates*. A potential difference ΔV exists between the conductors due to the presence of the charges.

What determines how much charge is on the plates of a capacitor for a given voltage? Experiments show that the quantity of charge Q on a capacitor[1] is linearly proportional to the potential difference between the conductors; that is, $Q \propto \Delta V$. The proportionality constant depends on the shape and separation of the conductors.[2] We can write this relationship as $Q = C\,\Delta V$ if we define capacitance as follows:

The **capacitance** C of a capacitor is defined as the ratio of the magnitude of the charge on either conductor to the magnitude of the potential difference between the conductors:

$$C \equiv \frac{Q}{\Delta V} \qquad (26.1)$$

[1] Although the total charge on the capacitor is zero (because there is as much excess positive charge on one conductor as there is excess negative charge on the other), it is common practice to refer to the magnitude of the charge on either conductor as "the charge on the capacitor."

[2] The proportionality between ΔV and Q can be proved from Coulomb's law or by experiment.

Note that by definition *capacitance is always a positive quantity.* Furthermore, the charge Q and the potential difference ΔV are always expressed in Equation 26.1 as positive quantities. Because the potential difference increases linearly with the stored charge, the ratio $Q/\Delta V$ is constant for a given capacitor. Therefore, capacitance is a measure of a capacitor's ability to store charge. Because positive and negative charges are separated in the system of two conductors in a capacitor, there is electric potential energy stored in the system.

From Equation 26.1, we see that capacitance has SI units of coulombs per volt. The SI unit of capacitance is the **farad** (F), which was named in honor of Michael Faraday:

$$1 \text{ F} = 1 \text{ C/V}$$

The farad is a very large unit of capacitance. In practice, typical devices have capacitances ranging from microfarads (10^{-6} F) to picofarads (10^{-12} F). We shall use the symbol μF to represent microfarads. To avoid the use of Greek letters, in practice, physical capacitors often are labeled "mF" for microfarads and "mmF" for micromicrofarads or, equivalently, "pF" for picofarads.

Let us consider a capacitor formed from a pair of parallel plates, as shown in Figure 26.2. Each plate is connected to one terminal of a battery, which acts as a source of potential difference. If the capacitor is initially uncharged, the battery establishes an electric field in the connecting wires when the connections are made. Let us focus on the plate connected to the negative terminal of the battery. The electric field applies a force on electrons in the wire just outside this plate; this force causes the electrons to move onto the plate. This movement continues until the plate, the wire, and the terminal are all at the same electric potential. Once this equilibrium point is attained, a potential difference no longer exists between the terminal and the plate, and as a result no electric field is present in the wire, and the movement of electrons stops. The plate now carries a negative charge. A similar process occurs at the other capacitor plate, with electrons moving from the plate to the wire, leaving the plate positively charged. In this final configuration, the potential difference across the capacitor plates is the same as that between the terminals of the battery.

Suppose that we have a capacitor rated at 4 pF. This rating means that the capacitor can store 4 pC of charge for each volt of potential difference between the two conductors. If a 9-V battery is connected across this capacitor, one of the conductors ends up with a net charge of -36 pC and the other ends up with a net charge of $+36$ pC.

Quick Quiz 26.1 A capacitor stores charge Q at a potential difference ΔV. If the voltage applied by a battery to the capacitor is doubled to $2\,\Delta V$, (a) the capacitance falls to half its initial value and the charge remains the same (b) the capacitance and the charge both fall to half their initial values (c) the capacitance and the charge both double (d) the capacitance remains the same and the charge doubles.

26.2 Calculating Capacitance

We can derive an expression for the capacitance of a pair of oppositely charged conductors in the following manner: assume a charge of magnitude Q, and calculate the potential difference using the techniques described in the preceding chapter. We then use the expression $C = Q/\Delta V$ to evaluate the capacitance. As we might expect, we can perform this calculation relatively easily if the geometry of the capacitor is simple.

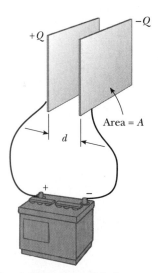

Figure 26.2 A parallel-plate capacitor consists of two parallel conducting plates, each of area A, separated by a distance d. When the capacitor is charged by connecting the plates to the terminals of a battery, the plates carry equal amounts of charge. One plate carries positive charge, and the other carries negative charge.

While the most common situation is that of two conductors, a single conductor also has a capacitance. For example, imagine a spherical charged conductor. The electric field lines around this conductor are exactly the same as if there were a conducting shell of infinite radius, concentric with the sphere and carrying a charge of the same magnitude but opposite sign. Thus, we can identify the imaginary shell as the second conductor of a two-conductor capacitor. We now calculate the capacitance for this situation. The electric potential of the sphere of radius R is simply $k_e Q/R$, and setting $V = 0$ for the infinitely large shell, we have

Capacitance of an isolated charged sphere

$$C = \frac{Q}{\Delta V} = \frac{Q}{k_e Q/R} = \frac{R}{k_e} = 4\pi\epsilon_0 R \qquad (26.2)$$

This expression shows that the capacitance of an isolated charged sphere is proportional to its radius and is independent of both the charge on the sphere and the potential difference.

The capacitance of a pair of conductors depends on the geometry of the conductors. Let us illustrate this with three familiar geometries, namely, parallel plates, concentric cylinders, and concentric spheres. In these examples, we assume that the charged conductors are separated by a vacuum. The effect of a dielectric material placed between the conductors is treated in Section 26.5.

Parallel-Plate Capacitors

Two parallel metallic plates of equal area A are separated by a distance d, as shown in Figure 26.2. One plate carries a charge Q, and the other carries a charge $-Q$. Let us consider how the geometry of these conductors influences the capacity of the combination to store charge. Recall that charges of the same sign repel one another. As a capacitor is being charged by a battery, electrons flow into the negative plate and out of the positive plate. If the capacitor plates are large, the accumulated charges are able to distribute themselves over a substantial area, and the amount of charge that can be stored on a plate for a given potential difference increases as the plate area is increased. Thus, we expect the capacitance to be proportional to the plate area A.

Now let us consider the region that separates the plates. If the battery has a constant potential difference between its terminals, then the electric field between the plates must increase as d is decreased. Let us imagine that we move the plates closer together and consider the situation before any charges have had a chance to move in response to this change. Because no charges have moved, the electric field between the plates has the same value but extends over a shorter distance. Thus, the magnitude of the potential difference between the plates $\Delta V = Ed$ (Eq. 25.6) is now smaller. The difference between this new capacitor voltage and the terminal voltage of the battery now exists as a potential difference across the wires connecting the battery to the capacitor. This potential difference results in the electric field in the wires that drives more charge onto the plates, increasing the potential difference between the plates. When the potential difference between the plates again matches that of the battery, the potential difference across the wires falls back to zero, and the flow of charge stops. Thus, moving the plates closer together causes the charge on the capacitor to increase. If d is increased, the charge decreases. As a result, we expect the capacitance of the pair of plates to be inversely proportional to d.

We can verify these physical arguments with the following derivation. The surface charge density on either plate is $\sigma = Q/A$. If the plates are very close together (in comparison with their length and width), we can assume that the electric field is uniform between the plates and is zero elsewhere. According to the **What If?** feature in Example 24.8, the value of the electric field between the plates is

$$E = \frac{\sigma}{\epsilon_0} = \frac{Q}{\epsilon_0 A}$$

Because the field between the plates is uniform, the magnitude of the potential difference between the plates equals Ed (see Eq. 25.6); therefore,

$$\Delta V = Ed = \frac{Qd}{\epsilon_0 A}$$

Substituting this result into Equation 26.1, we find that the capacitance is

$$C = \frac{Q}{\Delta V} = \frac{Q}{Qd/\epsilon_0 A}$$

$$C = \frac{\epsilon_0 A}{d} \qquad\qquad (26.3) \qquad \textbf{Capacitance of parallel plates}$$

That is, **the capacitance of a parallel-plate capacitor is proportional to the area of its plates and inversely proportional to the plate separation,** just as we expected from our conceptual argument.

A careful inspection of the electric field lines for a parallel-plate capacitor reveals that the field is uniform in the central region between the plates, as shown in Figure 26.3a. However, the field is nonuniform at the edges of the plates. Figure 26.3b is a photograph of the electric field pattern of a parallel-plate capacitor. Note the nonuniform nature of the electric field at the ends of the plates. Such end effects can be neglected if the plate separation is small compared with the length of the plates.

Figure 26.4 shows a battery connected to a single parallel-plate capacitor with a switch in the circuit. Let us identify the circuit as a system. When the switch is closed, the battery establishes an electric field in the wires and charges flow between the wires and the capacitor. As this occurs, there is a transformation of energy within the system. Before the switch is closed, energy is stored as chemical energy in the battery. This energy is transformed during the chemical reaction that occurs within the battery when it is operating in an electric circuit. When the switch is closed, some of the chemical energy in the battery is converted to electric potential energy related to the separation of positive and negative charges on the plates. As a result, we can describe a capacitor as a device that stores energy as well as charge. We will explore this energy storage in more detail in Section 26.4.

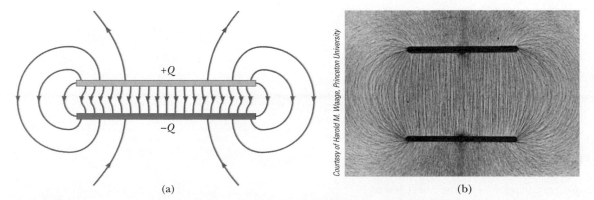

(a)   (b)

Figure 26.3 (a) The electric field between the plates of a parallel-plate capacitor is uniform near the center but nonuniform near the edges. (b) Electric field pattern of two oppositely charged conducting parallel plates. Small pieces of thread on an oil surface align with the electric field.

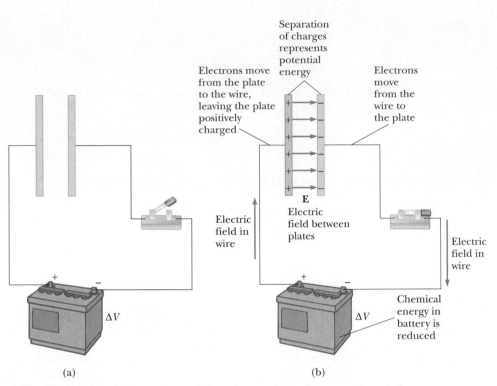

(a)

(b)

At the Active Figures link at http://www.pse6.com, you can adjust the battery voltage and see the resulting charge on the plates and the electric field between the plates.

Active Figure 26.4 (a) A circuit consisting of a capacitor, a battery, and a switch. (b) When the switch is closed, the battery establishes an electric field in the wire that causes electrons to move from the left plate into the wire and into the right plate from the wire. As a result, a separation of charge exists on the plates, which represents an increase in electric potential energy of the system of the circuit. This energy in the system has been transformed from chemical energy in the battery.

Quick Quiz 26.2 Many computer keyboard buttons are constructed of capacitors, as shown in Figure 26.5. When a key is pushed down, the soft insulator between the movable plate and the fixed plate is compressed. When the key is pressed, the capacitance (a) increases, (b) decreases, or (c) changes in a way that we cannot determine because the complicated electric circuit connected to the keyboard button may cause a change in ΔV.

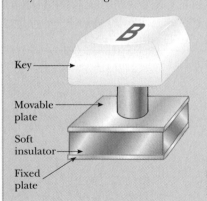

Figure 26.5 (Quick Quiz 26.2) One type of computer keyboard button.

Example 26.1 Parallel-Plate Capacitor

A parallel-plate capacitor with air between the plates has an area $A = 2.00 \times 10^{-4}$ m^2 and a plate separation $d = 1.00$ mm. Find its capacitance.

Solution From Equation 26.3, we find that

$$C = \frac{\epsilon_0 A}{d} = \frac{(8.85 \times 10^{-12} \text{ C}^2/\text{N} \cdot \text{m}^2)(2.00 \times 10^{-4} \text{ m}^2)}{1.00 \times 10^{-3} \text{ m}}$$

$$= 1.77 \times 10^{-12} \text{ F} = \boxed{1.77 \text{ pF}}$$

Cylindrical and Spherical Capacitors

From the definition of capacitance, we can, in principle, find the capacitance of any geometric arrangement of conductors. The following examples demonstrate the use of this definition to calculate the capacitance of the other familiar geometries that we mentioned: cylinders and spheres.

Example 26.2 The Cylindrical Capacitor

A solid cylindrical conductor of radius a and charge Q is coaxial with a cylindrical shell of negligible thickness, radius $b > a$, and charge $- Q$ (Fig. 26.6a). Find the capacitance of this cylindrical capacitor if its length is ℓ.

Solution It is difficult to apply physical arguments to this configuration, although we can reasonably expect the capacitance to be proportional to the cylinder length ℓ for the same reason that parallel-plate capacitance is proportional to plate area: stored charges have more room in which to be distributed. If we assume that ℓ is much greater than a and b, we can neglect end effects. In this case, the electric field is perpendicular to the long axis of the cylinders and is confined to the region between them (Fig. 26.6b). We must first calculate the potential difference between the two cylinders, which is given in general by

$$V_b - V_a = -\int_a^b \mathbf{E} \cdot d\mathbf{s}$$

where $\mathbf{E}$ is the electric field in the region between the cylinders. In Chapter 24, we showed using Gauss's law that the magnitude of the electric field of a cylindrical charge distribution having linear charge density λ is $E = 2k_e\lambda/r$ (Eq. 24.7). The same result applies here because, according to Gauss's law, the charge on the outer cylinder does not contribute to the electric field inside it. Using this result and noting from Figure 26.6b that $\mathbf{E}$ is along r, we find that

$$V_b - V_a = -\int_a^b E_r\, dr = -2k_e\lambda \int_a^b \frac{dr}{r} = -2k_e\lambda \ln\left(\frac{b}{a}\right)$$

Substituting this result into Equation 26.1 and using the fact that $\lambda = Q/\ell$, we obtain

$$C = \frac{Q}{\Delta V} = \frac{Q}{(2k_eQ/\ell)\ln(b/a)} = \boxed{\frac{\ell}{2k_e\ln(b/a)}} \quad (26.4)$$

where ΔV is the magnitude of the potential difference between the cylinders, given by $\Delta V = |V_a - V_b| = 2k_e\lambda\ln(b/a)$, a positive quantity. As predicted, the capacitance is proportional to the length of the cylinders. As we might expect, the capacitance also depends on the radii of the two cylindrical conductors. From Equation 26.4, we see that the capacitance per unit length of a combination of concentric cylindrical conductors is

$$\frac{C}{\ell} = \frac{1}{2k_e\ln(b/a)} \quad (26.5)$$

An example of this type of geometric arrangement is a *coaxial cable*, which consists of two concentric cylindrical conductors separated by an insulator. You are likely to have a coaxial cable attached to your television set or VCR if you are a subscriber to cable television. The cable carries electrical signals in the inner and outer conductors. Such a geometry is especially useful for shielding the signals from any possible external influences.

What If? Suppose $b = 2.00a$ for the cylindrical capacitor. We would like to increase the capacitance, and we can do so by choosing to increase ℓ by 10% or by increasing a by 10%. Which choice is more effective at increasing the capacitance?

Answer According to Equation 26.4, C is proportional to ℓ, so increasing ℓ by 10% results in a 10% increase in C. For the result of the change in a, let us first evaluate C for $b = 2.00a$:

$$C = \frac{\ell}{2k_e\ln(b/a)} = \frac{\ell}{2k_e\ln(2.00)} = \frac{\ell}{2k_e(0.693)}$$

$$= 0.721\,\frac{\ell}{k_e}$$

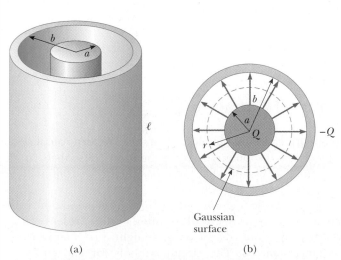

(a)   (b)

Figure 26.6 (Example 26.2) (a) A cylindrical capacitor consists of a solid cylindrical conductor of radius a and length ℓ surrounded by a coaxial cylindrical shell of radius b. (b) End view. The electric field lines are radial. The dashed line represents the end of the cylindrical gaussian surface of radius r and length ℓ.

Now, for a 10% increase in a, the new value is $a' = 1.10a$, so

$$C' = \frac{\ell}{2k_e \ln(b/a')} = \frac{\ell}{2k_e \ln(2.00a/1.10a)}$$

$$= \frac{\ell}{2k_e \ln(2.00/1.10)} = \frac{\ell}{2k_e(0.598)} = 0.836\,\frac{\ell}{k_e}$$

The ratio of the new and old capacitances is

$$\frac{C'}{C} = \frac{0.836\,\ell/k_e}{0.721\,\ell/k_e} = 1.16$$

corresponding to a 16% increase in capacitance. Thus, it is more effective to increase a than to increase ℓ.

Note two more extensions of this problem. First, the advantage goes to increasing a only for a range of relationships between a and b. It is a valuable exercise to show that if $b > 2.85a$, increasing ℓ by 10% is more effective than increasing a (Problem 77). Second, if we increase b, we *reduce* the capacitance, so we would need to decrease b to increase the capacitance. Increasing a and decreasing b both have the effect of bringing the plates closer together, which increases the capacitance.

Example 26.3 The Spherical Capacitor

A spherical capacitor consists of a spherical conducting shell of radius b and charge $-Q$ concentric with a smaller conducting sphere of radius a and charge Q (Fig. 26.7). Find the capacitance of this device.

Solution As we showed in Chapter 24, the field outside a spherically symmetric charge distribution is radial and given by the expression k_eQ/r^2. In this case, this result applies to the field *between* the spheres ($a < r < b$). From Gauss's law we see that only the inner sphere contributes to this field. Thus, the potential difference between the spheres is

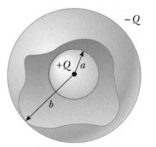

Figure 26.7 (Example 26.3) A spherical capacitor consists of an inner sphere of radius a surrounded by a concentric spherical shell of radius b. The electric field between the spheres is directed radially outward when the inner sphere is positively charged.

$$V_b - V_a = -\int_a^b E_r\,dr = -k_eQ\int_a^b \frac{dr}{r^2} = k_eQ\left[\frac{1}{r}\right]_a^b$$

$$= k_eQ\left(\frac{1}{b} - \frac{1}{a}\right)$$

The magnitude of the potential difference is

$$\Delta V = |V_b - V_a| = k_eQ\,\frac{(b-a)}{ab}$$

Substituting this value for ΔV into Equation 26.1, we obtain

$$C = \frac{Q}{\Delta V} = \frac{ab}{k_e(b-a)} \qquad (26.6)$$

What If? What if the radius b of the outer sphere approaches infinity? What does the capacitance become?

Answer In Equation 26.6, we let $b \to \infty$:

$$C = \lim_{b\to\infty}\frac{ab}{k_e(b-a)} = \frac{ab}{k_e(b)} = \frac{a}{k_e} = 4\pi\epsilon_0 a$$

Note that this is the same expression as Equation 26.2, the capacitance of an isolated spherical conductor.

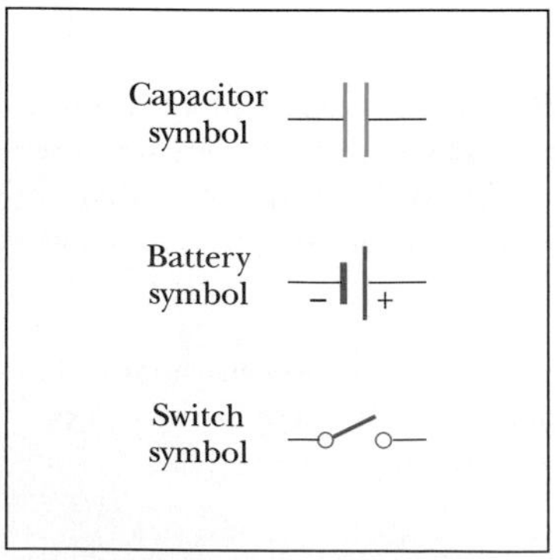

26.3 Combinations of Capacitors

Two or more capacitors often are combined in electric circuits. We can calculate the equivalent capacitance of certain combinations using methods described in this section. Throughout this section, we assume that the capacitors to be combined are initially uncharged.

In studying electric circuits, we use a simplified pictorial representation called a **circuit diagram.** Such a diagram uses **circuit symbols** to represent various circuit elements. The circuit symbols are connected by straight lines that represent the wires between the circuit elements. The circuit symbols for capacitors and batteries, as well as the color codes used for them in this text, are given in Figure 26.8. The symbol for the capacitor reflects the geometry of the most common model for a capacitor—a pair of parallel plates. The positive terminal of the battery is at the higher potential and is represented in the circuit symbol by the longer line.

Capacitor symbol

Battery symbol

Switch symbol

Figure 26.8 Circuit symbols for capacitors, batteries, and switches. Note that capacitors are in blue and batteries and switches are in red.

Parallel Combination

Two capacitors connected as shown in Figure 26.9a are known as a *parallel combination* of capacitors. Figure 26.9b shows a circuit diagram for this combination of capacitors. The left plates of the capacitors are connected by a conducting wire to the positive terminal of the battery and are therefore both at the same electric potential as the positive terminal. Likewise, the right plates are connected to the negative terminal and are therefore both at the same potential as the negative terminal. Thus, **the individual potential differences across capacitors connected in parallel are the same and are equal to the potential difference applied across the combination.**

In a circuit such as that shown in Figure 26.9, the voltage applied across the combination is the terminal voltage of the battery. Situations can occur in which the parallel combination is in a circuit with other circuit elements; in such situations, we must determine the potential difference across the combination by analyzing the entire circuit.

When the capacitors are first connected in the circuit shown in Figure 26.9, electrons are transferred between the wires and the plates; this transfer leaves the left plates positively charged and the right plates negatively charged. The flow of charge ceases when the voltage across the capacitors is equal to that across the battery terminals. The capacitors reach their maximum charge when the flow of charge ceases. Let us call the maximum charges on the two capacitors Q_1 and Q_2. The *total charge Q* stored by the two capacitors is

$$Q = Q_1 + Q_2 \tag{26.7}$$

That is, **the total charge on capacitors connected in parallel is the sum of the charges on the individual capacitors.** Because the voltages across the capacitors are the same, the charges that they carry are

$$Q_1 = C_1 \, \Delta V \qquad Q_2 = C_2 \, \Delta V$$

Suppose that we wish to replace these two capacitors by one *equivalent capacitor* having a capacitance C_{eq}, as in Figure 26.9c. The effect this equivalent capacitor has on the circuit must be exactly the same as the effect of the combination of the two

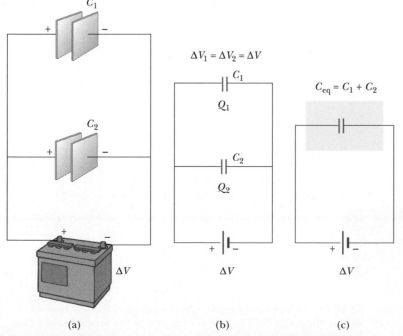

(a)   (b)   (c)

Active Figure 26.9 (a) A parallel combination of two capacitors in an electric circuit in which the potential difference across the battery terminals is ΔV. (b) The circuit diagram for the parallel combination. (c) The equivalent capacitance is $C_{eq} = C_1 + C_2$.

At the Active Figures link at http://www.pse6.com, you can adjust the battery voltage and the individual capacitances to see the resulting charges and voltages on the capacitors. You can combine up to four capacitors in parallel.

individual capacitors. That is, the equivalent capacitor must store Q units of charge when connected to the battery. We can see from Figure 26.9c that the voltage across the equivalent capacitor also is ΔV because the equivalent capacitor is connected directly across the battery terminals. Thus, for the equivalent capacitor,

$$Q = C_{eq} \Delta V$$

Substituting these three relationships for charge into Equation 26.7, we have

$$C_{eq} \Delta V = C_1 \Delta V + C_2 \Delta V$$

$$C_{eq} = C_1 + C_2 \qquad \text{(parallel combination)}$$

If we extend this treatment to three or more capacitors connected in parallel, we find the equivalent capacitance to be

Capacitors in parallel

$$C_{eq} = C_1 + C_2 + C_3 + \cdots \qquad \text{(parallel combination)} \qquad (26.8)$$

Thus, **the equivalent capacitance of a parallel combination of capacitors is the algebraic sum of the individual capacitances and is greater than any of the individual capacitances.** This makes sense because we are essentially combining the areas of all the capacitor plates when we connect them with conducting wire, and capacitance of parallel plates is proportional to area (Eq. 26.3).

Series Combination

Two capacitors connected as shown in Figure 26.10a and the equivalent circuit diagram in Figure 26.10b are known as a *series combination* of capacitors. The left plate of capacitor 1 and the right plate of capacitor 2 are connected to the terminals of a battery. The other two plates are connected to each other and to nothing else; hence, they form an isolated conductor that is initially uncharged and must continue to have zero net charge. To analyze this combination, let us begin by considering the uncharged capacitors and follow what happens just after a battery is connected to the circuit. When the battery is connected, electrons are transferred out of the left plate of C_1 and into the right plate of C_2. As this negative charge accumulates on the right plate of C_2, an equivalent amount of negative charge is forced off the left plate of C_2, and this left plate therefore has an excess positive charge. The negative charge leaving

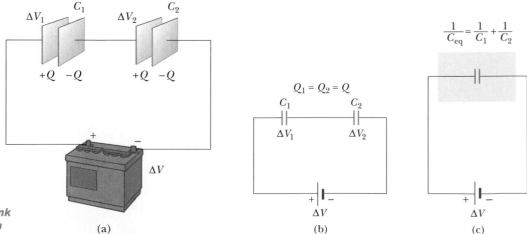

At the Active Figures link at http://www.pse6.com, you can adjust the battery voltage and the individual capacitances to see the resulting charges and voltages on the capacitors. You can combine up to four capacitors in series.

Active Figure 26.10 (a) A series combination of two capacitors. The charges on the two capacitors are the same. (b) The circuit diagram for the series combination. (c) The equivalent capacitance can be calculated from the relationship
$$\frac{1}{C_{eq}} = \frac{1}{C_1} + \frac{1}{C_2}.$$

the left plate of C_2 causes negative charges to accumulate on the right plate of C_1. As a result, all the right plates end up with a charge $- Q$, and all the left plates end up with a charge $+ Q$. Thus, **the charges on capacitors connected in series are the same.**

From Figure 26.10a, we see that the voltage ΔV across the battery terminals is split between the two capacitors:

$$\Delta V = \Delta V_1 + \Delta V_2 \qquad (26.9)$$

where ΔV_1 and ΔV_2 are the potential differences across capacitors C_1 and C_2, respectively. In general, **the total potential difference across any number of capacitors connected in series is the sum of the potential differences across the individual capacitors.**

Suppose that the equivalent single capacitor in Figure 26.10c has the same effect on the circuit as the series combination when it is connected to the battery. After it is fully charged, the equivalent capacitor must have a charge of $- Q$ on its right plate and a charge of $+ Q$ on its left plate. Applying the definition of capacitance to the circuit in Figure 26.10c, we have

$$\Delta V = \frac{Q}{C_{eq}}$$

Because we can apply the expression $Q = C \Delta V$ to each capacitor shown in Figure 26.10b, the potential differences across them are

$$\Delta V_1 = \frac{Q}{C_1} \qquad \Delta V_2 = \frac{Q}{C_2}$$

Substituting these expressions into Equation 26.9, we have

$$\frac{Q}{C_{eq}} = \frac{Q}{C_1} + \frac{Q}{C_2}$$

Canceling Q, we arrive at the relationship

$$\frac{1}{C_{eq}} = \frac{1}{C_1} + \frac{1}{C_2} \qquad \text{(series combination)}$$

When this analysis is applied to three or more capacitors connected in series, the relationship for the equivalent capacitance is

$$\frac{1}{C_{eq}} = \frac{1}{C_1} + \frac{1}{C_2} + \frac{1}{C_3} + \cdots \qquad \text{(series combination)} \qquad (26.10) \qquad \textbf{Capacitors in series}$$

This shows that **the inverse of the equivalent capacitance is the algebraic sum of the inverses of the individual capacitances and the equivalent capacitance of a series combination is always less than any individual capacitance in the combination.**

Quick Quiz 26.3 Two capacitors are identical. They can be connected in series or in parallel. If you want the *smallest* equivalent capacitance for the combination, do you connect them in (a) series, in (b) parallel, or (c) do the combinations have the same capacitance?

Quick Quiz 26.4 Consider the two capacitors in Quick Quiz 26.3 again. Each capacitor is charged to a voltage of 10 V. If you want the largest combined potential difference across the combination, do you connect them in (a) series, in (b) parallel, or (c) do the combinations have the same potential difference?

PROBLEM-SOLVING HINTS

Capacitors

- Be careful with units. When you calculate capacitance in farads, make sure that distances are expressed in meters. When checking consistency of units, remember that the unit for electric fields can be either N/C or V/m.

- When two or more capacitors are connected in parallel, the potential difference across each is the same. The charge on each capacitor is proportional to its capacitance; hence, the capacitances can be added directly to give the equivalent capacitance of the parallel combination. The equivalent capacitance is always larger than the individual capacitances.

- When two or more capacitors are connected in series, they carry the same charge, and the sum of the potential differences equals the total potential difference applied to the combination. The sum of the reciprocals of the capacitances equals the reciprocal of the equivalent capacitance, which is always less than the capacitance of the smallest individual capacitor.

Example 26.4 Equivalent Capacitance
Interactive

Find the equivalent capacitance between *a* and *b* for the combination of capacitors shown in Figure 26.11a. All capacitances are in microfarads.

Solution Using Equations 26.8 and 26.10, we reduce the combination step by step as indicated in the figure. The 1.0-μF and 3.0-μF capacitors are in parallel and combine according to the expression $C_{eq} = C_1 + C_2 = 4.0\ \mu$F. The 2.0-$\mu$F and 6.0-$\mu$F capacitors also are in parallel and have an equivalent capacitance of 8.0 μF. Thus, the upper branch in Figure 26.11b consists of two 4.0-μF capacitors in series, which combine as follows:

$$\frac{1}{C_{eq}} = \frac{1}{C_1} + \frac{1}{C_2} = \frac{1}{4.0\ \mu F} + \frac{1}{4.0\ \mu F} = \frac{1}{2.0\ \mu F}$$

$$C_{eq} = 2.0\ \mu F$$

The lower branch in Figure 26.11b consists of two 8.0-μF capacitors in series, which combine to yield an equivalent capacitance of 4.0 μF. Finally, the 2.0-μF and 4.0-μF capacitors in Figure 26.11c are in parallel and thus have an

equivalent capacitance of   6.0 μF.

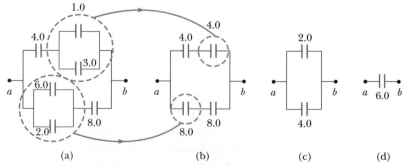

(a)   (b)   (c)   (d)

Figure 26.11 (Example 26.4) To find the equivalent capacitance of the capacitors in part (a), we reduce the various combinations in steps as indicated in parts (b), (c), and (d), using the series and parallel rules described in the text.

Practice reducing a combination of capacitors to a single equivalent capacitance at the Interactive Worked Example link at http://www.pse6.com.

26.4   Energy Stored in a Charged Capacitor

Almost everyone who works with electronic equipment has at some time verified that a capacitor can store energy. If the plates of a charged capacitor are connected by a conductor, such as a wire, charge moves between each plate and its connecting wire until the capacitor is uncharged. The discharge can often be observed as a visible spark. If you should accidentally touch the opposite plates of a charged capacitor, your fingers act as a pathway for discharge, and the result is an electric shock. The degree of shock you receive depends on the capacitance and on the voltage applied to the capacitor. Such a shock could be fatal if high voltages are present, such as in the power supply of a television set. Because the charges can be stored in a capacitor even when the set is turned off, unplugging the television does not make it safe to open the case and touch the components inside.

To calculate the energy stored in the capacitor, we shall assume a charging process that is different from the actual process described in Section 26.1 but which gives the same final result. We can make this assumption because the energy in the final configuration does not depend on the actual charge-transfer process. We imagine that the charge is transferred mechanically through the space between the plates. We reach in and grab a small amount of positive charge on the plate connected to the negative terminal and apply a force that causes this positive charge to move over to the plate connected to the positive terminal. Thus, we do work on the charge as we transfer it from one plate to the other. At first, no work is required to transfer a small amount of charge dq from one plate to the other.[3] However, once this charge has been transferred, a small potential difference exists between the plates. Therefore, work must be done to move additional charge through this potential difference. As more and more charge is transferred from one plate to the other, the potential difference increases in proportion, and more work is required.

Suppose that q is the charge on the capacitor at some instant during the charging process. At the same instant, the potential difference across the capacitor is $\Delta V = q/C$. From Section 25.2, we know that the work necessary to transfer an increment of charge dq from the plate carrying charge $-q$ to the plate carrying charge q (which is at the higher electric potential) is

$$dW = \Delta V\, dq = \frac{q}{C}\, dq$$

This is illustrated in Figure 26.12. The total work required to charge the capacitor from $q = 0$ to some final charge $q = Q$ is

$$W = \int_0^Q \frac{q}{C}\, dq = \frac{1}{C} \int_0^Q q\, dq = \frac{Q^2}{2C}$$

The work done in charging the capacitor appears as electric potential energy U stored in the capacitor. Using Equation 26.1, we can express the potential energy stored in a charged capacitor in the following forms:

$$U = \frac{Q^2}{2C} = \tfrac{1}{2}Q\,\Delta V = \tfrac{1}{2}C(\Delta V)^2 \qquad (26.11)$$

Energy stored in a charged capacitor

This result applies to any capacitor, regardless of its geometry. We see that for a given capacitance, the stored energy increases as the charge increases and as the potential difference increases. In practice, there is a limit to the maximum energy (or charge) that can be stored because, at a sufficiently great value of ΔV, discharge ultimately occurs between the plates. For this reason, capacitors are usually labeled with a maximum operating voltage.

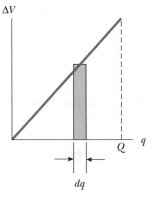

Figure 26.12 A plot of potential difference versus charge for a capacitor is a straight line having a slope $1/C$. The work required to move charge dq through the potential difference ΔV existing at the time across the capacitor plates is given approximately by the area of the shaded rectangle. The total work required to charge the capacitor to a final charge Q is the triangular area under the straight line, $W = \tfrac{1}{2}Q\Delta V$. (Don't forget that $1\ \text{V} = \text{J}/\text{C}$; hence, the unit for the triangular area is the joule.)

---

[3]   We shall use lowercase q for the time-varying charge on the capacitor while it is charging, to distinguish it from uppercase Q, which is the total charge on the capacitor after it is completely charged.

We can consider the energy stored in a capacitor as being stored in the electric field created between the plates as the capacitor is charged. This description is reasonable because the electric field is proportional to the charge on the capacitor. For a parallel-plate capacitor, the potential difference is related to the electric field through the relationship $\Delta V = Ed$. Furthermore, its capacitance is $C = \epsilon_0 A/d$ (Eq. 26.3). Substituting these expressions into Equation 26.11, we obtain

$$U = \tfrac{1}{2}\frac{\epsilon_0 A}{d}(E^2 d^2) = \tfrac{1}{2}(\epsilon_0 Ad)E^2 \tag{26.12}$$

Because the volume occupied by the electric field is Ad, the *energy per unit volume* $u_E = U/Ad$, known as the *energy density*, is

Energy density in an electric field

$$u_E = \tfrac{1}{2}\epsilon_0 E^2 \tag{26.13}$$

Although Equation 26.13 was derived for a parallel-plate capacitor, the expression is generally valid, regardless of the source of the electric field. That is, **the energy density in any electric field is proportional to the square of the magnitude of the electric field at a given point.**

![triangle] **PITFALL PREVENTION**

26.4 Not a New Kind of Energy

The energy given by Equation 26.13 is not a new kind of energy. It is familiar electric potential energy associated with a system of separated source charges. Equation 26.13 provides a new *interpretation*, or a new way of *modeling* the energy, as energy associated with the electric field, regardless of the source of the field.

Quick Quiz 26.5 You have three capacitors and a battery. In which of the following combinations of the three capacitors will the maximum possible energy be stored when the combination is attached to the battery? (a) series (b) parallel (c) Both combinations will store the same amount of energy.

Quick Quiz 26.6 You charge a parallel-plate capacitor, remove it from the battery, and prevent the wires connected to the plates from touching each other. When you pull the plates apart to a larger separation, do the following quantities increase, decrease, or stay the same? (a) C; (b) Q; (c) E between the plates; (d) ΔV; (e) energy stored in the capacitor.

Quick Quiz 26.7 Repeat Quick Quiz 26.6, but this time answer the questions for the situation in which the battery remains connected to the capacitor while you pull the plates apart.

Example 26.5 Rewiring Two Charged Capacitors   `Interactive`

Two capacitors C_1 and C_2 (where $C_1 > C_2$) are charged to the same initial potential difference ΔV_i. The charged capacitors are removed from the battery, and their plates are connected with opposite polarity as in Figure 26.13a. The switches S_1 and S_2 are then closed, as in Figure 26.13b.

(A) Find the final potential difference ΔV_f between a and b after the switches are closed.

Solution Figure 26.13 helps us conceptualize the initial and final configurations of the system. In Figure 26.13b, it might appear as if the capacitors are connected in parallel, but there is no battery in this circuit that is applying a voltage across the combination. Thus, we *cannot* categorize this as a problem in which capacitors are connected in parallel. We *can* categorize this as a problem involving an isolated system for electric charge—the left-hand plates of the capac-

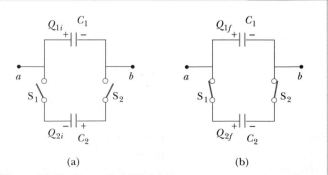

Figure 26.13 (Example 26.5) (a) Two capacitors are charged to the same initial potential difference and connected together with plates of opposite sign to be in contact when the switches are closed. (b) When the switches are closed, the charges redistribute.

itors form an isolated system because they are not connected to the right-hand plates by conductors. To analyze the problem, note that the charges on the left-hand plates before the switches are closed are

$$Q_{1i} = C_1 \Delta V_i \quad \text{and} \quad Q_{2i} = -C_2 \Delta V_i$$

The negative sign for Q_{2i} is necessary because the charge on the left plate of capacitor C_2 is negative. The total charge Q in the system is

$$(1) \qquad Q = Q_{1i} + Q_{2i} = (C_1 - C_2)\Delta V_i$$

After the switches are closed, the total charge Q in the system remains the same but the charges on the individual capacitors change to new values Q_{1f} and Q_{2f}. Because the system is isolated,

$$(2) \qquad Q = Q_{1f} + Q_{2f}$$

The charges redistribute until the potential difference is the same across both capacitors, ΔV_f. To satisfy this requirement, the charges on the capacitors after the switches are closed are

$$Q_{1f} = C_1 \Delta V_f \quad \text{and} \quad Q_{2f} = C_2 \Delta V_f$$

Dividing the first equation by the second, we have

$$(3) \qquad Q_{1f} = \frac{C_1}{C_2} Q_{2f}$$

Combining Equations (2) and (3), we obtain

$$Q = Q_{1f} + Q_{2f} = \frac{C_1}{C_2} Q_{2f} + Q_{2f} = Q_{2f}\left(1 + \frac{C_1}{C_2}\right)$$

$$(4) \qquad Q_{2f} = Q\left(\frac{C_2}{C_1 + C_2}\right)$$

Using Equations (3) and (4) to find Q_{1f} in terms of Q, we have

$$(5) \qquad Q_{1f} = \frac{C_1}{C_2} Q_{2f} = \frac{C_1}{C_2} Q\left(\frac{C_2}{C_1 + C_2}\right)$$

$$= Q\left(\frac{C_1}{C_1 + C_2}\right)$$

Finally, using Equation 26.1 to find the voltage across each capacitor, we find that

$$(6) \qquad \Delta V_{1f} = \frac{Q_{1f}}{C_1} = \frac{Q[C_1/(C_1 + C_2)]}{C_1} = \frac{Q}{C_1 + C_2}$$

$$(7) \qquad \Delta V_{2f} = \frac{Q_{2f}}{C_2} = \frac{Q[C_2/(C_1 + C_2)]}{C_2} = \frac{Q}{C_1 + C_2}$$

As noted earlier, $\Delta V_{1f} = \Delta V_{2f} = \Delta V_f$.

To express ΔV_f in terms of the given quantities C_1, C_2, and ΔV_i, we substitute the value of Q from Equation (1) into either Equation (6) or (7) to obtain

$$\Delta V_f = \left(\frac{C_1 - C_2}{C_1 + C_2}\right)\Delta V_i$$

(B) Find the total energy stored in the capacitors before and after the switches are closed and the ratio of the final energy to the initial energy.

Solution Before the switches are closed, the total energy stored in the capacitors is

$$U_i = \tfrac{1}{2}C_1(\Delta V_i)^2 + \tfrac{1}{2}C_2(\Delta V_i)^2 = \tfrac{1}{2}(C_1 + C_2)(\Delta V_i)^2$$

After the switches are closed, the total energy stored in the capacitors is

$$U_f = \tfrac{1}{2}C_1(\Delta V_f)^2 + \tfrac{1}{2}C_2(\Delta V_f)^2 = \tfrac{1}{2}(C_1 + C_2)(\Delta V_f)^2$$

Using the results of part (A), we can express this as

$$U_f = \frac{1}{2}\frac{(C_1 - C_2)^2(\Delta V_i)^2}{(C_1 + C_2)}$$

Therefore, the ratio of the final energy stored to the initial energy stored is

$$(8) \qquad \frac{U_f}{U_i} = \frac{\tfrac{1}{2}(C_1 - C_2)^2(\Delta V_i)^2/(C_1 + C_2)}{\tfrac{1}{2}(C_1 + C_2)(\Delta V_i)^2}$$

$$= \left(\frac{C_1 - C_2}{C_1 + C_2}\right)^2$$

To finalize this problem, note that this ratio is *less* than unity, indicating that the final energy is *less* than the initial energy. At first, you might think that the law of energy conservation has been violated, but this is not the case. The "missing" energy is transferred out of the system of the capacitors by the mechanism of electromagnetic waves, as we shall see in Chapter 34.

What If? **What if the two capacitors have the same capacitance? What would we expect to happen when the switches are closed?**

Answer The equal-magnitude charges on the two capacitors should simply cancel each other and the capacitors will be uncharged afterward.

Let us test our results to see if this is the case mathematically. In Equation (1), because the charges are of equal magnitude and opposite sign, we see that $Q = 0$. Thus, Equations (4) and (5) show us that $Q_{1f} = Q_{2f} = 0$, consistent with our prediction. Furthermore, Equations (6) and (7) show us that $\Delta V_{1f} = \Delta V_{2f} = 0$, which is consistent with uncharged capacitors. Finally, if $C_1 = C_2$, Equation (8) shows us that $U_f = 0$, which is also consistent with uncharged capacitors.

At the Interactive Worked Example link at **http://www.pse6.com,** *explore this situation for various initial values of the voltage and the capacitances.*

Figure 26.14 In a hospital or at an emergency scene, you might see a patient being revived with a defibrillator. The defibrillator's paddles are applied to the patient's chest, and an electric shock is sent through the chest cavity. The aim of this technique is to restore the heart's normal rhythm pattern.

One device in which capacitors have an important role is the *defibrillator* (Fig. 26.14). Up to 360 J is stored in the electric field of a large capacitor in a defibrillator when it is fully charged. The defibrillator can deliver all this energy to a patient in about 2 ms. (This is roughly equivalent to 3 000 times the power delivered to a 60-W lightbulb!) Under the proper conditions, the defibrillator can be used to stop cardiac fibrillation (random contractions) in heart attack victims. When fibrillation occurs, the heart produces a rapid, irregular pattern of beats. A fast discharge of energy through the heart can return the organ to its normal beat pattern. Emergency medical teams use portable defibrillators that contain batteries capable of charging a capacitor to a high voltage. (The circuitry actually permits the capacitor to be charged to a much higher voltage than that of the battery.) The stored energy is released through the heart by conducting electrodes, called paddles, that are placed on both sides of the victim's chest. The paramedics must wait between applications of the energy due to the time necessary for the capacitors to become fully charged. In this case and others (e.g., camera flash units and lasers used for fusion experiments), capacitors serve as energy reservoirs which can be slowly charged and then discharged quickly to provide large amounts of energy in a short pulse.

A camera's flash unit also uses a capacitor, although the total amount of energy stored is much less than that stored in a defibrillator. After the flash unit's capacitor is charged, tripping the camera's shutter causes the stored energy to be sent through a special lightbulb that briefly illuminates the subject being photographed.

26.5 Capacitors with Dielectrics

A **dielectric** is a nonconducting material, such as rubber, glass, or waxed paper. When a dielectric is inserted between the plates of a capacitor, the capacitance increases. If the dielectric completely fills the space between the plates, the capacitance increases by a dimensionless factor κ, which is called the **dielectric constant** of the material. The dielectric constant varies from one material to another. In this section, we analyze this change in capacitance in terms of electrical parameters such as electric charge, electric field, and potential difference; in Section 26.7, we shall discuss the microscopic origin of these changes.

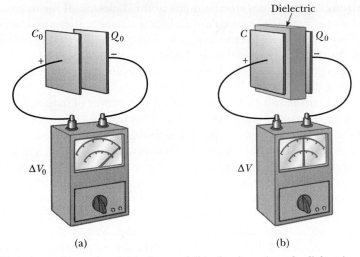

Figure 26.15 A charged capacitor (a) before and (b) after insertion of a dielectric between the plates. The charge on the plates remains unchanged, but the potential difference decreases from ΔV_0 to $\Delta V = \Delta V_0/\kappa$. Thus, the capacitance increases from C_0 to κC_0.

We can perform the following experiment to illustrate the effect of a dielectric in a capacitor. Consider a parallel-plate capacitor that without a dielectric has a charge Q_0 and a capacitance C_0. The potential difference across the capacitor is $\Delta V_0 = Q_0/C_0$. Figure 26.15a illustrates this situation. The potential difference is measured by a *voltmeter*, which we shall study in greater detail in Chapter 28. Note that no battery is shown in the figure; also, we must assume that no charge can flow through an ideal voltmeter. Hence, there is no path by which charge can flow and alter the charge on the capacitor. If a dielectric is now inserted between the plates, as in Figure 26.15b, the voltmeter indicates that the voltage between the plates decreases to a value ΔV. The voltages with and without the dielectric are related by the factor κ as follows:

$$\Delta V = \frac{\Delta V_0}{\kappa}$$

Because $\Delta V < \Delta V_0$, we see that $\kappa > 1$.

Because the charge Q_0 on the capacitor does not change, we conclude that the capacitance must change to the value

$$C = \frac{Q_0}{\Delta V} = \frac{Q_0}{\Delta V_0/\kappa} = \kappa \frac{Q_0}{\Delta V_0}$$

$$C = \kappa C_0 \qquad\qquad (26.14)$$

That is, the capacitance *increases* by the factor κ when the dielectric completely fills the region between the plates.[4] For a parallel-plate capacitor, where $C_0 = \epsilon_0 A/d$ (Eq. 26.3), we can express the capacitance when the capacitor is filled with a dielectric as

$$C = \kappa \frac{\epsilon_0 A}{d} \qquad\qquad (26.15)$$

From Equations 26.3 and 26.15, it would appear that we could make the capacitance very large by decreasing d, the distance between the plates. In practice, the lowest value of d is limited by the electric discharge that could occur through the dielectric medium separating the plates. For any given separation d, the maximum voltage that can be applied to a capacitor without causing a discharge depends on the

> ▲ **PITFALL PREVENTION**
>
> **26.5 Is the Capacitor Connected to a Battery?**
>
> In problems in which you are modifying a capacitor (by insertion of a dielectric, for example), you must note whether modifications to the capacitor are being made while the capacitor is connected to a battery or after it is disconnected. If the capacitor remains connected to the battery, the voltage across the capacitor necessarily remains the same. If you disconnect the capacitor from the battery before making any modifications to the capacitor, the capacitor is an isolated system and its charge remains the same.

Capacitance of a capacitor filled with a material of dielectric constant κ

---

[4]   If the dielectric is introduced while the potential difference is held constant by a battery, the charge increases to a value $Q = \kappa Q_0$. The additional charge comes from the wires attached to the capacitor, and the capacitance again increases by the factor κ.

Figure 26.16 Dielectric breakdown in air. Sparks are produced when the high voltage between the wires causes the electric field to exceed the dielectric strength of air.

dielectric strength (maximum electric field) of the dielectric. If the magnitude of the electric field in the dielectric exceeds the dielectric strength, then the insulating properties break down and the dielectric begins to conduct. Figure 26.16 shows the effect of exceeding the dielectric strength of air. Sparks appear between the two wires, due to ionization of atoms and recombination with electrons in the air, similar to the process that produced corona discharge in Section 25.6.

Physical capacitors have a specification called by a variety of names, including *working voltage, breakdown voltage,* and *rated voltage.* This parameter represents the largest voltage that can be applied to the capacitor without exceeding the dielectric strength of the dielectric material in the capacitor. Consequently, when selecting a capacitor for a given application, you must consider the capacitance of the device along with the expected voltage across the capacitor in the circuit, making sure that the expected voltage will be smaller than the rated voltage of the capacitor. You can see the rated voltage on several of the capacitors in the opening photograph for this chapter.

Insulating materials have values of κ greater than unity and dielectric strengths greater than that of air, as Table 26.1 indicates. Thus, we see that a dielectric provides the following advantages:

- Increase in capacitance
- Increase in maximum operating voltage
- Possible mechanical support between the plates, which allows the plates to be close together without touching, thereby decreasing d and increasing C.

Types of Capacitors

Commercial capacitors are often made from metallic foil interlaced with thin sheets of either paraffin-impregnated paper or Mylar as the dielectric material. These alternate layers of metallic foil and dielectric are rolled into a cylinder to form a small package (Fig. 26.17a). High-voltage capacitors commonly consist of a number of interwoven

Table 26.1

Approximate Dielectric Constants and Dielectric Strengths of Various Materials at Room Temperature		
Material	**Dielectric Constant κ**	**Dielectric Strength[a] (10^6 V/m)**
Air (dry)	1.000 59	3
Bakelite	4.9	24
Fused quartz	3.78	8
Mylar	3.2	7
Neoprene rubber	6.7	12
Nylon	3.4	14
Paper	3.7	16
Paraffin-impregnated paper	3.5	11
Polystyrene	2.56	24
Polyvinyl chloride	3.4	40
Porcelain	6	12
Pyrex glass	5.6	14
Silicone oil	2.5	15
Strontium titanate	233	8
Teflon	2.1	60
Vacuum	1.000 00	—
Water	80	—

[a] The dielectric strength equals the maximum electric field that can exist in a dielectric without electrical breakdown. Note that these values depend strongly on the presence of impurities and flaws in the materials.

© Loren Winters/Visuals Unlimited

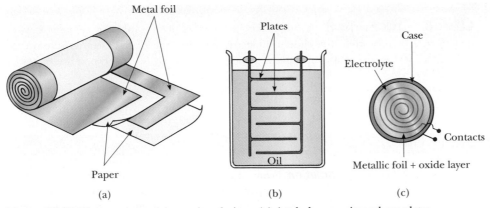

Figure 26.17 Three commercial capacitor designs. (a) A tubular capacitor, whose plates are separated by paper and then rolled into a cylinder. (b) A high-voltage capacitor consisting of many parallel plates separated by insulating oil. (c) An electrolytic capacitor.

metallic plates immersed in silicone oil (Fig. 26.17b). Small capacitors are often constructed from ceramic materials.

Often, an *electrolytic capacitor* is used to store large amounts of charge at relatively low voltages. This device, shown in Figure 26.17c, consists of a metallic foil in contact with an *electrolyte*—a solution that conducts electricity by virtue of the motion of ions contained in the solution. When a voltage is applied between the foil and the electrolyte, a thin layer of metal oxide (an insulator) is formed on the foil, and this layer serves as the dielectric. Very large values of capacitance can be obtained in an electrolytic capacitor because the dielectric layer is very thin, and thus the plate separation is very small.

Electrolytic capacitors are not reversible as are many other capacitors—they have a polarity, which is indicated by positive and negative signs marked on the device. When electrolytic capacitors are used in circuits, the polarity must be aligned properly. If the polarity of the applied voltage is opposite that which is intended, the oxide layer is removed and the capacitor conducts electricity instead of storing charge.

Variable capacitors (typically 10 to 500 pF) usually consist of two interwoven sets of metallic plates, one fixed and the other movable, and contain air as the dielectric (Fig. 26.18). These types of capacitors are often used in radio tuning circuits.

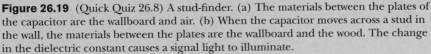

Figure 26.18 A variable capacitor. When one set of metal plates is rotated so as to lie between a fixed set of plates, the capacitance of the device changes.

Quick Quiz 26.8 If you have ever tried to hang a picture or a mirror, you know it can be difficult to locate a wooden stud in which to anchor your nail or screw. A carpenter's stud-finder is basically a capacitor with its plates arranged side by side instead of facing one another, as shown in Figure 26.19. When the device is moved over a stud, does the capacitance increase or decrease?

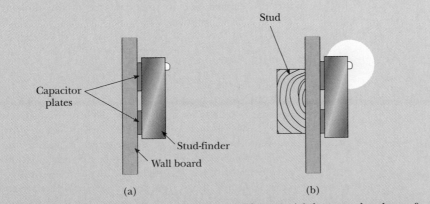

Figure 26.19 (Quick Quiz 26.8) A stud-finder. (a) The materials between the plates of the capacitor are the wallboard and air. (b) When the capacitor moves across a stud in the wall, the materials between the plates are the wallboard and the wood. The change in the dielectric constant causes a signal light to illuminate.

Quick Quiz 26.9 A fully charged parallel-plate capacitor remains connected to a battery while you slide a dielectric between the plates. Do the following quantities increase, decrease, or stay the same? (a) C; (b) Q; (c) E between the plates; (d) ΔV.

Example 26.6   A Paper-Filled Capacitor

A parallel-plate capacitor has plates of dimensions 2.0 cm by 3.0 cm separated by a 1.0-mm thickness of paper.

(A) Find its capacitance.

Solution Because $\kappa = 3.7$ for paper (see Table 26.1), we have

$$C = \kappa \frac{\epsilon_0 A}{d}$$

$$= 3.7 \left(\frac{(8.85 \times 10^{-12}\, \text{C}^2/\text{N} \cdot \text{m}^2)(6.0 \times 10^{-4}\, \text{m}^2)}{1.0 \times 10^{-3}\, \text{m}} \right)$$

$$= 20 \times 10^{-12}\, \text{F} = \boxed{20\ \text{pF}}$$

(B) What is the maximum charge that can be placed on the capacitor?

Solution From Table 26.1 we see that the dielectric strength of paper is 16×10^6 V/m. Because the thickness of the paper is 1.0 mm, the maximum voltage that can be applied before breakdown is

$$\Delta V_{\max} = E_{\max} d = (16 \times 10^6\, \text{V/m})(1.0 \times 10^{-3}\, \text{m})$$

$$= 16 \times 10^3\, \text{V}$$

Hence, the maximum charge is

$$Q_{\max} = C\,\Delta V_{\max} = (20 \times 10^{-12}\, \text{F})(16 \times 10^3\, \text{V})$$

$$= \boxed{0.32\ \mu\text{C}}$$

Example 26.7   Energy Stored Before and After

A parallel-plate capacitor is charged with a battery to a charge Q_0, as shown in Figure 26.20a. The battery is then removed, and a slab of material that has a dielectric constant κ is inserted between the plates, as shown in Figure 26.20b. Find the energy stored in the capacitor before and after the dielectric is inserted.

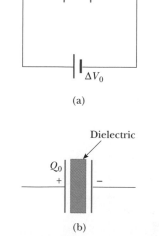

(a)

(b)

Figure 26.20 (Example 26.7) (a) A battery charges up a parallel-plate capacitor. (b) The battery is removed and a slab of dielectric material is inserted between the plates.

Solution From Equation 26.11, we see that the energy stored in the absence of the dielectric is

$$U_0 = \frac{Q_0{}^2}{2C_0}$$

After the battery is removed and the dielectric inserted, the *charge on the capacitor remains the same*. Hence, the energy stored in the presence of the dielectric is

$$U = \frac{Q_0{}^2}{2C}$$

But the capacitance in the presence of the dielectric is $C = \kappa C_0$, so U becomes

$$U = \frac{Q_0{}^2}{2\kappa C_0} = \frac{U_0}{\kappa}$$

Because $\kappa > 1$, the final energy is less than the initial energy. We can account for the "missing" energy by noting that the dielectric, when inserted, is pulled into the device (see Section 26.7). An external agent must do negative work to keep the dielectric from accelerating. This work is simply the difference $U - U_0$. (Alternatively, the positive work done by the system on the external agent is $U_0 - U$.)

26.6 Electric Dipole in an Electric Field

We have discussed the effect on the capacitance of placing a dielectric between the plates of a capacitor. In Section 26.7, we shall describe the microscopic origin of this effect. Before we can do so, however, we need to expand upon the discussion of the electric dipole that we began in Section 23.4 (see Example 23.6). The electric dipole consists of two charges of equal magnitude and opposite sign separated by a distance $2a$, as shown in Figure 26.21. The **electric dipole moment** of this configuration is defined as the vector $\mathbf{p}$ directed from $-q$ toward $+q$ along the line joining the charges and having magnitude $2aq$:

$$p \equiv 2aq \qquad (26.16)$$

Now suppose that an electric dipole is placed in a uniform electric field $\mathbf{E}$, as shown in Figure 26.22. We identify $\mathbf{E}$ as the field *external* to the dipole, distinguishing it from the field *due to* the dipole, which we discussed in Section 23.4. The field $\mathbf{E}$ is established by some other charge distribution, and we place the dipole into this field. Let us imagine that the dipole moment makes an angle θ with the field.

The electric forces acting on the two charges are equal in magnitude ($F = qE$) and opposite in direction as shown in Figure 26.22. Thus, the net force on the dipole is zero. However, the two forces produce a net torque on the dipole; as a result, the dipole rotates in the direction that brings the dipole moment vector into greater alignment with the field. The torque due to the force on the positive charge about an axis through O in Figure 26.22 has magnitude $Fa \sin \theta$, where $a \sin \theta$ is the moment arm of F about O. This force tends to produce a clockwise rotation. The torque about O on the negative charge is also of magnitude $Fa \sin \theta$; here again, the force tends to produce a clockwise rotation. Thus, the magnitude of the net torque about O is

$$\tau = 2Fa \sin \theta$$

Because $F = qE$ and $p = 2aq$, we can express τ as

$$\tau = 2aqE \sin \theta = pE \sin \theta \qquad (26.17)$$

It is convenient to express the torque in vector form as the cross product of the vectors $\mathbf{p}$ and $\mathbf{E}$:

$$\boxed{\boldsymbol{\tau} = \mathbf{p} \times \mathbf{E}} \qquad (26.18)$$

We can determine the potential energy of the system—an electric dipole in an external electric field—as a function of the orientation of the dipole with respect to the field. To do this, we recognize that work must be done by an external agent to rotate the dipole through an angle so as to cause the dipole moment vector to become less aligned with the field. The work done is then stored as potential energy in the system. The work dW required to rotate the dipole through an angle $d\theta$ is $dW = \tau \, d\theta$ (Eq. 10.22). Because $\tau = pE \sin \theta$ and because the work results in an increase in the potential energy U, we find that for a rotation from θ_i to θ_f the change in potential energy of the system is

$$U_f - U_i = \int_{\theta_i}^{\theta_f} \tau \, d\theta = \int_{\theta_i}^{\theta_f} pE \sin \theta \, d\theta = pE \int_{\theta_i}^{\theta_f} \sin \theta \, d\theta$$

$$= pE[-\cos \theta]_{\theta_i}^{\theta_f} = pE(\cos \theta_i - \cos \theta_f)$$

The term that contains $\cos \theta_i$ is a constant that depends on the initial orientation of the dipole. It is convenient for us to choose a reference angle of $\theta_i = 90°$, so that $\cos \theta_i = \cos 90° = 0$. Furthermore, let us choose $U_i = 0$ at $\theta_i = 90°$ as our reference of potential energy. Hence, we can express a general value of $U = U_f$ as

$$U = -pE \cos \theta \qquad (26.19)$$

We can write this expression for the potential energy of a dipole in an electric field as the dot product of the vectors $\mathbf{p}$ and $\mathbf{E}$:

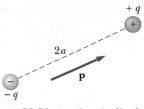

Figure 26.21 An electric dipole consists of two charges of equal magnitude and opposite sign separated by a distance of $2a$. The electric dipole moment $\mathbf{p}$ is directed from $-q$ toward $+q$.

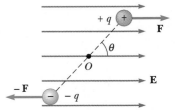

Figure 26.22 An electric dipole in a uniform external electric field. The dipole moment $\mathbf{p}$ is at an angle θ to the field, causing the dipole to experience a torque.

Torque on an electric dipole in an external electric field

Potential energy of the system of an electric dipole in an external electric field

$$U = -\mathbf{p} \cdot \mathbf{E} \qquad (26.20)$$

To develop a conceptual understanding of Equation 26.19, compare this expression with the expression for the potential energy of the system of an object in the gravitational field of the Earth, $U = mgh$ (see Chapter 8). The gravitational expression includes a parameter associated with the object we place in the field—its mass m. Likewise, Equation 26.19 includes a parameter of the object in the electric field—its dipole moment p. The gravitational expression includes the magnitude of the gravitational field g. Similarly, Equation 26.19 includes the magnitude of the electric field E. So far, these two contributions to the potential energy expressions appear analogous. However, the final contribution is somewhat different in the two cases. In the gravitational expression, the potential energy depends on how high we lift the object, measured by h. In Equation 26.19, the potential energy depends on the angle θ through which we rotate the dipole. In both cases, we are making a change in the configuration of the system. In the gravitational case, the change involves moving an object in a *translational* sense, whereas in the electrical case, the change involves moving an object in a *rotational* sense. In both cases, however, once the change is made, the system tends to return to the original configuration when the object is released: the object of mass m falls back to the ground, and the dipole begins to rotate back toward the configuration in which it is aligned with the field. Thus, apart from the type of motion, the expressions for potential energy in these two cases are similar.

Molecules are said to be *polarized* when a separation exists between the average position of the negative charges and the average position of the positive charges in the molecule. In some molecules, such as water, this condition is always present—such molecules are called **polar molecules.** Molecules that do not possess a permanent polarization are called **nonpolar molecules.**

We can understand the permanent polarization of water by inspecting the geometry of the water molecule. In the water molecule, the oxygen atom is bonded to the hydrogen atoms such that an angle of 105° is formed between the two bonds (Fig. 26.23). The center of the negative charge distribution is near the oxygen atom, and the center of the positive charge distribution lies at a point midway along the line joining the hydrogen atoms (the point labeled × in Fig. 26.23). We can model the water molecule and other polar molecules as dipoles because the average positions of the positive and negative charges act as point charges. As a result, we can apply our discussion of dipoles to the behavior of polar molecules.

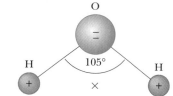

Figure 26.23 The water molecule, H_2O, has a permanent polarization resulting from its nonlinear geometry. The center of the positive charge distribution is at the point ×.

Microwave ovens take advantage of the polar nature of the water molecule. When in operation, microwave ovens generate a rapidly changing electric field that causes the polar molecules to swing back and forth, absorbing energy from the field in the process. Because the jostling molecules collide with each other, the energy they absorb from the field is converted to internal energy, which corresponds to an increase in temperature of the food.

Another household scenario in which the dipole structure of water is exploited is washing with soap and water. Grease and oil are made up of nonpolar molecules, which are generally not attracted to water. Plain water is not very useful for removing this type of grime. Soap contains long molecules called *surfactants*. In a long molecule, the polarity characteristics of one end of the molecule can be different from those at the other end. In a surfactant molecule, one end acts like a nonpolar molecule and the other acts like a polar molecule. The nonpolar end can attach to a grease or oil molecule, and the polar end can attach to a water molecule. Thus, the soap serves as a chain, linking the dirt and water molecules together. When the water is rinsed away, the grease and oil go with it.

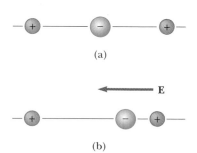

Figure 26.24 (a) A linear symmetric molecule has no permanent polarization. (b) An external electric field induces a polarization in the molecule.

A symmetric molecule (Fig. 26.24a) has no permanent polarization, but polarization can be induced by placing the molecule in an electric field. A field directed to the left, as shown in Figure 26.24b, would cause the center of the positive charge distribution to shift to the left from its initial position and the center of the negative charge distribution to shift to the right. This *induced polarization* is the effect that predominates in most materials used as dielectrics in capacitors.

Example 26.8   The H_2O Molecule

The water (H_2O) molecule has an electric dipole moment of 6.3×10^{-30} C·m. A sample contains 10^{21} water molecules, with the dipole moments all oriented in the direction of an electric field of magnitude 2.5×10^5 N/C. How much work is required to rotate the dipoles from this orientation ($\theta = 0°$) to one in which all the moments are perpendicular to the field ($\theta = 90°$)?

Solution The work required to rotate one molecule 90° is equal to the difference in potential energy between the 90° orientation and the 0° orientation. Using Equation 26.19,

we obtain

$$W = U_{90°} - U_{0°} = (-pE \cos 90°) - (-pE \cos 0°)$$
$$= pE = (6.3 \times 10^{-30}\ \text{C·m})(2.5 \times 10^5\ \text{N/C})$$
$$= 1.6 \times 10^{-24}\ \text{J}$$

Because there are 10^{21} molecules in the sample, the *total* work required is

$$W_{\text{total}} = (10^{21})(1.6 \times 10^{-24}\ \text{J}) = \boxed{1.6 \times 10^{-3}\ \text{J}}$$

26.7   An Atomic Description of Dielectrics

In Section 26.5 we found that the potential difference ΔV_0 between the plates of a capacitor is reduced to $\Delta V_0/\kappa$ when a dielectric is introduced. The potential difference is reduced because the magnitude of the electric field decreases between the plates. In particular, if $\mathbf{E}_0$ is the electric field without the dielectric, the field in the presence of a dielectric is

$$\mathbf{E} = \frac{\mathbf{E}_0}{\kappa} \qquad (26.21)$$

Let us first consider a dielectric made up of polar molecules placed in the electric field between the plates of a capacitor. The dipoles (that is, the polar molecules making up the dielectric) are randomly oriented in the absence of an electric field, as shown in Figure 26.25a. When an external field $\mathbf{E}_0$ due to charges on the capacitor plates is applied, a torque is exerted on the dipoles, causing them to partially align with the field, as shown in Figure 26.25b. We can now describe the dielectric as being polarized. The degree of alignment of the molecules with the electric field depends on temperature and on the magnitude of the field. In general, the alignment increases with decreasing temperature and with increasing electric field.

If the molecules of the dielectric are nonpolar, then the electric field due to the plates produces some charge separation and an *induced dipole moment*. These induced dipole moments tend to align with the external field, and the dielectric is polarized. Thus, we can polarize a dielectric with an external field regardless of whether the molecules are polar or nonpolar.

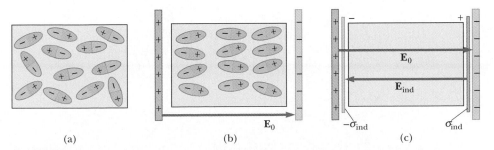

(a)   (b)   (c)

Figure 26.25 (a) Polar molecules are randomly oriented in the absence of an external electric field. (b) When an external electric field is applied, the molecules partially align with the field. (c) The charged edges of the dielectric can be modeled as an additional pair of parallel plates establishing an electric field $\mathbf{E}_{\text{ind}}$ in the direction opposite to that of $\mathbf{E}_0$.

With these ideas in mind, consider a slab of dielectric material placed between the plates of a capacitor so that it is in a uniform electric field $\mathbf{E}_0$, as shown in Figure 26.25b. The electric field due to the plates is directed to the right and polarizes the dielectric. The net effect on the dielectric is the formation of an *induced* positive surface charge density σ_{ind} on the right face and an equal-magnitude negative surface charge density $-\sigma_{ind}$ on the left face, as shown in Figure 26.25c. Because we can model these surface charge distributions as being due to parallel plates, the induced surface charges on the dielectric give rise to an induced electric field $\mathbf{E}_{ind}$ in the direction opposite the external field $\mathbf{E}_0$. Therefore, the net electric field $\mathbf{E}$ in the dielectric has a magnitude

$$E = E_0 - E_{ind} \tag{26.22}$$

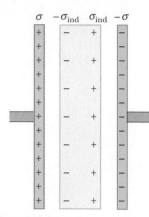

$$
\begin{array}{cccc}
\sigma & -\sigma_{ind} & \sigma_{ind} & -\sigma
\end{array}
$$

Figure 26.26 Induced charge on a dielectric placed between the plates of a charged capacitor. Note that the induced charge density on the dielectric is *less* than the charge density on the plates.

In the parallel-plate capacitor shown in Figure 26.26, the external field E_0 is related to the charge density σ on the plates through the relationship $E_0 = \sigma/\epsilon_0$. The induced electric field in the dielectric is related to the induced charge density σ_{ind} through the relationship $E_{ind} = \sigma_{ind}/\epsilon_0$. Because $E = E_0/\kappa = \sigma/\kappa\epsilon_0$, substitution into Equation 26.22 gives

$$\frac{\sigma}{\kappa\epsilon_0} = \frac{\sigma}{\epsilon_0} - \frac{\sigma_{ind}}{\epsilon_0}$$

$$\sigma_{ind} = \left(\frac{\kappa - 1}{\kappa}\right)\sigma \tag{26.23}$$

Because $\kappa > 1$, this expression shows that the charge density σ_{ind} induced on the dielectric is less than the charge density σ on the plates. For instance, if $\kappa = 3$ we see that the induced charge density is two-thirds the charge density on the plates. If no dielectric is present, then $\kappa = 1$ and $\sigma_{ind} = 0$ as expected. However, if the dielectric is replaced by an electrical conductor, for which $E = 0$, then Equation 26.22 indicates that $E_0 = E_{ind}$; this corresponds to $\sigma_{ind} = \sigma$. That is, the surface charge induced on the conductor is equal in magnitude but opposite in sign to that on the plates, resulting in a net electric field of zero in the conductor (see Fig. 24.16).

We can use the existence of the induced surface charge distributions on the dielectric to explain the result of Example 26.7. As we saw there, the energy of a capacitor not connected to a battery is lowered when a dielectric is inserted between the plates; this means that negative work is done on the dielectric by the external agent inserting the dielectric into the capacitor. This, in turn, implies that a force must be acting on the dielectric that draws it into the capacitor. This force originates from the nonuniform nature of the electric field of the capacitor near its edges, as indicated in Figure 26.27.

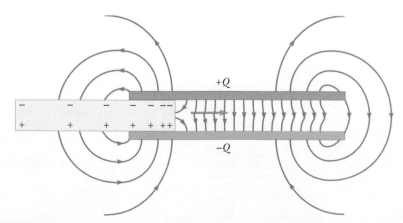

Figure 26.27 The nonuniform electric field near the edges of a parallel-plate capacitor causes a dielectric to be pulled into the capacitor. Note that the field acts on the induced surface charges on the dielectric, which are nonuniformly distributed.

The horizontal component of this *fringe field* acts on the induced charges on the surface of the dielectric, producing a net horizontal force directed into the space between the capacitor plates.

Example 26.9   Effect of a Metallic Slab

A parallel-plate capacitor has a plate separation d and plate area A. An uncharged metallic slab of thickness a is inserted midway between the plates.

(A) Find the capacitance of the device.

Solution We can solve this problem by noting that any charge that appears on one plate of the capacitor must induce a charge of equal magnitude and opposite sign on the near side of the slab, as shown in Figure 26.28a. Consequently, the net charge on the slab remains zero, and the electric field inside the slab is zero. Hence, the capacitor is equivalent to two capacitors in series, each having a plate separation $(d - a)/2$, as shown in Figure 26.28b.

Using Eq. 26.3 and the rule for adding two capacitors in series (Eq. 26.10), we obtain

$$\frac{1}{C} = \frac{1}{C_1} + \frac{1}{C_2} = \frac{1}{\left[\dfrac{\epsilon_0 A}{(d-a)/2}\right]} + \frac{1}{\left[\dfrac{\epsilon_0 A}{(d-a)/2}\right]}$$

$$C = \boxed{\frac{\epsilon_0 A}{d - a}}$$

Note that C approaches infinity as a approaches d. Why?

(B) Show that the capacitance of the original capacitor is unaffected by the insertion of the metallic slab if the slab is infinitesimally thin.

Solution In the result for part (A), we let $a \to 0$:

$$C = \lim_{a \to 0} \frac{\epsilon_0 A}{d - a} = \frac{\epsilon_0 A}{d}$$

which is the original capacitance.

What If? What if the metallic slab in part (A) is not midway between the plates? How does this affect the capacitance?

Answer Let us imagine that the slab in Figure 26.27a is moved upward so that the distance between the upper edge of the slab and the upper plate is b. Then, the distance between the lower edge of the slab and the lower plate is $d - b - a$. As in part (A), we find the total capacitance of the series combination:

$$\frac{1}{C} = \frac{1}{C_1} + \frac{1}{C_2} = \frac{1}{(\epsilon_0 A/b)} + \frac{1}{\epsilon_0 A/(d - b - a)}$$

$$= \frac{b}{\epsilon_0 A} + \frac{d - b - a}{\epsilon_0 A} = \frac{d - a}{\epsilon_0 A}$$

$$C = \frac{\epsilon_0 A}{d - a}$$

This is the same result as in part (A). It is independent of the value of b, so it does not matter where the slab is located. In Figure 26.28b, when the central structure is moved up or down, the decrease in plate separation of one capacitor is compensated by the increase in plate separation for the other.

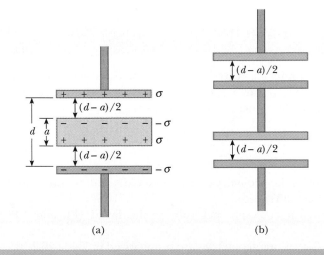

(a)   (b)

Figure 26.28 (Example 26.9) (a) A parallel-plate capacitor of plate separation d partially filled with a metallic slab of thickness a. (b) The equivalent circuit of the device in part (a) consists of two capacitors in series, each having a plate separation $(d - a)/2$.

Example 26.10   A Partially Filled Capacitor

A parallel-plate capacitor with a plate separation d has a capacitance C_0 in the absence of a dielectric. What is the capacitance when a slab of dielectric material of dielectric constant κ and thickness $\frac{1}{3}d$ is inserted between the plates (Fig. 26.29a)?

Solution In Example 26.9, we found that we could insert a metallic slab between the plates of a capacitor and consider the combination as two capacitors in series. The resulting capacitance was independent of the location of the slab. Furthermore, if the thickness of the slab approaches zero,

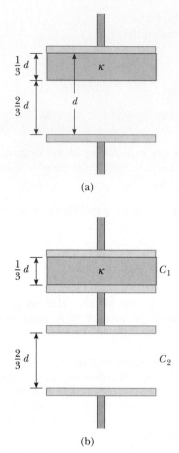

(a)

(b)

Figure 26.29 (Example 26.10) (a) A parallel-plate capacitor of plate separation d partially filled with a dielectric of thickness $d/3$. (b) The equivalent circuit of the capacitor consists of two capacitors connected in series.

then the capacitance of the system approaches the capacitance when the slab is absent. From this, we conclude that we can insert an infinitesimally thin metallic slab anywhere between the plates of a capacitor without affecting the capacitance. Thus, let us imagine sliding an infinitesimally thin metallic slab along the bottom face of the dielectric shown in Figure 26.29a. We can then consider this system to be the series combination of the two capacitors shown in Figure 26.29b: one having a plate separation $d/3$ and filled with a dielectric, and the other having a plate separation $2d/3$ and air between its plates.

From Equations 26.15 and 26.3, the two capacitances are

$$C_1 = \frac{\kappa \epsilon_0 A}{d/3} \quad \text{and} \quad C_2 = \frac{\epsilon_0 A}{2d/3}$$

Using Equation 26.10 for two capacitors combined in series, we have

$$\frac{1}{C} = \frac{1}{C_1} + \frac{1}{C_2} = \frac{d/3}{\kappa \epsilon_0 A} + \frac{2d/3}{\epsilon_0 A}$$

$$\frac{1}{C} = \frac{d}{3\epsilon_0 A}\left(\frac{1}{\kappa} + 2\right) = \frac{d}{3\epsilon_0 A}\left(\frac{1 + 2\kappa}{\kappa}\right)$$

$$C = \left(\frac{3\kappa}{2\kappa + 1}\right)\frac{\epsilon_0 A}{d}$$

Because the capacitance without the dielectric is $C_0 = \epsilon_0 A/d$, we see that

$$C = \left(\frac{3\kappa}{2\kappa + 1}\right)C_0$$

SUMMARY

Take a practice test for this chapter by clicking on the Practice Test link at http://www.pse6.com.

A **capacitor** consists of two conductors carrying charges of equal magnitude and opposite sign. The **capacitance** C of any capacitor is the ratio of the charge Q on either conductor to the potential difference ΔV between them:

$$C \equiv \frac{Q}{\Delta V} \tag{26.1}$$

The capacitance depends only on the geometry of the conductors and not on an external source of charge or potential difference.

The SI unit of capacitance is coulombs per volt, or the **farad** (F), and $1\ \text{F} = 1\ \text{C/V}$.

Capacitance expressions for various geometries are summarized in Table 26.2.

If two or more capacitors are connected in parallel, then the potential difference is the same across all of them. The equivalent capacitance of a parallel combination of capacitors is

$$C_{\text{eq}} = C_1 + C_2 + C_3 + \cdots \tag{26.8}$$

If two or more capacitors are connected in series, the charge is the same on all of them, and the equivalent capacitance of the series combination is given by

Table 26.2

Capacitance and Geometry		
Geometry	**Capacitance**	**Equation**
Isolated sphere of radius R (second spherical conductor assumed to have infinite radius)	$C = 4\pi\epsilon_0 R$	26.2
Parallel-plate capacitor of plate area A and plate separation d	$C = \epsilon_0 \dfrac{A}{d}$	26.3
Cylindrical capacitor of length ℓ and inner and outer radii a and b, respectively	$C = \dfrac{\ell}{2k_e \ln(b/a)}$	26.4
Spherical capacitor with inner and outer radii a and b, respectively	$C = \dfrac{ab}{k_e(b-a)}$	26.6

$$\frac{1}{C_{eq}} = \frac{1}{C_1} + \frac{1}{C_2} + \frac{1}{C_3} + \cdots \tag{26.10}$$

These two equations enable you to simplify many electric circuits by replacing multiple capacitors with a single equivalent capacitance.

Energy is stored in a capacitor because the charging process is equivalent to the transfer of charges from one conductor at a lower electric potential to another conductor at a higher potential. The energy stored in a capacitor with charge Q is

$$U = \frac{Q^2}{2C} = \tfrac{1}{2}Q\,\Delta V = \tfrac{1}{2}C(\Delta V)^2 \tag{26.11}$$

When a dielectric material is inserted between the plates of a capacitor, the capacitance increases by a dimensionless factor κ, called the **dielectric constant:**

$$C = \kappa C_0 \tag{26.14}$$

where C_0 is the capacitance in the absence of the dielectric. The increase in capacitance is due to a decrease in the magnitude of the electric field in the presence of the dielectric. The decrease in the magnitude of **E** arises from an internal electric field produced by aligned dipoles in the dielectric.

The **electric dipole moment p** of an electric dipole has a magnitude

$$p \equiv 2aq \tag{26.16}$$

The direction of the electric dipole moment vector is from the negative charge toward the positive charge.

The torque acting on an electric dipole in a uniform electric field **E** is

$$\boldsymbol{\tau} = \mathbf{p} \times \mathbf{E} \tag{26.18}$$

The potential energy of the system of an electric dipole in a uniform external electric field **E** is

$$U = -\mathbf{p} \cdot \mathbf{E} \tag{26.20}$$

QUESTIONS

1. The plates of a capacitor are connected to a battery. What happens to the charge on the plates if the connecting wires are removed from the battery? What happens to the charge if the wires are removed from the battery and connected to each other?

2. A farad is a very large unit of capacitance. Calculate the length of one side of a square, air-filled capacitor that has a capacitance of 1 F and a plate separation of 1 m.

3. A pair of capacitors are connected in parallel while an identical pair are connected in series. Which pair would be

more dangerous to handle after being connected to the same battery? Explain.

4. If you are given three different capacitors C_1, C_2, C_3, how many different combinations of capacitance can you produce?

5. What advantage might there be in using two identical capacitors in parallel connected in series with another identical parallel pair, rather than using a single capacitor?

6. Is it always possible to reduce a combination of capacitors to one equivalent capacitor with the rules we have developed? Explain.

7. The sum of the charges on both plates of a capacitor is zero. What does a capacitor store?

8. Because the charges on the plates of a parallel-plate capacitor are opposite in sign, they attract each other. Hence, it would take positive work to increase the plate separation. What type of energy in the system changes due to the external work done in this process?

9. Why is it dangerous to touch the terminals of a high-voltage capacitor even after the applied potential difference has been turned off? What can be done to make the capacitor safe to handle after the voltage source has been removed?

10. Explain why the work needed to move a charge Q through a potential difference ΔV is $W = Q\,\Delta V$ whereas the energy stored in a charged capacitor is $U = \frac{1}{2}Q\,\Delta V$. Where does the $\frac{1}{2}$ factor come from?

11. If the potential difference across a capacitor is doubled, by what factor does the energy stored change?

12. It is possible to obtain large potential differences by first charging a group of capacitors connected in parallel and then activating a switch arrangement that in effect dis-

connects the capacitors from the charging source and from each other and reconnects them in a series arrangement. The group of charged capacitors is then discharged in series. What is the maximum potential difference that can be obtained in this manner by using ten capacitors each of 500 μF and a charging source of 800 V?

13. Assume you want to increase the maximum operating voltage of a parallel-plate capacitor. Describe how you can do this for a fixed plate separation.

14. An air-filled capacitor is charged, then disconnected from the power supply, and finally connected to a voltmeter. Explain how and why the potential difference changes when a dielectric is inserted between the plates of the capacitor.

15. Using the polar molecule description of a dielectric, explain how a dielectric affects the electric field inside a capacitor.

16. Explain why a dielectric increases the maximum operating voltage of a capacitor although the physical size of the capacitor does not change.

17. What is the difference between dielectric strength and the dielectric constant?

18. Explain why a water molecule is permanently polarized. What type of molecule has no permanent polarization?

19. If a dielectric-filled capacitor is heated, how will its capacitance change? (Ignore thermal expansion and assume that the dipole orientations are temperature-dependent.)

20. If you were asked to design a capacitor where small size and large capacitance were required, what factors would be important in your design?

PROBLEMS

1, 2, 3 = straightforward, intermediate, challenging ☐ = full solution available in the *Student Solutions Manual and Study Guide*

= coached solution with hints available at http://www.pse6.com 🖳 = computer useful in solving problem

= paired numerical and symbolic problems

Section 26.1 Definition of Capacitance

1. (a) How much charge is on each plate of a 4.00-μF capacitor when it is connected to a 12.0-V battery? (b) If this same capacitor is connected to a 1.50-V battery, what charge is stored?

2. Two conductors having net charges of $+10.0\ \mu$C and $-10.0\ \mu$C have a potential difference of 10.0 V between them. (a) Determine the capacitance of the system. (b) What is the potential difference between the two conductors if the charges on each are increased to $+100\ \mu$C and $-100\ \mu$C?

Section 26.2 Calculating Capacitance

3. An isolated charged conducting sphere of radius 12.0 cm creates an electric field of 4.90×10^4 N/C at a distance

21.0 cm from its center. (a) What is its surface charge density? (b) What is its capacitance?

4. (a) If a drop of liquid has capacitance 1.00 pF, what is its radius? (b) If another drop has radius 2.00 mm, what is its capacitance? (c) What is the charge on the smaller drop if its potential is 100 V?

5. Two conducting spheres with diameters of 0.400 m and 1.00 m are separated by a distance that is large compared with the diameters. The spheres are connected by a thin wire and are charged to 7.00 μC. (a) How is this total charge shared between the spheres? (Ignore any charge on the wire.) (b) What is the potential of the system of spheres when the reference potential is taken to be $V = 0$ at $r = \infty$?

6. Regarding the Earth and a cloud layer 800 m above the Earth as the "plates" of a capacitor, calculate the

capacitance. Assume the cloud layer has an area of 1.00 km^2 and that the air between the cloud and the ground is pure and dry. Assume charge builds up on the cloud and on the ground until a uniform electric field of 3.00×10^6 N/C throughout the space between them makes the air break down and conduct electricity as a lightning bolt. What is the maximum charge the cloud can hold?

7. ✏️🌀 An air-filled capacitor consists of two parallel plates, each with an area of 7.60 cm^2, separated by a distance of 1.80 mm. A 20.0-V potential difference is applied to these plates. Calculate (a) the electric field between the plates, (b) the surface charge density, (c) the capacitance, and (d) the charge on each plate.

8. A 1-megabit computer memory chip contains many 60.0-fF capacitors. Each capacitor has a plate area of 21.0×10^{-12} m^2. Determine the plate separation of such a capacitor (assume a parallel-plate configuration). The order of magnitude of the diameter of an atom is 10^{-10} m = 0.1 nm. Express the plate separation in nanometers.

9. When a potential difference of 150 V is applied to the plates of a parallel-plate capacitor, the plates carry a surface charge density of 30.0 nC/cm^2. What is the spacing between the plates?

10. A variable air capacitor used in a radio tuning circuit is made of N semicircular plates each of radius R and positioned a distance d from its neighbors, to which it is electrically connected. As shown in Figure P26.10, a second identical set of plates is enmeshed with its plates halfway between those of the first set. The second set can rotate as a unit. Determine the capacitance as a function of the angle of rotation θ, where $\theta = 0$ corresponds to the maximum capacitance.

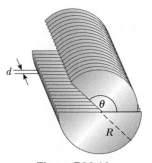

Figure P26.10

11. ✏️🌀 A 50.0-m length of coaxial cable has an inner conductor that has a diameter of 2.58 mm and carries a charge of 8.10 μC. The surrounding conductor has an inner diameter of 7.27 mm and a charge of -8.10 μC. (a) What is the capacitance of this cable? (b) What is the potential difference between the two conductors? Assume the region between the conductors is air.

12. A 20.0-μF spherical capacitor is composed of two concentric metal spheres, one having a radius twice as large as the

other. The region between the spheres is a vacuum. Determine the volume of this region.

13. An air-filled spherical capacitor is constructed with inner and outer shell radii of 7.00 and 14.0 cm, respectively. (a) Calculate the capacitance of the device. (b) What potential difference between the spheres results in a charge of 4.00 μC on the capacitor?

14. A small object of mass m carries a charge q and is suspended by a thread between the vertical plates of a parallel-plate capacitor. The plate separation is d. If the thread makes an angle θ with the vertical, what is the potential difference between the plates?

15. Find the capacitance of the Earth. (*Suggestion:* The outer conductor of the "spherical capacitor" may be considered as a conducting sphere at infinity where V approaches zero.)

Section 26.3   Combinations of Capacitors

16. Two capacitors, $C_1 = 5.00$ μF and $C_2 = 12.0$ μF, are connected in parallel, and the resulting combination is connected to a 9.00-V battery. (a) What is the equivalent capacitance of the combination? What are (b) the potential difference across each capacitor and (c) the charge stored on each capacitor?

17. **What If?** The two capacitors of Problem 16 are now connected in series and to a 9.00-V battery. Find (a) the equivalent capacitance of the combination, (b) the potential difference across each capacitor, and (c) the charge on each capacitor.

18. Evaluate the equivalent capacitance of the configuration shown in Figure P26.18. All the capacitors are identical, and each has capacitance C.

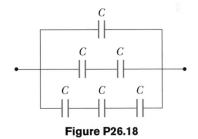

Figure P26.18

19. Two capacitors when connected in parallel give an equivalent capacitance of 9.00 pF and give an equivalent capacitance of 2.00 pF when connected in series. What is the capacitance of each capacitor?

20. Two capacitors when connected in parallel give an equivalent capacitance of C_p and an equivalent capacitance of C_s when connected in series. What is the capacitance of each capacitor?

21. ✏️🌀 Four capacitors are connected as shown in Figure P26.21. (a) Find the equivalent capacitance between points a and b. (b) Calculate the charge on each capacitor if $\Delta V_{ab} = 15.0$ V.

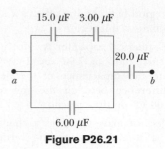

15.0 μF   3.00 μF

20.0 μF

a   *b*

6.00 μF

Figure P26.21

22. Three capacitors are connected to a battery as shown in Figure P26.22. Their capacitances are $C_1 = 3C$, $C_2 = C$, and $C_3 = 5C$. (a) What is the equivalent capacitance of this set of capacitors? (b) State the ranking of the capacitors according to the charge they store, from largest to smallest. (c) Rank the capacitors according to the potential differences across them, from largest to smallest. (d) **What If?** If C_3 is increased, what happens to the charge stored by each of the capacitors?

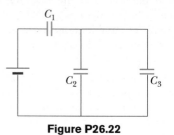

C_1

C_2 C_3

Figure P26.22

23. Consider the circuit shown in Figure P26.23, where $C_1 = 6.00$ μF, $C_2 = 3.00$ μF, and $\Delta V = 20.0$ V. Capacitor C_1 is first charged by the closing of switch S_1. Switch S_1 is then opened, and the charged capacitor is connected to the uncharged capacitor by the closing of S_2. Calculate the initial charge acquired by C_1 and the final charge on each capacitor.

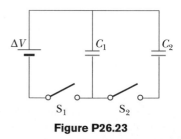

ΔV C_1 C_2

S_1 S_2

Figure P26.23

24. According to its design specification, the timer circuit delaying the closing of an elevator door is to have a capacitance of 32.0 μF between two points A and B. (a) When one circuit is being constructed, the inexpensive but durable capacitor installed between these two points is found to have capacitance 34.8 μF. To meet the specification, one additional capacitor can be placed between the two points. Should it be in series or in parallel with the 34.8-μF capacitor? What should be its capacitance? (b) **What If?** The next circuit comes down the assembly line with capacitance 29.8 μF between A and B. What additional capacitor should be installed in series or in parallel in that circuit, to meet the specification?

25. A group of identical capacitors is connected first in series and then in parallel. The combined capacitance in parallel is 100 times larger than for the series connection. How many capacitors are in the group?

26. Consider three capacitors C_1, C_2, C_3, and a battery. If C_1 is connected to the battery, the charge on C_1 is 30.8 μC. Now C_1 is disconnected, discharged, and connected in series with C_2. When the series combination of C_2 and C_1 is connected across the battery, the charge on C_1 is 23.1 μC. The circuit is disconnected and the capacitors discharged. Capacitor C_3, capacitor C_1, and the battery are connected in series, resulting in a charge on C_1 of 25.2 μC. If, after being disconnected and discharged, C_1, C_2, and C_3 are connected in series with one another and with the battery, what is the charge on C_1?

27. Find the equivalent capacitance between points a and b for the group of capacitors connected as shown in Figure P26.27. Take $C_1 = 5.00$ μF, $C_2 = 10.0$ μF, and $C_3 = 2.00$ μF.

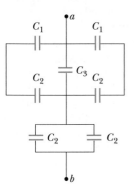

a

C_1 C_1

C_2 C_3 C_2

C_2 C_2

b

Figure P26.27 Problems 27 and 28.

28. For the network described in the previous problem, if the potential difference between points a and b is 60.0 V, what charge is stored on C_3?

29. Find the equivalent capacitance between points a and b in the combination of capacitors shown in Figure P26.29.

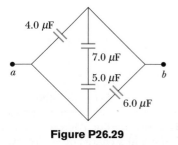

4.0 μF

7.0 μF

a 5.0 μF b

6.0 μF

Figure P26.29

30. Some physical systems possessing capacitance continuously distributed over space can be modeled as an infinite array of discrete circuit elements. Examples are a microwave waveguide and the axon of a nerve cell. To practice analy-

sis of an infinite array, determine the equivalent capacitance C between terminals X and Y of the infinite set of capacitors represented in Figure P26.30. Each capacitor has capacitance C_0. *Suggestion:* Imagine that the ladder is cut at the line AB, and note that the equivalent capacitance of the infinite section to the right of AB is also C.

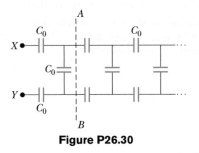

Figure P26.30

Section 26.4   Energy Stored in a Charged Capacitor

31. (a) A 3.00-μF capacitor is connected to a 12.0-V battery. How much energy is stored in the capacitor? (b) If the capacitor had been connected to a 6.00-V battery, how much energy would have been stored?

32. The immediate cause of many deaths is ventricular fibrillation, uncoordinated quivering of the heart as opposed to proper beating. An electric shock to the chest can cause momentary paralysis of the heart muscle, after which the heart will sometimes start organized beating again. A *defibrillator* (Fig. 26.14) is a device that applies a strong electric shock to the chest over a time interval of a few milliseconds. The device contains a capacitor of several microfarads, charged to several thousand volts. Electrodes called paddles, about 8 cm across and coated with conducting paste, are held against the chest on both sides of the heart. Their handles are insulated to prevent injury to the operator, who calls, "Clear!" and pushes a button on one paddle to discharge the capacitor through the patient's chest. Assume that an energy of 300 J is to be delivered from a 30.0-μF capacitor. To what potential difference must it be charged?

33. Two capacitors, $C_1 = 25.0\ \mu$F and $C_2 = 5.00\ \mu$F, are connected in parallel and charged with a 100-V power supply. (a) Draw a circuit diagram and calculate the total energy stored in the two capacitors. (b) **What If?** What potential difference would be required across the same two capacitors connected in series in order that the combination stores the same amount of energy as in (a)? Draw a circuit diagram of this circuit.

34. A parallel-plate capacitor is charged and then disconnected from a battery. By what fraction does the stored energy change (increase or decrease) when the plate separation is doubled?

35. As a person moves about in a dry environment, electric charge accumulates on his body. Once it is at high voltage, either positive or negative, the body can discharge via sometimes noticeable sparks and shocks. Consider a human body well separated from ground, with the typical capacitance 150 pF. (a) What charge on the body will produce a potential of 10.0 kV? (b) Sensitive electronic devices can be destroyed by electrostatic discharge from a person. A particular device can be destroyed by a discharge releasing an energy of 250 μJ. To what voltage on the body does this correspond?

36. A uniform electric field $E = 3\ 000$ V/m exists within a certain region. What volume of space contains an energy equal to 1.00×10^{-7} J? Express your answer in cubic meters and in liters.

37. A parallel-plate capacitor has a charge Q and plates of area A. What force acts on one plate to attract it toward the other plate? Because the electric field between the plates is $E = Q/A\epsilon_0$, you might think that the force is $F = QE = Q^2/A\epsilon_0$. This is wrong, because the field E includes contributions from both plates, and the field created by the positive plate cannot exert any force on the positive plate. Show that the force exerted on each plate is actually $F = Q^2/2\epsilon_0 A$. (*Suggestion:* Let $C = \epsilon_0 A/x$ for an arbitrary plate separation x; then require that the work done in separating the two charged plates be $W = \int F\,dx$.) The force exerted by one charged plate on another is sometimes used in a machine shop to hold a workpiece stationary.

38. The circuit in Figure P26.38 consists of two identical parallel metal plates connected by identical metal springs to a 100-V battery. With the switch open, the plates are uncharged, are separated by a distance $d = 8.00$ mm, and have a capacitance $C = 2.00\ \mu$F. When the switch is closed, the distance between the plates decreases by a factor of 0.500. (a) How much charge collects on each plate and (b) what is the spring constant for each spring? (*Suggestion:* Use the result of Problem 37.)

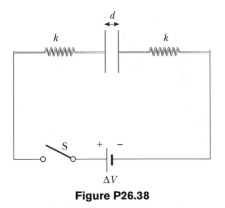

Figure P26.38

39. **Review problem.** A certain storm cloud has a potential of 1.00×10^8 V relative to a tree. If, during a lightning storm, 50.0 C of charge is transferred through this potential difference and 1.00% of the energy is absorbed by the tree, how much sap in the tree can be boiled away? Model the sap as water initially at 30.0°C. Water has a specific heat of 4 186 J/kg°C, a boiling point of 100°C, and a latent heat of vaporization of 2.26×10^6 J/kg.

40. Two identical parallel-plate capacitors, each with capacitance C, are charged to potential difference ΔV and connected in parallel. Then the plate separation in one of the capacitors is doubled. (a) Find the total energy of the system of two capacitors *before* the plate separation is doubled. (b) Find the potential difference across each capacitor *after* the plate separation is doubled. (c) Find the

total energy of the system *after* the plate separation is doubled. (d) Reconcile the difference in the answers to parts (a) and (c) with the law of conservation of energy.

41. Show that the energy associated with a conducting sphere of radius R and charge Q surrounded by a vacuum is $U = k_e Q^2/2R$.

42. Consider two conducting spheres with radii R_1 and R_2. They are separated by a distance much greater than either radius. A total charge Q is shared between the spheres, subject to the condition that the electric potential energy of the system has the smallest possible value. The total charge Q is equal to $q_1 + q_2$, where q_1 represents the charge on the first sphere and q_2 the charge on the second. Because the spheres are very far apart, you can assume that the charge of each is uniformly distributed over its surface. You may use the result of Problem 41. (a) Determine the values of q_1 and q_2 in terms of Q, R_1, and R_2. (b) Show that the potential difference between the spheres is zero. (We saw in Chapter 25 that two conductors joined by a conducting wire will be at the same potential in a static situation. This problem illustrates the general principle that static charge on a conductor will distribute itself so that the electric potential energy of the system is a minimum.)

Section 26.5 Capacitors with Dielectrics

43. Determine (a) the capacitance and (b) the maximum potential difference that can be applied to a Teflon-filled parallel-plate capacitor having a plate area of 1.75 cm² and plate separation of 0.040 0 mm.

44. (a) How much charge can be placed on a capacitor with air between the plates before it breaks down, if the area of each of the plates is 5.00 cm²? (b) **What If?** Find the maximum charge if polystyrene is used between the plates instead of air.

45. A commercial capacitor is to be constructed as shown in Figure 26.17a. This particular capacitor is made from two strips of aluminum separated by a strip of paraffin-coated paper. Each strip of foil and paper is 7.00 cm wide. The foil is 0.004 00 mm thick, and the paper is 0.025 0 mm thick and has a dielectric constant of 3.70. What length should the strips have, if a capacitance of 9.50×10^{-8} F is desired before the capacitor is rolled up? (Adding a second strip of paper and rolling the capacitor effectively doubles its capacitance, by allowing charge storage on both sides of each strip of foil.)

46. The supermarket sells rolls of aluminum foil, of plastic wrap, and of waxed paper. Describe a capacitor made from supermarket materials. Compute order-of-magnitude estimates for its capacitance and its breakdown voltage.

47. A parallel-plate capacitor in air has a plate separation of 1.50 cm and a plate area of 25.0 cm². The plates are charged to a potential difference of 250 V and disconnected from the source. The capacitor is then immersed in distilled water. Determine (a) the charge on the plates before and after immersion, (b) the capacitance and potential difference after immersion, and (c) the change in energy of the capacitor. Assume the liquid is an insulator.

48. A wafer of titanium dioxide ($\kappa = 173$) of area 1.00 cm² has a thickness of 0.100 mm. Aluminum is evaporated on the parallel faces to form a parallel-plate capacitor. (a) Calculate the capacitance. (b) When the capacitor is charged with a 12.0-V battery, what is the magnitude of charge delivered to each plate? (c) For the situation in part (b), what are the free and induced surface charge densities? (d) What is the magnitude of the electric field?

49. Each capacitor in the combination shown in Figure P26.49 has a breakdown voltage of 15.0 V. What is the breakdown voltage of the combination?

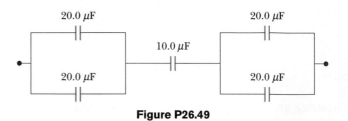

20.0 μF   20.0 μF

10.0 μF

20.0 μF   20.0 μF

Figure P26.49

Section 26.6 Electric Dipole in an Electric Field

50. A small rigid object carries positive and negative 3.50-nC charges. It is oriented so that the positive charge has coordinates $(-1.20$ mm, 1.10 mm) and the negative charge is at the point (1.40 mm, -1.30 mm). (a) Find the electric dipole moment of the object. The object is placed in an electric field $\mathbf{E} = (7\,800\hat{\mathbf{i}} - 4\,900\hat{\mathbf{j}})$ N/C. (b) Find the torque acting on the object. (c) Find the potential energy of the object–field system when the object is in this orientation. (d) If the orientation of the object can change, find the difference between the maximum and minimum potential energies of the system.

51. A small object with electric dipole moment $\mathbf{p}$ is placed in a nonuniform electric field $\mathbf{E} = E(x)\hat{\mathbf{i}}$. That is, the field is in the x direction and its magnitude depends on the coordinate x. Let θ represent the angle between the dipole moment and the x direction. (a) Prove that the dipole feels a net force

$$F = p\left(\frac{dE}{dx}\right)\cos\theta$$

in the direction toward which the field increases. (b) Consider a spherical balloon centered at the origin, with radius 15.0 cm and carrying charge 2.00 μC. Evaluate dE/dx at the point (16 cm, 0, 0). Assume a water droplet at this point has an induced dipole moment of $6.30\hat{\mathbf{i}}$ nC·m. Find the force on it.

Section 26.7 An Atomic Description of Dielectrics

52. A detector of radiation called a Geiger tube consists of a closed, hollow, conducting cylinder with a fine wire along its axis. Suppose that the internal diameter of the cylinder is 2.50 cm and that the wire along the axis has a diameter of 0.200 mm. The dielectric strength of the gas between the central wire and the cylinder is 1.20×10^6 V/m. Calculate the maximum potential difference that can be applied between the wire and the cylinder before breakdown occurs in the gas.

53. The general form of Gauss's law describes how a charge creates an electric field in a material, as well as in vacuum. It is

$$\oint \mathbf{E} \cdot d\mathbf{A} = \frac{q}{\epsilon}$$

where $\epsilon = \kappa\epsilon_0$ is the permittivity of the material. (a) A sheet with charge Q uniformly distributed over its area A is surrounded by a dielectric. Show that the sheet creates a uniform electric field at nearby points, with magnitude $E = Q/2A\epsilon$. (b) Two large sheets of area A, carrying opposite charges of equal magnitude Q, are a small distance d apart. Show that they create uniform electric field in the space between them, with magnitude $E = Q/A\epsilon$. (c) Assume that the negative plate is at zero potential. Show that the positive plate is at potential $Qd/A\epsilon$. (d) Show that the capacitance of the pair of plates is $A\epsilon/d = \kappa A\epsilon_0/d$.

Additional Problems

54. For the system of capacitors shown in Figure P26.54, find (a) the equivalent capacitance of the system, (b) the potential across each capacitor, (c) the charge on each capacitor, and (d) the total energy stored by the group.

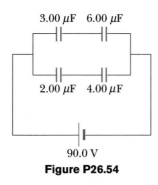

3.00 μF   6.00 μF

2.00 μF   4.00 μF

90.0 V

Figure P26.54

55. Four parallel metal plates P_1, P_2, P_3, and P_4, each of area 7.50 cm^2, are separated successively by a distance $d = 1.19$ mm, as shown in Figure P26.55. P_1 is connected to the negative terminal of a battery, and P_2 to the positive terminal. The battery maintains a potential difference of 12.0 V. (a) If P_3 is connected to the negative terminal, what is the

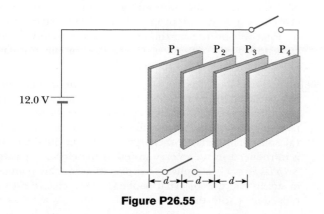

12.0 V

P_1 P_2 P_3 P_4

$\leftarrow d \rightarrow \leftarrow d \rightarrow \leftarrow d \rightarrow$

Figure P26.55

capacitance of the three-plate system $P_1P_2P_3$? (b) What is the charge on P_2? (c) If P_4 is now connected to the positive terminal of the battery, what is the capacitance of the four-plate system $P_1P_2P_3P_4$? (d) What is the charge on P_4?

56. One conductor of an overhead electric transmission line is a long aluminum wire 2.40 cm in radius. Suppose that at a particular moment it carries charge per length 1.40 μC/m and is at potential 345 kV. Find the potential 12.0 m below the wire. Ignore the other conductors of the transmission line and assume the electric field is everywhere purely radial.

57. Two large parallel metal plates are oriented horizontally and separated by a distance $3d$. A grounded conducting wire joins them, and initially each plate carries no charge. Now a third identical plate carrying charge Q is inserted between the two plates, parallel to them and located a distance d from the upper plate, as in Figure P26.57. (a) What induced charge appears on each of the two original plates? (b) What potential difference appears between the middle plate and each of the other plates? Each plate has area A.

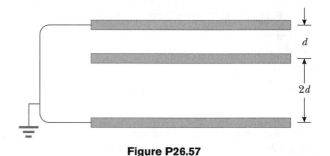

d

$2d$

Figure P26.57

58. A 2.00-nF parallel-plate capacitor is charged to an initial potential difference $\Delta V_i = 100$ V and then isolated. The dielectric material between the plates is mica, with a dielectric constant of 5.00. (a) How much work is required to withdraw the mica sheet? (b) What is the potential difference of the capacitor after the mica is withdrawn?

59. A parallel-plate capacitor is constructed using a dielectric material whose dielectric constant is 3.00 and whose dielectric strength is 2.00×10^8 V/m. The desired capacitance is 0.250 μF, and the capacitor must withstand a maximum potential difference of 4 000 V. Find the minimum area of the capacitor plates.

60. A 10.0-μF capacitor has plates with vacuum between them. Each plate carries a charge of magnitude 1 000 μC. A particle with charge -3.00 μC and mass 2.00×10^{-16} kg is fired from the positive plate toward the negative plate with an initial speed of 2.00×10^6 m/s. Does it reach the negative plate? If so, find its impact speed. If not, what fraction of the way across the capacitor does it travel?

61. A parallel-plate capacitor is constructed by filling the space between two square plates with blocks of three dielectric materials, as in Figure P26.61. You may assume that $\ell \gg d$. (a) Find an expression for the capacitance of the device in terms of the plate area A and d, κ_1, κ_2, and κ_3. (b) Calculate the capacitance using the values $A = 1.00$ cm^2, $d = 2.00$ mm, $\kappa_1 = 4.90$, $\kappa_2 = 5.60$, and $\kappa_3 = 2.10$.

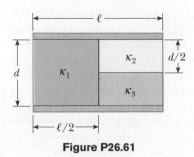

Figure P26.61

62. A 10.0-μF capacitor is charged to 15.0 V. It is next connected in series with an uncharged 5.00-μF capacitor. The series combination is finally connected across a 50.0-V battery, as diagrammed in Figure P26.62. Find the new potential differences across the 5-μF and 10-μF capacitors.

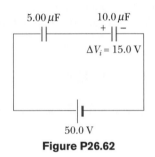

Figure P26.62

63. (a) Two spheres have radii a and b and their centers are a distance d apart. Show that the capacitance of this system is

$$C = \frac{4\pi\epsilon_0}{\dfrac{1}{a} + \dfrac{1}{b} - \dfrac{2}{d}}$$

provided that d is large compared with a and b. (*Suggestion:* Because the spheres are far apart, assume that the potential of each equals the sum of the potentials due to each sphere, and when calculating those potentials assume that $V = k_e Q/r$ applies.) (b) Show that as d approaches infinity the above result reduces to that of two spherical capacitors in series.

64. A capacitor is constructed from two square plates of sides ℓ and separation d. A material of dielectric constant κ is inserted a distance x into the capacitor, as shown in Figure P26.64. Assume that d is much smaller than x. (a) Find the equivalent capacitance of the device. (b) Calculate the energy stored in the capacitor, letting ΔV repre-

sent the potential difference. (c) Find the direction and magnitude of the force exerted on the dielectric, assuming a constant potential difference ΔV. Ignore friction. (d) Obtain a numerical value for the force assuming that $\ell = 5.00$ cm, $\Delta V = 2\,000$ V, $d = 2.00$ mm, and the dielectric is glass ($\kappa = 4.50$). (*Suggestion:* The system can be considered as two capacitors connected in parallel.)

65. A capacitor is constructed from two square plates of sides ℓ and separation d, as suggested in Figure P26.64. You may assume that d is much less than ℓ. The plates carry charges $+Q_0$ and $-Q_0$. A block of metal has a width ℓ, a length ℓ, and a thickness slightly less than d. It is inserted a distance x into the capacitor. The charges on the plates are not disturbed as the block slides in. In a static situation, a metal prevents an electric field from penetrating inside it. The metal can be thought of as a perfect dielectric, with $\kappa \rightarrow \infty$. (a) Calculate the stored energy as a function of x. (b) Find the direction and magnitude of the force that acts on the metallic block. (c) The area of the advancing front face of the block is essentially equal to ℓd. Considering the force on the block as acting on this face, find the stress (force per area) on it. (d) For comparison, express the energy density in the electric field between the capacitor plates in terms of Q_0, ℓ, d, and ϵ_0.

66. When considering the energy supply for an automobile, the energy per unit mass of the energy source is an important parameter. Using the following data, compare the energy per unit mass (J/kg) for gasoline, lead–acid batteries, and capacitors. (The ampere A will be introduced in the next chapter as the SI unit of electric current. 1 A = 1 C/s.)
Gasoline: 126 000 Btu/gal; density = 670 kg/m³.
Lead–acid battery: 12.0 V; 100 A·h; mass = 16.0 kg.
Capacitor: potential difference at full charge = 12.0 V; capacitance = 0.100 F; mass = 0.100 kg.

67. An isolated capacitor of unknown capacitance has been charged to a potential difference of 100 V. When the charged capacitor is then connected in parallel to an uncharged 10.0-μF capacitor, the potential difference across the combination is 30.0 V. Calculate the unknown capacitance.

68. To repair a power supply for a stereo amplifier, an electronics technician needs a 100-μF capacitor capable of withstanding a potential difference of 90 V between the plates. The only available supply is a box of five 100-μF capacitors, each having a maximum voltage capability of 50 V. Can the technician substitute a combination of these capacitors that has the proper electrical characteristics? If so, what will be the maximum voltage across any of the capacitors used? (*Suggestion:* The technician may not have to use all the capacitors in the box.)

69. A parallel-plate capacitor of plate separation d is charged to a potential difference ΔV_0. A dielectric slab of thickness d and dielectric constant κ is introduced between the plates while the battery remains connected to the plates. (a) Show that the ratio of energy stored after the dielectric is introduced to the energy stored in the empty capacitor is $U/U_0 = \kappa$. Give a physical explanation for this increase in stored energy. (b) What happens to the charge on the capacitor? (Note that this situation is not the same as in

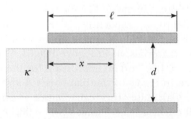

Figure P26.64 Problems 64 and 65.

Example 26.7, in which the battery was removed from the circuit before the dielectric was introduced.)

70. A vertical parallel-plate capacitor is half filled with a dielectric for which the dielectric constant is 2.00 (Fig. P26.70a). When this capacitor is positioned horizontally, what fraction of it should be filled with the same dielectric (Fig. P26.70b) in order for the two capacitors to have equal capacitance?

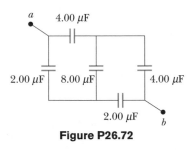

(a)   (b)

Figure P26.70

71. Capacitors $C_1 = 6.00\ \mu F$ and $C_2 = 2.00\ \mu F$ are charged as a parallel combination across a 250-V battery. The capacitors are disconnected from the battery and from each other. They are then connected positive plate to negative plate and negative plate to positive plate. Calculate the resulting charge on each capacitor.

72. Calculate the equivalent capacitance between the points a and b in Figure P26.72. Note that this is not a simple series or parallel combination. (*Suggestion:* Assume a potential difference ΔV between points a and b. Write expressions for ΔV_{ab} in terms of the charges and capacitances for the various possible pathways from a to b, and require conservation of charge for those capacitor plates that are connected to each other.)

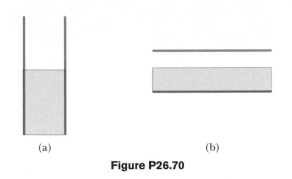

Figure P26.72

73. The inner conductor of a coaxial cable has a radius of 0.800 mm, and the outer conductor's inside radius is 3.00 mm. The space between the conductors is filled with polyethylene, which has a dielectric constant of 2.30 and a dielectric strength of 18.0×10^6 V/m. What is the maximum potential difference that this cable can withstand?

74. You are optimizing coaxial cable design for a major manufacturer. Show that for a given outer conductor radius b, maximum potential difference capability is attained when the radius of the inner conductor is $a = b/e$ where e is the base of natural logarithms.

75. Determine the equivalent capacitance of the combination shown in Figure P26.75. (*Suggestion:* Consider the symmetry involved.)

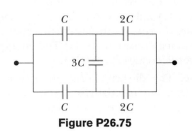

Figure P26.75

76. Consider two long, parallel, and oppositely charged wires of radius d with their centers separated by a distance D. Assuming the charge is distributed uniformly on the surface of each wire, show that the capacitance per unit length of this pair of wires is

$$\frac{C}{\ell} = \frac{\pi\epsilon_0}{\ln[(D-d)/d]}$$

77. Example 26.2 explored a cylindrical capacitor of length ℓ and radii a and b of the two conductors. In the **What If?** section, it was claimed that increasing ℓ by 10% is more effective in terms of increasing the capacitance than increasing a by 10% if $b > 2.85a$. Verify this claim mathematically.

Answers to Quick Quizzes

26.1 (d). The capacitance is a property of the physical system and does not vary with applied voltage. According to Equation 26.1, if the voltage is doubled, the charge is doubled.

26.2 (a). When the key is pressed, the plate separation is decreased and the capacitance increases. Capacitance depends only on how a capacitor is constructed and not on the external circuit.

26.3 (a). When connecting capacitors in series, the inverses of the capacitances add, resulting in a smaller overall equivalent capacitance.

26.4 (a). When capacitors are connected in series, the voltages add, for a total of 20 V in this case. If they are combined in parallel, the voltage across the combination is still 10 V.

26.5 (b). For a given voltage, the energy stored in a capacitor is proportional to C: $U = C(\Delta V)^2/2$. Thus, you want to maximize the equivalent capacitance. You do this by connecting the three capacitors in parallel, so that the capacitances add.

26.6 (a) C decreases (Eq. 26.3). (b) Q stays the same because there is no place for the charge to flow. (c) E remains constant (see Eq. 24.8 and the paragraph following it). (d) ΔV increases because $\Delta V = Q/C$, Q is constant (part b), and C decreases (part a). (e) The energy stored in the capacitor is proportional to both Q and ΔV (Eq.

26.11) and thus increases. The additional energy comes from the work you do in pulling the two plates apart.

26.7 (a) C decreases (Eq. 26.3). (b) Q decreases. The battery supplies a constant potential difference ΔV; thus, charge must flow out of the capacitor if $C = Q/\Delta V$ is to decrease. (c) E decreases because the charge density on the plates decreases. (d) ΔV remains constant because of the presence of the battery. (e) The energy stored in the capacitor decreases (Eq. 26.11).

26.8 Increase. The dielectric constant of wood (and of all other insulating materials, for that matter) is greater than 1; therefore, the capacitance increases (Eq. 26.14). This increase is sensed by the stud-finder's special circuitry, which causes an indicator on the device to light up.

26.9 (a) C increases (Eq. 26.14). (b) Q increases. Because the battery maintains a constant ΔV, Q must increase if C increases. (c) E between the plates remains constant because $\Delta V = Ed$ and neither ΔV nor d changes. The electric field due to the charges on the plates increases because more charge has flowed onto the plates. The induced surface charges on the dielectric create a field that opposes the increase in the field caused by the greater number of charges on the plates (see Section 26.7). (d) The battery maintains a constant ΔV.

Current and Resistance

▲ These power lines transfer energy from the power company to homes and businesses. The energy is transferred at a very high voltage, possibly hundreds of thousands of volts in some cases. Despite the fact that this makes power lines very dangerous, the high voltage results in less loss of power due to resistance in the wires. (Telegraph Colour Library/FPG)

Thus far our treatment of electrical phenomena has been confined to the study of charges in equilibrium situations, or *electrostatics*. We now consider situations involving electric charges that are *not* in equilibrium. We use the term *electric current*, or simply *current*, to describe the rate of flow of charge through some region of space. Most practical applications of electricity deal with electric currents. For example, the battery in a flashlight produces a current in the filament of the bulb when the switch is turned on. A variety of home appliances operate on alternating current. In these common situations, current exists in a conductor, such as a copper wire. It also is possible for currents to exist outside a conductor. For instance, a beam of electrons in a television picture tube constitutes a current.

This chapter begins with the definition of current. A microscopic description of current is given, and some of the factors that contribute to the opposition to the flow of charge in conductors are discussed. A classical model is used to describe electrical conduction in metals, and some of the limitations of this model are cited. We also define electrical resistance and introduce a new circuit element, the resistor. We conclude by discussing the rate at which energy is transferred to a device in an electric circuit.

27.1 Electric Current

In this section, we study the flow of electric charges through a piece of material. The amount of flow depends on the material through which the charges are passing and the potential difference across the material. Whenever there is a net flow of charge through some region, an electric **current** is said to exist.

It is instructive to draw an analogy between water flow and current. In many localities it is common practice to install low-flow showerheads in homes as a water-conservation measure. We quantify the flow of water from these and similar devices by specifying the amount of water that emerges during a given time interval, which is often measured in liters per minute. On a grander scale, we can characterize a river current by describing the rate at which the water flows past a particular location. For example, the flow over the brink at Niagara Falls is maintained at rates between $1\,400 \text{ m}^3/\text{s}$ and $2\,800 \text{ m}^3/\text{s}$.

There is also an analogy between thermal conduction and current. In Section 20.7, we discussed the flow of energy by heat through a sample of material. The rate of energy flow is determined by the material as well as the temperature difference across the material, as described by Equation 20.14.

To define current more precisely, suppose that charges are moving perpendicular to a surface of area A, as shown in Figure 27.1. (This area could be the cross-sectional area of a wire, for example.) **The current is the rate at which charge flows through this surface.** If ΔQ is the amount of charge that passes through this area in a time interval Δt, the **average current** I_{av} is equal to the charge that passes through A per unit time:

$$I_{av} = \frac{\Delta Q}{\Delta t} \tag{27.1}$$

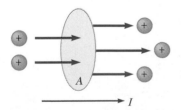

Figure 27.1 Charges in motion through an area A. The time rate at which charge flows through the area is defined as the current I. The direction of the current is the direction in which positive charges flow when free to do so.

If the rate at which charge flows varies in time, then the current varies in time; we define the **instantaneous current** I as the differential limit of average current:

$$I \equiv \frac{dQ}{dt} \qquad (27.2)$$

The SI unit of current is the **ampere** (A):

$$1\text{ A} = \frac{1\text{ C}}{1\text{ s}} \qquad (27.3)$$

That is, 1 A of current is equivalent to 1 C of charge passing through the surface area in 1 s.

The charges passing through the surface in Figure 27.1 can be positive or negative, or both. **It is conventional to assign to the current the same direction as the flow of positive charge.** In electrical conductors, such as copper or aluminum, the current is due to the motion of negatively charged electrons. Therefore, when we speak of current in an ordinary conductor, **the direction of the current is opposite the direction of flow of electrons.** However, if we are considering a beam of positively charged protons in an accelerator, the current is in the direction of motion of the protons. In some cases—such as those involving gases and electrolytes, for instance—the current is the result of the flow of both positive and negative charges.

If the ends of a conducting wire are connected to form a loop, all points on the loop are at the same electric potential, and hence the electric field is zero within and at the surface of the conductor. Because the electric field is zero, there is no net transport of charge through the wire, and therefore there is no current. However, if the ends of the conducting wire are connected to a battery, all points on the loop are not at the same potential. The battery sets up a potential difference between the ends of the loop, creating an electric field within the wire. The electric field exerts forces on the conduction electrons in the wire, causing them to move in the wire, thus creating a current.

It is common to refer to a moving charge (positive or negative) as a mobile **charge carrier.** For example, the mobile charge carriers in a metal are electrons.

Microscopic Model of Current

We can relate current to the motion of the charge carriers by describing a microscopic model of conduction in a metal. Consider the current in a conductor of cross-sectional area A (Fig. 27.2). The volume of a section of the conductor of length Δx (the gray region shown in Fig. 27.2) is $A \Delta x$. If n represents the number of mobile charge carriers per unit volume (in other words, the charge carrier density), the number of carriers in the gray section is $nA \Delta x$. Therefore, the total charge ΔQ in this section is

$$\Delta Q = \text{number of carriers in section} \times \text{charge per carrier} = (nA \, \Delta x)q$$

where q is the charge on each carrier. If the carriers move with a speed v_d, the displacement they experience in the x direction in a time interval Δt is $\Delta x = v_d \, \Delta t$. Let us choose Δt to be the time interval required for the charges in the cylinder to move through a displacement whose magnitude is equal to the length of the cylinder. This time interval is also that required for all of the charges in the cylinder to pass through the circular area at one end. With this choice, we can write ΔQ in the form

$$\Delta Q = (nAv_d \, \Delta t)q$$

If we divide both sides of this equation by Δt, we see that the average current in the conductor is

$$I_{\text{av}} = \frac{\Delta Q}{\Delta t} = nqv_d A \qquad (27.4)$$

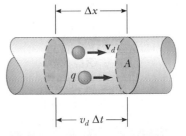

Figure 27.2 A section of a uniform conductor of cross-sectional area A. The mobile charge carriers move with a speed v_d, and the displacement they experience in the x direction in a time interval Δt is $\Delta x = v_d \, \Delta t$. If we choose Δt to be the time interval during which the charges are displaced, on the average, by the length of the cylinder, the number of carriers in the section of length Δx is $nAv_d \, \Delta t$, where n is the number of carriers per unit volume.

Current in a conductor in terms of microscopic quantities

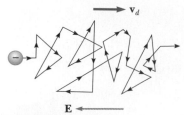

Figure 27.3 A schematic representation of the zigzag motion of an electron in a conductor. The changes in direction are the result of collisions between the electron and atoms in the conductor. Note that the net motion of the electron is opposite the direction of the electric field. Because of the acceleration of the charge carriers due to the electric force, the paths are actually parabolic. However, the drift speed is much smaller than the average speed, so the parabolic shape is not visible on this scale.

The speed of the charge carriers v_d is an average speed called the **drift speed.** To understand the meaning of drift speed, consider a conductor in which the charge carriers are free electrons. If the conductor is isolated—that is, the potential difference across it is zero—then these electrons undergo random motion that is analogous to the motion of gas molecules. As we discussed earlier, when a potential difference is applied across the conductor (for example, by means of a battery), an electric field is set up in the conductor; this field exerts an electric force on the electrons, producing a current. However, the electrons do not move in straight lines along the conductor. Instead, they collide repeatedly with the metal atoms, and their resultant motion is complicated and zigzag (Fig. 27.3). Despite the collisions, the electrons move slowly along the conductor (in a direction opposite that of **E**) at the drift velocity $\mathbf{v}_d$.

We can think of the atom–electron collisions in a conductor as an effective internal friction (or drag force) similar to that experienced by the molecules of a liquid flowing through a pipe stuffed with steel wool. The energy transferred from the electrons to the metal atoms during collisions causes an increase in the vibrational energy of the atoms and a corresponding increase in the temperature of the conductor.

Quick Quiz 27.1 Consider positive and negative charges moving horizontally through the four regions shown in Figure 27.4. Rank the current in these four regions, from lowest to highest.

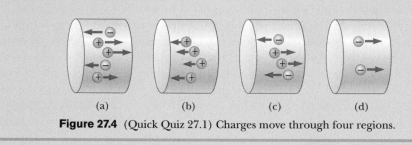

(a)   (b)   (c)   (d)

Figure 27.4 (Quick Quiz 27.1) Charges move through four regions.

Quick Quiz 27.2 Electric charge is conserved. As a consequence, when current arrives at a junction of wires, the charges can take either of two paths out of the junction and the numerical sum of the currents in the two paths equals the current that entered the junction. Thus, current is (a) a vector (b) a scalar (c) neither a vector nor a scalar.

Example 27.1   Drift Speed in a Copper Wire

The 12-gauge copper wire in a typical residential building has a cross-sectional area of 3.31×10^{-6} m². If it carries a current of 10.0 A, what is the drift speed of the electrons? Assume that each copper atom contributes one free electron to the current. The density of copper is 8.95 g/cm³.

Solution From the periodic table of the elements in Appendix C, we find that the molar mass of copper is 63.5 g/mol. Recall that 1 mol of any substance contains Avogadro's number of atoms (6.02×10^{23}). Knowing the density of copper, we can calculate the volume occupied by 63.5 g ($= 1$ mol) of copper:

$$V = \frac{m}{\rho} = \frac{63.5 \text{ g}}{8.95 \text{ g/cm}^3} = 7.09 \text{ cm}^3$$

Because each copper atom contributes one free electron to the current, we have

$$n = \frac{6.02 \times 10^{23} \text{ electrons}}{7.09 \text{ cm}^3}\left(\frac{1.00 \times 10^6 \text{ cm}^3}{1 \text{ m}^3}\right)$$

$$= 8.49 \times 10^{28} \text{ electrons/m}^3$$

From Equation 27.4, we find that the drift speed is

$$v_d = \frac{I}{nqA}$$

where q is the absolute value of the charge on each electron. Thus,

$$v_d = \frac{I}{nqA}$$

$$= \frac{10.0 \text{ C/s}}{(8.49 \times 10^{28} \text{ m}^{-3})(1.60 \times 10^{-19} \text{ C})(3.31 \times 10^{-6} \text{ m}^2)}$$

$$= \boxed{2.22 \times 10^{-4} \text{ m/s}}$$

Example 27.1 shows that typical drift speeds are very low. For instance, electrons traveling with a speed of 2.22×10^{-4} m/s would take about 75 min to travel 1 m! In view of this, you might wonder why a light turns on almost instantaneously when a switch is thrown. In a conductor, changes in the electric field that drives the free electrons travel through the conductor with a speed close to that of light. Thus, when you flip on a light switch, electrons already in the filament of the lightbulb experience electric forces and begin moving after a time interval on the order of nanoseconds.

27.2 Resistance

In Chapter 24 we found that the electric field inside a conductor is zero. However, this statement is true *only* if the conductor is in static equilibrium. The purpose of this section is to describe what happens when the charges in the conductor are not in equilibrium, in which case there is an electric field in the conductor.

Consider a conductor of cross-sectional area A carrying a current I. The **current density** J in the conductor is defined as the current per unit area. Because the current $I = nqv_d A$, the current density is

$$J \equiv \frac{I}{A} = nqv_d \qquad (27.5)$$

where J has SI units of A/m^2. This expression is valid only if the current density is uniform and only if the surface of cross-sectional area A is perpendicular to the direction of the current. In general, current density is a vector quantity:

$$\mathbf{J} = nq\mathbf{v}_d \qquad (27.6)$$

From this equation, we see that current density is in the direction of charge motion for positive charge carriers and opposite the direction of motion for negative charge carriers.

A current density J and an electric field E are established in a conductor whenever a potential difference is maintained across the conductor. In some materials, the current density is proportional to the electric field:

$$\mathbf{J} = \sigma\mathbf{E} \qquad (27.7)$$

where the constant of proportionality σ is called the **conductivity** of the conductor.[1] Materials that obey Equation 27.7 are said to follow **Ohm's law,** named after Georg Simon Ohm (1789–1854). More specifically, Ohm's law states that

> for many materials (including most metals), the ratio of the current density to the electric field is a constant σ that is independent of the electric field producing the current.

Materials that obey Ohm's law and hence demonstrate this simple relationship between **E** and **J** are said to be *ohmic*. Experimentally, however, it is found that not all materials have this property. Materials and devices that do not obey Ohm's law are said to be *nonohmic*. Ohm's law is not a fundamental law of nature but rather an empirical relationship valid only for certain materials.

We can obtain an equation useful in practical applications by considering a segment of straight wire of uniform cross-sectional area A and length ℓ, as shown in

---

[1]   Do not confuse conductivity σ with surface charge density, for which the same symbol is used.

▲ PITFALL PREVENTION

27.2 Electrons Are Available Everywhere

Electrons do not have to travel from the light switch to the light in order for the light to operate. Electrons already in the filament of the lightbulb move in response to the electric field set up by the battery. Notice also that a battery does not provide electrons to the circuit. It establishes the electric field that exerts a force on electrons already in the wires and elements of the circuit.

Current density

Georg Simon Ohm
German physicist (1789–1854)

Ohm, a high school teacher and later a professor at the University of Munich, formulated the concept of resistance and discovered the proportionalities expressed in Equations 27.7 and 27.8. *(© Bettmann/Corbis)*

▲ PITFALL PREVENTION

27.3 We've Seen Something Like Equation 27.8 Before

In Chapter 5, we introduced Newton's second law, $\Sigma F = ma$, for a net force on an object of mass m. This can be written as

$$m = \frac{\Sigma F}{a}$$

In that chapter, we defined mass as *resistance to a change in motion in response to an external force.* Mass as resistance to changes in motion is analogous to electrical resistance to charge flow, and Equation 27.8 is analogous to the form of Newton's second law shown here.

▲ PITFALL PREVENTION

27.4 Equation 27.8 Is Not Ohm's Law

Many individuals call Equation 27.8 Ohm's law, but this is incorrect. This equation is simply the definition of resistance, and provides an important relationship between voltage, current, and resistance. Ohm's law is related to a linear relationship between $\mathbf{J}$ and $\mathbf{E}$ (Eq. 27.7) or, equivalently, between I and ΔV, which, from Equation 27.8, indicates that the resistance is constant, independent of the applied voltage.

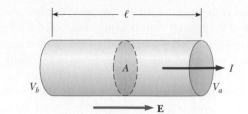

Figure 27.5 A uniform conductor of length ℓ and cross-sectional area A. A potential difference $\Delta V = V_b - V_a$ maintained across the conductor sets up an electric field $\mathbf{E}$, and this field produces a current I that is proportional to the potential difference.

Figure 27.5. A potential difference $\Delta V = V_b - V_a$ is maintained across the wire, creating in the wire an electric field and a current. If the field is assumed to be uniform, the potential difference is related to the field through the relationship[2]

$$\Delta V = E\ell$$

Therefore, we can express the magnitude of the current density in the wire as

$$J = \sigma E = \sigma \frac{\Delta V}{\ell}$$

Because $J = I/A$, we can write the potential difference as

$$\Delta V = \frac{\ell}{\sigma} J = \left(\frac{\ell}{\sigma A}\right) I = RI$$

The quantity $R = \ell/\sigma A$ is called the **resistance** of the conductor. We can define the resistance as the ratio of the potential difference across a conductor to the current in the conductor:

$$R \equiv \frac{\Delta V}{I} \tag{27.8}$$

We will use this equation over and over again when studying electric circuits. From this result we see that resistance has SI units of volts per ampere. One volt per ampere is defined to be one **ohm** (Ω):

$$1\,\Omega \equiv \frac{1\,\text{V}}{1\,\text{A}} \tag{27.9}$$

This expression shows that if a potential difference of 1 V across a conductor causes a current of 1 A, the resistance of the conductor is 1 Ω. For example, if an electrical appliance connected to a 120-V source of potential difference carries a current of 6 A, its resistance is 20 Ω.

The inverse of conductivity is **resistivity**[3] ρ:

$$\rho = \frac{1}{\sigma} \tag{27.10}$$

Resistivity is the inverse of conductivity

where ρ has the units ohm-meters ($\Omega \cdot$m). Because $R = \ell/\sigma A$, we can express the resistance of a uniform block of material along the length ℓ as

Resistance of a uniform material along the length ℓ

$$R = \rho \frac{\ell}{A} \tag{27.11}$$

---

[2] This result follows from the definition of potential difference:

$$V_b - V_a = -\int_a^b \mathbf{E} \cdot d\mathbf{s} = E \int_0^\ell dx = E\ell$$

[3] Do not confuse resistivity ρ with mass density or charge density, for which the same symbol is used.

Table 27.1

Resistivities and Temperature Coefficients of Resistivity for Various Materials		
Material	**Resistivity[a] $(\Omega \cdot m)$**	**Temperature Coefficient[b] $\alpha[(^\circ C)^{-1}]$**
Silver	1.59×10^{-8}	3.8×10^{-3}
Copper	1.7×10^{-8}	3.9×10^{-3}
Gold	2.44×10^{-8}	3.4×10^{-3}
Aluminum	2.82×10^{-8}	3.9×10^{-3}
Tungsten	5.6×10^{-8}	4.5×10^{-3}
Iron	10×10^{-8}	5.0×10^{-3}
Platinum	11×10^{-8}	3.92×10^{-3}
Lead	22×10^{-8}	3.9×10^{-3}
Nichrome[c]	1.50×10^{-6}	0.4×10^{-3}
Carbon	3.5×10^{-5}	-0.5×10^{-3}
Germanium	0.46	-48×10^{-3}
Silicon	640	-75×10^{-3}
Glass	10^{10} to 10^{14}	
Hard rubber	$\sim 10^{13}$	
Sulfur	10^{15}	
Quartz (fused)	75×10^{16}	

[a] All values at 20°C.

[b] See Section 27.4.

[c] A nickel–chromium alloy commonly used in heating elements.

Every ohmic material has a characteristic resistivity that depends on the properties of the material and on temperature. Additionally, as you can see from Equation 27.11, the resistance of a sample depends on geometry as well as on resistivity. Table 27.1 gives the resistivities of a variety of materials at 20°C. Note the enormous range, from very low values for good conductors such as copper and silver, to very high values for good insulators such as glass and rubber. An ideal conductor would have zero resistivity, and an ideal insulator would have infinite resistivity.

Equation 27.11 shows that the resistance of a given cylindrical conductor such as a wire is proportional to its length and inversely proportional to its cross-sectional area. If the length of a wire is doubled, then its resistance doubles. If its cross-sectional area is doubled, then its resistance decreases by one half. The situation is analogous to the flow of a liquid through a pipe. As the pipe's length is increased, the resistance to flow increases. As the pipe's cross-sectional area is increased, more liquid crosses a given cross section of the pipe per unit time interval. Thus, more liquid flows for the same pressure differential applied to the pipe, and the resistance to flow decreases.

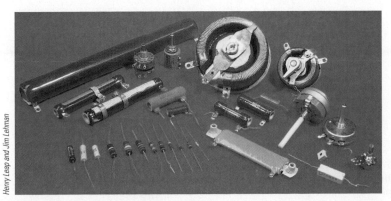

Henry Leap and Jim Lehman

An assortment of resistors used in electrical circuits.

Figure 27.6 The colored bands on a resistor represent a code for determining resistance. The first two colors give the first two digits in the resistance value. The third color represents the power of ten for the multiplier of the resistance value. The last color is the tolerance of the resistance value. As an example, the four colors on the circled resistors are red ($= 2$), black ($= 0$), orange ($= 10^3$), and gold ($= 5\%$), and so the resistance value is $20 \times 10^3 \, \Omega = 20 \, k\Omega$ with a tolerance value of $5\% = 1 \, k\Omega$. (The values for the colors are from Table 27.2.)

Table 27.2

Color Coding for Resistors			
Color	**Number**	**Multiplier**	**Tolerance**
Black	0	1	
Brown	1	10^1	
Red	2	10^2	
Orange	3	10^3	
Yellow	4	10^4	
Green	5	10^5	
Blue	6	10^6	
Violet	7	10^7	
Gray	8	10^8	
White	9	10^9	
Gold		10^{-1}	5%
Silver		10^{-2}	10%
Colorless			20%

Most electric circuits use circuit elements called **resistors** to control the current level in the various parts of the circuit. Two common types of resistors are the *composition resistor*, which contains carbon, and the *wire-wound resistor*, which consists of a coil of wire. Values of resistors in ohms are normally indicated by color-coding, as shown in Figure 27.6 and Table 27.2.

Ohmic materials and devices have a linear current–potential difference relationship over a broad range of applied potential differences (Fig. 27.7a). The slope of the *I*-versus-ΔV curve in the linear region yields a value for $1/R$. Nonohmic materials have a nonlinear current–potential difference relationship. One common semiconducting device that has nonlinear *I*-versus-ΔV characteristics is the *junction diode* (Fig. 27.7b). The resistance of this device is low for currents in one direction (positive ΔV) and high for currents in the reverse direction (negative ΔV). In fact, most modern electronic devices, such as transistors, have nonlinear current–potential difference relationships; their proper operation depends on the particular way in which they violate Ohm's law.

Quick Quiz 27.3 Suppose that a current-carrying ohmic metal wire has a cross-sectional area that gradually becomes smaller from one end of the wire to the other. The current must have the same value in each section of the wire so that charge does not accumulate at any one point. How do the drift velocity and the resistance per

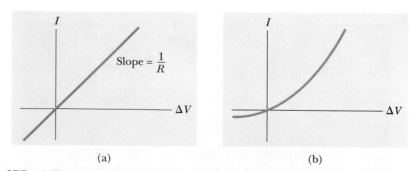

(a)   (b)

Figure 27.7 (a) The current–potential difference curve for an ohmic material. The curve is linear, and the slope is equal to the inverse of the resistance of the conductor. (b) A nonlinear current–potential difference curve for a junction diode. This device does not obey Ohm's law.

unit length vary along the wire as the area becomes smaller? (a) The drift velocity and resistance both increase. (b) The drift velocity and resistance both decrease. (c) The drift velocity increases and the resistance decreases. (d) The drift velocity decreases and the resistance increases.

Quick Quiz 27.4 A cylindrical wire has a radius r and length ℓ. If both r and ℓ are doubled, the resistance of the wire (a) increases (b) decreases (c) remains the same.

Quick Quiz 27.5 In Figure 27.7b, as the applied voltage increases, the resistance of the diode (a) increases (b) decreases (c) remains the same.

Example 27.2 The Resistance of a Conductor

Calculate the resistance of an aluminum cylinder that has a length of 10.0 cm and a cross-sectional area of 2.00×10^{-4} m². Repeat the calculation for a cylinder of the same dimensions and made of glass having a resistivity of 3.0×10^{10} Ω·m.

Solution From Equation 27.11 and Table 27.1, we can calculate the resistance of the aluminum cylinder as follows:

$$R = \rho \frac{\ell}{A} = (2.82 \times 10^{-8}\ \Omega \cdot m) \left(\frac{0.100\ m}{2.00 \times 10^{-4}\ m^2} \right)$$

$$= 1.41 \times 10^{-5}\ \Omega$$

Similarly, for glass we find that

$$R = \rho \frac{\ell}{A} = (3.0 \times 10^{10}\ \Omega \cdot m) \left(\frac{0.100\ m}{2.00 \times 10^{-4}\ m^2} \right)$$

$$= 1.5 \times 10^{13}\ \Omega$$

As you might guess from the large difference in resistivities, the resistances of identically shaped cylinders of aluminum and glass differ widely. The resistance of the glass cylinder is 18 orders of magnitude greater than that of the aluminum cylinder.

Example 27.3 The Resistance of Nichrome Wire   Interactive

(A) Calculate the resistance per unit length of a 22-gauge Nichrome wire, which has a radius of 0.321 mm.

Solution The cross-sectional area of this wire is

$$A = \pi r^2 = \pi (0.321 \times 10^{-3}\ m)^2 = 3.24 \times 10^{-7}\ m^2$$

The resistivity of Nichrome is 1.5×10^{-6} Ω·m (see Table 27.1). Thus, we can use Equation 27.11 to find the resistance per unit length:

$$\frac{R}{\ell} = \frac{\rho}{A} = \frac{1.5 \times 10^{-6}\ \Omega \cdot m}{3.24 \times 10^{-7}\ m^2} = 4.6\ \Omega/m$$

(B) If a potential difference of 10 V is maintained across a 1.0-m length of the Nichrome wire, what is the current in the wire?

Solution Because a 1.0-m length of this wire has a resistance of 4.6 Ω, Equation 27.8 gives

$$I = \frac{\Delta V}{R} = \frac{10\ V}{4.6\ \Omega} = 2.2\ A$$

Note from Table 27.1 that the resistivity of Nichrome wire is about 100 times that of copper. A copper wire of the same radius would have a resistance per unit length of only 0.052 Ω/m. A 1.0-m length of copper wire of the same radius would carry the same current (2.2 A) with an applied potential difference of only 0.11 V.

Because of its high resistivity and its resistance to oxidation, Nichrome is often used for heating elements in toasters, irons, and electric heaters.

Explore the resistance of different materials at the Interactive Worked Example link at **http://www.pse6.com.**

Example 27.4 The Radial Resistance of a Coaxial Cable

Coaxial cables are used extensively for cable television and other electronic applications. A coaxial cable consists of two concentric cylindrical conductors. The region between the conductors is completely filled with silicon, as shown in Figure 27.8a, and current leakage through the

silicon, in the *radial* direction, is unwanted. (The cable is designed to conduct current along its length—this is *not* the current we are considering here.) The radius of the inner conductor is $a = 0.500$ cm, the radius of the outer one is $b = 1.75$ cm, and the length is $L = 15.0$ cm.

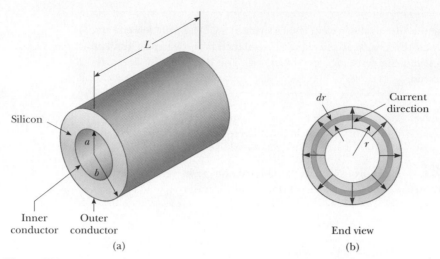

Figure 27.8 (Example 27.4) A coaxial cable. (a) Silicon fills the gap between the two conductors. (b) End view, showing current leakage.

Calculate the resistance of the silicon between the two conductors.

Solution Conceptualize by imagining two currents, as suggested in the text of the problem. The desired current is along the cable, carried within the conductors. The undesired current corresponds to charge leakage through the silicon and its direction is radial. Because we know the resistivity and the geometry of the silicon, we categorize this as a problem in which we find the resistance of the silicon from these parameters, using Equation 27.11. Because the area through which the charges pass depends on the radial position, we must use integral calculus to determine the answer.

To analyze the problem, we divide the silicon into concentric elements of infinitesimal thickness dr (Fig. 27.8b). We start by using the differential form of Equation 27.11, replacing ℓ with r for the distance variable: $dR = \rho \, dr/A$, where dR is the resistance of an element of silicon of thickness dr and surface area A. In this example, we take as our representative concentric element a hollow silicon cylinder of radius r, thickness dr, and length L, as in Figure 27.8. Any charge that passes from the inner conductor to the outer one must pass radially through this concentric element, and the area through which this charge passes is $A = 2\pi rL$. (This is the curved surface area—circumference multiplied by length—of our hollow silicon cylinder of thickness dr.) Hence, we can write the resistance of our hollow cylinder of silicon as

$$dR = \frac{\rho}{2\pi rL} \, dr$$

Because we wish to know the total resistance across the entire thickness of the silicon, we must integrate this expression from $r = a$ to $r = b$:

$$(1) \qquad R = \int_a^b dR = \frac{\rho}{2\pi L} \int_a^b \frac{dr}{r} = \frac{\rho}{2\pi L} \ln\left(\frac{b}{a}\right)$$

Substituting in the values given, and using $\rho = 640 \; \Omega \cdot \text{m}$ for silicon, we obtain

$$R = \frac{640 \; \Omega \cdot \text{m}}{2\pi(0.150 \; \text{m})} \ln\left(\frac{1.75 \; \text{cm}}{0.500 \; \text{cm}}\right) = \boxed{851 \; \Omega}$$

To finalize this problem, let us compare this resistance to that of the inner conductor of the cable along the 15.0-cm length. Assuming that the conductor is made of copper, we have

$$R = \rho \frac{\ell}{A} = (1.7 \times 10^{-8} \; \Omega \cdot \text{m}) \left(\frac{0.150 \; \text{m}}{\pi(5.00 \times 10^{-3} \; \text{m})^2}\right)$$
$$= 3.2 \times 10^{-5} \; \Omega$$

This resistance is much smaller than the radial resistance. As a consequence, almost all of the current corresponds to charge moving along the length of the cable, with a very small fraction leaking in the radial direction.

What If? Suppose the coaxial cable is enlarged to twice the overall diameter with two possibilities: (1) the ratio b/a is held fixed, or (2) the difference $b - a$ is held fixed. For which possibility does the leakage current between the inner and outer conductors increase when the voltage is applied between the two conductors?

Answer In order for the current to increase, the resistance must decrease. For possibility (1), in which b/a is held fixed, Equation (1) tells us that the resistance is unaffected. For possibility (2), we do not have an equation involving the difference $b - a$ to inspect. Looking at Figure 27.8b, however, we see that increasing b and a while holding the voltage constant results in charge flowing through the same thickness of silicon but through a larger overall area perpendicular to the flow. This larger area will result in lower resistance and a higher current.

27.3   A Model for Electrical Conduction

In this section we describe a classical model of electrical conduction in metals that was first proposed by Paul Drude (1863–1906) in 1900. This model leads to Ohm's law and shows that resistivity can be related to the motion of electrons in metals. Although the Drude model described here does have limitations, it nevertheless introduces concepts that are still applied in more elaborate treatments.

Consider a conductor as a regular array of atoms plus a collection of free electrons, which are sometimes called *conduction* electrons. The conduction electrons, although bound to their respective atoms when the atoms are not part of a solid, gain mobility when the free atoms condense into a solid. In the absence of an electric field, the conduction electrons move in random directions through the conductor with average speeds on the order of 10^6 m/s. The situation is similar to the motion of gas molecules confined in a vessel. In fact, some scientists refer to conduction electrons in a metal as an *electron gas*. There is no current in the conductor in the absence of an electric field because the drift velocity of the free electrons is zero. That is, on the average, just as many electrons move in one direction as in the opposite direction, and so there is no net flow of charge.

This situation changes when an electric field is applied. Now, in addition to undergoing the random motion just described, the free electrons drift slowly in a direction opposite that of the electric field, with an average drift speed v_d that is much smaller (typically 10^{-4} m/s) than their average speed between collisions (typically 10^6 m/s).

Figure 27.9 provides a crude description of the motion of free electrons in a conductor. In the absence of an electric field, there is no net displacement after many collisions (Fig. 27.9a). An electric field **E** modifies the random motion and causes the electrons to drift in a direction opposite that of **E** (Fig. 27.9b).

In our model, we assume that the motion of an electron after a collision is independent of its motion before the collision. We also assume that the excess energy acquired by the electrons in the electric field is lost to the atoms of the conductor when the electrons and atoms collide. The energy given up to the atoms increases their vibrational energy, and this causes the temperature of the conductor to increase. The temperature increase of a conductor due to resistance is utilized in electric toasters and other familiar appliances.

We are now in a position to derive an expression for the drift velocity. When a free electron of mass m_e and charge $q(= -e)$ is subjected to an electric field **E**, it experiences a force $\mathbf{F} = q\mathbf{E}$. Because this force is related to the acceleration of the electron through Newton's second law, $\mathbf{F} = m_e\mathbf{a}$, we conclude that the acceleration of the electron is

$$\mathbf{a} = \frac{q\mathbf{E}}{m_e} \tag{27.12}$$

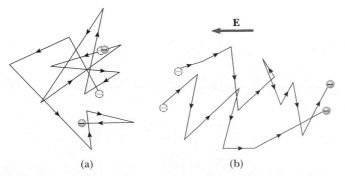

(a)   (b)

Active Figure 27.9 (a) A schematic diagram of the random motion of two charge carriers in a conductor in the absence of an electric field. The drift velocity is zero. (b) The motion of the charge carriers in a conductor in the presence of an electric field. Note that the random motion is modified by the field, and the charge carriers have a drift velocity.

At the Active Figures link at http://www.pse6.com, *you can adjust the electric field to see the resulting effect on the motion of an electron.*

This acceleration, which occurs for only a short time interval between collisions, enables the electron to acquire a small drift velocity. If $\mathbf{v}_i$ is the electron's initial velocity the instant after a collision (which occurs at a time that we define as $t = 0$), then the velocity of the electron at time t (at which the next collision occurs) is

$$\mathbf{v}_f = \mathbf{v}_i + \mathbf{a}t = \mathbf{v}_i + \frac{q\mathbf{E}}{m_e} t \tag{27.13}$$

We now take the average value of $\mathbf{v}_f$ over all possible collision times t and all possible values of $\mathbf{v}_i$. If we assume that the initial velocities are randomly distributed over all possible values, we see that the average value of $\mathbf{v}_i$ is zero. The term $(q\mathbf{E}/m_e)t$ is the velocity change of the electron due to the electric field during one trip between atoms. The average value of the second term of Equation 27.13 is $(q\mathbf{E}/m_e)\tau$, where τ is the *average time interval between successive collisions*. Because the average value of $\mathbf{v}_f$ is equal to the drift velocity, we have

Drift velocity in terms of microscopic quantities

$$\overline{\mathbf{v}_f} = \mathbf{v}_d = \frac{q\mathbf{E}}{m_e} \tau \tag{27.14}$$

We can relate this expression for drift velocity to the current in the conductor. Substituting Equation 27.14 into Equation 27.6, we find that the magnitude of the current density is

Current density in terms of microscopic quantities

$$J = nqv_d = \frac{nq^2E}{m_e} \tau \tag{27.15}$$

where n is the number of charge carriers per unit volume. Comparing this expression with Ohm's law, $J = \sigma E$, we obtain the following relationships for conductivity and resistivity of a conductor:

Conductivity in terms of microscopic quantities

$$\sigma = \frac{nq^2\tau}{m_e} \tag{27.16}$$

Resistivity in terms of microscopic quantities

$$\rho = \frac{1}{\sigma} = \frac{m_e}{nq^2\tau} \tag{27.17}$$

According to this classical model, conductivity and resistivity do not depend on the strength of the electric field. This feature is characteristic of a conductor obeying Ohm's law.

The average time interval τ between collisions is related to the average distance between collisions ℓ (that is, the *mean free path*; see Section 21.7) and the average speed $\overline{v}$ through the expression

$$\tau = \frac{\ell}{\overline{v}} \tag{27.18}$$

Example 27.5 Electron Collisions in a Wire

(A) Using the data and results from Example 27.1 and the classical model of electron conduction, estimate the average time interval between collisions for electrons in household copper wiring.

Solution From Equation 27.17, we see that

$$\tau = \frac{m_e}{nq^2\rho}$$

where $\rho = 1.7 \times 10^{-8}$ $\Omega \cdot$m for copper and the carrier density is $n = 8.49 \times 10^{28}$ electrons/m^3 for the wire described

in Example 27.1. Substitution of these values into the expression above gives

$$\tau = \frac{9.11 \times 10^{-31} \text{ kg}}{(8.49 \times 10^{28} \text{ m}^{-3})(1.6 \times 10^{-19} \text{ C})^2 (1.7 \times 10^{-8} \Omega \cdot \text{m})}$$

$$= 2.5 \times 10^{-14} \text{ s}$$

(B) Assuming that the average speed for free electrons in copper is 1.6×10^6 m/s and using the result from part (A), calculate the mean free path for electrons in copper.

Solution From Equation 27.18,

$$\ell = \bar{v}\tau = (1.6 \times 10^6 \text{ m/s})(2.5 \times 10^{-14} \text{ s})$$

$$= 4.0 \times 10^{-8} \text{ m}$$

which is equivalent to 40 nm (compared with atomic spacings of about 0.2 nm). Thus, although the time interval between collisions is very short, an electron in the wire travels about 200 atomic spacings between collisions.

27.4 Resistance and Temperature

Over a limited temperature range, the resistivity of a conductor varies approximately linearly with temperature according to the expression

$$\rho = \rho_0[1 + \alpha(T - T_0)] \qquad (27.19)$$

Variation of ρ with temperature

where ρ is the resistivity at some temperature T (in degrees Celsius), ρ_0 is the resistivity at some reference temperature T_0 (usually taken to be 20°C), and α is the **temperature coefficient of resistivity.** From Equation 27.19, we see that the temperature coefficient of resistivity can be expressed as

$$\alpha = \frac{1}{\rho_0}\frac{\Delta\rho}{\Delta T} \qquad (27.20)$$

Temperature coefficient of resistivity

where $\Delta\rho = \rho - \rho_0$ is the change in resistivity in the temperature interval $\Delta T = T - T_0$.

The temperature coefficients of resistivity for various materials are given in Table 27.1. Note that the unit for α is degrees Celsius^{-1} [$(°C)^{-1}$]. Because resistance is proportional to resistivity (Eq. 27.11), we can write the variation of resistance as

$$R = R_0[1 + \alpha(T - T_0)] \qquad (27.21)$$

Use of this property enables us to make precise temperature measurements, as shown in Example 27.6.

Quick Quiz 27.6 When does a lightbulb carry more current: (a) just after it is turned on and the glow of the metal filament is increasing, or (b) after it has been on for a few milliseconds and the glow is steady?

Example 27.6   A Platinum Resistance Thermometer

A resistance thermometer, which measures temperature by measuring the change in resistance of a conductor, is made from platinum and has a resistance of 50.0 Ω at 20.0°C. When immersed in a vessel containing melting indium, its resistance increases to 76.8 Ω. Calculate the melting point of the indium.

Solution Solving Equation 27.21 for ΔT and using the α value for platinum given in Table 27.1, we obtain

$$\Delta T = \frac{R - R_0}{\alpha R_0} = \frac{76.8\ \Omega - 50.0\ \Omega}{[3.92 \times 10^{-3}(°C)^{-1}](50.0\ \Omega)}$$

$$= 137°C$$

Because $T_0 = 20.0°C$, we find that T, the temperature of the melting indium sample, is   157°C.

For metals like copper, resistivity is nearly proportional to temperature, as shown in Figure 27.10. However, a nonlinear region always exists at very low temperatures, and the resistivity usually reaches some finite value as the temperature approaches absolute zero. This residual resistivity near absolute zero is caused primarily by the

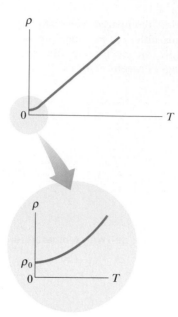

Figure 27.10 Resistivity versus temperature for a metal such as copper. The curve is linear over a wide range of temperatures, and ρ increases with increasing temperature. As T approaches absolute zero (inset), the resistivity approaches a finite value ρ_0.

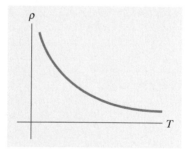

Figure 27.11 Resistivity versus temperature for a pure semiconductor, such as silicon or germanium.

collision of electrons with impurities and imperfections in the metal. In contrast, high-temperature resistivity (the linear region) is predominantly characterized by collisions between electrons and metal atoms.

Notice that three of the α values in Table 27.1 are negative; this indicates that the resistivity of these materials decreases with increasing temperature (Fig. 27.11), which is indicative of a class of materials called *semiconductors*. This behavior is due to an increase in the density of charge carriers at higher temperatures.

Because the charge carriers in a semiconductor are often associated with impurity atoms, the resistivity of these materials is very sensitive to the type and concentration of such impurities. We shall return to the study of semiconductors in Chapter 43.

27.5 Superconductors

There is a class of metals and compounds whose resistance decreases to zero when they are below a certain temperature T_c, known as the **critical temperature.** These materials are known as **superconductors.** The resistance–temperature graph for a superconductor follows that of a normal metal at temperatures above T_c (Fig. 27.12). When the temperature is at or below T_c, the resistivity drops suddenly to zero. This phenomenon was discovered in 1911 by the Dutch physicist Heike Kamerlingh-Onnes (1853–1926) as he worked with mercury, which is a superconductor below 4.2 K. Recent measurements have shown that the resistivities of superconductors below their T_c values are less than $4 \times 10^{-25}\ \Omega \cdot m$—around 10^{17} times smaller than the resistivity of copper and in practice considered to be zero.

Today thousands of superconductors are known, and as Table 27.3 illustrates, the critical temperatures of recently discovered superconductors are substantially higher than initially thought possible. Two kinds of superconductors are recognized. The more recently identified ones are essentially ceramics with high critical temperatures, whereas superconducting materials such as those observed by Kamerlingh-Onnes are metals. If a room-temperature superconductor is ever identified, its impact on technology could be tremendous.

The value of T_c is sensitive to chemical composition, pressure, and molecular structure. It is interesting to note that copper, silver, and gold, which are excellent conductors, do not exhibit superconductivity.

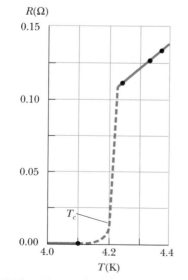

Figure 27.12 Resistance versus temperature for a sample of mercury (Hg). The graph follows that of a normal metal above the critical temperature T_c. The resistance drops to zero at T_c, which is 4.2 K for mercury.

Table 27.3

Critical Temperatures for Various Superconductors	
Material	**T_c(K)**
$HgBa_2Ca_2Cu_3O_8$	134
Tl–Ba–Ca–Cu–O	125
Bi–Sr–Ca–Cu–O	105
$YBa_2Cu_3O_7$	92
Nb_3Ge	23.2
Nb_3Sn	18.05
Nb	9.46
Pb	7.18
Hg	4.15
Sn	3.72
Al	1.19
Zn	0.88

One of the truly remarkable features of superconductors is that once a current is set up in them, it persists *without any applied potential difference* (because $R = 0$). Steady currents have been observed to persist in superconducting loops for several years with no apparent decay!

An important and useful application of superconductivity is in the development of superconducting magnets, in which the magnitudes of the magnetic field are about ten times greater than those produced by the best normal electromagnets. Such superconducting magnets are being considered as a means of storing energy. Superconducting magnets are currently used in medical magnetic resonance imaging (MRI) units, which produce high-quality images of internal organs without the need for excessive exposure of patients to x-rays or other harmful radiation.

For further information on superconductivity, see Section 43.8.

27.6 Electrical Power

If a battery is used to establish an electric current in a conductor, there is a continuous transformation of chemical energy in the battery to kinetic energy of the electrons to internal energy in the conductor, resulting in an increase in the temperature of the conductor.

In typical electric circuits, energy is transferred from a source such as a battery, to some device, such as a lightbulb or a radio receiver. Let us determine an expression that will allow us to calculate the rate of this energy transfer. First, consider the simple circuit in Figure 27.13, where we imagine energy is being delivered to a resistor. (Resistors are designated by the circuit symbol —\/\/\/—.) Because the connecting wires also have resistance, some energy is delivered to the wires and some energy to the resistor. Unless noted otherwise, we shall assume that the resistance of the wires is so small compared to the resistance of the circuit element that we ignore the energy delivered to the wires.

Imagine following a positive quantity of charge Q that is moving clockwise around the circuit in Figure 27.13 from point a through the battery and resistor back to point a. We identify the entire circuit as our system. As the charge moves from a to b through the battery, the electric potential energy of the system *increases* by an amount $Q\,\Delta V$ while the chemical potential energy in the battery *decreases* by the same amount. (Recall from Eq. 25.9 that $\Delta U = q\,\Delta V$.) However, as the charge moves from c to d through the resistor, the system *loses* this electric potential energy during collisions of electrons with atoms in the resistor. In this process, the energy is transformed to internal energy corresponding to increased vibrational motion of the atoms in the resistor. Because we have neglected the resistance of the interconnecting wires, no energy transformation occurs for paths bc and da. When the charge returns to point a, the net result is that some of the chemical energy in the battery has been delivered to the resistor and resides in the resistor as internal energy associated with molecular vibration.

The resistor is normally in contact with air, so its increased temperature will result in a transfer of energy by heat into the air. In addition, the resistor emits thermal

A small permanent magnet levitated above a disk of the superconductor $YBa_2Cu_3O_7$, which is at 77 K.

▲ PITFALL PREVENTION

27.6 Misconceptions About Current

There are several common misconceptions associated with current in a circuit like that in Figure 27.13. One is that current comes out of one terminal of the battery and is then "used up" as it passes through the resistor, leaving current in only one part of the circuit. The truth is that the current is the same *everywhere* in the circuit. A related misconception has the current coming out of the resistor being smaller than that going in, because some of the current is "used up." Another misconception has current coming out of both terminals of the battery, in opposite directions, and then "clashing" in the resistor, delivering the energy in this manner. This is not the case—the charges flow in the same rotational sense at *all* points in the circuit.

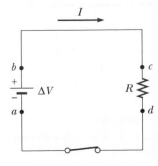

Active Figure 27.13 A circuit consisting of a resistor of resistance R and a battery having a potential difference ΔV across its terminals. Positive charge flows in the clockwise direction.

 *At the Active Figures link at http://www.pse6.com, you can adjust the battery voltage and the resistance to see the resulting current in the circuit and power delivered to the resistor.*

27.7 Charges Do Not Move All the Way Around a Circuit in a Short Time

Due to the very small magnitude of the drift velocity, it might take *hours* for a single electron to make one complete trip around the circuit. In terms of understanding the energy transfer in a circuit, however, it is useful to *imagine* a charge moving all the way around the circuit.

Power delivered to a device

Power delivered to a resistor

27.8 Energy Is Not "Dissipated"

In some books, you may see Equation 27.23 described as the power "dissipated in" a resistor, suggesting that energy disappears. Instead we say energy is "delivered to" a resistor. The notion of *dissipation* arises because a warm resistor will expel energy by radiation and heat, so that energy delivered by the battery leaves the circuit. (It does not disappear!)

radiation, representing another means of escape for the energy. After some time interval has passed, the resistor reaches a constant temperature, at which time the input of energy from the battery is balanced by the output of energy by heat and radiation. Some electrical devices include *heat sinks*[4] connected to parts of the circuit to prevent these parts from reaching dangerously high temperatures. These are pieces of metal with many fins. The high thermal conductivity of the metal provides a rapid transfer of energy by heat away from the hot component, while the large number of fins provides a large surface area in contact with the air, so that energy can transfer by radiation and into the air by heat at a high rate.

Let us consider now the rate at which the system loses electric potential energy as the charge Q passes through the resistor:

$$\frac{dU}{dt} = \frac{d}{dt}(Q\Delta V) = \frac{dQ}{dt}\Delta V = I\Delta V$$

where I is the current in the circuit. The system regains this potential energy when the charge passes through the battery, at the expense of chemical energy in the battery. The rate at which the system loses potential energy as the charge passes through the resistor is equal to the rate at which the system gains internal energy in the resistor. Thus, the power $\mathcal{P}$, representing the rate at which energy is delivered to the resistor, is

$$\mathcal{P} = I\Delta V \tag{27.22}$$

We derived this result by considering a battery delivering energy to a resistor. However, Equation 27.22 can be used to calculate the power delivered by a voltage source to *any* device carrying a current I and having a potential difference ΔV between its terminals.

Using Equation 27.22 and the fact that $\Delta V = IR$ for a resistor, we can express the power delivered to the resistor in the alternative forms

$$\mathcal{P} = I^2R = \frac{(\Delta V)^2}{R} \tag{27.23}$$

When I is expressed in amperes, ΔV in volts, and R in ohms, the SI unit of power is the watt, as it was in Chapter 7 in our discussion of mechanical power. The process by which power is lost as internal energy in a conductor of resistance R is often called *joule heating*[5]; this transformation is also often referred to as an I^2R loss.

When transporting energy by electricity through power lines, such as those shown in the opening photograph for this chapter, we cannot make the simplifying assumption that the lines have zero resistance. Real power lines do indeed have resistance, and power is delivered to the resistance of these wires. Utility companies seek to minimize the power transformed to internal energy in the lines and maximize the energy delivered to the consumer. Because $\mathcal{P} = I\Delta V$, the same amount of power can be transported either at high currents and low potential differences or at low currents and high potential differences. Utility companies choose to transport energy at low currents and high potential differences primarily for economic reasons. Copper wire is very expensive, and so it is cheaper to use high-resistance wire (that is, wire having a small cross-sectional area; see Eq. 27.11). Thus, in the expression for the power delivered to a resistor, $\mathcal{P} = I^2R$, the resistance of the wire is fixed at a relatively high value for economic considerations. The I^2R loss can be reduced by keeping the current I as low as possible, which means transferring the energy at a high voltage. In some instances, power is transported at potential differences as great as 765 kV. Once the electricity reaches your city, the potential difference is usually reduced to 4 kV by a device called a *transformer*. Another

[4] This is another misuse of the word *heat* that is ingrained in our common language.

[5] It is commonly called *joule heating* even though the process of heat does not occur. This is another example of incorrect usage of the word *heat* that has become entrenched in our language.

transformer drops the potential difference to 240 V before the electricity finally reaches your home. Of course, each time the potential difference decreases, the current increases by the same factor, and the power remains the same. We shall discuss transformers in greater detail in Chapter 33.

Demands on our dwindling energy supplies have made it necessary for us to be aware of the energy requirements of our electrical devices. Every electrical appliance carries a label that contains the information you need to calculate the appliance's power requirements. In many cases, the power consumption in watts is stated directly, as it is on a lightbulb. In other cases, the amount of current used by the device and the potential difference at which it operates are given. This information and Equation 27.22 are sufficient for calculating the power requirement of any electrical device.

Quick Quiz 27.7 The same potential difference is applied to the two lightbulbs shown in Figure 27.14. Which one of the following statements is true? (a) The 30-W bulb carries the greater current and has the higher resistance. (b) The 30-W bulb carries the greater current, but the 60-W bulb has the higher resistance. (c) The 30-W bulb has the higher resistance, but the 60-W bulb carries the greater current. (d) The 60-W bulb carries the greater current and has the higher resistance.

Figure 27.14 (Quick Quiz 27.7) These lightbulbs operate at their rated power only when they are connected to a 120-V source.

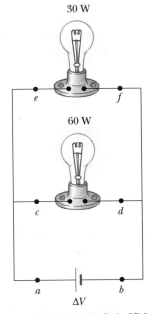

Figure 27.15 (Quick Quiz 27.8) Two lightbulbs connected across the same potential difference.

Quick Quiz 27.8 For the two lightbulbs shown in Figure 27.15, rank the current values at points *a* through *f*, from greatest to least.

Example 27.7   Power in an Electric Heater

An electric heater is constructed by applying a potential difference of 120 V to a Nichrome wire that has a total resistance of 8.00 Ω. Find the current carried by the wire and the power rating of the heater.

Solution Because $\Delta V = IR$, we have

$$I = \frac{\Delta V}{R} = \frac{120 \text{ V}}{8.00 \text{ }\Omega} = \boxed{15.0 \text{ A}}$$

We can find the power rating using the expression $\mathcal{P} = I^2 R$:

$$\mathcal{P} = I^2 R = (15.0 \text{ A})^2 (8.00 \text{ }\Omega) = 1.80 \times 10^3 \text{ W}$$

$$\mathcal{P} = \boxed{1.80 \text{ kW}}$$

What If? What if the heater were accidentally connected to a 240-V supply? (This is difficult to do because the shape and orientation of the metal contacts in 240-V plugs are different from those in 120-V plugs.) How would this affect the current carried by the heater and the power rating of the heater?

Answer If we doubled the applied potential difference, Equation 27.8 tells us that the current would double. According to Equation 27.23, $\mathcal{P} = (\Delta V)^2 / R$, the power would be four times larger.

Example 27.8   Linking Electricity and Thermodynamics

(A) What is the required resistance of an immersion heater that will increase the temperature of 1.50 kg of water from 10.0°C to 50.0°C in 10.0 min while operating at 110 V?

(B) Estimate the cost of heating the water.

Solution This example allows us to link our new understanding of power in electricity with our experience with specific heat in thermodynamics (Chapter 20). An immersion heater is a resistor that is inserted into a container of water. As energy is delivered to the immersion heater, raising its temperature, energy leaves the surface of the resistor by heat, going into the water. When the immersion heater reaches a constant temperature, the rate of energy delivered to the resistance by electrical transmission is equal to the rate of energy delivered by heat to the water.

(A) To simplify the analysis, we ignore the initial period during which the temperature of the resistor increases, and also ignore any variation of resistance with temperature. Thus, we imagine a constant rate of energy transfer for the entire 10.0 min. Setting the rate of energy delivered to the resistor equal to the rate of energy entering the water by heat, we have

$$\mathcal{P} = \frac{(\Delta V)^2}{R} = \frac{Q}{\Delta t}$$

where Q represents an amount of energy transfer by heat into the water and we have used Equation 27.23 to express

the electrical power. The amount of energy transfer by heat necessary to raise the temperature of the water is given by Equation 20.4, $Q = mc\,\Delta T$. Thus,

$$\frac{(\Delta V)^2}{R} = \frac{mc\,\Delta T}{\Delta t} \quad \longrightarrow \quad R = \frac{(\Delta V)^2\,\Delta t}{mc\,\Delta T}$$

Substituting the values given in the statement of the problem, we have

$$R = \frac{(110\text{ V})^2(600\text{ s})}{(1.50\text{ kg})(4186\text{ J/kg}\cdot°\text{C})(50.0°\text{C} - 10.0°\text{C})}$$

$$= \boxed{28.9\ \Omega}$$

(B) Because the energy transferred equals power multiplied by time interval, the amount of energy transferred is

$$\mathcal{P}\,\Delta t = \frac{(\Delta V)^2}{R}\,\Delta t = \frac{(110\text{ V})^2}{28.9\ \Omega}(10.0\text{ min})\left(\frac{1\text{ h}}{60.0\text{ min}}\right)$$

$$= 69.8\text{ Wh} = 0.069\ 8\text{ kWh}$$

If the energy is purchased at an estimated price of 10.0¢ per kilowatt-hour, the cost is

$$\text{Cost} = (0.069\ 8\text{ kWh})(\$0.100/\text{kWh}) = \$0.006\ 98$$

$$\approx \boxed{0.7\ ¢}$$

At the Interactive Worked Example link at **http://www.pse6.com,** *you can explore the heating of the water.*

Example 27.9   Current in an Electron Beam

In a certain particle accelerator, electrons emerge with an energy of 40.0 MeV ($1\text{ MeV} = 1.60 \times 10^{-13}$ J). The electrons emerge not in a steady stream but rather in pulses at the rate of 250 pulses/s. This corresponds to a time interval between pulses of 4.00 ms (Fig. 27.16). Each pulse has a duration of 200 ns, and the electrons in the pulse constitute a current of 250 mA. The current is zero between pulses.

(A) How many electrons are delivered by the accelerator per pulse?

Solution We use Equation 27.2 in the form $dQ = I\,dt$ and integrate to find the charge per pulse. While the pulse is on, the current is constant; thus,

$$Q_{\text{pulse}} = I\int dt = I\,\Delta t = (250 \times 10^{-3}\text{ A})(200 \times 10^{-9}\text{ s})$$

$$= 5.00 \times 10^{-8}\text{ C}$$

Dividing this quantity of charge per pulse by the electronic charge gives the number of electrons per pulse:

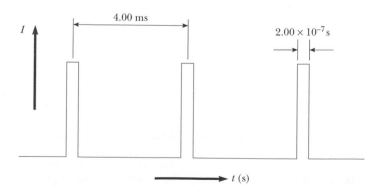

Figure 27.16 (Example 27.9) Current versus time for a pulsed beam of electrons.

$$\text{Electrons per pulse} = \frac{5.00 \times 10^{-8}\,\text{C/pulse}}{1.60 \times 10^{-19}\,\text{C/electron}}$$

$$= 3.13 \times 10^{11}\,\text{electrons/pulse}$$

(B) What is the average current per pulse delivered by the accelerator?

Solution Average current is given by Equation 27.1, $I_{av} = \Delta Q/\Delta t$. Because the time interval between pulses is 4.00 ms, and because we know the charge per pulse from part (A), we obtain

$$I_{av} = \frac{Q_{pulse}}{\Delta t} = \frac{5.00 \times 10^{-8}\,\text{C}}{4.00 \times 10^{-3}\,\text{s}} = 12.5\,\mu\text{A}$$

This represents only 0.005% of the peak current, which is 250 mA.

(C) What is the peak power delivered by the electron beam?

Solution By definition, power is energy delivered per unit time interval. Thus, the peak power is equal to the energy delivered by a pulse divided by the pulse duration:

$$(1) \qquad \mathcal{P}_{peak} = \frac{\text{pulse energy}}{\text{pulse duration}}$$

$$= \frac{(3.13 \times 10^{11}\,\text{electrons/pulse})(40.0\,\text{MeV/electron})}{2.00 \times 10^{-7}\,\text{s/pulse}}$$

$$\times \left(\frac{1.60 \times 10^{-13}\,\text{J}}{1\,\text{MeV}}\right)$$

$$= 1.00 \times 10^7\,\text{W} = 10.0\,\text{MW}$$

We could also compute this power directly. We assume that each electron has zero energy before being accelerated. Thus, by definition, each electron must go through a potential difference of 40.0 MV to acquire a final energy of 40.0 MeV. Hence, we have

$$(2) \qquad \mathcal{P}_{peak} = I_{peak}\Delta V$$

$$= (250 \times 10^{-3}\,\text{A})(40.0 \times 10^6\,\text{V})$$

$$= 10.0\,\text{MW}$$

What If? What if the requested quantity in part (C) were the *average* power rather than the *peak* power?

Answer Instead of Equation (1), we would use the time interval between pulses rather than the duration of a pulse:

$$\mathcal{P}_{av} = \frac{\text{pulse energy}}{\text{time interval between pulses}}$$

$$= \frac{(3.13 \times 10^{11}\,\text{electrons/pulse})(40.0\,\text{MeV/electron})}{4.00 \times 10^{-3}\,\text{s/pulse}}$$

$$\times \left(\frac{1.60 \times 10^{-13}\,\text{J}}{1\,\text{MeV}}\right)$$

$$= 500\,\text{W}$$

Instead of Equation (2), we would use the average current found in part (B):

$$\mathcal{P}_{av} = I_{av}\Delta V = (12.5 \times 10^{-6}\,\text{A})(40.0 \times 10^6\,\text{V})$$

$$= 500\,\text{W}$$

Notice that these two calculations agree with each other and that the average power is much lower than the peak power.

SUMMARY

The **electric current** I in a conductor is defined as

$$I \equiv \frac{dQ}{dt} \qquad (27.2)$$

Take a practice test for this chapter by clicking on the Practice Test link at http://www.pse6.com.

where dQ is the charge that passes through a cross section of the conductor in a time interval dt. The SI unit of current is the **ampere** (A), where $1\,\text{A} = 1\,\text{C/s}$.

The average current in a conductor is related to the motion of the charge carriers through the relationship

$$I_{av} = nqv_d A \qquad (27.4)$$

where n is the density of charge carriers, q is the charge on each carrier, v_d is the drift speed, and A is the cross-sectional area of the conductor.

The magnitude of the **current density** J in a conductor is the current per unit area:

$$J \equiv \frac{I}{A} = nqv_d \qquad (27.5)$$

The current density in an ohmic conductor is proportional to the electric field according to the expression

$$\mathbf{J} = \sigma \mathbf{E} \qquad (27.7)$$

The proportionality constant σ is called the **conductivity** of the material of which the conductor is made. The inverse of σ is known as **resistivity** ρ (that is, $\rho = 1/\sigma$). Equation 27.7 is known as **Ohm's law,** and a material is said to obey this law if the ratio of its current density $\mathbf{J}$ to its applied electric field $\mathbf{E}$ is a constant that is independent of the applied field.

The **resistance** R of a conductor is defined as

$$R \equiv \frac{\Delta V}{I} \qquad (27.8)$$

where ΔV is the potential difference across it, and I is the current it carries.

The SI unit of resistance is volts per ampere, which is defined to be 1 **ohm** (Ω); that is, $1\ \Omega = 1\ \text{V/A}$. If the resistance is independent of the applied potential difference, the conductor obeys Ohm's law.

For a uniform block of material of cross sectional area A and length ℓ, the resistance over the length ℓ is

$$R = \rho \frac{\ell}{A} \qquad (27.11)$$

where ρ is the resistivity of the material.

In a classical model of electrical conduction in metals, the electrons are treated as molecules of a gas. In the absence of an electric field, the average velocity of the electrons is zero. When an electric field is applied, the electrons move (on the average) with a **drift velocity** $\mathbf{v}_d$ that is opposite the electric field and given by the expression

$$\mathbf{v}_d = \frac{q\mathbf{E}}{m_e} \tau \qquad (27.14)$$

where τ is the average time interval between electron–atom collisions, m_e is the mass of the electron, and q is its charge. According to this model, the resistivity of the metal is

$$\rho = \frac{m_e}{nq^2\tau} \qquad (27.17)$$

where n is the number of free electrons per unit volume.

The resistivity of a conductor varies approximately linearly with temperature according to the expression

$$\rho = \rho_0[1 + \alpha(T - T_0)] \qquad (27.19)$$

where α is the **temperature coefficient of resistivity** and ρ_0 is the resistivity at some reference temperature T_0.

If a potential difference ΔV is maintained across a circuit element, the **power,** or rate at which energy is supplied to the element, is

$$\mathcal{P} = I\,\Delta V \qquad (27.22)$$

Because the potential difference across a resistor is given by $\Delta V = IR$, we can express the power delivered to a resistor in the form

$$\mathcal{P} = I^2 R = \frac{(\Delta V)^2}{R} \qquad (27.23)$$

The energy delivered to a resistor by electrical transmission appears in the form of internal energy in the resistor.

QUESTIONS

1. In an analogy between electric current and automobile traffic flow, what would correspond to charge? What would correspond to current?

2. Newspaper articles often contain a statement such as "10 000 volts of electricity surged through the victim's body." What is wrong with this statement?

3. What factors affect the resistance of a conductor?

4. What is the difference between resistance and resistivity?

5. Two wires A and B of circular cross section are made of the same metal and have equal lengths, but the resistance of wire A is three times greater than that of wire B. What is the ratio of their cross-sectional areas? How do their radii compare?

6. Do all conductors obey Ohm's law? Give examples to justify your answer.

7. We have seen that an electric field must exist inside a conductor that carries a current. How is it possible in view of the fact that in electrostatics we concluded that the electric field must be zero inside a conductor?

8. A very large potential difference is not necessarily required to produce long sparks in air. With a device called *Jacob's ladder*, a potential difference of about 10 kV produces an electric arc a few millimeters long between the bottom ends of two curved rods that project upward from the power supply. (The device is seen in classic mad-scientist horror movies and in Figure Q27.8.) The arc rises, climbing the rods and getting longer and longer. It disappears when it reaches the top; then a new spark immediately forms at the bottom and the process repeats. Explain these phenomena. Why does the arc rise? Why does a new arc appear only after the previous one is gone?

Figure Q27.8

9. When the voltage across a certain conductor is doubled, the current is observed to increase by a factor of three. What can you conclude about the conductor?

10. In the water analogy of an electric circuit, what corresponds to the power supply, resistor, charge, and potential difference?

11. Use the atomic theory of matter to explain why the resistance of a material should increase as its temperature increases.

12. Why might a "good" electrical conductor also be a "good" thermal conductor?

13. How does the resistance for copper and for silicon change with temperature? Why are the behaviors of these two materials different?

14. Explain how a current can persist in a superconductor without any applied voltage.

15. What single experimental requirement makes superconducting devices expensive to operate? In principle, can this limitation be overcome?

16. What would happen to the drift velocity of the electrons in a wire and to the current in the wire if the electrons could move freely without resistance through the wire?

17. If charges flow very slowly through a metal, why does it not require several hours for a light to come on when you throw a switch?

18. In a conductor, changes in the electric field that drives the electrons through the conductor propagate with a speed close to the speed of light, although the drift velocity of the electrons is very small. Explain how these statements can both be true. Does one particular electron move from one end of the conductor to the other?

19. Two conductors of the same length and radius are connected across the same potential difference. One conductor has twice the resistance of the other. To which conductor is more power delivered?

20. Two lightbulbs both operate from 120 V. One has a power of 25 W and the other 100 W. Which bulb has higher resistance? Which bulb carries more current?

21. Car batteries are often rated in ampere-hours. Does this designate the amount of current, power, energy, or charge that can be drawn from the battery?

22. If you were to design an electric heater using Nichrome wire as the heating element, what parameters of the wire could you vary to meet a specific power output, such as 1 000 W?

PROBLEMS

1, 2, 3 = straightforward, intermediate, challenging ☐ = full solution available in the *Student Solutions Manual and Study Guide*

🌐 = coached solution with hints available at http://www.pse6.com 🖥️ = computer useful in solving problem

▨ = paired numerical and symbolic problems

Section 27.1 Electric Current

1. In a particular cathode ray tube, the measured beam current is 30.0 μA. How many electrons strike the tube screen every 40.0 s?

2. A teapot with a surface area of 700 cm^2 is to be silver plated. It is attached to the negative electrode of an electrolytic cell containing silver nitrate ($Ag^+ NO_3^-$). If the cell is powered by a 12.0-V battery and has a resistance of 1.80 Ω, how long does it take for a 0.133-mm layer of silver to build up on the teapot? (The density of silver is 10.5×10^3 kg/m^3.)

3. 🌐 Suppose that the current through a conductor decreases exponentially with time according to the equation $I(t) = I_0 e^{-t/\tau}$ where I_0 is the initial current (at $t = 0$), and τ is a constant having dimensions of time. Consider a fixed observation point within the conductor. (a) How much charge passes this point between $t = 0$ and $t = \tau$? (b) How much charge passes this point between $t = 0$ and $t = 10\tau$? (c) **What If?** How much charge passes this point between $t = 0$ and $t = \infty$?

4. In the Bohr model of the hydrogen atom, an electron in the lowest energy state follows a circular path 5.29×10^{-11} m from the proton. (a) Show that the speed of the electron is 2.19×10^6 m/s. (b) What is the effective current associated with this orbiting electron?

5. A small sphere that carries a charge q is whirled in a circle at the end of an insulating string. The angular frequency of rotation is ω. What average current does this rotating charge represent?

6. The quantity of charge q (in coulombs) that has passed through a surface of area 2.00 cm^2 varies with time according to the equation $q = 4t^3 + 5t + 6$, where t is in seconds. (a) What is the instantaneous current through the surface at $t = 1.00$ s? (b) What is the value of the current density?

7. An electric current is given by the expression $I(t) = 100 \sin(120\pi t)$, where I is in amperes and t is in seconds. What is the total charge carried by the current from $t = 0$ to $t = (1/240)$ s?

8. Figure P27.8 represents a section of a circular conductor of nonuniform diameter carrying a current of 5.00 A. The

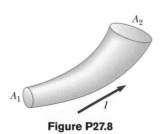

Figure P27.8

radius of cross section A_1 is 0.400 cm. (a) What is the magnitude of the current density across A_1? (b) If the current density across A_2 is one-fourth the value across A_1, what is the radius of the conductor at A_2?

9. The electron beam emerging from a certain high-energy electron accelerator has a circular cross section of radius 1.00 mm. (a) The beam current is 8.00 μA. Find the current density in the beam, assuming that it is uniform throughout. (b) The speed of the electrons is so close to the speed of light that their speed can be taken as $c = 3.00 \times 10^8$ m/s with negligible error. Find the electron density in the beam. (c) How long does it take for Avogadro's number of electrons to emerge from the accelerator?

10. A Van de Graaff generator produces a beam of 2.00-MeV deuterons, which are heavy hydrogen nuclei containing a proton and a neutron. (a) If the beam current is 10.0 μA, how far apart are the deuterons? (b) Is the electric force of repulsion among them a significant factor in beam stability? Explain.

11. An aluminum wire having a cross-sectional area of 4.00×10^{-6} m^2 carries a current of 5.00 A. Find the drift speed of the electrons in the wire. The density of aluminum is 2.70 g/cm^3. Assume that one conduction electron is supplied by each atom.

Section 27.2 Resistance

12. Calculate the current density in a gold wire at 20°C, if an electric field of 0.740 V/m exists in the wire.

13. A lightbulb has a resistance of 240 Ω when operating with a potential difference of 120 V across it. What is the current in the lightbulb?

14. A resistor is constructed of a carbon rod that has a uniform cross-sectional area of 5.00 mm^2. When a potential difference of 15.0 V is applied across the ends of the rod, the rod carries a current of 4.00×10^{-3} A. Find (a) the resistance of the rod and (b) the rod's length.

15. 🌐 A 0.900-V potential difference is maintained across a 1.50-m length of tungsten wire that has a cross-sectional area of 0.600 mm^2. What is the current in the wire?

16. A conductor of uniform radius 1.20 cm carries a current of 3.00 A produced by an electric field of 120 V/m. What is the resistivity of the material?

17. Suppose that you wish to fabricate a uniform wire out of 1.00 g of copper. If the wire is to have a resistance of $R = 0.500$ Ω, and if all of the copper is to be used, what will be (a) the length and (b) the diameter of this wire?

18. Gold is the most ductile of all metals. For example, one gram of gold can be drawn into a wire 2.40 km long. What is the resistance of such a wire at 20°C? You can find the necessary reference information in this textbook.

19. (a) Make an order-of-magnitude estimate of the resistance between the ends of a rubber band. (b) Make an order-of-magnitude estimate of the resistance between the 'heads' and 'tails' sides of a penny. In each case state what quantities you take as data and the values you measure or estimate for them. (c) WARNING! Do not try this at home! What is the order of magnitude of the current that each would carry if it were connected across a 120-V power supply?

20. A solid cube of silver (density = 10.5 g/cm^3) has a mass of 90.0 g. (a) What is the resistance between opposite faces of the cube? (b) Assume each silver atom contributes one conduction electron. Find the average drift speed of electrons when a potential difference of 1.00×10^{-5} V is applied to opposite faces. The atomic number of silver is 47, and its molar mass is 107.87 g/mol.

21. A metal wire of resistance R is cut into three equal pieces that are then connected side by side to form a new wire the length of which is equal to one-third the original length. What is the resistance of this new wire?

22. Aluminum and copper wires of equal length are found to have the same resistance. What is the ratio of their radii?

23. A current density of 6.00×10^{-13} A/m^2 exists in the atmosphere at a location where the electric field is 100 V/m. Calculate the electrical conductivity of the Earth's atmosphere in this region.

24. The rod in Figure P27.24 is made of two materials. The figure is not drawn to scale. Each conductor has a square cross section 3.00 mm on a side. The first material has a resistivity of 4.00×10^{-3} $\Omega \cdot$m and is 25.0 cm long, while the second material has a resistivity of 6.00×10^{-3} $\Omega \cdot$m and is 40.0 cm long. What is the resistance between the ends of the rod?

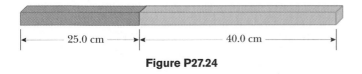

|← 25.0 cm →|← 40.0 cm →|

Figure P27.24

Section 27.3   A Model for Electrical Conduction

25. If the magnitude of the drift velocity of free electrons in a copper wire is 7.84×10^{-4} m/s, what is the electric field in the conductor?

26. If the current carried by a conductor is doubled, what happens to the (a) charge carrier density? (b) current density? (c) electron drift velocity? (d) average time interval between collisions?

27. Use data from Example 27.1 to calculate the collision mean free path of electrons in copper. Assume the average thermal speed of conduction electrons is 8.60×10^5 m/s.

Section 27.4   Resistance and Temperature

28. While taking photographs in Death Valley on a day when the temperature is 58.0°C, Bill Hiker finds that a certain voltage applied to a copper wire produces a current of 1.000 A. Bill then travels to Antarctica and applies the same voltage to the same wire. What current does he register there if the temperature is -88.0°C? Assume that no change occurs in the wire's shape and size.

29. A certain lightbulb has a tungsten filament with a resistance of 19.0 Ω when cold and 140 Ω when hot. Assume that the resistivity of tungsten varies linearly with temperature even over the large temperature range involved here, and find the temperature of the hot filament. Assume the initial temperature is 20.0°C.

30. A carbon wire and a Nichrome wire are connected in series, so that the same current exists in both wires. If the combination has a resistance of 10.0 kΩ at 0°C, what is the resistance of each wire at 0°C so that the resistance of the combination does not change with temperature? The total or equivalent resistance of resistors in series is the sum of their individual resistances.

31. An aluminum wire with a diameter of 0.100 mm has a uniform electric field of 0.200 V/m imposed along its entire length. The temperature of the wire is 50.0°C. Assume one free electron per atom. (a) Use the information in Table 27.1 and determine the resistivity. (b) What is the current density in the wire? (c) What is the total current in the wire? (d) What is the drift speed of the conduction electrons? (e) What potential difference must exist between the ends of a 2.00-m length of the wire to produce the stated electric field?

32. **Review problem.** An aluminum rod has a resistance of 1.234 Ω at 20.0°C. Calculate the resistance of the rod at 120°C by accounting for the changes in both the resistivity and the dimensions of the rod.

33. What is the fractional change in the resistance of an iron filament when its temperature changes from 25.0°C to 50.0°C?

34. The resistance of a platinum wire is to be calibrated for low-temperature measurements. A platinum wire with resistance 1.00 Ω at 20.0°C is immersed in liquid nitrogen at 77 K (-196°C). If the temperature response of the platinum wire is linear, what is the expected resistance of the platinum wire at -196°C? ($\alpha_{platinum} = 3.92 \times 10^{-3}/$°C)

35. The temperature of a sample of tungsten is raised while a sample of copper is maintained at 20.0°C. At what temperature will the resistivity of the tungsten be four times that of the copper?

Section 27.6   Electrical Power

36. A toaster is rated at 600 W when connected to a 120-V source. What current does the toaster carry, and what is its resistance?

37. A Van de Graaff generator (see Figure 25.29) is operating so that the potential difference between the high-voltage electrode B and the charging needles at A is 15.0 kV. Calculate the power required to drive the belt against electrical forces at an instant when the effective current delivered to the high-voltage electrode is 500 μA.

38. In a hydroelectric installation, a turbine delivers 1 500 hp to a generator, which in turn transfers 80.0% of the mechanical energy out by electrical transmission. Under these conditions, what current does the generator deliver at a terminal potential difference of 2 000 V?

39. What is the required resistance of an immersion heater that increases the temperature of 1.50 kg of water from 10.0°C to 50.0°C in 10.0 min while operating at 110 V?

40. One rechargeable battery of mass 15.0 g delivers to a CD player an average current of 18.0 mA at 1.60 V for 2.40 h before the battery needs to be recharged. The recharger maintains a potential difference of 2.30 V across the battery and delivers a charging current of 13.5 mA for 4.20 h. (a) What is the efficiency of the battery as an energy storage device? (b) How much internal energy is produced in the battery during one charge–discharge cycle? (b) If the battery is surrounded by ideal thermal insulation and has an overall effective specific heat of 975 J/kg°C, by how much will its temperature increase during the cycle?

41. Suppose that a voltage surge produces 140 V for a moment. By what percentage does the power output of a 120-V, 100-W lightbulb increase? Assume that its resistance does not change.

42. A 500-W heating coil designed to operate from 110 V is made of Nichrome wire 0.500 mm in diameter. (a) Assuming that the resistivity of the Nichrome remains constant at its 20.0°C value, find the length of wire used. (b) **What If?** Now consider the variation of resistivity with temperature. What power will the coil of part (a) actually deliver when it is heated to 1 200°C?

43. A coil of Nichrome wire is 25.0 m long. The wire has a diameter of 0.400 mm and is at 20.0°C. If it carries a current of 0.500 A, what are (a) the magnitude of the electric field in the wire, and (b) the power delivered to it? (c) **What If?** If the temperature is increased to 340°C and the voltage across the wire remains constant, what is the power delivered?

44. Batteries are rated in terms of ampere-hours (A·h). For example, a battery that can produce a current of 2.00 A for 3.00 h is rated at 6.00 A·h. (a) What is the total energy, in kilowatt-hours, stored in a 12.0-V battery rated at 55.0 A·h? (b) At $0.060 0 per kilowatt-hour, what is the value of the electricity produced by this battery?

45. A 10.0-V battery is connected to a 120-Ω resistor. Ignoring the internal resistance of the battery, calculate the power delivered to the resistor.

46. Residential building codes typically require the use of 12-gauge copper wire (diameter 0.205 3 cm) for wiring receptacles. Such circuits carry currents as large as 20 A. A wire of smaller diameter (with a higher gauge number) could carry this much current, but the wire could rise to a high temperature and cause a fire. (a) Calculate the rate at which internal energy is produced in 1.00 m of 12-gauge copper wire carrying a current of 20.0 A. (b) **What If?** Repeat the calculation for an aluminum wire. Would a 12-gauge aluminum wire be as safe as a copper wire?

47. An 11.0-W energy-efficient fluorescent lamp is designed to produce the same illumination as a conventional 40.0-W incandescent lightbulb. How much money does the user of the energy-efficient lamp save during 100 hours of use? Assume a cost of $0.080 0/kWh for energy from the power company.

48. We estimate that 270 million plug-in electric clocks are in the United States, approximately one clock for each person. The clocks convert energy at the average rate 2.50 W. To supply this energy, how many metric tons of coal are burned per hour in coal-fired electric generating plants that are, on average, 25.0% efficient? The heat of combustion for coal is 33.0 MJ/kg.

49. Compute the cost per day of operating a lamp that draws a current of 1.70 A from a 110-V line. Assume the cost of energy from the power company is $0.060 0/kWh.

50. **Review problem.** The heating element of a coffee maker operates at 120 V and carries a current of 2.00 A. Assuming that the water absorbs all of the energy delivered to the resistor, calculate how long it takes to raise the temperature of 0.500 kg of water from room temperature (23.0°C) to the boiling point.

51. A certain toaster has a heating element made of Nichrome wire. When the toaster is first connected to a 120-V source (and the wire is at a temperature of 20.0°C), the initial current is 1.80 A. However, the current begins to decrease as the heating element warms up. When the toaster reaches its final operating temperature, the current drops to 1.53 A. (a) Find the power delivered to the toaster when it is at its operating temperature. (b) What is the final temperature of the heating element?

52. The cost of electricity varies widely through the United States; $0.120/kWh is one typical value. At this unit price, calculate the cost of (a) leaving a 40.0-W porch light on for two weeks while you are on vacation, (b) making a piece of dark toast in 3.00 min with a 970-W toaster, and (c) drying a load of clothes in 40.0 min in a 5 200-W dryer.

53. Make an order-of-magnitude estimate of the cost of one person's routine use of a hair dryer for 1 yr. If you do not use a blow dryer yourself, observe or interview someone who does. State the quantities you estimate and their values.

Additional Problems

54. One lightbulb is marked '25 W 120 V,' and another '100 W 120 V'; this means that each bulb has its respective power delivered to it when plugged into a constant 120-V potential difference. (a) Find the resistance of each bulb. (b) How long does it take for 1.00 C to pass through the dim bulb? Is the charge different in any way upon its exit from the bulb versus its entry? (c) How long does it take for 1.00 J to pass through the dim bulb? By what mechanisms does this energy enter and exit the bulb? (d) Find how much it costs to run the dim bulb continuously for 30.0 days if the electric company sells its product at $0.070 0 per kWh. What product *does* the electric company sell? What is its price for one SI unit of this quantity?

55. A charge Q is placed on a capacitor of capacitance C. The capacitor is connected into the circuit shown in Figure P27.55, with an open switch, a resistor, and an initially uncharged capacitor of capacitance 3C. The switch is then closed and the circuit comes to equilibrium. In terms of Q and C, find (a) the final potential difference between the plates of each capacitor, (b) the charge on each capacitor, and (c) the final energy stored in each capacitor. (d) Find the internal energy appearing in the resistor.

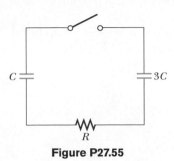

Figure P27.55

56. A high-voltage transmission line with a diameter of 2.00 cm and a length of 200 km carries a steady current of 1 000 A. If the conductor is copper wire with a free charge density of 8.49×10^{28} electrons/m^3, how long does it take one electron to travel the full length of the line?

57. A more general definition of the temperature coefficient of resistivity is

$$\alpha = \frac{1}{\rho} \frac{d\rho}{dT}$$

where ρ is the resistivity at temperature T. (a) Assuming that α is constant, show that

$$\rho = \rho_0 e^{\alpha(T - T_0)}$$

where ρ_0 is the resistivity at temperature T_0. (b) Using the series expansion $e^x \approx 1 + x$ for $x \ll 1$, show that the resistivity is given approximately by the expression $\rho = \rho_0[1 + \alpha(T - T_0)]$ for $\alpha(T - T_0) \ll 1$.

58. A high-voltage transmission line carries 1 000 A starting at 700 kV for a distance of 100 mi. If the resistance in the wire is 0.500 Ω/mi, what is the power loss due to resistive losses?

59. An experiment is conducted to measure the electrical resistivity of Nichrome in the form of wires with different lengths and cross-sectional areas. For one set of measurements, a student uses 30-gauge wire, which has a cross-sectional area of 7.30×10^{-8} m^2. The student measures the potential difference across the wire and the current in the wire with a voltmeter and an ammeter, respectively. For each of the measurements given in the table taken on wires of three different lengths, calculate the resistance of the wires and the corresponding values of the resistivity. What is the average value of the resistivity, and how does this value compare with the value given in Table 27.1?

L (m)	ΔV (V)	I (A)	R (Ω)	ρ($\Omega \cdot$m)
0.540	5.22	0.500		
1.028	5.82	0.276		
1.543	5.94	0.187		

60. An electric utility company supplies a customer's house from the main power lines (120 V) with two copper wires, each of which is 50.0 m long and has a resistance of 0.108 Ω per 300 m. (a) Find the voltage at the customer's

house for a load current of 110 A. For this load current, find (b) the power the customer is receiving and (c) the electric power lost in the copper wires.

61. A straight cylindrical wire lying along the x axis has a length of 0.500 m and a diameter of 0.200 mm. It is made of a material that obeys Ohm's law with a resistivity of $\rho = 4.00 \times 10^{-8}\ \Omega \cdot$m. Assume that a potential of 4.00 V is maintained at $x = 0$, and that $V = 0$ at $x = 0.500$ m. Find (a) the electric field **E** in the wire, (b) the resistance of the wire, (c) the electric current in the wire, and (d) the current density **J** in the wire. Express vectors in vector notation. (e) Show that $\mathbf{E} = \rho\mathbf{J}$.

62. A straight cylindrical wire lying along the x axis has a length L and a diameter d. It is made of a material that obeys Ohm's law with a resistivity ρ. Assume that potential V is maintained at $x = 0$, and that the potential is zero at $x = L$. In terms of L, d, V, ρ, and physical constants, derive expressions for (a) the electric field in the wire, (b) the resistance of the wire, (c) the electric current in the wire, and (d) the current density in the wire. Express vectors in vector notation. (e) Prove that $\mathbf{E} = \rho\mathbf{J}$.

63. The potential difference across the filament of a lamp is maintained at a constant level while equilibrium temperature is being reached. It is observed that the steady-state current in the lamp is only one tenth of the current drawn by the lamp when it is first turned on. If the temperature coefficient of resistivity for the lamp at 20.0°C is 0.004 50 (°C)$^{-1}$, and if the resistance increases linearly with increasing temperature, what is the final operating temperature of the filament?

64. The current in a resistor decreases by 3.00 A when the voltage applied across the resistor decreases from 12.0 V to 6.00 V. Find the resistance of the resistor.

65. An electric car is designed to run off a bank of 12.0-V batteries with total energy storage of 2.00×10^7 J. (a) If the electric motor draws 8.00 kW, what is the current delivered to the motor? (b) If the electric motor draws 8.00 kW as the car moves at a steady speed of 20.0 m/s, how far will the car travel before it is "out of juice"?

66. **Review problem.** When a straight wire is heated, its resistance is given by $R = R_0[1 + \alpha(T - T_0)]$ according to Equation 27.21, where α is the temperature coefficient of resistivity. (a) Show that a more precise result, one that includes the fact that the length and area of the wire change when heated, is

$$R = \frac{R_0[1 + \alpha(T - T_0)][1 + \alpha'(T - T_0)]}{[1 + 2\alpha'(T - T_0)]}$$

where α' is the coefficient of linear expansion (see Chapter 19). (b) Compare these two results for a 2.00-m-long copper wire of radius 0.100 mm, first at 20.0°C and then heated to 100.0°C.

67. The temperature coefficients of resistivity in Table 27.1 were determined at a temperature of 20°C. What would they be at 0°C? Note that the temperature coefficient of resistivity at 20°C satisfies $\rho = \rho_0[1 + \alpha(T - T_0)]$, where ρ_0 is the resistivity of the material at $T_0 = 20$°C. The temperature

coefficient of resistivity α' at $0°C$ must satisfy the expression $\rho = \rho'_0[1 + \alpha'T]$, where ρ'_0 is the resistivity of the material at $0°C$.

68. An oceanographer is studying how the ion concentration in sea water depends on depth. She does this by lowering into the water a pair of concentric metallic cylinders (Fig. P27.68) at the end of a cable and taking data to determine the resistance between these electrodes as a function of depth. The water between the two cylinders forms a cylindrical shell of inner radius r_a, outer radius r_b, and length L much larger than r_b. The scientist applies a potential difference ΔV between the inner and outer surfaces, producing an outward radial current I. Let ρ represent the resistivity of the water. (a) Find the resistance of the water between the cylinders in terms of L, ρ, r_a, and r_b. (b) Express the resistivity of the water in terms of the measured quantities L, r_a, r_b, ΔV, and I.

Figure P27.68

69. In a certain stereo system, each speaker has a resistance of $4.00\ \Omega$. The system is rated at 60.0 W in each channel, and each speaker circuit includes a fuse rated 4.00 A. Is this system adequately protected against overload? Explain your reasoning.

70. A close analogy exists between the flow of energy by heat because of a temperature difference (see Section 20.7) and the flow of electric charge because of a potential difference. The energy dQ and the electric charge dq can both be transported by free electrons in the conducting material. Consequently, a good electrical conductor is usually a good thermal conductor as well. Consider a thin conducting slab of thickness dx, area A, and electrical conductivity σ, with a potential difference dV between opposite faces. Show that the current $I = dq/dt$ is given by the equation on the left below:

Charge Conduction	Thermal Conduction (Eq. 20.14)
$\dfrac{dq}{dt} = \sigma A \left\| \dfrac{dV}{dx} \right\|$	$\dfrac{dQ}{dt} = kA \left\| \dfrac{dT}{dx} \right\|$

In the analogous thermal conduction equation on the right, the rate of energy flow dQ/dt (in SI units of joules per second) is due to a temperature gradient dT/dx, in a material of thermal conductivity k. State analogous rules relating the direction of the electric current to the change in potential, and relating the direction of energy flow to the change in temperature.

71. Material with uniform resistivity ρ is formed into a wedge as shown in Figure P27.71. Show that the resistance between face A and face B of this wedge is

$$R = \rho \frac{L}{w(y_2 - y_1)} \ln\left(\frac{y_2}{y_1}\right)$$

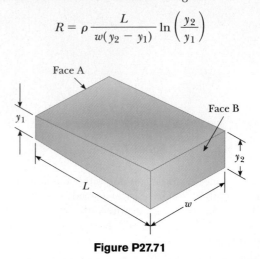

Figure P27.71

72. A material of resistivity ρ is formed into the shape of a truncated cone of altitude h as shown in Figure P27.72. The bottom end has radius b, and the top end has radius a. Assume that the current is distributed uniformly over any circular cross section of the cone, so that the current density does not depend on radial position. (The current density does vary with position along the axis of the cone.) Show that the resistance between the two ends is described by the expression

$$R = \frac{\rho}{\pi}\left(\frac{h}{ab}\right)$$

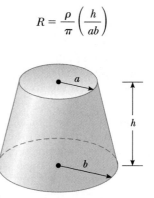

Figure P27.72

73. The dielectric material between the plates of a parallel-plate capacitor always has some nonzero conductivity σ. Let A represent the area of each plate and d the distance between them. Let κ represent the dielectric constant of the material. (a) Show that the resistance R and the capacitance C of the capacitor are related by

$$RC = \frac{\kappa\epsilon_0}{\sigma}$$

(b) Find the resistance between the plates of a 14.0-nF capacitor with a fused quartz dielectric.

74. 🖥 The current–voltage characteristic curve for a semiconductor diode as a function of temperature T is given by the equation

$$I = I_0(e^{e\,\Delta V/k_\mathrm{B}T} - 1)$$

Here the first symbol e represents Euler's number, the base of natural logarithms. The second e is the charge on the electron. The k_B stands for Boltzmann's constant, and T is the absolute temperature. Set up a spreadsheet to calculate I and $R = \Delta V/I$ for $\Delta V = 0.400$ V to 0.600 V in increments of 0.005 V. Assume $I_0 = 1.00$ nA. Plot R versus ΔV for $T = 280$ K, 300 K, and 320 K.

75. **Review problem.** A parallel-plate capacitor consists of square plates of edge length ℓ that are separated by a distance d, where $d \ll \ell$. A potential difference ΔV is maintained between the plates. A material of dielectric constant κ fills half of the space between the plates. The dielectric slab is now withdrawn from the capacitor, as shown in Figure P27.75. (a) Find the capacitance when the left edge of the dielectric is at a distance x from the center of the capacitor. (b) If the dielectric is removed at a constant speed v, what is the current in the circuit as the dielectric is being withdrawn?

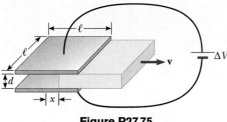

Figure P27.75

Answers to Quick Quizzes

27.1 d, b = c, a. The current in part (d) is equivalent to two positive charges moving to the left. Parts (b) and (c) each represent four positive charges moving in the same direction because negative charges moving to the left are equivalent to positive charges moving to the right. The current in part (a) is equivalent to five positive charges moving to the right.

27.2 (b). The currents in the two paths add numerically to equal the current coming into the junction, without regard for the directions of the two wires coming out of the junction. This is indicative of scalar addition. Even though we can assign a direction to a current, it is not a vector. This suggests a deeper meaning for vectors besides that of a quantity with magnitude and direction.

27.3 (a). The current in each section of the wire is the same even though the wire constricts. As the cross-sectional area A decreases, the drift velocity must increase in order for the constant current to be maintained, in accordance with Equation 27.4. As A decreases, Equation 27.11 tells us that R increases.

27.4 (b). The doubling of the radius causes the area A to be four times as large, so Equation 27.11 tells us that the resistance decreases.

27.5 (b). The slope of the tangent to the graph line at a point is the reciprocal of the resistance at that point. Because the slope is increasing, the resistance is decreasing.

27.6 (a). When the filament is at room temperature, its resistance is low, and hence the current is relatively large. As the filament warms up, its resistance increases, and the current decreases. Older lightbulbs often fail just as they are turned on because this large initial current "spike" produces rapid temperature increase and mechanical stress on the filament, causing it to break.

27.7 (c). Because the potential difference ΔV is the same across the two bulbs and because the power delivered to a conductor is $\mathcal{P} = I\Delta V$, the 60-W bulb, with its higher power rating, must carry the greater current. The 30-W bulb has the higher resistance because it draws less current at the same potential difference.

27.8 $I_a = I_b > I_c = I_d > I_e = I_f$. The current I_a leaves the positive terminal of the battery and then splits to flow through the two bulbs; thus, $I_a = I_c + I_e$. From Quick Quiz 27.7, we know that the current in the 60-W bulb is greater than that in the 30-W bulb. Because charge does not build up in the bulbs, we know that the same amount of charge flowing into a bulb from the left must flow out on the right; consequently, $I_c = I_d$ and $I_e = I_f$. The two currents leaving the bulbs recombine to form the current back into the battery, $I_f + I_d = I_b$.

Chapter 28

Direct Current Circuits

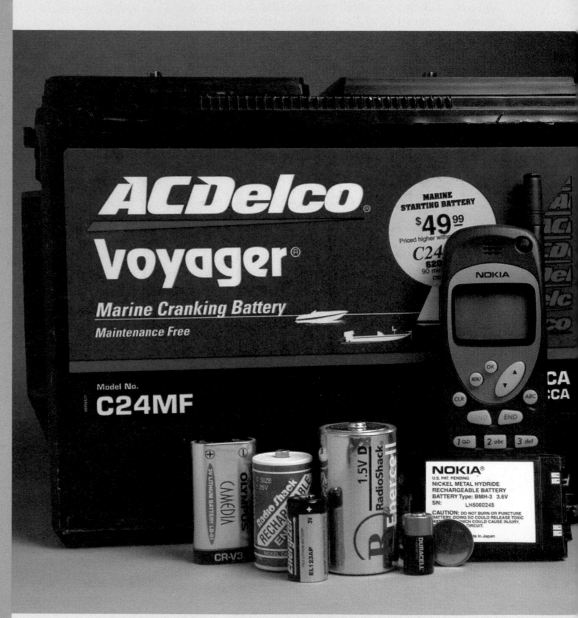

▲ *An assortment of batteries that can be used to provide energy for various devices. Batteries provide a voltage with a fixed polarity, resulting in a direct current in a circuit, that is, a current for which the drift velocity of the charges is always in the same direction. (George Semple)*

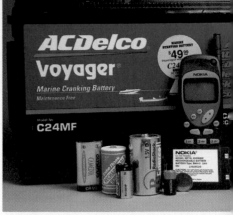

This chapter is concerned with the analysis of simple electric circuits that contain batteries, resistors, and capacitors in various combinations. We will see some circuits in which resistors can be combined using simple rules. The analysis of more complicated circuits is simplified using two rules known as *Kirchhoff's rules*, which follow from the laws of conservation of energy and conservation of electric charge for isolated systems. Most of the circuits analyzed are assumed to be in *steady state,* which means that currents in the circuit are constant in magnitude and direction. A current that is constant in direction is called a *direct current* (DC). We will study *alternating current* (AC), in which the current changes direction periodically, in Chapter 33. Finally, we describe electrical meters for measuring current and potential difference, and discuss electrical circuits in the home.

28.1 Electromotive Force

In Section 27.6 we discussed a closed circuit in which a battery produces a potential difference and causes charges to move. We will generally use a battery in our discussion and in our circuit diagrams as a source of energy for the circuit. Because the potential difference at the battery terminals is constant in a particular circuit, the current in the circuit is constant in magnitude and direction and is called **direct current.** A battery is called either a *source of electromotive force* or, more commonly, a *source of emf.* (The phrase *electromotive force* is an unfortunate historical term, describing not a force but rather a potential difference in volts.) **The emf $\mathcal{E}$ of a battery is the maximum possible voltage that the battery can provide between its terminals.** You can think of a source of emf as a "charge pump." When an electric potential difference exists between two points, the source moves charges "uphill" from the lower potential to the higher.

Consider the circuit shown in Figure 28.1, consisting of a battery connected to a resistor. We shall generally assume that the connecting wires have no resistance.

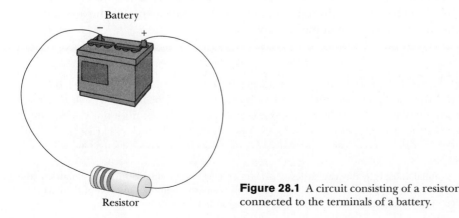

Figure 28.1 A circuit consisting of a resistor connected to the terminals of a battery.

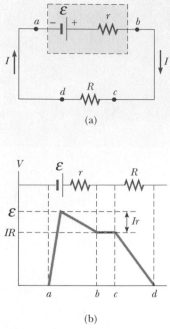

Active Figure 28.2 (a) Circuit diagram of a source of emf $\mathcal{E}$ (in this case, a battery), of internal resistance r, connected to an external resistor of resistance R. (b) Graphical representation showing how the electric potential changes as the circuit in part (a) is traversed clockwise.

At the Active Figures link at http://www.pse6.com, you can adjust the emf and resistances r and R to see the effect on the current and on the graph in part (b).

⚠ **PITFALL PREVENTION**

28.1   What Is Constant in a Battery?

It is a common misconception that a battery is a source of constant current. Equation 28.3 clearly shows that this is not true. The current in the circuit depends on the resistance connected to the battery. It is also not true that a battery is a source of constant terminal voltage, as shown by Equation 28.1. **A battery is a source of constant emf.**

The positive terminal of the battery is at a higher potential than the negative terminal. Because a real battery is made of matter, there is resistance to the flow of charge within the battery. This resistance is called **internal resistance** r. For an idealized battery with zero internal resistance, the potential difference across the battery (called its *terminal voltage*) equals its emf. However, for a real battery, the terminal voltage is *not* equal to the emf for a battery in a circuit in which there is a current. To understand why this is so, consider the circuit diagram in Figure 28.2a, where the battery of Figure 28.1 is represented by the dashed rectangle containing an ideal, resistance-free emf $\mathcal{E}$ in series with an internal resistance r. Now imagine moving through the battery from a to b and measuring the electric potential at various locations. As we pass from the negative terminal to the positive terminal, the potential *increases* by an amount $\mathcal{E}$. However, as we move through the resistance r, the potential *decreases* by an amount Ir, where I is the current in the circuit. Thus, the terminal voltage of the battery $\Delta V = V_b - V_a$ is[1]

$$\Delta V = \mathcal{E} - Ir \qquad (28.1)$$

From this expression, note that $\mathcal{E}$ is equivalent to the **open-circuit voltage**—that is, the *terminal voltage when the current is zero*. The emf is the voltage labeled on a battery—for example, the emf of a D cell is 1.5 V. The actual potential difference between the terminals of the battery depends on the current in the battery, as described by Equation 28.1.

Figure 28.2b is a graphical representation of the changes in electric potential as the circuit is traversed in the clockwise direction. By inspecting Figure 28.2a, we see that the terminal voltage ΔV must equal the potential difference across the external resistance R, often called the **load resistance.** The load resistor might be a simple resistive circuit element, as in Figure 28.1, or it could be the resistance of some electrical device (such as a toaster, an electric heater, or a lightbulb) connected to the battery (or, in the case of household devices, to the wall outlet). The resistor represents a *load* on the battery because the battery must supply energy to operate the device. The potential difference across the load resistance is $\Delta V = IR$. Combining this expression with Equation 28.1, we see that

$$\mathcal{E} = IR + Ir \qquad (28.2)$$

Solving for the current gives

$$I = \frac{\mathcal{E}}{R + r} \qquad (28.3)$$

This equation shows that the current in this simple circuit depends on both the load resistance R external to the battery and the internal resistance r. If R is much greater than r, as it is in many real-world circuits, we can neglect r.

If we multiply Equation 28.2 by the current I, we obtain

$$I\mathcal{E} = I^2R + I^2r \qquad (28.4)$$

This equation indicates that, because power $\mathcal{P} = I\,\Delta V$ (see Eq. 27.22), the total power output $I\mathcal{E}$ of the battery is delivered to the external load resistance in the amount I^2R and to the internal resistance in the amount I^2r.

Quick Quiz 28.1 In order to maximize the percentage of the power that is delivered from a battery to a device, the internal resistance of the battery should be (a) as low as possible (b) as high as possible (c) The percentage does not depend on the internal resistance.

[1]   The terminal voltage in this case is less than the emf by an amount Ir. In some situations, the terminal voltage may *exceed* the emf by an amount Ir. This happens when the direction of the current is *opposite* that of the emf, as in the case of charging a battery with another source of emf.

Example 28.1 Terminal Voltage of a Battery

Interactive

A battery has an emf of 12.0 V and an internal resistance of 0.05 Ω. Its terminals are connected to a load resistance of 3.00 Ω.

(A) Find the current in the circuit and the terminal voltage of the battery.

Solution Equation 28.3 gives us the current:

$$I = \frac{\mathcal{E}}{R + r} = \frac{12.0 \text{ V}}{3.05 \text{ Ω}} = \boxed{3.93 \text{ A}}$$

and from Equation 28.1, we find the terminal voltage:

$$\Delta V = \mathcal{E} - Ir = 12.0 \text{ V} - (3.93 \text{ A})(0.05 \text{ Ω}) = \boxed{11.8 \text{ V}}$$

To check this result, we can calculate the voltage across the load resistance R:

$$\Delta V = IR = (3.93 \text{ A})(3.00 \text{ Ω}) = 11.8 \text{ V}$$

(B) Calculate the power delivered to the load resistor, the power delivered to the internal resistance of the battery, and the power delivered by the battery.

Solution The power delivered to the load resistor is

$$\mathcal{P}_R = I^2R = (3.93 \text{ A})^2 (3.00 \text{ Ω}) = \boxed{46.3 \text{ W}}$$

The power delivered to the internal resistance is

$$\mathcal{P}_r = I^2r = (3.93 \text{ A})^2 (0.05 \text{ Ω}) = \boxed{0.772 \text{ W}}$$

Hence, the power delivered by the battery is the sum of these quantities, or 47.1 W. You should check this result, using the expression $\mathcal{P} = I\mathcal{E}$.

What If? As a battery ages, its internal resistance increases. Suppose the internal resistance of this battery rises to 2.00 Ω toward the end of its useful life. How does this alter the ability of the battery to deliver energy?

Answer Let us connect the same 3.00-Ω load resistor to the battery. The current in the battery now is

$$I = \frac{\mathcal{E}}{R + r} = \frac{12.0 \text{ V}}{(3.00 \text{ Ω} + 2.00 \text{ Ω})} = 2.40 \text{ A}$$

and the terminal voltage is

$$\Delta V = \mathcal{E} - Ir = 12.0 \text{ V} - (2.40 \text{ A})(2.00 \text{ Ω}) = 7.2 \text{ V}$$

Notice that the terminal voltage is only 60% of the emf. The powers delivered to the load resistor and internal resistance are

$$\mathcal{P}_R = I^2R = (2.40 \text{ A})^2 (3.00 \text{ Ω}) = \boxed{17.3 \text{ W}}$$

$$\mathcal{P}_r = I^2r = (2.40 \text{ A})^2 (2.00 \text{ Ω}) = 11.5 \text{ W}$$

Notice that 40% of the power from the battery is delivered to the internal resistance. In part (B), this percentage is 1.6%. Consequently, even though the emf remains fixed, the increasing internal resistance significantly reduces the ability of the battery to deliver energy.

At the Interactive Worked Example link at **http://www.pse6.com,** you can vary the load resistance and internal resistance, observing the power delivered to each.

Example 28.2 Matching the Load

Show that the maximum power delivered to the load resistance R in Figure 28.2a occurs when the load resistance matches the internal resistance—that is, when $R = r$.

Solution The power delivered to the load resistance is equal to I^2R, where I is given by Equation 28.3:

$$\mathcal{P} = I^2R = \frac{\mathcal{E}^2R}{(R + r)^2}$$

When $\mathcal{P}$ is plotted versus R as in Figure 28.3, we find that $\mathcal{P}$ reaches a maximum value of $\mathcal{E}^2/4r$ at $R = r$. When R is large, there is very little current, so that the power I^2R delivered to the load resistor is small. When R is small, the current is large and there is significant loss of power I^2r as energy is delivered to the internal resistance. When $R = r$, these effects balance to give a maximum transfer of power.

We can also prove that the power maximizes at $R = r$ by differentiating $\mathcal{P}$ with respect to R, setting the result equal

to zero, and solving for R. The details are left as a problem for you to solve (Problem 57).

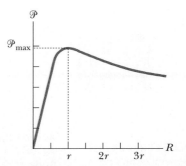

Figure 28.3 (Example 28.2) Graph of the power $\mathcal{P}$ delivered by a battery to a load resistor of resistance R as a function of R. The power delivered to the resistor is a maximum when the load resistance equals the internal resistance of the battery.

28.2   Resistors in Series and Parallel

Suppose that you and your friends are at a crowded basketball game in a sports arena and decide to leave early. You have two choices: (1) your group can exit through a single door and push your way down a long hallway containing several concession stands, each surrounded by a large crowd of people waiting to buy food or souvenirs; or (2) each member of your group can exit through a separate door in the main hall of the arena, where each will have to push his or her way through a single group of people standing by the door. In which scenario will less time be required for your group to leave the arena?

It should be clear that your group will be able to leave faster through the separate doors than down the hallway where each of you has to push through several groups of people. We could describe the groups of people in the hallway as being in *series*, because each of you must push your way through all of the groups. The groups of people around the doors in the arena can be described as being in *parallel*. Each member of your group must push through only one group of people, and each member pushes through a *different* group of people. This simple analogy will help us understand the behavior of currents in electric circuits containing more than one resistor.

When two or more resistors are connected together as are the lightbulbs in Figure 28.4a, they are said to be in *series*. Figure 28.4b is the circuit diagram for the lightbulbs, which are shown as resistors, and the battery. In a series connection, if an amount of charge Q exits resistor R_1, charge Q must also enter the second resistor R_2. (This is analogous to all members of your group pushing through each crowd in the single hallway of the sports arena.) Otherwise, charge will accumulate on the wire between the resistors. Thus, the same amount of charge passes through both resistors in a given time interval. Hence,

> for a series combination of two resistors, the currents are the same in both resistors because the amount of charge that passes through R_1 must also pass through R_2 in the same time interval.

The potential difference applied across the series combination of resistors will divide between the resistors. In Figure 28.4b, because the voltage drop[2] from a to b equals IR_1 and the voltage drop from b to c equals IR_2, the voltage drop from a to c is

$$\Delta V = IR_1 + IR_2 = I(R_1 + R_2)$$

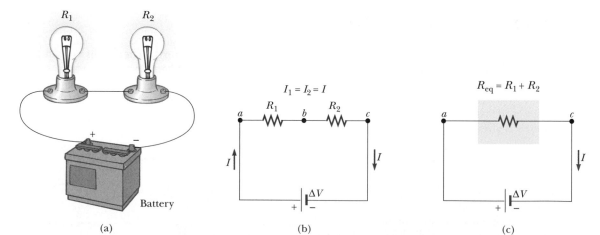

Active Figure 28.4 (a) A series connection of two lightbulbs with resistances R_1 and R_2. (b) Circuit diagram for the two-resistor circuit. The current in R_1 is the same as that in R_2. (c) The resistors replaced with a single resistor having an equivalent resistance $R_{eq} = R_1 + R_2$.

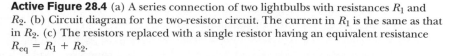

[2]   The term *voltage drop* is synonymous with a decrease in electric potential across a resistor and is used often by individuals working with electric circuits.

The potential difference across the battery is also applied to the **equivalent resistance** R_{eq} in Figure 28.4c:

$$\Delta V = IR_{eq}$$

where we have indicated that the equivalent resistance has the same effect on the circuit because it results in the same current in the battery as the combination of resistors. Combining these equations, we see that we can replace the two resistors in series with a single equivalent resistance whose value is the *sum* of the individual resistances:

$$\Delta V = IR_{eq} = I(R_1 + R_2) \longrightarrow R_{eq} = R_1 + R_2 \qquad (28.5)$$

The resistance R_{eq} is equivalent to the series combination $R_1 + R_2$ in the sense that the circuit current is unchanged when R_{eq} replaces $R_1 + R_2$.

The equivalent resistance of three or more resistors connected in series is

$$R_{eq} = R_1 + R_2 + R_3 + \cdots \qquad (28.6)$$

◀ The equivalent resistance of several resistors in series

This relationship indicates that **the equivalent resistance of a series connection of resistors is the numerical sum of the individual resistances and is always greater than any individual resistance.**

Looking back at Equation 28.3, the denominator is the simple algebraic sum of the external and internal resistances. This is consistent with the fact that internal and external resistances are in series in Figure 28.2a.

Note that if the filament of one lightbulb in Figure 28.4 were to fail, the circuit would no longer be complete (resulting in an open-circuit condition) and the second bulb would also go out. This is a general feature of a series circuit—if one device in the series creates an open circuit, all devices are inoperative.

▲ **PITFALL PREVENTION**

28.2 Lightbulbs Don't Burn

We will describe the end of the life of a lightbulb by saying that *the filament fails*, rather than by saying that the lightbulb "burns out." The word *burn* suggests a combustion process, which is not what occurs in a lightbulb.

Quick Quiz 28.2 In Figure 28.4, imagine positive charges pass first through R_1 and then through R_2. Compared to the current in R_1, the current in R_2 is (a) smaller, (b) larger, or (c) the same.

Quick Quiz 28.3 If a piece of wire is used to connect points b and c in Figure 28.4b, does the brightness of bulb R_1 (a) increase, (b) decrease, or (c) remain the same?

Quick Quiz 28.4 With the switch in the circuit of Figure 28.5 closed (left), there is no current in R_2, because the current has an alternate zero-resistance path through the switch. There is current in R_1 and this current is measured with the ammeter (a device for measuring current) at the right side of the circuit. If the switch is opened (Fig. 28.5, right), there is current in R_2. What happens to the reading on the ammeter when the switch is opened? (a) the reading goes up; (b) the reading goes down; (c) the reading does not change.

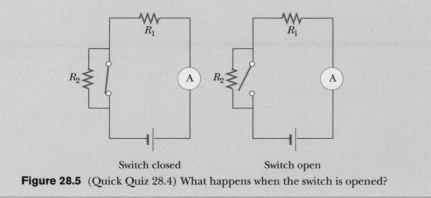

Switch closed   Switch open

Figure 28.5 (Quick Quiz 28.4) What happens when the switch is opened?

At the Active Figures link at http://www.pse6.com, you can adjust the battery voltage and resistances R_1 and R_2 to see the effect on the currents and voltages in the individual resistors.

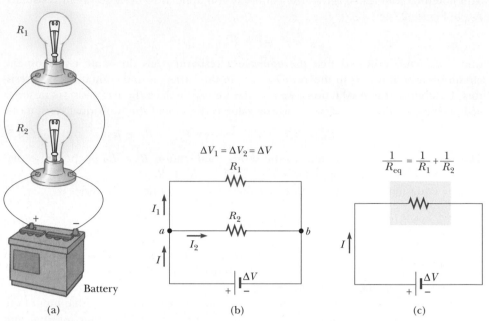

Active Figure 28.6 (a) A parallel connection of two lightbulbs with resistances R_1 and R_2. (b) Circuit diagram for the two-resistor circuit. The potential difference across R_1 is the same as that across R_2. (c) The resistors replaced with a single resistor having an equivalent resistance given by Equation 28.7.

▲ **PITFALL PREVENTION**

28.3 Local and Global Changes

A local change in one part of a circuit may result in a global change throughout the circuit. For example, if a single resistance is changed in a circuit containing several resistors and batteries, the currents in all resistors and batteries, the terminal voltages of all batteries, and the voltages across all resistors may change as a result.

▲ **PITFALL PREVENTION**

28.4 Current Does Not Take the Path of Least Resistance

You may have heard a phrase like "current takes the path of least resistance" in reference to a parallel combination of current paths, such that there are two or more paths for the current to take. The phrase is incorrect. The current takes *all* paths. Those paths with lower resistance will have large currents, but even very high-resistance paths will carry *some* of the current.

Now consider two resistors connected in *parallel*, as shown in Figure 28.6. When charges reach point a in Figure 28.6b, called a *junction*, they split into two parts, with some going through R_1 and the rest going through R_2. A **junction** is any point in a circuit where a current can split (just as your group might split up and leave the sports arena through several doors, as described earlier.) This split results in less current in each individual resistor than the current leaving the battery. Because electric charge is conserved, the current I that enters point a must equal the total current leaving that point:

$$I = I_1 + I_2$$

where I_1 is the current in R_1 and I_2 is the current in R_2.

As can be seen from Figure 28.6, both resistors are connected directly across the terminals of the battery. Therefore,

> when resistors are connected in parallel, the potential differences across the resistors is the same.

Because the potential differences across the resistors are the same, the expression $\Delta V = IR$ gives

$$I = I_1 + I_2 = \frac{\Delta V}{R_1} + \frac{\Delta V}{R_2} = \Delta V \left(\frac{1}{R_1} + \frac{1}{R_2} \right) = \frac{\Delta V}{R_{eq}}$$

where R_{eq} is an equivalent single resistance which will have the same effect on the circuit as the two resistors in parallel; that is, it will draw the same current from the battery (Fig. 28.6c). From this result, we see that the equivalent resistance of two resistors in parallel is given by

$$\frac{1}{R_{eq}} = \frac{1}{R_1} + \frac{1}{R_2} \tag{28.7}$$

or

$$R_{eq} = \frac{1}{\dfrac{1}{R_1} + \dfrac{1}{R_2}} = \frac{R_1 R_2}{R_1 + R_2}$$

An extension of this analysis to three or more resistors in parallel gives

$$\frac{1}{R_{eq}} = \frac{1}{R_1} + \frac{1}{R_2} + \frac{1}{R_3} + \cdots$$

(28.8)   **The equivalent resistance of several resistors in parallel**

We can see from this expression that **the inverse of the equivalent resistance of two or more resistors connected in parallel is equal to the sum of the inverses of the individual resistances. Furthermore, the equivalent resistance is always less than the smallest resistance in the group.**

Household circuits are always wired such that the appliances are connected in parallel. Each device operates independently of the others so that if one is switched off, the others remain on. In addition, in this type of connection, all of the devices operate on the same voltage.

Quick Quiz 28.5 In Figure 28.4, imagine that we add a third resistor in series with the first two. Does the current in the battery (a) increase, (b) decrease, or (c) remain the same? Does the terminal voltage of the battery (d) increase, (e) decrease, or (f) remain the same?

Quick Quiz 28.6 In Figure 28.6, imagine that we add a third resistor in parallel with the first two. Does the current in the battery (a) increase, (b) decrease, or (c) remain the same? Does the terminal voltage of the battery (d) increase, (e) decrease, or (f) remain the same?

Quick Quiz 28.7 With the switch in the circuit of Figure 28.7 open (left), there is no current in R_2. There is current in R_1 and this current is measured with the ammeter at the right side of the circuit. If the switch is closed (Fig. 28.7, right), there is current in R_2. What happens to the reading on the ammeter when the switch is closed? (a) the reading goes up; (b) the reading goes down; (c) the reading does not change.

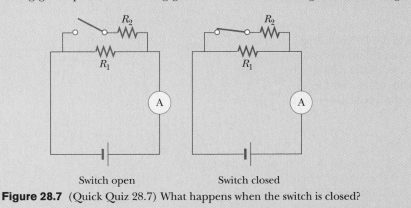

Switch open   Switch closed

Figure 28.7 (Quick Quiz 28.7) What happens when the switch is closed?

Conceptual Example 28.3   Landscape Lights

A homeowner wishes to install 12-volt landscape lighting in his back yard. To save money, he purchases inexpensive 18-gauge cable, which has a relatively high resistance per unit length. This cable consists of two side-by-side wires separated by insulation, like the cord on an appliance. He runs a 200-foot length of this cable from the power supply to the farthest point at which he plans to position a light fixture. He attaches light fixtures across the two wires on the cable at 10-foot intervals, so the light fixtures are in parallel. Because of the cable's resistance, the brightness of the bulbs in the light fixtures is not as desired. Which problem does the homeowner have? (a) All of the bulbs glow equally less brightly than they would if lower-resistance cable had been used. (b) The brightness of the bulbs decreases as you move farther from the power supply.

Solution A circuit diagram for the system appears in Figure 28.8. The horizontal resistors (such as R_A and R_B) represent the resistance of the wires in the cable between the light fixtures while the vertical resistors (such as R_C) represent the resistance of the light fixtures themselves. Part of the terminal voltage of the power supply is dropped across resistors R_A and R_B. Thus, the voltage across light

fixture R_C is less than the terminal voltage. There is a further voltage drop across resistors R_D and R_E. Consequently, the voltage across light fixture R_F is smaller than that across R_C. This continues on down the line of light fixtures, so the correct choice is (b). Each successive light fixture has a smaller voltage across it and glows less brightly than the one before.

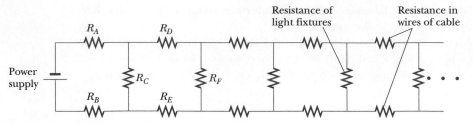

Figure 28.8 (Conceptual Example 28.3) The circuit diagram for a set of landscape light fixtures connected in parallel across the two wires of a two-wire cable. The horizontal resistors represent resistance in the wires of the cable. The vertical resistors represent the light fixtures.

Example 28.4 Find the Equivalent Resistance

Four resistors are connected as shown in Figure 28.9a.

(A) Find the equivalent resistance between points a and c.

Solution The combination of resistors can be reduced in steps, as shown in Figure 28.9. The 8.0-Ω and 4.0-Ω resistors are in series; thus, the equivalent resistance between a and b is 12.0 Ω (see Eq. 28.5). The 6.0-Ω and 3.0-Ω resistors are in parallel, so from Equation 28.7 we find that the equivalent resistance from b to c is 2.0 Ω. Hence, the equivalent resistance from a to c is 14.0 Ω.

(B) What is the current in each resistor if a potential difference of 42 V is maintained between a and c?

Solution The currents in the 8.0-Ω and 4.0-Ω resistors are the same because they are in series. In addition, this is the same as the current that would exist in the 14.0-Ω equivalent resistor subject to the 42-V potential difference. Therefore, using Equation 27.8 ($R = \Delta V/I$) and the result from part (A), we obtain

$$I = \frac{\Delta V_{ac}}{R_{eq}} = \frac{42 \text{ V}}{14.0 \text{ }\Omega} = 3.0 \text{ A}$$

This is the current in the 8.0-Ω and 4.0-Ω resistors. When this 3.0-A current enters the junction at b, however, it splits, with part passing through the 6.0-Ω resistor (I_1) and part through the 3.0-Ω resistor (I_2). Because the potential difference is ΔV_{bc} across each of these parallel resistors, we see that $(6.0 \text{ }\Omega)I_1 = (3.0 \text{ }\Omega)I_2$, or $I_2 = 2I_1$. Using this result and the fact that $I_1 + I_2 = 3.0$ A, we find that $I_1 = 1.0$ A and

$I_2 = 2.0$ A. We could have guessed this at the start by noting that the current in the 3.0-Ω resistor has to be twice that in the 6.0-Ω resistor, in view of their relative resistances and the fact that the same voltage is applied to each of them.

As a final check of our results, note that $\Delta V_{bc} = (6.0 \text{ }\Omega)I_1 = (3.0 \text{ }\Omega)I_2 = 6.0$ V and $\Delta V_{ab} = (12.0 \text{ }\Omega)I = 36$ V; therefore, $\Delta V_{ac} = \Delta V_{ab} + \Delta V_{bc} = 42$ V, as it must.

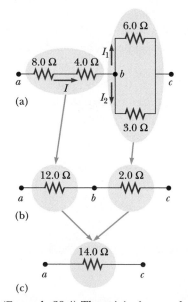

Figure 28.9 (Example 28.4) The original network of resistors is reduced to a single equivalent resistance.

Example 28.5 Finding R_{eq} by Symmetry Arguments

Consider five resistors connected as shown in Figure 28.10a. Find the equivalent resistance between points a and b.

Solution If we inspect this system of resistors, we realize that we cannot reduce it by using our rules for series and parallel

connections. We can, however, assume a current entering junction a and then apply symmetry arguments. Because of the symmetry in the circuit (all 1-Ω resistors in the outside loop), the currents in branches ac and ad must be equal; hence, the electric potentials at points c and d must be equal.

This means that $\Delta V_{cd} = 0$ and there is no current between points c and d. As a result, points c and d may be connected together without affecting the circuit, as in Figure 28.10b. Thus, the 5-Ω resistor may be removed from the circuit and the remaining circuit then reduced as in Figures 28.10c and d. From this reduction we see that the equivalent resistance of the combination is 1 Ω. Note that the result is 1 Ω regardless of the value of the resistor connected between c and d.

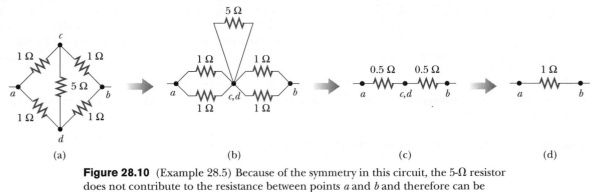

(a)   (b)   (c)   (d)

Figure 28.10 (Example 28.5) Because of the symmetry in this circuit, the 5-Ω resistor does not contribute to the resistance between points a and b and therefore can be disregarded when we calculate the equivalent resistance.

Example 28.6 Three Resistors in Parallel   Interactive

Three resistors are connected in parallel as shown in Figure 28.11a. A potential difference of 18.0 V is maintained between points a and b.

(A) Find the current in each resistor.

Solution The resistors are in parallel, and so the potential difference across each must be 18.0 V. Applying the relationship $\Delta V = IR$ to each resistor gives

$$I_1 = \frac{\Delta V}{R_1} = \frac{18.0\ \text{V}}{3.00\ \Omega} = \boxed{6.00\ \text{A}}$$

$$I_2 = \frac{\Delta V}{R_2} = \frac{18.0\ \text{V}}{6.00\ \Omega} = \boxed{3.00\ \text{A}}$$

$$I_3 = \frac{\Delta V}{R_3} = \frac{18.0\ \text{V}}{9.00\ \Omega} = \boxed{2.00\ \text{A}}$$

(B) Calculate the power delivered to each resistor and the total power delivered to the combination of resistors.

Solution We apply the relationship $\mathcal{P} = I^2 R$ to each resistor and obtain

3.00-Ω: $\mathcal{P}_1 = I_1{}^2 R_1 = (6.00\ \text{A})^2 (3.00\ \Omega) = \boxed{108\ \text{W}}$

6.00-Ω: $\mathcal{P}_2 = I_2{}^2 R_2 = (3.00\ \text{A})^2 (6.00\ \Omega) = \boxed{54.0\ \text{W}}$

9.00-Ω: $\mathcal{P}_3 = I_3{}^2 R_3 = (2.00\ \text{A})^2 (9.00\ \Omega) = \boxed{36.0\ \text{W}}$

This shows that the smallest resistor receives the most power. Summing the three quantities gives a total power of 198 W.

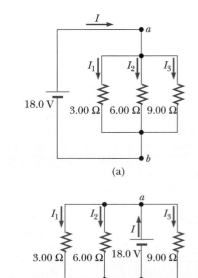

(a)

(b)

Figure 28.11 (Example 28.6) (a) Three resistors connected in parallel. The voltage across each resistor is 18.0 V. (b) Another circuit with three resistors and a battery. Is this equivalent to the circuit in part (a) of the figure?

(C) Calculate the equivalent resistance of the circuit.

Solution We can use Equation 28.8 to find R_{eq}:

$$\frac{1}{R_{eq}} = \frac{1}{3.00\ \Omega} + \frac{1}{6.00\ \Omega} + \frac{1}{9.00\ \Omega}$$

$$R_{eq} = \frac{18.0\ \Omega}{11.0} = \boxed{1.64\ \Omega}$$

What If? What if the circuit is as shown in Figure 28.11b instead of as in Figure 28.11a? How does this affect the calculation?

Answer There is no effect on the calculation. The physical placement of the battery is not important. In Figure 28.11b, the battery still applies a potential difference of 18.0 V between points a and b, so the two circuits in Figure 28.11 are electrically identical.

At the Interactive Worked Example link at http://www.pse6.com, you can explore different configurations of the battery and resistors.

Conceptual Example 28.7   Operation of a Three-Way Lightbulb

Figure 28.12 illustrates how a three-way lightbulb is constructed to provide three levels of light intensity. The socket of the lamp is equipped with a three-way switch for selecting different light intensities. The bulb contains two filaments. When the lamp is connected to a 120-V source, one filament receives 100 W of power, and the other receives 75 W. Explain how the two filaments are used to provide three different light intensities.

Solution The three light intensities are made possible by applying the 120 V to one filament alone, to the other filament alone, or to the two filaments in parallel. When switch S_1 is closed and switch S_2 is opened, current exists only in the 75-W filament. When switch S_1 is open and switch S_2 is closed, current exists only in the 100-W filament. When both switches are closed, current exists in both filaments, and the total power is 175 W.

If the filaments were connected in series and one of them were to break, no charges could pass through the bulb, and the bulb would give no illumination, regardless of the switch position. However, with the filaments connected

in parallel, if one of them (for example, the 75-W filament) breaks, the bulb will still operate in two of the switch positions as current exists in the other (100-W) filament.

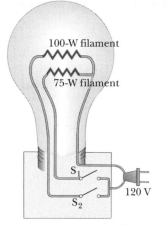

Figure 28.12 (Conceptual Example 28.7) A three-way lightbulb.

Application   Strings of Lights

Strings of lights are used for many ornamental purposes, such as decorating Christmas trees.[3] Over the years, both parallel and series connections have been used for strings of lights powered by 120 V. Series-wired bulbs are safer than parallel-wired bulbs for indoor Christmas-tree use because series-wired bulbs operate with less energy per bulb and at a lower temperature. However, if the filament of a single bulb fails (or if the bulb is removed from its socket), all the lights on the string go out. The popularity of series-wired light strings diminished because troubleshooting a failed bulb was a tedious, time-consuming chore that involved trial-and-error substitution of a good bulb in each socket along the string until the defective bulb was found.

In a parallel-wired string, each bulb operates at 120 V. By design, the bulbs are brighter and hotter than those on

a series-wired string. As a result, these bulbs are inherently more dangerous (more likely to start a fire, for instance), but if one bulb in a parallel-wired string fails or is removed, the rest of the bulbs continue to glow. (A 25-bulb string of 4-W bulbs results in a power of 100 W; the total power becomes substantial when several strings are used.)

A new design was developed for so-called "miniature" lights wired in series, to prevent the failure of one bulb from causing the entire string to go out. This design creates a connection (called a jumper) across the filament after it fails. When the filament breaks in one of these miniature lightbulbs, the break in the filament represents the largest resistance in the series, much larger than that of the intact filaments. As a result, most of the applied 120 V appears across the bulb with the broken filament. Inside the

---

[3] These and other household devices, such as the three-way lightbulb in Conceptual Example 28.7 and the kitchen appliances discussed in Section 28.6, actually operate on alternating current (AC), to be introduced in Chapter 33.

lightbulb, a small jumper loop covered by an insulating material is wrapped around the filament leads. When the filament fails and 120 V appears across the bulb, an arc burns the insulation on the jumper and connects the filament leads. This connection now completes the circuit through the bulb even though its filament is no longer active (Fig. 28.13).

Suppose that all the bulbs in a 50-bulb miniature-light string are operating. A 2.40-V potential drop occurs across each bulb because the bulbs are in series. A typical power input to this style of bulb is 0.340 W. The filament resistance of each bulb at the operating temperature is $(2.40\text{ V})^2/(0.340\text{ W}) = 16.9\ \Omega$. The current in each bulb is $2.40\text{ V}/16.9\ \Omega = 0.142$ A. When a bulb fails, the resistance across its terminals is reduced to zero because of the alternate

jumper connection mentioned in the preceding paragraph. All the other bulbs not only stay on but glow more brightly because the total resistance of the string is reduced and consequently the current in each bulb increases.

Let us assume that the resistance of a bulb remains at $16.9\ \Omega$ even though its temperature rises as a result of the increased current. If one bulb fails, the potential difference across each of the remaining bulbs increases to $120\text{ V}/49 = 2.45$ V, the current increases from 0.142 A to 0.145 A, and the power increases to 0.355 W. As more bulbs fail, the current keeps rising, the filament of each bulb operates at a higher temperature, and the lifetime of the bulb is reduced. For this reason, you should check for failed (nonglowing) bulbs in such a series-wired string and replace them as soon as possible, in order to maximize the lifetimes of all the bulbs.

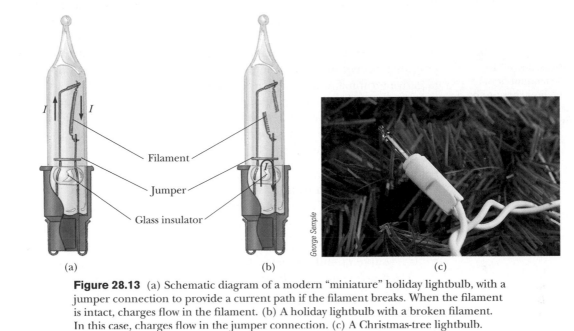

(a)   (b)   (c)

Figure 28.13 (a) Schematic diagram of a modern "miniature" holiday lightbulb, with a jumper connection to provide a current path if the filament breaks. When the filament is intact, charges flow in the filament. (b) A holiday lightbulb with a broken filament. In this case, charges flow in the jumper connection. (c) A Christmas-tree lightbulb.

28.3 Kirchhoff's Rules

As we saw in the preceding section, simple circuits can be analyzed using the expression $\Delta V = IR$ and the rules for series and parallel combinations of resistors. Very often, however, it is not possible to reduce a circuit to a single loop. The procedure for analyzing more complex circuits is greatly simplified if we use two principles called **Kirchhoff's rules:**

1. **Junction rule.** The sum of the currents entering any junction in a circuit must equal the sum of the currents leaving that junction:

$$\sum I_{\text{in}} = \sum I_{\text{out}} \qquad (28.9)$$

2. **Loop rule.** The sum of the potential differences across all elements around any closed circuit loop must be zero:

$$\sum_{\substack{\text{closed}\\\text{loop}}} \Delta V = 0 \qquad (28.10)$$

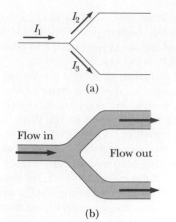

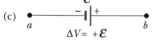

Figure 28.14 (a) Kirchhoff's junction rule. Conservation of charge requires that all charges entering a junction must leave that junction. Therefore, $I_1 = I_2 + I_3$. (b) A mechanical analog of the junction rule: the amount of water flowing out of the branches on the right must equal the amount flowing into the single branch on the left.

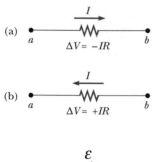

Figure 28.15 Rules for determining the potential differences across a resistor and a battery. (The battery is assumed to have no internal resistance.) Each circuit element is traversed from left to right.

Kirchhoff's first rule is a statement of conservation of electric charge. All charges that enter a given point in a circuit must leave that point because charge cannot build up at a point. If we apply this rule to the junction shown in Figure 28.14a, we obtain

$$I_1 = I_2 + I_3$$

Figure 28.14b represents a mechanical analog of this situation, in which water flows through a branched pipe having no leaks. Because water does not build up anywhere in the pipe, the flow rate into the pipe equals the total flow rate out of the two branches on the right.

Kirchhoff's second rule follows from the law of conservation of energy. Let us imagine moving a charge around a closed loop of a circuit. When the charge returns to the starting point, the charge–circuit system must have the same total energy as it had before the charge was moved. The sum of the increases in energy as the charge passes through some circuit elements must equal the sum of the decreases in energy as it passes through other elements. The potential energy decreases whenever the charge moves through a potential drop $-IR$ across a resistor or whenever it moves in the reverse direction through a source of emf. The potential energy increases whenever the charge passes through a battery from the negative terminal to the positive terminal.

When applying Kirchhoff's second rule in practice, we imagine *traveling* around the loop and consider changes in *electric potential,* rather than the changes in *potential energy* described in the preceding paragraph. You should note the following sign conventions when using the second rule:

- Because charges move from the high-potential end of a resistor toward the low-potential end, if a resistor is traversed in the direction of the current, the potential difference ΔV across the resistor is $-IR$ (Fig. 28.15a).
- If a resistor is traversed in the direction *opposite* the current, the potential difference ΔV across the resistor is $+IR$ (Fig. 28.15b).
- If a source of emf (assumed to have zero internal resistance) is traversed in the direction of the emf (from $-$ to $+$), the potential difference ΔV is $+\mathcal{E}$ (Fig. 28.15c). The emf of the battery increases the electric potential as we move through it in this direction.
- If a source of emf (assumed to have zero internal resistance) is traversed in the direction opposite the emf (from $+$ to $-$), the potential difference ΔV is $-\mathcal{E}$ (Fig. 28.15d). In this case the emf of the battery reduces the electric potential as we move through it.

Limitations exist on the numbers of times you can usefully apply Kirchhoff's rules in analyzing a circuit. You can use the junction rule as often as you need, so long as each time you write an equation you include in it a current that has not been used in a preceding junction-rule equation. In general, the number of times you can use the junction rule is one fewer than the number of junction points in the circuit. You can apply the loop rule as often as needed, as long as a new circuit element (resistor or battery) or a new current appears in each new equation. In general, **in order to solve a particular circuit problem, the number of independent equations you need to obtain from the two rules equals the number of unknown currents.**

Complex networks containing many loops and junctions generate great numbers of independent linear equations and a correspondingly great number of unknowns. Such situations can be handled formally through the use of matrix algebra. Computer software can also be used to solve for the unknowns.

The following examples illustrate how to use Kirchhoff's rules. In all cases, it is assumed that the circuits have reached steady-state conditions—that is, the currents in the various branches are constant. **Any capacitor acts as an open branch in a circuit;** that is, the current in the branch containing the capacitor is zero under steady-state conditions.

PROBLEM-SOLVING HINTS

Kirchhoff's Rules

- Draw a circuit diagram, and label all the known and unknown quantities. You must assign a *direction* to the current in each branch of the circuit. Although the assignment of current directions is arbitrary, you must adhere rigorously to the assigned directions when applying Kirchhoff's rules.

- Apply the junction rule to any junctions in the circuit that provide new relationships among the various currents.

- Apply the loop rule to as many loops in the circuit as are needed to solve for the unknowns. To apply this rule, you must correctly identify the potential difference as you imagine crossing each element while traversing the closed loop (either clockwise or counterclockwise). Watch out for errors in sign!

- Solve the equations simultaneously for the unknown quantities. Do not be alarmed if a current turns out to be negative; *its magnitude will be correct and the direction is opposite to that which you assigned.*

Gustav Kirchhoff
German Physicist (1824–1887)

Kirchhoff, a professor at Heidelberg, and Robert Bunsen invented the spectroscope and founded the science of spectroscopy, which we shall study in Chapter 42. They discovered the elements cesium and rubidium and invented astronomical spectroscopy. *(AIP ESVA/W.F. Meggers Collection)*

Quick Quiz 28.8 In using Kirchhoff's rules, you generally assign a separate unknown current to (a) each resistor in the circuit (b) each loop in the circuit (c) each branch in the circuit (d) each battery in the circuit.

Example 28.8   A Single-Loop Circuit

A single-loop circuit contains two resistors and two batteries, as shown in Figure 28.16. (Neglect the internal resistances of the batteries.)

(A) Find the current in the circuit.

Solution We do not need Kirchhoff's rules to analyze this simple circuit, but let us use them anyway just to see how they are applied. There are no junctions in this single-loop circuit; thus, the current is the same in all elements. Let us assume that the current is clockwise, as shown in Figure 28.16. Traversing the circuit in the clockwise direction, starting at a, we see that $a \rightarrow b$ represents a potential difference of $+\mathcal{E}_1$, $b \rightarrow c$ represents a potential difference of $-IR_1$, $c \rightarrow d$ represents a potential difference of $-\mathcal{E}_2$, and

$d \rightarrow a$ represents a potential difference of $-IR_2$. Applying Kirchhoff's loop rule gives

$$\sum \Delta V = 0$$

$$\mathcal{E}_1 - IR_1 - \mathcal{E}_2 - IR_2 = 0$$

Solving for I and using the values given in Figure 28.16, we obtain

$$(1) \quad I = \frac{\mathcal{E}_1 - \mathcal{E}_2}{R_1 + R_2} = \frac{6.0\ \text{V} - 12\ \text{V}}{8.0\ \Omega + 10\ \Omega} = \boxed{-0.33\ \text{A}}$$

The negative sign for I indicates that the direction of the current is opposite the assumed direction. Notice that the emfs in the numerator subtract because the batteries have opposite polarities in Figure 28.16. In the denominator, the resistances add because the two resistors are in series.

(B) What power is delivered to each resistor? What power is delivered by the 12-V battery?

Solution Using Equation 27.23,

$$\mathcal{P}_1 = I^2 R_1 = (0.33\ \text{A})^2 (8.0\ \Omega) = \boxed{0.87\ \text{W}}$$

$$\mathcal{P}_2 = I^2 R_2 = (0.33\ \text{A})^2 (10\ \Omega) = \boxed{1.1\ \text{W}}$$

Hence, the total power delivered to the resistors is $\mathcal{P}_1 + \mathcal{P}_2 = 2.0$ W.

The 12-V battery delivers power $I\mathcal{E}_2 = 4.0$ W. Half of this power is delivered to the two resistors, as we just calculated. The other half is delivered to the 6-V battery, which is being

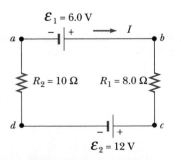

$\mathcal{E}_1 = 6.0$ V

$R_2 = 10\ \Omega$ $R_1 = 8.0\ \Omega$

$\mathcal{E}_2 = 12$ V

Figure 28.16 (Example 28.8) A series circuit containing two batteries and two resistors, where the polarities of the batteries are in opposition.

charged by the 12-V battery. If we had included the internal resistances of the batteries in our analysis, some of the power would appear as internal energy in the batteries; as a result, we would have found that less power was being delivered to the 6-V battery.

What If? What if the polarity of the 12.0-V battery were reversed? How would this affect the circuit?

Answer While we could repeat the Kirchhoff's rules calculation, let us examine Equation (1) and modify it accordingly. Because the polarities of the two batteries are now in the same direction, the signs of $\mathcal{E}_1$ and $\mathcal{E}_2$ are the same and Equation (1) becomes

$$I = \frac{\mathcal{E}_1 + \mathcal{E}_2}{R_1 + R_2} = \frac{6.0 \text{ V} + 12 \text{ V}}{8.0 \text{ }\Omega + 10 \text{ }\Omega} = 1.0 \text{ A}$$

The new powers delivered to the resistors are

$$\mathcal{P}_1 = I^2 R_1 = (1.0 \text{ A})^2 (8.0 \text{ }\Omega) = 8.0 \text{ W}$$

$$\mathcal{P}_2 = I^2 R_2 = (1.0 \text{ A})^2 (10 \text{ }\Omega) = 10 \text{ W}$$

This totals 18 W, nine times as much as in the original circuit, in which the batteries were opposing each other.

Example 28.9 Applying Kirchhoff's Rules

Interactive

Find the currents I_1, I_2, and I_3 in the circuit shown in Figure 28.17.

Solution Conceptualize by noting that we cannot simplify the circuit by the rules of adding resistances in series and in parallel. (If the 10.0-V battery were taken away, we could reduce the remaining circuit with series and parallel combinations.) Thus, we categorize this problem as one in which we must use Kirchhoff's rules. To analyze the circuit, we arbitrarily choose the directions of the currents as labeled in Figure 28.17. Applying Kirchhoff's junction rule to junction c gives

$$(1) \qquad I_1 + I_2 = I_3$$

We now have one equation with three unknowns—I_1, I_2, and I_3. There are three loops in the circuit—*abcda, befcb,* and *aefda.* We therefore need only two loop equations to determine the unknown currents. (The third loop equation would give no new information.) Applying Kirchhoff's loop rule to loops *abcda* and *befcb* and traversing these loops clockwise, we obtain the expressions

$$(2) \qquad abcda \quad 10.0 \text{ V} - (6.0 \text{ }\Omega) I_1 - (2.0 \text{ }\Omega) I_3 = 0$$

$$(3) \quad befcb \quad -14.0 \text{ V} + (6.0 \text{ }\Omega) I_1 - 10.0 \text{ V} - (4.0 \text{ }\Omega) I_2 = 0$$

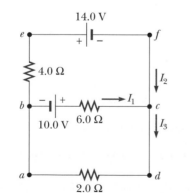

Figure 28.17 (Example 28.9) A circuit containing different branches.

Note that in loop *befcb* we obtain a positive value when traversing the 6.0-Ω resistor because our direction of travel is opposite the assumed direction of I_1. Expressions (1), (2), and (3) represent three independent equations with three unknowns. Substituting Equation (1) into Equation (2) gives

$$10.0 \text{ V} - (6.0 \text{ }\Omega) I_1 - (2.0 \text{ }\Omega) (I_1 + I_2) = 0$$

$$(4) \qquad 10.0 \text{ V} = (8.0 \text{ }\Omega) I_1 + (2.0 \text{ }\Omega) I_2$$

Dividing each term in Equation (3) by 2 and rearranging gives

$$(5) \qquad -12.0 \text{ V} = -(3.0 \text{ }\Omega) I_1 + (2.0 \text{ }\Omega) I_2$$

Subtracting Equation (5) from Equation (4) eliminates I_2, giving

$$22.0 \text{ V} = (11.0 \text{ }\Omega) I_1$$

$$I_1 = \boxed{2.0 \text{ A}}$$

Using this value of I_1 in Equation (5) gives a value for I_2:

$$(2.0 \text{ }\Omega) I_2 = (3.0 \text{ }\Omega) I_1 - 12.0 \text{ V}$$

$$= (3.0 \text{ }\Omega)(2.0 \text{ A}) - 12.0 \text{ V} = -6.0 \text{ V}$$

$$I_2 = \boxed{-3.0 \text{ A}}$$

Finally,

$$I_3 = I_1 + I_2 = \boxed{-1.0 \text{ A}}$$

To finalize the problem, note that I_2 and I_3 are both negative. This indicates only that the currents are opposite the direction we chose for them. However, the numerical values are correct. What would have happened had we left the current directions as labeled in Figure 28.17 but traversed the loops in the opposite direction?

Practice applying Kirchhoff's rules at the Interactive Worked Example link at http://www.pse6.com.

Example 28.10   A Multiloop Circuit

(A) Under steady-state conditions, find the unknown currents I_1, I_2, and I_3 in the multiloop circuit shown in Figure 28.18.

Solution First note that because the capacitor represents an open circuit, there is no current between g and b along path $ghab$ under steady-state conditions. Therefore, when the charges associated with I_1 reach point g, they all go toward point b through the 8.00-V battery; hence, $I_{gb} = I_1$. Labeling the currents as shown in Figure 28.18 and applying Equation 28.9 to junction c, we obtain

$$(1) \qquad I_1 + I_2 = I_3$$

Equation 28.10 applied to loops $defcd$ and $cfgbc$, traversed clockwise, gives

$$(2) \qquad defcd \quad 4.00 \text{ V} - (3.00 \ \Omega) I_2 - (5.00 \ \Omega) I_3 = 0$$

$$(3) \qquad cfgbc \quad (3.00 \ \Omega) I_2 - (5.00 \ \Omega) I_1 + 8.00 \text{ V} = 0$$

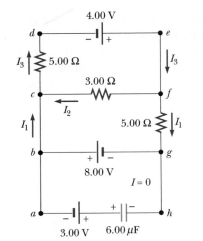

Figure 28.18 (Example 28.10) A multiloop circuit. Kirchhoff's loop rule can be applied to *any* closed loop, including the one containing the capacitor.

From Equation (1) we see that $I_1 = I_3 - I_2$, which, when substituted into Equation (3), gives

$$(4) \qquad (8.00 \ \Omega) I_2 - (5.00 \ \Omega) I_3 + 8.00 \text{ V} = 0$$

Subtracting Equation (4) from Equation (2), we eliminate I_3 and find that

$$I_2 = -\frac{4.00 \text{ V}}{11.0 \ \Omega} = \boxed{-0.364 \text{ A}}$$

Because our value for I_2 is negative, we conclude that the direction of I_2 is from c to f in the 3.00-Ω resistor. Despite this interpretation of the direction, however, we must continue to use this negative value for I_2 in subsequent calculations because our equations were established with our original choice of direction.

Using $I_2 = -0.364$ A in Equations (3) and (1) gives

$$I_1 = \boxed{1.38 \text{ A}} \qquad I_3 = \boxed{1.02 \text{ A}}$$

(B) What is the charge on the capacitor?

Solution We can apply Kirchhoff's loop rule to loop $bghab$ (or any other loop that contains the capacitor) to find the potential difference ΔV_{cap} across the capacitor. We use this potential difference in the loop equation without reference to a sign convention because the charge on the capacitor depends only on the magnitude of the potential difference. Moving clockwise around this loop, we obtain

$$-8.00 \text{ V} + \Delta V_{cap} - 3.00 \text{ V} = 0$$

$$\Delta V_{cap} = 11.0 \text{ V}$$

Because $Q = C \Delta V_{cap}$ (see Eq. 26.1), the charge on the capacitor is

$$Q = (6.00 \ \mu\text{F})(11.0 \text{ V}) = \boxed{66.0 \ \mu\text{C}}$$

Why is the left side of the capacitor positively charged?

28.4   *RC* Circuits

So far we have analyzed direct current circuits in which the current is constant. In DC circuits containing capacitors, the current is always in the same direction but may vary in time. A circuit containing a series combination of a resistor and a capacitor is called an **RC circuit.**

Charging a Capacitor

Figure 28.19 shows a simple series *RC* circuit. Let us assume that the capacitor in this circuit is initially uncharged. There is no current while switch S is open (Fig. 28.19b). If the switch is closed at $t = 0$, however, charge begins to flow, setting up a current in the circuit, and the capacitor begins to charge.[4] Note that during charging, charges do

---

[4]   In previous discussions of capacitors, we assumed a steady-state situation, in which no current was present in any branch of the circuit containing a capacitor. Now we are considering the case *before* the steady-state condition is realized; in this situation, charges are moving and a current exists in the wires connected to the capacitor.

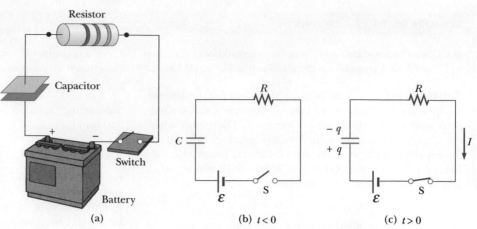

Active Figure 28.19 (a) A capacitor in series with a resistor, switch, and battery.
(b) Circuit diagram representing this system at time $t < 0$, before the switch is closed.
(c) Circuit diagram at time $t > 0$, after the switch has been closed.

At the Active Figures link
at http://www.pse6.com, you
can adjust the values of R and
C to see the effect on the
charging of the capacitor.

not jump across the capacitor plates because the gap between the plates represents an open circuit. Instead, charge is transferred between each plate and its connecting wires due to the electric field established in the wires by the battery, until the capacitor is fully charged. As the plates are being charged, the potential difference across the capacitor increases. The value of the maximum charge on the plates depends on the voltage of the battery. Once the maximum charge is reached, the current in the circuit is zero because the potential difference across the capacitor matches that supplied by the battery.

To analyze this circuit quantitatively, let us apply Kirchhoff's loop rule to the circuit after the switch is closed. Traversing the loop in Fig. 28.19c clockwise gives

$$\mathcal{E} - \frac{q}{C} - IR = 0 \tag{28.11}$$

where q/C is the potential difference across the capacitor and IR is the potential difference across the resistor. We have used the sign conventions discussed earlier for the signs on $\mathcal{E}$ and IR. For the capacitor, notice that we are traveling in the direction from the positive plate to the negative plate; this represents a decrease in potential. Thus, we use a negative sign for this potential difference in Equation 28.11. Note that q and I are *instantaneous* values that depend on time (as opposed to steady-state values) as the capacitor is being charged.

We can use Equation 28.11 to find the initial current in the circuit and the maximum charge on the capacitor. At the instant the switch is closed ($t = 0$), the charge on the capacitor is zero, and from Equation 28.11 we find that the initial current I_0 in the circuit is a maximum and is equal to

$$I_0 = \frac{\mathcal{E}}{R} \quad \text{(current at } t = 0\text{)} \tag{28.12}$$

At this time, the potential difference from the battery terminals appears entirely across the resistor. Later, when the capacitor is charged to its maximum value Q, charges cease to flow, the current in the circuit is zero, and the potential difference from the battery terminals appears entirely across the capacitor. Substituting $I = 0$ into Equation 28.11 gives the charge on the capacitor at this time:

$$Q = C\mathcal{E} \quad \text{(maximum charge)} \tag{28.13}$$

To determine analytical expressions for the time dependence of the charge and current, we must solve Equation 28.11—a single equation containing two variables, q and I. The current in all parts of the series circuit must be the same. Thus, the current in the resistance R must be the same as the current between the capacitor plates and the wires. This current is equal to the time rate of change of the charge on the capacitor plates. Thus, we substitute $I = dq/dt$ into Equation 28.11 and rearrange the equation:

$$\frac{dq}{dt} = \frac{\mathcal{E}}{R} - \frac{q}{RC}$$

To find an expression for q, we solve this separable differential equation. We first combine the terms on the right-hand side:

$$\frac{dq}{dt} = \frac{C\mathcal{E}}{RC} - \frac{q}{RC} = -\frac{q - C\mathcal{E}}{RC}$$

Now we multiply by dt and divide by $q - C\mathcal{E}$ to obtain

$$\frac{dq}{q - C\mathcal{E}} = -\frac{1}{RC}\,dt$$

Integrating this expression, using the fact that $q = 0$ at $t = 0$, we obtain

$$\int_0^q \frac{dq}{(q - C\mathcal{E})} = -\frac{1}{RC}\int_0^t dt$$

$$\ln\left(\frac{q - C\mathcal{E}}{-C\mathcal{E}}\right) = -\frac{t}{RC}$$

From the definition of the natural logarithm, we can write this expression as

$$q(t) = C\mathcal{E}(1 - e^{-t/RC}) = Q(1 - e^{-t/RC}) \qquad (28.14)$$

Charge as a function of time for a capacitor being charged

where e is the base of the natural logarithm and we have made the substitution from Equation 28.13.

We can find an expression for the charging current by differentiating Equation 28.14 with respect to time. Using $I = dq/dt$, we find that

$$I(t) = \frac{\mathcal{E}}{R}\,e^{-t/RC} \qquad (28.15)$$

Current as a function of time for a capacitor being charged

Plots of capacitor charge and circuit current versus time are shown in Figure 28.20. Note that the charge is zero at $t = 0$ and approaches the maximum value $C\mathcal{E}$ as $t \rightarrow \infty$. The current has its maximum value $I_0 = \mathcal{E}/R$ at $t = 0$ and decays exponentially to zero as $t \rightarrow \infty$. The quantity RC, which appears in the exponents of Equations 28.14 and 28.15, is called the **time constant** τ of the circuit. It represents the time interval during which the current decreases to $1/e$ of its initial value; that is, in a time interval τ, $I = e^{-1}I_0 = 0.368I_0$. In a time interval 2τ, $I = e^{-2}I_0 = 0.135I_0$, and so forth. Likewise, in a time interval τ, the charge increases from zero to $C\mathcal{E}[1 - e^{-1}] = 0.632C\mathcal{E}$.

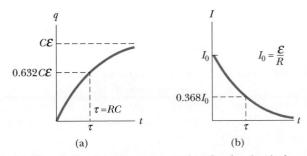

(a)   (b)

Figure 28.20 (a) Plot of capacitor charge versus time for the circuit shown in Figure 28.19. After a time interval equal to one time constant τ has passed, the charge is 63.2% of the maximum value $C\mathcal{E}$. The charge approaches its maximum value as t approaches infinity. (b) Plot of current versus time for the circuit shown in Figure 28.19. The current has its maximum value $I_0 = \mathcal{E}/R$ at $t = 0$ and decays to zero exponentially as t approaches infinity. After a time interval equal to one time constant τ has passed, the current is 36.8% of its initial value.

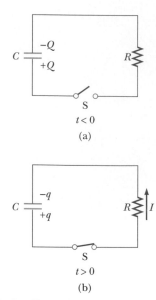

Active Figure 28.21 (a) A charged capacitor connected to a resistor and a switch, which is open for $t < 0$. (b) After the switch is closed at $t = 0$, a current that decreases in magnitude with time is set up in the direction shown, and the charge on the capacitor decreases exponentially with time.

At the Active Figures link at http://www.pse6.com, you can adjust the values of R and C to see the effect on the discharging of the capacitor.

Charge as a function of time for a discharging capacitor

Current as a function of time for a discharging capacitor

The following dimensional analysis shows that τ has the units of time:

$$[\tau] = [RC] = \left[\frac{\Delta V}{I} \times \frac{Q}{\Delta V}\right] = \left[\frac{Q}{Q / \Delta t}\right] = [\Delta t] = \text{T}$$

Because $\tau = RC$ has units of time, the combination τ/RC is dimensionless, as it must be in order to be an exponent of e in Equations 28.14 and 28.15.

The energy output of the battery as the capacitor is fully charged is $Q\mathcal{E} = C\mathcal{E}^2$. After the capacitor is fully charged, the energy stored in the capacitor is $\frac{1}{2}Q\mathcal{E} = \frac{1}{2}C\mathcal{E}^2$, which is just half the energy output of the battery. It is left as a problem (Problem 64) to show that the remaining half of the energy supplied by the battery appears as internal energy in the resistor.

Discharging a Capacitor

Now consider the circuit shown in Figure 28.21, which consists of a capacitor carrying an initial charge Q, a resistor, and a switch. When the switch is open, a potential difference Q/C exists across the capacitor and there is zero potential difference across the resistor because $I = 0$. If the switch is closed at $t = 0$, the capacitor begins to discharge through the resistor. At some time t during the discharge, the current in the circuit is I and the charge on the capacitor is q (Fig. 28.21b). The circuit in Figure 28.21 is the same as the circuit in Figure 28.19 except for the absence of the battery. Thus, we eliminate the emf $\mathcal{E}$ from Equation 28.11 to obtain the appropriate loop equation for the circuit in Figure 28.21:

$$-\frac{q}{C} - IR = 0 \tag{28.16}$$

When we substitute $I = dq/dt$ into this expression, it becomes

$$-R\frac{dq}{dt} = \frac{q}{C}$$

$$\frac{dq}{q} = -\frac{1}{RC}\,dt$$

Integrating this expression, using the fact that $q = Q$ at $t = 0$ gives

$$\int_Q^q \frac{dq}{q} = -\frac{1}{RC}\int_0^t dt$$

$$\ln\left(\frac{q}{Q}\right) = -\frac{t}{RC}$$

$$q(t) = Qe^{-t/RC} \tag{28.17}$$

Differentiating this expression with respect to time gives the instantaneous current as a function of time:

$$I(t) = \frac{dq}{dt} = \frac{d}{dt}(Qe^{-t/RC}) = -\frac{Q}{RC}e^{-t/RC} \tag{28.18}$$

where $Q/RC = I_0$ is the initial current. The negative sign indicates that as the capacitor discharges, the current direction is opposite its direction when the capacitor was being charged. (Compare the current directions in Figs. 28.19c and 28.21b.) We see that both the charge on the capacitor and the current decay exponentially at a rate characterized by the time constant $\tau = RC$.

Quick Quiz 28.9 Consider the circuit in Figure 28.19 and assume that the battery has no internal resistance. Just after the switch is closed, the potential difference across which of the following is equal to the emf of the battery? (a) C (b) R (c) neither C nor R. After a very long time, the potential difference across which of the following is equal to the emf of the battery? (d) C (e) R (f) neither C nor R.

Quick Quiz 28.10 Consider the circuit in Figure 28.22 and assume that the battery has no internal resistance. Just after the switch is closed, the current in the battery is (a) zero (b) $\mathcal{E}/2R$ (c) $2\mathcal{E}/R$ (d) $\mathcal{E}/R$ (e) impossible to determine. After a very long time, the current in the battery is (f) zero (g) $\mathcal{E}/2R$ (h) $2\mathcal{E}/R$ (i) $\mathcal{E}/R$ (j) impossible to determine.

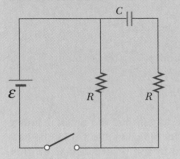

Figure 28.22 (Quick Quiz 28.10) How does the current vary after the switch is closed?

Conceptual Example 28.11   Intermittent Windshield Wipers

Many automobiles are equipped with windshield wipers that can operate intermittently during a light rainfall. How does the operation of such wipers depend on the charging and discharging of a capacitor?

Solution The wipers are part of an RC circuit whose time constant can be varied by selecting different values of R

through a multiposition switch. As it increases with time, the voltage across the capacitor reaches a point at which it triggers the wipers and discharges, ready to begin another charging cycle. The time interval between the individual sweeps of the wipers is determined by the value of the time constant.

Example 28.12   Charging a Capacitor in an *RC* Circuit   **Interactive**

An uncharged capacitor and a resistor are connected in series to a battery, as shown in Figure 28.23. If $\mathcal{E}$ = 12.0 V, C = 5.00 μF, and R = 8.00 $\times$ 10^5 Ω, find the time constant of the circuit, the maximum charge on the capacitor, the maximum current in the circuit, and the charge and current as functions of time.

Solution The time constant of the circuit is $\tau = RC$ = $(8.00 \times 10^5 \ \Omega)(5.00 \times 10^{-6} \ \text{F})$ = 4.00 s. The maximum charge on the capacitor is $Q = C\mathcal{E}$ = (5.00 μF)(12.0 V) = 60.0 μC. The maximum current in the circuit is I_0 = $\mathcal{E}/R$ = (12.0 V)/(8.00 $\times$ 10^5 Ω) = 15.0 μA. Using these values and Equations 28.14 and 28.15, we find that

$$q(t) = (60.0 \ \mu\text{C})(1 - e^{-t/4.00 \ \text{s}})$$

$$I(t) = (15.0 \ \mu\text{A})e^{-t/4.00 \ \text{s}}$$

Graphs of these functions are provided in Figure 28.24.

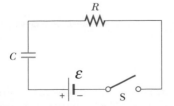

Figure 28.23 (Example 28.12) The switch in this series RC circuit, open for times $t < 0$, is closed at $t = 0$.

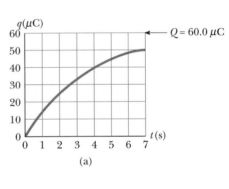

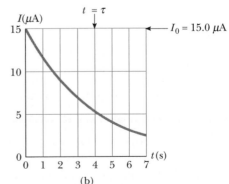

Figure 28.24 (Example 28.12) Plots of (a) charge versus time and (b) current versus time for the RC circuit shown in Figure 28.23, with $\mathcal{E}$ = 12.0 V, R = 8.00 $\times$ 10^5 Ω, and C = 5.00 μF.

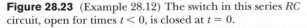 *At the Interactive Worked Example link at* **http://www.pse6.com,** *you can vary R, C, and $\mathcal{E}$ and observe the charge and current as functions of time while charging or discharging the capacitor.*

Example 28.13   Discharging a Capacitor in an *RC* Circuit

Consider a capacitor of capacitance C that is being discharged through a resistor of resistance R, as shown in Figure 28.21.

(A) After how many time constants is the charge on the capacitor one-fourth its initial value?

Solution The charge on the capacitor varies with time according to Equation 28.17, $q(t) = Qe^{-t/RC}$. To find the time interval during which q drops to one-fourth its initial value, we substitute $q(t) = Q/4$ into this expression and solve for t:

$$\frac{Q}{4} = Qe^{-t/RC}$$

$$\tfrac{1}{4} = e^{-t/RC}$$

Taking logarithms of both sides, we find

$$-\ln 4 = -\frac{t}{RC}$$

$$t = RC\,(\ln 4) = 1.39RC = \boxed{1.39\tau}$$

(B) The energy stored in the capacitor decreases with time as the capacitor discharges. After how many time constants is this stored energy one-fourth its initial value?

Solution Using Equations 26.11 ($U = Q^2/2C$) and 28.17, we can express the energy stored in the capacitor at any time t as

$$U = \frac{q^2}{2C} = \frac{Q^2}{2C}e^{-2t/RC} = U_0 e^{-2t/RC}$$

where $U_0 = Q^2/2C$ is the initial energy stored in the capacitor. As in part (A), we now set $U = U_0/4$ and solve for t:

$$\frac{U_0}{4} = U_0 e^{-2t/RC}$$

$$\tfrac{1}{4} = e^{-2t/RC}$$

Again, taking logarithms of both sides and solving for t gives

$$t = \tfrac{1}{2}RC\ln 4 = 0.693RC = \boxed{0.693\tau}$$

What If? What if we wanted to describe the circuit in terms of the time interval required for the charge to fall to one-half its original value, rather than by the time constant τ? This would give a parameter for the circuit called its *half-life* $t_{1/2}$. How is the half-life related to the time constant?

Answer After one half-life, the charge has fallen from Q to $Q/2$. Thus, from Equation 28.17,

$$\frac{Q}{2} = Qe^{-t_{1/2}/RC}$$

$$\tfrac{1}{2} = e^{-t_{1/2}/RC}$$

leading to

$$t_{1/2} = 0.693\tau$$

The concept of half-life will be important to us when we study nuclear decay in Chapter 44. The radioactive decay of an unstable sample behaves in a mathematically similar manner to a discharging capacitor in an *RC* circuit.

Example 28.14   Energy Delivered to a Resistor

A 5.00-μF capacitor is charged to a potential difference of 800 V and then discharged through a 25.0-kV resistor. How much energy is delivered to the resistor in the time interval required to fully discharge the capacitor?

Solution We shall solve this problem in two ways. The first way is to note that the initial energy in the circuit equals the energy stored in the capacitor, $C\mathcal{E}^2/2$ (see Eq. 26.11). Once the capacitor is fully discharged, the energy stored in it is zero. Because energy in an isolated system is conserved, the initial energy stored in the capacitor is transformed into internal energy in the resistor. Using the given values of C and $\mathcal{E}$, we find

$$\text{Energy} = \tfrac{1}{2}C\mathcal{E}^2 = \tfrac{1}{2}(5.00 \times 10^{-6}\text{ F})(800\text{ V})^2 = \boxed{1.60\text{ J}}$$

The second way, which is more difficult but perhaps more instructive, is to note that as the capacitor discharges through the resistor, the rate at which energy is delivered to the resistor is given by I^2R, where I is the instantaneous current given by Equation 28.18. Because power is defined as the rate at which energy is transferred, we conclude that

the energy delivered to the resistor must equal the time integral of $I^2R\,dt$:

$$\text{Energy} = \int_0^\infty I^2 R\,dt = \int_0^\infty (-I_0 e^{-t/RC})^2\,R\,dt$$

To evaluate this integral, we note that the initial current I_0 is equal to $\mathcal{E}/R$ and that all parameters except t are constant. Thus, we find

$$(1) \qquad \text{Energy} = \frac{\mathcal{E}^2}{R}\int_0^\infty e^{-2t/RC}\,dt$$

This integral has a value of $RC/2$ (see Problem 35); hence, we find

$$\text{Energy} = \tfrac{1}{2}C\mathcal{E}^2$$

which agrees with the result we obtained using the simpler approach, as it must. Note that we can use this second approach to find the total energy delivered to the resistor at *any* time after the switch is closed by simply replacing the upper limit in the integral with that specific value of t.

28.5 Electrical Meters

The Galvanometer

The **galvanometer** is the main component in analog meters for measuring current and voltage. (Many analog meters are still in use although digital meters, which operate on a different principle, are currently in wide use.) Figure 28.25 illustrates the essential features of a common type called the *D'Arsonval galvanometer*. It consists of a coil of wire mounted so that it is free to rotate on a pivot in a magnetic field provided by a permanent magnet. The basic operation of the galvanometer uses the fact that a torque acts on a current loop in the presence of a magnetic field (Chapter 29). The torque experienced by the coil is proportional to the current in it: the larger the current, the greater the torque and the more the coil rotates before the spring tightens enough to stop the rotation. Hence, the deflection of a needle attached to the coil is proportional to the current. Once the instrument is properly calibrated, it can be used in conjunction with other circuit elements to measure either currents or potential differences.

The Ammeter

A device that measures current is called an **ammeter.** The charges constituting the current to be measured must pass directly through the ammeter, so the ammeter must be connected in series with other elements in the circuit, as shown in Figure 28.26. When using an ammeter to measure direct currents, you must connect it so that charges enter the instrument at the positive terminal and exit at the negative terminal.

Ideally, an ammeter should have zero resistance so that the current being measured is not altered. In the circuit shown in Figure 28.26, this condition requires that the resistance of the ammeter be much less than $R_1 + R_2$. Because any ammeter always has some internal resistance, the presence of the ammeter in the circuit slightly reduces the current from the value it would have in the meter's absence.

A typical off-the-shelf galvanometer is often not suitable for use as an ammeter, primarily because it has a resistance of about 60 Ω. An ammeter resistance this great considerably alters the current in a circuit. You can understand this by considering the following example. The current in a simple series circuit containing a 3-V battery and a 3-Ω resistor is 1 A. If you insert a 60-Ω galvanometer in this circuit to measure the current, the total resistance becomes 63 Ω and the current is reduced to 0.048 A!

A second factor that limits the use of a galvanometer as an ammeter is the fact that a typical galvanometer gives a full-scale deflection for currents on the order of 1 mA or less. Consequently, such a galvanometer cannot be used directly to measure currents greater than this value. However, it can be converted to a useful ammeter by placing a shunt resistor R_p in parallel with the galvanometer, as shown in Figure 28.27. The value of R_p must be much less than the galvanometer resistance so that most of the current to be measured is directed to the shunt resistor.

The Voltmeter

A device that measures potential difference is called a **voltmeter.** The potential difference between any two points in a circuit can be measured by attaching the terminals of the voltmeter between these points without breaking the circuit, as shown in Figure 28.28. The potential difference across resistor R_2 is measured by connecting the voltmeter in parallel with R_2. Again, it is necessary to observe the polarity of the instrument. The positive terminal of the voltmeter must be connected to the end of the resistor that is at the higher potential, and the negative terminal to the end of the resistor at the lower potential.

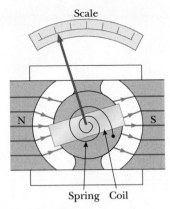

Figure 28.25 The principal components of a D'Arsonval galvanometer. When the coil situated in a magnetic field carries a current, the magnetic torque causes the coil to twist. The angle through which the coil rotates is proportional to the current in the coil because of the counteracting torque of the spring.

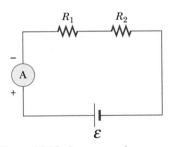

Figure 28.26 Current can be measured with an ammeter connected in series with the elements in which the measurement of a current is desired. An ideal ammeter has zero resistance.

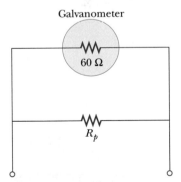

Active Figure 28.27 A galvanometer is represented here by its internal resistance of 60 Ω. When a galvanometer is to be used as an ammeter, a shunt resistor R_p is connected in parallel with the galvanometer.

At the Active Figures link at http://www.pse6.com, you can predict the value of R_p needed to cause full-scale deflection in the circuit of Figure 28.26, and test your result.

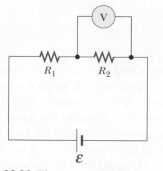

Figure 28.28 The potential difference across a resistor can be measured with a voltmeter connected in parallel with the resistor. An ideal voltmeter has infinite resistance.

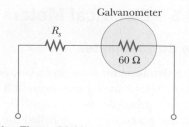

Active Figure 28.29 When the galvanometer is used as a voltmeter, a resistor R_s is connected in series with the galvanometer.

At the Active Figures link at http://www.pse6.com, you can predict the value of R_s needed to cause full-scale deflection in the circuit of Figure 28.28, and test your result.

An ideal voltmeter has infinite resistance so that no current exists in it. In Figure 28.28, this condition requires that the voltmeter have a resistance much greater than R_2. In practice, if this condition is not met, corrections should be made for the known resistance of the voltmeter.

A galvanometer can also be used as a voltmeter by adding an external resistor R_s in series with it, as shown in Figure 28.29. In this case, the external resistor must have a value much greater than the resistance of the galvanometer to ensure that the galvanometer does not significantly alter the voltage being measured.

28.6   Household Wiring and Electrical Safety

Household circuits represent a practical application of some of the ideas presented in this chapter. In our world of electrical appliances, it is useful to understand the power requirements and limitations of conventional electrical systems and the safety measures that prevent accidents.

In a conventional installation, the utility company distributes electric power to individual homes by means of a pair of wires, with each home connected in parallel to these wires. One wire is called the *live wire*,[5] as illustrated in Figure 28.30, and the other is called the *neutral wire*. The neutral wire is grounded; that is, its electric potential is taken to be zero. The potential difference between the live and neutral wires is about 120 V. This voltage alternates in time, and the potential of the live wire oscillates relative to ground. Much of what we have learned so far for the constant-emf situation (direct current) can also be applied to the alternating current that power companies supply to businesses and households. (Alternating voltage and current are discussed in Chapter 33.)

A meter is connected in series with the live wire entering the house to record the household's energy consumption. After the meter, the wire splits so that there are several separate circuits in parallel distributed throughout the house. Each circuit contains a circuit breaker (or, in older installations, a fuse). The wire and circuit breaker for each circuit are carefully selected to meet the current demands for that circuit. If a circuit is to carry currents as large as 30 A, a heavy wire and an appropriate circuit breaker must be selected to handle this current. A circuit used to power only lamps and small appliances often requires only 20 A. Each circuit has its own circuit breaker to provide protection for that part of the entire electrical system of the house.

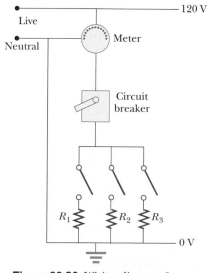

Figure 28.30 Wiring diagram for a household circuit. The resistances represent appliances or other electrical devices that operate with an applied voltage of 120 V.

---

[5]   *Live wire* is a common expression for a conductor whose electric potential is above or below ground potential.

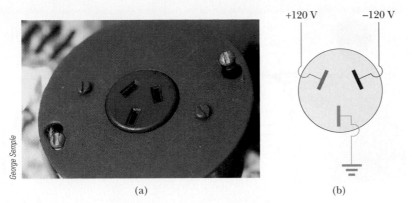

+120 V   −120 V

Figure 28.31 (a) An outlet for connection to a 240-V supply. (b) The connections for each of the openings in a 240-V outlet.

As an example, consider a circuit in which a toaster oven, a microwave oven, and a coffee maker are connected (corresponding to R_1, R_2, and R_3 in Fig. 28.30). We can calculate the current in each appliance by using the expression $\mathcal{P} = I\,\Delta V$. The toaster oven, rated at 1 000 W, draws a current of 1 000 W/120 V = 8.33 A. The microwave oven, rated at 1 300 W, draws 10.8 A, and the coffee maker, rated at 800 W, draws 6.67 A. If the three appliances are operated simultaneously, they draw a total current of 25.8 A. Therefore, the circuit should be wired to handle at least this much current. If the rating of the circuit breaker protecting the circuit is too small—say, 20 A—the breaker will be tripped when the third appliance is turned on, preventing all three appliances from operating. To avoid this situation, the toaster oven and coffee maker can be operated on one 20-A circuit and the microwave oven on a separate 20-A circuit.

Many heavy-duty appliances, such as electric ranges and clothes dryers, require 240 V for their operation. The power company supplies this voltage by providing a third wire that is 120 V below ground potential (Fig. 28.31). The potential difference between this live wire and the other live wire (which is 120 V above ground potential) is 240 V. An appliance that operates from a 240-V line requires half as much current compared to operating it at 120 V; therefore, smaller wires can be used in the higher-voltage circuit without overheating.

Electrical Safety

When the live wire of an electrical outlet is connected directly to ground, the circuit is completed and a short-circuit condition exists. A *short circuit* occurs when almost zero resistance exists between two points at different potentials; this results in a very large current. When this happens accidentally, a properly operating circuit breaker opens the circuit and no damage is done. However, a person in contact with ground can be electrocuted by touching the live wire of a frayed cord or other exposed conductor. An exceptionally effective (and dangerous!) ground contact is made when the person either touches a water pipe (normally at ground potential) or stands on the ground with wet feet. The latter situation represents effective ground contact because normal, nondistilled water is a conductor due to the large number of ions associated with impurities. This situation should be avoided at all cost.

Electric shock can result in fatal burns, or it can cause the muscles of vital organs, such as the heart, to malfunction. The degree of damage to the body depends on the magnitude of the current, the length of time it acts, the part of the body touched by the live wire, and the part of the body in which the current exists. Currents of 5 mA or less cause a sensation of shock but ordinarily do little or no damage. If the current is larger than about 10 mA, the muscles contract and the person may be unable to release the live wire. If a current of about 100 mA passes through the body for only a few seconds, the result can be fatal. Such a large current paralyzes the respiratory

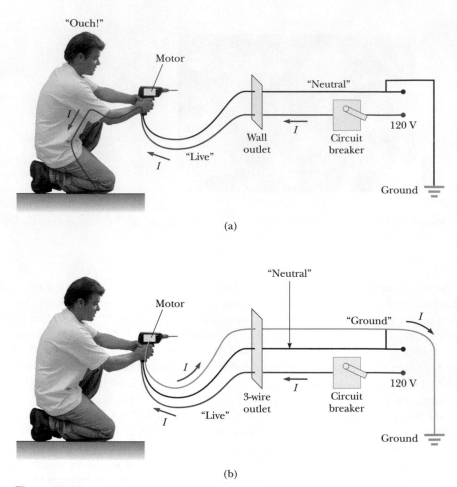

Figure 28.32 (a) A diagram of the circuit for an electric drill with only two connecting wires. The normal current path is from the live wire through the motor connections and back to ground through the neutral wire. In the situation shown, the live wire has come into contact with the drill case. As a result, the person holding the drill acts as a current path to ground and receives an electric shock. (b) This shock can be avoided by connecting the drill case to ground through a third ground wire. In this situation, the drill case remains at ground potential and no current exists in the person.

muscles and prevents breathing. In some cases, currents of about 1 A can produce serious (and sometimes fatal) burns. In practice, no contact with live wires is regarded as safe whenever the voltage is greater than 24 V.

Many 120-V outlets are designed to accept a three-pronged power cord. (This feature is required in all new electrical installations.) One of these prongs is the live wire at a nominal potential of 120 V. The second is the neutral wire, nominally at 0 V, and carries current to ground. The third, round prong is a safety ground wire that normally carries no current but is both grounded and connected directly to the casing of the appliance (see Figure 28.32). If the live wire is accidentally shorted to the casing (which can occur if the wire insulation wears off), most of the current takes the low-resistance path through the appliance to ground. In contrast, if the casing of the appliance is not properly grounded and a short occurs, anyone in contact with the appliance experiences an electric shock because the body provides a low-resistance path to ground.

Special power outlets called *ground-fault interrupters* (GFIs) are now used in kitchens, bathrooms, basements, exterior outlets, and other hazardous areas of new homes. These devices are designed to protect persons from electric shock by sensing small currents (≈ 5 mA) leaking to ground. (The principle of their operation is described in Chapter 31.) When an excessive leakage current is detected, the current is shut off in less than 1 ms.

SUMMARY

Take a practice test for this chapter by clicking on the Practice Test link at http://www.pse6.com.

The **emf** of a battery is equal to the voltage across its terminals when the current is zero. That is, the emf is equivalent to the **open-circuit voltage** of the battery.

The **equivalent resistance** of a set of resistors connected in **series** is

$$R_{eq} = R_1 + R_2 + R_3 + \cdots \tag{28.6}$$

The **equivalent resistance** of a set of resistors connected in **parallel** is found from the relationship

$$\frac{1}{R_{eq}} = \frac{1}{R_1} + \frac{1}{R_2} + \frac{1}{R_3} + \cdots \tag{28.8}$$

If it is possible to combine resistors into series or parallel equivalents, the preceding two equations make it easy to determine how the resistors influence the rest of the circuit.

Circuits involving more than one loop are conveniently analyzed with the use of **Kirchhoff's rules:**

1. **Junction rule.** The sum of the currents entering any junction in an electric circuit must equal the sum of the currents leaving that junction:

$$\sum I_{in} = \sum I_{out} \tag{28.9}$$

2. **Loop rule.** The sum of the potential differences across all elements around any circuit loop must be zero:

$$\sum_{\substack{closed \\ loop}} \Delta V = 0 \tag{28.10}$$

The first rule is a statement of conservation of charge; the second is equivalent to a statement of conservation of energy.

When a resistor is traversed in the direction of the current, the potential difference ΔV across the resistor is $-IR$. When a resistor is traversed in the direction opposite the current, $\Delta V = +IR$. When a source of emf is traversed in the direction of the emf (negative terminal to positive terminal), the potential difference is $+\mathcal{E}$. When a source of emf is traversed opposite the emf (positive to negative), the potential difference is $-\mathcal{E}$. The use of these rules together with Equations 28.9 and 28.10 allows you to analyze electric circuits.

If a capacitor is charged with a battery through a resistor of resistance R, the charge on the capacitor and the current in the circuit vary in time according to the expressions

$$q(t) = Q(1 - e^{-t/RC}) \tag{28.14}$$

$$I(t) = \frac{\mathcal{E}}{R} e^{-t/RC} \tag{28.15}$$

where $Q = C\mathcal{E}$ is the maximum charge on the capacitor. The product RC is called the **time constant** τ of the circuit. If a charged capacitor is discharged through a resistor of resistance R, the charge and current decrease exponentially in time according to the expressions

$$q(t) = Qe^{-t/RC} \tag{28.17}$$

$$I(t) = -I_0 e^{-t/RC} \tag{28.18}$$

where Q is the initial charge on the capacitor and $I_0 = Q/RC$ is the initial current in the circuit.

QUESTIONS

1. Explain the difference between load resistance in a circuit and internal resistance in a battery.

2. Under what condition does the potential difference across the terminals of a battery equal its emf? Can the terminal voltage ever exceed the emf? Explain.

3. Is the direction of current through a battery always from the negative terminal to the positive terminal? Explain.

4. How would you connect resistors so that the equivalent resistance is larger than the greatest individual resistance? Give an example involving three resistors.

5. How would you connect resistors so that the equivalent resistance is smaller than the least individual resistance? Give an example involving three resistors.

6. Given three lightbulbs and a battery, sketch as many different electric circuits as you can.

7. When resistors are connected in series, which of the following would be the same for each resistor: potential difference, current, power?

8. When resistors are connected in parallel, which of the following would be the same for each resistor: potential difference, current, power?

9. What advantage might there be in using two identical resistors in parallel connected in series with another identical parallel pair, rather than just using a single resistor?

10. An incandescent lamp connected to a 120-V source with a short extension cord provides more illumination than the same lamp connected to the same source with a very long extension cord. Explain.

11. Why is it possible for a bird to sit on a high-voltage wire without being electrocuted?

12. When can the potential difference across a resistor be positive?

13. Referring to Figure Q28.13, describe what happens to the lightbulb after the switch is closed. Assume that the capacitor has a large capacitance and is initially uncharged, and assume that the light illuminates when connected directly across the battery terminals.

14. What is the internal resistance of an ideal ammeter? Of an ideal voltmeter? Do real meters ever attain these ideals?

15. A "short circuit" is a path of very low resistance in a circuit in parallel with some other part of the circuit. Discuss the effect of the short circuit on the portion of the circuit it parallels. Use a lamp with a frayed cord as an example.

16. If electric power is transmitted over long distances, the resistance of the wires becomes significant. Why? Which method of transmission would result in less energy wasted—high current and low voltage or low current and high voltage? Explain your answer.

17. Are the two headlights of a car wired in series or in parallel? How can you tell?

18. Embodied in Kirchhoff's rules are two conservation laws. What are they?

19. Figure Q28.19 shows a series combination of three lightbulbs, all rated at 120 V with power ratings of 60 W, 75 W, and 200 W. Why is the 60-W lamp the brightest and the 200-W lamp the dimmest? Which bulb has the greatest resistance? How would their intensities differ if they were connected in parallel?

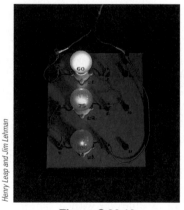

Figure Q28.19

20. A student claims that the second lightbulb in series is less bright than the first, because the first bulb uses up some of the current. How would you respond to this statement?

21. Is a circuit breaker wired in series or in parallel with the device it is protecting?

22. So that your grandmother can listen to *A Prairie Home Companion*, you take her bedside radio to the hospital where she is staying. You are required to have a maintenance worker test it for electrical safety. Finding that it develops 120 V on one of its knobs, he does not let you take it up to your grandmother's room. She complains that she has had the radio for many years and nobody has ever gotten a shock from it. You end up having to buy a new plastic radio. Is this fair? Will the old radio be safe back in her bedroom?

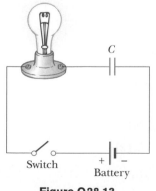

Figure Q28.13

23. Suppose you fall from a building and on the way down grab a high-voltage wire. If the wire supports you as you hang from it, will you be electrocuted? If the wire then breaks, should you continue to hold onto an end of the wire as you fall?

24. What advantage does 120-V operation offer over 240 V? What disadvantages?

25. When electricians work with potentially live wires, they often use the backs of their hands or fingers to move wires. Why do you suppose they use this technique?

26. What procedure would you use to try to save a person who is "frozen" to a live high-voltage wire without endangering your own life?

27. If it is the current through the body that determines how serious a shock will be, why do we see warnings of *high voltage* rather than *high current* near electrical equipment?

28. Suppose you are flying a kite when it strikes a high-voltage wire. What factors determine how great a shock you receive?

29. A series circuit consists of three identical lamps connected to a battery as shown in Figure Q28.29. When the switch S is closed, what happens (a) to the intensities of lamps A and B; (b) to the intensity of lamp C; (c) to the current in the circuit; and (d) to the voltage across the three lamps? (e) Does the power delivered to the circuit increase, decrease, or remain the same?

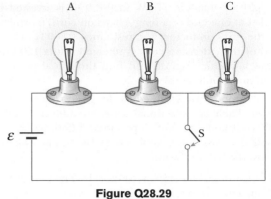

Figure Q28.29

30. If your car's headlights are on when you start the ignition, why do they dim while the car is starting?

31. A ski resort consists of a few chair lifts and several interconnected downhill runs on the side of a mountain, with a lodge at the bottom. The lifts are analogous to batteries, and the runs are analogous to resistors. Describe how two runs can be in series. Describe how three runs can be in parallel. Sketch a junction of one lift and two runs. State Kirchhoff's junction rule for ski resorts. One of the skiers happens to be carrying a skydiver's altimeter. She never takes the same set of lifts and runs twice, but keeps passing you at the fixed location where you are working. State Kirchhoff's loop rule for ski resorts.

PROBLEMS

1, 2, 3 = straightforward, intermediate, challenging   ☐ = full solution available in the *Student Solutions Manual and Study Guide*

🌐 = coached solution with hints available at http://www.pse.com   💻 = computer useful in solving problem

▨ = paired numerical and symbolic problems

Section 28.1   Electromotive Force

1. 🌐 A battery has an emf of 15.0 V. The terminal voltage of the battery is 11.6 V when it is delivering 20.0 W of power to an external load resistor R. (a) What is the value of R? (b) What is the internal resistance of the battery?

2. (a) What is the current in a 5.60-Ω resistor connected to a battery that has a 0.200-Ω internal resistance if the terminal voltage of the battery is 10.0 V? (b) What is the emf of the battery?

3. Two 1.50-V batteries—with their positive terminals in the same direction—are inserted in series into the barrel of a flashlight. One battery has an internal resistance of 0.255 Ω, the other an internal resistance of 0.153 Ω. When the switch is closed, a current of 600 mA occurs in the lamp. (a) What is the lamp's resistance? (b) What fraction of the chemical energy transformed appears as internal energy in the batteries?

4. An automobile battery has an emf of 12.6 V and an internal resistance of 0.080 0 Ω. The headlights together present equivalent resistance 5.00 Ω (assumed constant). What is the potential difference across the headlight bulbs (a) when they are the only load on the battery and (b) when the starter motor is operated, taking an additional 35.0 A from the battery?

Section 28.2   Resistors in Series and Parallel

5. The current in a loop circuit that has a resistance of R_1 is 2.00 A. The current is reduced to 1.60 A when an additional resistor $R_2 = 3.00$ Ω is added in series with R_1. What is the value of R_1?

6. (a) Find the equivalent resistance between points a and b in Figure P28.6. (b) A potential difference of 34.0 V is applied between points a and b. Calculate the current in each resistor.

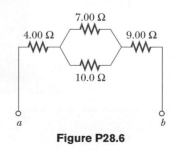

Figure P28.6

7. A lightbulb marked "75 W [at] 120 V" is screwed into a socket at one end of a long extension cord, in which each of the two conductors has resistance 0.800 Ω. The other end of the extension cord is plugged into a 120-V outlet. Draw a circuit diagram and find the actual power delivered to the bulb in this circuit.

8. Four copper wires of equal length are connected in series. Their cross-sectional areas are 1.00 cm², 2.00 cm², 3.00 cm², and 5.00 cm². A potential difference of 120 V is applied across the combination. Determine the voltage across the 2.00-cm² wire.

9. 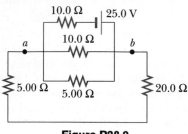 Consider the circuit shown in Figure P28.9. Find (a) the current in the 20.0-Ω resistor and (b) the potential difference between points a and b.

Figure P28.9

10. For the purpose of measuring the electric resistance of shoes through the body of the wearer to a metal ground plate, the American National Standards Institute (ANSI) specifies the circuit shown in Figure P28.10. The potential difference ΔV across the 1.00-MΩ resistor is measured with a high-resistance voltmeter. (a) Show that the resistance of the footwear is given by

$$R_{\text{shoes}} = 1.00 \text{ M}\Omega \left(\frac{50.0 \text{ V} - \Delta V}{\Delta V} \right)$$

(b) In a medical test, a current through the human body should not exceed 150 μA. Can the current delivered by the ANSI-specified circuit exceed 150 μA? To decide, consider a person standing barefoot on the ground plate.

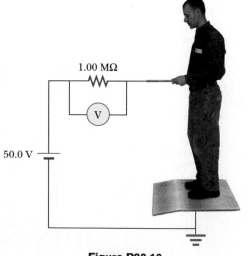

Figure P28.10

11. Three 100-Ω resistors are connected as shown in Figure P28.11. The maximum power that can safely be delivered to any one resistor is 25.0 W. (a) What is the maximum voltage that can be applied to the terminals a and b? For the voltage determined in part (a), what is the power delivered to each resistor? What is the total power delivered?

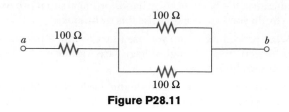

Figure P28.11

12. Using only three resistors—2.00 Ω, 3.00 Ω, and 4.00 Ω—find 17 resistance values that may be obtained by various combinations of one or more resistors. Tabulate the combinations in order of increasing resistance.

13. The current in a circuit is tripled by connecting a 500-Ω resistor in parallel with the resistance of the circuit. Determine the resistance of the circuit in the absence of the 500-Ω resistor.

14. A 6.00-V battery supplies current to the circuit shown in Figure P28.14. When the double-throw switch S is open, as shown in the figure, the current in the battery is 1.00 mA. When the switch is closed in position 1, the current in the battery is 1.20 mA. When the switch is closed in position 2, the current in the battery is 2.00 mA. Find the resistances R_1, R_2, and R_3.

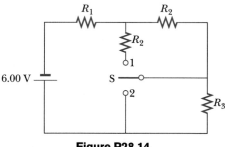

Figure P28.14

15. Calculate the power delivered to each resistor in the circuit shown in Figure P28.15.

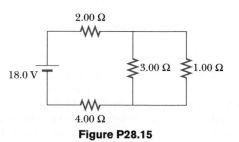

Figure P28.15

16. Two resistors connected in series have an equivalent resistance of 690 Ω. When they are connected in parallel, their equivalent resistance is 150 Ω. Find the resistance of each resistor.

17. An electric teakettle has a multiposition switch and two heating coils. When only one of the coils is switched on, the well-insulated kettle brings a full pot of water to a boil over the time interval Δt. When only the other coil is switched on, it requires a time interval of $2\Delta t$ to boil the same amount of water. Find the time interval required to boil the same amount of water if both coils are switched on (a) in a parallel connection and (b) in a series connection.

18. In Figures 28.4 and 28.6, let $R_1 = 11.0$ Ω, $R_2 = 22.0$ Ω, and let the battery have a terminal voltage of 33.0 V. (a) In the parallel circuit shown in Figure 28.6, to which resistor is more power delivered? (b) Verify that the sum of the power (I^2R) delivered to each resistor equals the power supplied by the battery ($\mathcal{P} = I\Delta V$). (c) In the series circuit, which resistor uses more power? (d) Verify that the sum of the power (I^2R) used by each resistor equals the power supplied by the battery ($\mathcal{P} = I\Delta V$). (e) Which circuit configuration uses more power?

19. Four resistors are connected to a battery as shown in Figure P28.19. The current in the battery is I, the battery emf is $\mathcal{E}$, and the resistor values are $R_1 = R$, $R_2 = 2R$, $R_3 = 4R$, $R_4 = 3R$. (a) Rank the resistors according to the potential difference across them, from largest to smallest. Note any cases of equal potential differences. (b) Determine the potential difference across each resistor in terms of $\mathcal{E}$. (c) Rank the resistors according to the current in them, from largest to smallest. Note any cases of equal currents. (d) Determine the current in each resistor in terms of I. (e) **What If?** If R_3 is increased, what happens to the current in each of the resistors? (f) In the limit that $R_3 \to \infty$, what are the new values of the current in each resistor in terms of I, the original current in the battery?

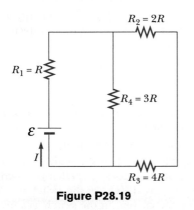

Figure P28.19

Section 28.3   Kirchhoff's Rules

Note: The currents are not necessarily in the direction shown for some circuits.

20. The ammeter shown in Figure P28.20 reads 2.00 A. Find I_1, I_2, and $\mathcal{E}$.

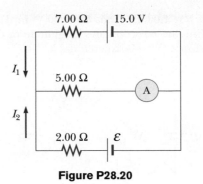

Figure P28.20

21. Determine the current in each branch of the circuit shown in Figure P28.21.

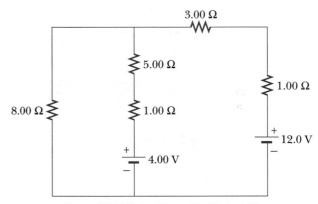

Figure P28.21   Problems 21, 22, and 23.

22. In Figure P28.21, show how to add just enough ammeters to measure every different current. Show how to add just enough voltmeters to measure the potential difference across each resistor and across each battery.

23. The circuit considered in Problem 21 and shown in Figure P28.21 is connected for 2.00 min. (a) Find the energy delivered by each battery. (b) Find the energy delivered to each resistor. (c) Identify the net energy transformation that occurs in the operation of the circuit and the total amount of energy transformed.

24. Using Kirchhoff's rules, (a) find the current in each resistor in Figure P28.24. (b) Find the potential difference between points c and f. Which point is at the higher potential?

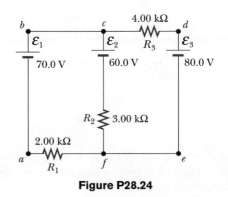

Figure P28.24

25. Taking $R = 1.00$ kΩ and $\mathcal{E} = 250$ V in Figure P28.25, determine the direction and magnitude of the current in the horizontal wire between a and e.

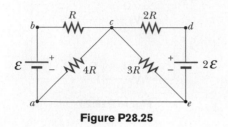

Figure P28.25

26. In the circuit of Figure P28.26, determine the current in each resistor and the voltage across the 200-Ω resistor.

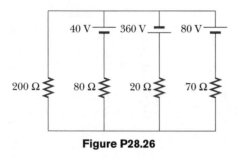

Figure P28.26

27. A dead battery is charged by connecting it to the live battery of another car with jumper cables (Fig. P28.27). Determine the current in the starter and in the dead battery.

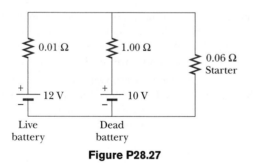

Figure P28.27

28. For the network shown in Figure P28.28, show that the resistance $R_{ab} = (27/17)$ Ω.

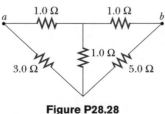

Figure P28.28

29. For the circuit shown in Figure P28.29, calculate (a) the current in the 2.00-Ω resistor and (b) the potential difference between points a and b.

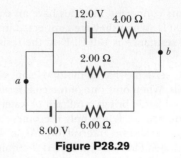

Figure P28.29

30. Calculate the power delivered to each resistor shown in Figure P28.30.

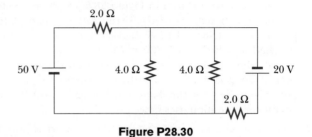

Figure P28.30

Section 28.4 RC Circuits

31. Consider a series RC circuit (see Fig. 28.19) for which $R = 1.00$ MΩ, $C = 5.00$ μF, and $\mathcal{E} = 30.0$ V. Find (a) the time constant of the circuit and (b) the maximum charge on the capacitor after the switch is closed. (c) Find the current in the resistor 10.0 s after the switch is closed.

32. A 2.00-nF capacitor with an initial charge of 5.10 μC is discharged through a 1.30-kΩ resistor. (a) Calculate the current in the resistor 9.00 μs after the resistor is connected across the terminals of the capacitor. (b) What charge remains on the capacitor after 8.00 μs? (c) What is the maximum current in the resistor?

33. A fully charged capacitor stores energy U_0. How much energy remains when its charge has decreased to half its original value?

34. A capacitor in an RC circuit is charged to 60.0% of its maximum value in 0.900 s. What is the time constant of the circuit?

35. Show that the integral in Equation (1) of Example 28.14 has the value $RC/2$.

36. In the circuit of Figure P28.36, the switch S has been open for a long time. It is then suddenly closed. Determine the time constant (a) before the switch is closed and (b) after the switch is closed. (c) Let the switch be closed at $t = 0$. Determine the current in the switch as a function of time.

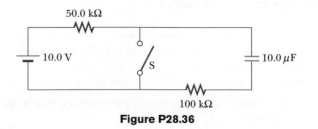

Figure P28.36

37. The circuit in Figure P28.37 has been connected for a long time. (a) What is the voltage across the capacitor? (b) If the battery is disconnected, how long does it take the capacitor to discharge to one tenth of its initial voltage?

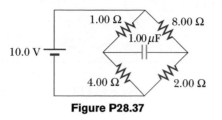

Figure P28.37

38. In places such as a hospital operating room and a factory for electronic circuit boards, electric sparks must be avoided. A person standing on a grounded floor and touching nothing else can typically have a body capacitance of 150 pF, in parallel with a foot capacitance of 80.0 pF produced by the dielectric soles of his or her shoes. The person acquires static electric charge from interactions with furniture, clothing, equipment, packaging materials, and essentially everything else. The static charge is conducted to ground through the equivalent resistance of the two shoe soles in parallel with each other. A pair of rubber-soled street shoes can present an equivalent resistance of 5 000 MΩ. A pair of shoes with special static-dissipative soles can have an equivalent resistance of 1.00 MΩ. Consider the person's body and shoes as forming an RC circuit with the ground. (a) How long does it take the rubber-soled shoes to reduce a 3 000-V static charge to 100 V? (b) How long does it take the static-dissipative shoes to do the same thing?

39. A 4.00-MΩ resistor and a 3.00-μF capacitor are connected in series with a 12.0-V power supply. (a) What is the time constant for the circuit? (b) Express the current in the circuit and the charge on the capacitor as functions of time.

40. Dielectric materials used in the manufacture of capacitors are characterized by conductivities that are small but not zero. Therefore, a charged capacitor slowly loses its charge by "leaking" across the dielectric. If a capacitor having capacitance C leaks charge such that the potential difference has decreased to half its initial ($t = 0$) value at a time t, what is the equivalent resistance of the dielectric?

Section 28.5   Electrical Meters

41. Assume that a galvanometer has an internal resistance of 60.0 Ω and requires a current of 0.500 mA to produce full-scale deflection. What resistance must be connected in parallel with the galvanometer if the combination is to serve as an ammeter that has a full-scale deflection for a current of 0.100 A?

42. A typical galvanometer, which requires a current of 1.50 mA for full-scale deflection and has a resistance of 75.0 Ω, may be used to measure currents of much greater values. To enable an operator to measure large currents without damage to the galvanometer, a relatively small shunt resistor is wired in parallel with the galvanometer, as suggested in Figure 28.27. Most of the current then goes through the shunt resistor. Calculate the value of the shunt resistor that allows the galvanometer to be used to measure a current of 1.00 A at full-scale deflection. (*Suggestion:* use Kirchhoff's rules.)

43. The same galvanometer described in the previous problem may be used to measure voltages. In this case a large resistor is wired in series with the galvanometer, as suggested in Figure 28.29. The effect is to limit the current in the galvanometer when large voltages are applied. Most of the potential drop occurs across the resistor placed in series. Calculate the value of the resistor that allows the galvanometer to measure an applied voltage of 25.0 V at full-scale deflection.

44. *Meter loading.* Work this problem to five-digit precision. Refer to Figure P28.44. (a) When a 180.00-Ω resistor is connected across a battery of emf 6.000 0 V and internal resistance 20.000 Ω, what is the current in the resistor? What is the potential difference across it? (b) Suppose now an ammeter of resistance 0.500 00 Ω and a voltmeter of resistance 20 000 Ω are added to the circuit as shown in Figure P28.44b. Find the reading of each. (c) **What If?** Now one terminal of one wire is moved, as shown in Figure P28.44c. Find the new meter readings.

45. Design a multirange ammeter capable of full-scale deflection for 25.0 mA, 50.0 mA, and 100 mA. Assume the meter movement is a galvanometer that has a resistance of 25.0 Ω and gives a full-scale deflection for 1.00 mA.

46. Design a multirange voltmeter capable of full-scale deflection for 20.0 V, 50.0 V, and 100 V. Assume the meter movement is a galvanometer that has a resistance of 60.0 Ω and gives a full-scale deflection for a current of 1.00 mA.

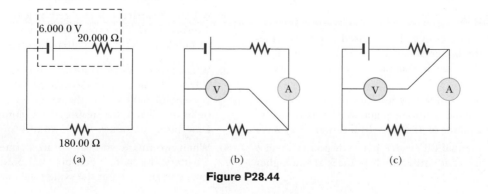

Figure P28.44

47. A particular galvanometer serves as a 2.00-V full-scale voltmeter when a 2 500-Ω resistor is connected in series with it. It serves as a 0.500-A full-scale ammeter when a 0.220-Ω resistor is connected in parallel with it. Determine the internal resistance of the galvanometer and the current required to produce full-scale deflection.

Section 28.6   Household Wiring and Electrical Safety

48. An 8.00-ft extension cord has two 18-gauge copper wires, each having a diameter of 1.024 mm. At what rate is energy delivered to the resistance in the cord when it is carrying a current of (a) 1.00 A and (b) 10.0 A?

49. [www] An electric heater is rated at 1 500 W, a toaster at 750 W, and an electric grill at 1 000 W. The three appliances are connected to a common 120-V household circuit. (a) How much current does each draw? (b) Is a circuit with a 25.0-A circuit breaker sufficient in this situation? Explain your answer.

50. Aluminum wiring has sometimes been used instead of copper for economy. According to the National Electrical Code, the maximum allowable current for 12-gauge copper wire with rubber insulation is 20 A. What should be the maximum allowable current in a 12-gauge aluminum wire if the power per unit length delivered to the resistance in the aluminum wire is the same as that delivered in the copper wire?

51. Turn on your desk lamp. Pick up the cord, with your thumb and index finger spanning the width of the cord. (a) Compute an order-of-magnitude estimate for the current in your hand. You assume that at a typical instant the conductor inside the lamp cord next to your thumb is at potential $\sim 10^2$ V and that the conductor next to your index finger is at ground potential (0 V). The resistance of your hand depends strongly on the thickness and the moisture content of the outer layers of your skin. Assume that the resistance of your hand between fingertip and thumb tip is $\sim 10^4$ Ω. You may model the cord as having rubber insulation. State the other quantities you measure or estimate and their values. Explain your reasoning. (b) Suppose that your body is isolated from any other charges or currents. In order-of-magnitude terms describe the potential of your thumb where it contacts the cord, and the potential of your finger where it touches the cord.

Additional Problems

52. Four 1.50-V AA batteries in series are used to power a transistor radio. If the batteries can move a charge of 240 C, how long will they last if the radio has a resistance of 200 Ω?

53. A battery has an emf of 9.20 V and an internal resistance of 1.20 Ω. (a) What resistance across the battery will extract from it a power of 12.8 W? (b) a power of 21.2 W?

54. Calculate the potential difference between points a and b in Figure P28.54 and identify which point is at the higher potential.

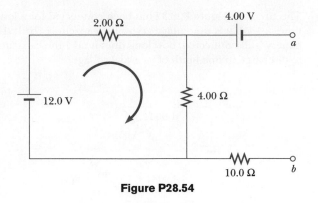

Figure P28.54

55. Assume you have a battery of emf $\mathcal{E}$ and three identical lightbulbs, each having constant resistance R. What is the total power delivered by the battery if the bulbs are connected (a) in series? (b) in parallel? (c) For which connection will the bulbs shine the brightest?

56. A group of students on spring break manages to reach a deserted island in their wrecked sailboat. They splash ashore with fuel, a European gasoline-powered 240-V generator, a box of North American 100-W 120-V lightbulbs, a 500-W 120-V hot pot, lamp sockets, and some insulated wire. While waiting to be rescued, they decide to use the generator to operate some lightbulbs. (a) Draw a diagram of a circuit they can use, containing the minimum number of lightbulbs with 120 V across each bulb, and no higher voltage. Find the current in the generator and its power output. (b) One student catches a fish and wants to cook it in the hot pot. Draw a diagram of a circuit containing the hot pot and the minimum number of lightbulbs with 120 V across each device, and not more. Find the current in the generator and its power output.

57. A battery has an emf $\mathcal{E}$ and internal resistance r. A variable load resistor R is connected across the terminals of the battery. (a) Determine the value of R such that the potential difference across the terminals is a maximum. (b) Determine the value of R so that the current in the circuit is a maximum. (c) Determine the value of R so that the power delivered to the load resistor is a maximum. Choosing the load resistance for maximum power transfer is a case of what is called *impedance matching* in general. Impedance matching is important in shifting gears on a bicycle, in connecting a loudspeaker to an audio amplifier, in connecting a battery charger to a bank of solar photoelectric cells, and in many other applications.

58. A 10.0-μF capacitor is charged by a 10.0-V battery through a resistance R. The capacitor reaches a potential difference of 4.00 V in a time 3.00 s after charging begins. Find R.

59. When two unknown resistors are connected in series with a battery, the battery delivers 225 W and carries a total current of 5.00 A. For the same total current, 50.0 W is delivered when the resistors are connected in parallel. Determine the values of the two resistors.

60. When two unknown resistors are connected in series with a battery, the battery delivers total power $\mathcal{P}_s$ and carries a total current of I. For the same total current, a total power

$\mathcal{P}_p$ is delivered when the resistors are connected in parallel. Determine the values of the two resistors.

61. A power supply has an open-circuit voltage of 40.0 V and an internal resistance of 2.00 Ω. It is used to charge two storage batteries connected in series, each having an emf of 6.00 V and internal resistance of 0.300 Ω. If the charging current is to be 4.00 A, (a) what additional resistance should be added in series? (b) At what rate does the internal energy increase in the supply, in the batteries, and in the added series resistance? (c) At what rate does the chemical energy increase in the batteries?

62. Two resistors R_1 and R_2 are in parallel with each other. Together they carry total current I. (a) Determine the current in each resistor. (b) Prove that this division of the total current I between the two resistors results in less power delivered to the combination than any other division. It is a general principle that *current in a direct current circuit distributes itself so that the total power delivered to the circuit is a minimum.*

63. The value of a resistor R is to be determined using the ammeter–voltmeter setup shown in Figure P28.63. The ammeter has a resistance of 0.500 Ω, and the voltmeter has a resistance of 20 000 Ω. Within what range of actual values of R will the measured values be correct to within 5.00% if the measurement is made using the circuit shown in (a) Figure P28.63a and (b) Figure P28.63b?

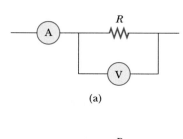

(a)

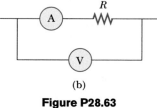

(b)

Figure P28.63

64. A battery is used to charge a capacitor through a resistor, as shown in Figure 28.19. Show that half the energy supplied by the battery appears as internal energy in the resistor and that half is stored in the capacitor.

65. The values of the components in a simple series RC circuit containing a switch (Fig. 28.19) are $C = 1.00\ \mu F$, $R = 2.00 \times 10^6$ Ω, and $\mathcal{E} = 10.0$ V. At the instant 10.0 s after the switch is closed, calculate (a) the charge on the capacitor, (b) the current in the resistor, (c) the rate at which energy is being stored in the capacitor, and (d) the rate at which energy is being delivered by the battery.

66. The switch in Figure P28.66a closes when $\Delta V_c > 2\Delta V/3$ and opens when $\Delta V_c < \Delta V/3$. The voltmeter reads a voltage as plotted in Figure P28.66b. What is the period T of the waveform in terms of R_1, R_2, and C?

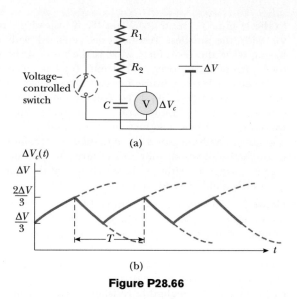

(a)

(b)

Figure P28.66

67. Three 60.0-W, 120-V lightbulbs are connected across a 120-V power source, as shown in Figure P28.67. Find (a) the total power delivered to the three bulbs and (b) the voltage across each. Assume that the resistance of each bulb is constant (even though in reality the resistance might increase markedly with current).

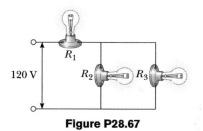

Figure P28.67

68. Switch S has been closed for a long time, and the electric circuit shown in Figure P28.68 carries a constant current. Take $C_1 = 3.00\ \mu F$, $C_2 = 6.00\ \mu F$, $R_1 = 4.00$ kΩ, and $R_2 = 7.00$ kΩ. The power delivered to R_2 is 2.40 W. (a) Find the charge on C_1. (b) Now the switch is opened. After many milliseconds, by how much has the charge on C_2 changed?

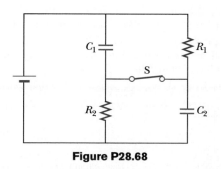

Figure P28.68

69. Four resistors are connected in parallel across a 9.20-V battery. They carry currents of 150 mA, 45.0 mA, 14.00 mA, and 4.00 mA. (a) If the resistor with the largest resistance is replaced with one having twice the resistance, what is the ratio of the new current in the battery

to the original current? (b) **What If?** If instead the resistor with the smallest resistance is replaced with one having twice the resistance, what is the ratio of the new total current to the original current? (c) On a February night, energy leaves a house by several heat leaks, including the following: 1 500 W by conduction through the ceiling; 450 W by infiltration (air flow) around the windows; 140 W by conduction through the basement wall above the foundation sill; and 40.0 W by conduction through the plywood door to the attic. To produce the biggest saving in heating bills, which one of these energy transfers should be reduced first?

70. Figure P28.70 shows a circuit model for the transmission of an electrical signal, such as cable TV, to a large number of subscribers. Each subscriber connects a load resistance R_L between the transmission line and the ground. The ground is assumed to be at zero potential and able to carry any current between any ground connections with negligible resistance. The resistance of the transmission line itself between the connection points of different subscribers is modeled as the constant resistance R_T. Show that the equivalent resistance across the signal source is

$$R_{eq} = \tfrac{1}{2}\,[(4R_T R_L + R_T^2)^{1/2} + R_T]$$

Suggestion: Because the number of subscribers is large, the equivalent resistance would not change noticeably if the first subscriber cancelled his service. Consequently, the equivalent resistance of the section of the circuit to the right of the first load resistor is nearly equal to R_{eq}.

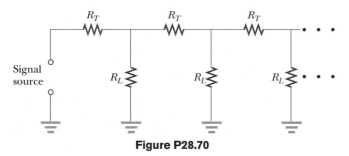

Figure P28.70

71. In Figure P28.71, suppose the switch has been closed for a time sufficiently long for the capacitor to become fully charged. Find (a) the steady-state current in each resistor and (b) the charge Q on the capacitor. (c) The switch is now opened at $t = 0$. Write an equation for the current I_{R_2} through R_2 as a function of time and (d) find the time interval required for the charge on the capacitor to fall to one-fifth its initial value.

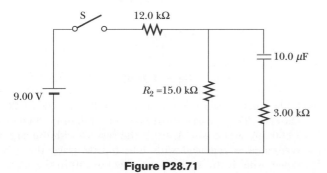

Figure P28.71

72. A regular tetrahedron is a pyramid with a triangular base. Six 10.0-Ω resistors are placed along its six edges, with junctions at its four vertices. A 12.0-V battery is connected to any two of the vertices. Find (a) the equivalent resistance of the tetrahedron between these vertices and (b) the current in the battery.

73. 🖳 The circuit shown in Figure P28.73 is set up in the laboratory to measure an unknown capacitance C with the use of a voltmeter of resistance $R = 10.0$ MΩ and a battery whose emf is 6.19 V. The data given in the table are the measured voltages across the capacitor as a function of time, where $t = 0$ represents the instant at which the switch is opened. (a) Construct a graph of $\ln(\mathcal{E}/\Delta V)$ versus t, and perform a linear least-squares fit to the data. (b) From the slope of your graph, obtain a value for the time constant of the circuit and a value for the capacitance.

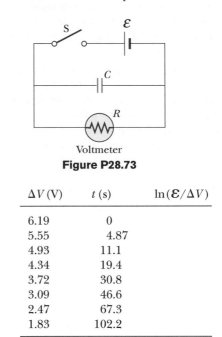

Figure P28.73

ΔV (V)	t (s)	$\ln(\mathcal{E}/\Delta V)$
6.19	0	
5.55	4.87	
4.93	11.1	
4.34	19.4	
3.72	30.8	
3.09	46.6	
2.47	67.3	
1.83	102.2	

74. The student engineer of a campus radio station wishes to verify the effectiveness of the lightning rod on the antenna mast (Fig. P28.74). The unknown resistance R_x is between points C and E. Point E is a true ground but is inaccessible for direct measurement since this stratum is several meters below the Earth's surface. Two identical rods are driven into the ground at A and B, introducing an unknown resistance R_y. The procedure is as follows. Measure resistance R_1 between points A and B, then connect A and B with a heavy conducting wire and measure resistance R_2 between

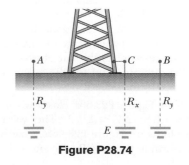

Figure P28.74

points A and C. (a) Derive an equation for R_x in terms of the observable resistances, R_1 and R_2. (b) A satisfactory ground resistance would be $R_x < 2.00\ \Omega$. Is the grounding of the station adequate if measurements give $R_1 = 13.0\ \Omega$ and $R_2 = 6.00\ \Omega$?

75. The circuit in Figure P28.75 contains two resistors, $R_1 = 2.00\ \text{k}\Omega$ and $R_2 = 3.00\ \text{k}\Omega$, and two capacitors, $C_1 = 2.00\ \mu\text{F}$ and $C_2 = 3.00\ \mu\text{F}$, connected to a battery with emf $\mathcal{E} = 120\ \text{V}$. No charge is on either capacitor before switch S is closed. Determine the charges q_1 and q_2 on capacitors C_1 and C_2, respectively, after the switch is closed. (*Suggestion:* First reconstruct the circuit so that it becomes a simple RC circuit containing a single resistor and single capacitor in series, connected to the battery, and then determine the total charge q stored in the equivalent circuit.)

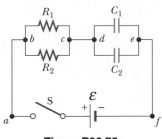

Figure P28.75

76. This problem[6] illustrates how a digital voltmeter affects the voltage across a capacitor in an RC circuit. A digital voltmeter of internal resistance r is used to measure the voltage across a capacitor after the switch in Figure P28.76 is closed. Because the meter has finite resistance, part of the current supplied by the battery passes through the meter. (a) Apply Kirchhoff's rules to this circuit, and use the fact that $i_C = dq/dt$ to show that this leads to the differential equation

$$R_{\text{eq}}\frac{dq}{dt} + \frac{q}{C} = \frac{r}{r+R}\,\mathcal{E}$$

where $R_{\text{eq}} = rR/(r+R)$. (b) Show that the solution to this differential equation is

$$q = \frac{r}{r+R}\,C\mathcal{E}\,(1 - e^{-t/R_{\text{eq}}C})$$

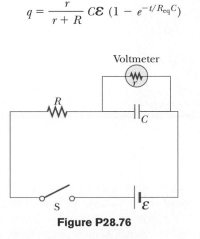

Figure P28.76

[6] After Joseph Priest, "Meter Resistance: Don't Forget It!" *The Physics Teacher*, January 2003, p. 40.

and that the voltage across the capacitor as a function of time is

$$V_C = \frac{r}{r+R}\,\mathcal{E}(1 - e^{-t/R_{\text{eq}}C})$$

(c) **What If?** If the capacitor is fully charged, and the switch is then opened, how does the voltage across the capacitor behave in this case?

Answers to Quick Quizzes

28.1 (a). Power is delivered to the internal resistance of a battery, so decreasing the internal resistance will decrease this "lost" power and increase the percentage of the power delivered to the device.

28.2 (c). In a series circuit, the current is the same in all resistors in series. Current is not "used up" as charges pass through a resistor.

28.3 (a). Connecting b to c "shorts out" bulb R_2 and changes the total resistance of the circuit from $R_1 + R_2$ to just R_1. Because the resistance of the circuit has decreased (and the emf supplied by the battery does not change), the current in the circuit increases.

28.4 (b). When the switch is opened, resistors R_1 and R_2 are in series, so that the total circuit resistance is larger than when the switch was closed. As a result, the current decreases.

28.5 (b), (d). Adding another series resistor increases the total resistance of the circuit and thus reduces the current in the circuit. The potential difference across the battery terminals increases because the reduced current results in a smaller voltage decrease across the internal resistance.

28.6 (a), (e). If the second resistor were connected in parallel, the total resistance of the circuit would decrease, and the current in the battery would increase. The potential difference across the terminals would decrease because the increased current results in a greater voltage drop across the internal resistance.

28.7 (a). When the switch is closed, resistors R_1 and R_2 are in parallel, so that the total circuit resistance is smaller than when the switch was open. As a result, the current increases.

28.8 (c). A current is assigned to a given branch of a circuit. There may be multiple resistors and batteries in a given branch.

28.9 (b), (d). Just after the switch is closed, there is no charge on the capacitor, so there is no voltage across it. Charges begin to flow in the circuit to charge up the capacitor, so that all of the voltage $\Delta V = IR$ appears across the resistor. After a long time, the capacitor is fully charged and the current drops to zero. Thus, the battery voltage is now entirely across the capacitor.

28.10 (c), (i). Just after the switch is closed, there is no charge on the capacitor. Current exists in both branches of the circuit as the capacitor begins to charge, so the right half of the circuit is equivalent to two resistances R in parallel for an equivalent resistance of $\frac{1}{2}R$. After a long time, the capacitor is fully charged and the current in the right-hand branch drops to zero. Now, current exists only in a resistance R across the battery.

Chapter 29

Magnetic Fields

▲ Magnetic fingerprinting allows fingerprints to be seen on surfaces that otherwise would not allow prints to be lifted. The powder spread on the surface is coated with an organic material that adheres to the greasy residue in a fingerprint. A magnetic "brush" removes the excess powder and makes the fingerprint visible. (James King-Holmes/Photo Researchers, Inc.)

Many historians of science believe that the compass, which uses a magnetic needle, was used in China as early as the 13th century B.C., its invention being of Arabic or Indian origin. The early Greeks knew about magnetism as early as 800 B.C. They discovered that the stone magnetite (Fe_3O_4) attracts pieces of iron. Legend ascribes the name *magnetite* to the shepherd Magnes, the nails of whose shoes and the tip of whose staff stuck fast to chunks of magnetite while he pastured his flocks.

In 1269 a Frenchman named Pierre de Maricourt found that the directions of a needle near a spherical natural magnet formed lines that encircled the sphere and passed through two points diametrically opposite each other, which he called the *poles* of the magnet. Subsequent experiments showed that every magnet, regardless of its shape, has two poles, called *north* (N) and *south* (S) poles, that exert forces on other magnetic poles similar to the way that electric charges exert forces on one another. That is, like poles (N–N or S–S) repel each other, and opposite poles (N–S) attract each other.

The poles received their names because of the way a magnet, such as that in a compass, behaves in the presence of the Earth's magnetic field. If a bar magnet is suspended from its midpoint and can swing freely in a horizontal plane, it will rotate until its north pole points to the Earth's geographic North Pole and its south pole points to the Earth's geographic South Pole.[1]

In 1600 William Gilbert (1540–1603) extended de Maricourt's experiments to a variety of materials. Using the fact that a compass needle orients in preferred directions, he suggested that the Earth itself is a large permanent magnet. In 1750 experimenters used a torsion balance to show that magnetic poles exert attractive or repulsive forces on each other and that these forces vary as the inverse square of the distance between interacting poles. Although the force between two magnetic poles is otherwise similar to the force between two electric charges, electric charges can be isolated (witness the electron and proton) whereas **a single magnetic pole has never been isolated.** That is, **magnetic poles are always found in pairs.** All attempts thus far to detect an isolated magnetic pole have been unsuccessful. No matter how many times a permanent magnet is cut in two, each piece always has a north and a south pole.[2]

The relationship between magnetism and electricity was discovered in 1819 when, during a lecture demonstration, the Danish scientist Hans Christian Oersted found that an electric current in a wire deflected a nearby compass needle.[3] In the 1820s,

Hans Christian Oersted

Danish Physicist and Chemist (1777–1851)

Oersted is best known for observing that a compass needle deflects when placed near a wire carrying a current. This important discovery was the first evidence of the connection between electric and magnetic phenomena. Oersted was also the first to prepare pure aluminum. *(North Wind Picture Archives)*

---

[1] Note that the Earth's geographic North Pole is magnetically a south pole, whereas its geographic South Pole is magnetically a north pole. Because *opposite* magnetic poles attract each other, the pole on a magnet that is attracted to the Earth's geographic North Pole is the magnet's *north* pole and the pole attracted to the Earth's geographic South Pole is the magnet's *south* pole.

[2] There is some theoretical basis for speculating that magnetic *monopoles*—isolated north or south poles—may exist in nature, and attempts to detect them are an active experimental field of investigation.

[3] The same discovery was reported in 1802 by an Italian jurist, Gian Dominico Romognosi, but was overlooked, probably because it was published in an obscure journal.

further connections between electricity and magnetism were demonstrated independently by Faraday and Joseph Henry (1797–1878). They showed that an electric current can be produced in a circuit either by moving a magnet near the circuit or by changing the current in a nearby circuit. These observations demonstrate that a changing magnetic field creates an electric field. Years later, theoretical work by Maxwell showed that the reverse is also true: a changing electric field creates a magnetic field.

This chapter examines the forces that act on moving charges and on current-carrying wires in the presence of a magnetic field. The source of the magnetic field is described in Chapter 30.

29.1 Magnetic Fields and Forces

In our study of electricity, we described the interactions between charged objects in terms of electric fields. Recall that an electric field surrounds any electric charge. In addition to containing an electric field, the region of space surrounding any *moving* electric charge also contains a magnetic field. A magnetic field also surrounds a magnetic substance making up a permanent magnet.

Historically, the symbol **B** has been used to represent a magnetic field, and this is the notation we use in this text. The direction of the magnetic field **B** at any location is the direction in which a compass needle points at that location. As with the electric field, we can represent the magnetic field by means of drawings with *magnetic field lines*.

Figure 29.1 shows how the magnetic field lines of a bar magnet can be traced with the aid of a compass. Note that the magnetic field lines outside the magnet point away from north poles and toward south poles. One can display magnetic field patterns of a bar magnet using small iron filings, as shown in Figure 29.2.

We can define a magnetic field **B** at some point in space in terms of the magnetic force $\mathbf{F}_B$ that the field exerts on a charged particle moving with a velocity **v**, which we call the test object. For the time being, let us assume that no electric or gravitational fields are present at the location of the test object. Experiments on various charged particles moving in a magnetic field give the following results:

Properties of the magnetic force on a charge moving in a magnetic field B

- The magnitude F_B of the magnetic force exerted on the particle is proportional to the charge q and to the speed v of the particle.

- The magnitude and direction of $\mathbf{F}_B$ depend on the velocity of the particle and on the magnitude and direction of the magnetic field **B**.

- When a charged particle moves parallel to the magnetic field vector, the magnetic force acting on the particle is zero.

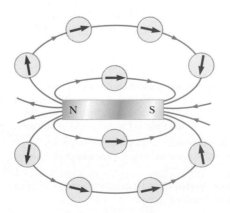

At the Active Figures link at http://www.pse6.com, *you can move the compass around and trace the magnetic field lines for yourself.*

Active Figure 29.1 Compass needles can be used to trace the magnetic field lines in the region outside a bar magnet.

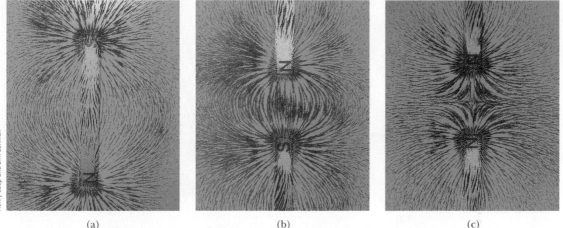

Figure 29.2 (a) Magnetic field pattern surrounding a bar magnet as displayed with iron filings. (b) Magnetic field pattern between *opposite* poles (N–S) of two bar magnets. (c) Magnetic field pattern between *like* poles (N–N) of two bar magnets.

- When the particle's velocity vector makes any angle $\theta \neq 0$ with the magnetic field, the magnetic force acts in a direction perpendicular to both **v** and **B**; that is, $\mathbf{F}_B$ is perpendicular to the plane formed by **v** and **B** (Fig. 29.3a).

- The magnetic force exerted on a positive charge is in the direction opposite the direction of the magnetic force exerted on a negative charge moving in the same direction (Fig. 29.3b).

- The magnitude of the magnetic force exerted on the moving particle is proportional to $\sin \theta$, where θ is the angle the particle's velocity vector makes with the direction of **B**.

We can summarize these observations by writing the magnetic force in the form

$$\mathbf{F}_B = q\mathbf{v} \times \mathbf{B} \qquad (29.1)$$

Vector expression for the magnetic force on a charged particle moving in a magnetic field

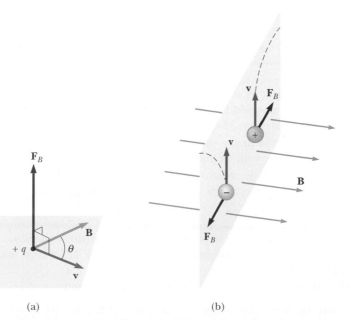

(a)   (b)

Figure 29.3 The direction of the magnetic force $\mathbf{F}_B$ acting on a charged particle moving with a velocity **v** in the presence of a magnetic field **B**. (a) The magnetic force is perpendicular to both **v** and **B**. (b) Oppositely directed magnetic forces $\mathbf{F}_B$ are exerted on two oppositely charged particles moving at the same velocity in a magnetic field. The dashed lines show the paths of the particles, which we will investigate in Section 29.4.

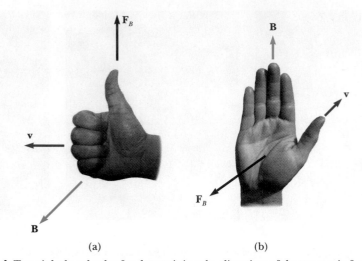

Figure 29.4 Two right-hand rules for determining the direction of the magnetic force $\mathbf{F}_B = q\mathbf{v} \times \mathbf{B}$ acting on a particle with charge q moving with a velocity $\mathbf{v}$ in a magnetic field $\mathbf{B}$. (a) In this rule, the fingers point in the direction of $\mathbf{v}$, with $\mathbf{B}$ coming out of your palm, so that you can curl your fingers in the direction of $\mathbf{B}$. The direction of $\mathbf{v} \times \mathbf{B}$, and the force on a positive charge, is the direction in which the thumb points. (b) In this rule, the vector $\mathbf{v}$ is in the direction of your thumb and $\mathbf{B}$ in the direction of your fingers. The force $\mathbf{F}_B$ on a positive charge is in the direction of your palm, as if you are pushing the particle with your hand.

which by definition of the cross product (see Section 11.1) is perpendicular to both $\mathbf{v}$ and $\mathbf{B}$. We can regard this equation as an operational definition of the magnetic field at some point in space. That is, the magnetic field is defined in terms of the force acting on a moving charged particle.

Figure 29.4 reviews two right-hand rules for determining the direction of the cross product $\mathbf{v} \times \mathbf{B}$ and determining the direction of $\mathbf{F}_B$. The rule in Figure 29.4a depends on our right-hand rule for the cross product in Figure 11.2. Point the four fingers of your right hand along the direction of $\mathbf{v}$ with the palm facing $\mathbf{B}$ and curl them toward $\mathbf{B}$. The extended thumb, which is at a right angle to the fingers, points in the direction of $\mathbf{v} \times \mathbf{B}$. Because $\mathbf{F}_B = q\mathbf{v} \times \mathbf{B}$, $\mathbf{F}_B$ is in the direction of your thumb if q is positive and opposite the direction of your thumb if q is negative. (If you need more help understanding the cross product, you should review pages 337 to 339, including Fig. 11.2.)

An alternative rule is shown in Figure 29.4b. Here the thumb points in the direction of $\mathbf{v}$ and the extended fingers in the direction of $\mathbf{B}$. Now, the force $\mathbf{F}_B$ on a positive charge extends outward from your palm. The advantage of this rule is that the force on the charge is in the direction that you would push on something with your hand—outward from your palm. The force on a negative charge is in the opposite direction. Feel free to use either of these two right-hand rules.

The magnitude of the magnetic force on a charged particle is

$$F_B = |q|vB \sin \theta \qquad (29.2)$$

Magnitude of the magnetic force on a charged particle moving in a magnetic field

where θ is the smaller angle between $\mathbf{v}$ and $\mathbf{B}$. From this expression, we see that F_B is zero when $\mathbf{v}$ is parallel or antiparallel to $\mathbf{B}$ ($\theta = 0$ or $180°$) and maximum when $\mathbf{v}$ is perpendicular to $\mathbf{B}$ ($\theta = 90°$).

There are several important differences between electric and magnetic forces:

- The electric force acts along the direction of the electric field, whereas the magnetic force acts perpendicular to the magnetic field.

- The electric force acts on a charged particle regardless of whether the particle is moving, whereas the magnetic force acts on a charged particle only when the particle is in motion.

- The electric force does work in displacing a charged particle, whereas the magnetic force associated with a steady magnetic field does no work when a particle is displaced because the force is perpendicular to the displacement.

From the last statement and on the basis of the work–kinetic energy theorem, we conclude that the kinetic energy of a charged particle moving through a magnetic field cannot be altered by the magnetic field alone. In other words, when a charged particle moves with a velocity $\mathbf{v}$ through a magnetic field, the field can alter the direction of the velocity vector but cannot change the speed or kinetic energy of the particle.

From Equation 29.2, we see that the SI unit of magnetic field is the newton per coulomb-meter per second, which is called the **tesla** (T):

$$1 \text{ T} = 1 \frac{\text{N}}{\text{C} \cdot \text{m/s}}$$

The tesla

Because a coulomb per second is defined to be an ampere, we see that

$$1 \text{ T} = 1 \frac{\text{N}}{\text{A} \cdot \text{m}}$$

A non-SI magnetic-field unit in common use, called the *gauss* (G), is related to the tesla through the conversion $1 \text{ T} = 10^4 \text{ G}$. Table 29.1 shows some typical values of magnetic fields.

Quick Quiz 29.1 The north-pole end of a bar magnet is held near a positively charged piece of plastic. Is the plastic (a) attracted, (b) repelled, or (c) unaffected by the magnet?

Quick Quiz 29.2 A charged particle moves with velocity $\mathbf{v}$ in a magnetic field $\mathbf{B}$. The magnetic force on the particle is a maximum when $\mathbf{v}$ is (a) parallel to $\mathbf{B}$, (b) perpendicular to $\mathbf{B}$, (c) zero.

Quick Quiz 29.3 An electron moves in the plane of this paper toward the top of the page. A magnetic field is also in the plane of the page and directed toward the right. The direction of the magnetic force on the electron is (a) toward the top of the page, (b) toward the bottom of the page, (c) toward the left edge of the page, (d) toward the right edge of the page, (e) upward out of the page, (f) downward into the page.

Table 29.1

Some Approximate Magnetic Field Magnitudes	
Source of Field	**Field Magnitude (T)**
Strong superconducting laboratory magnet	30
Strong conventional laboratory magnet	2
Medical MRI unit	1.5
Bar magnet	10^{-2}
Surface of the Sun	10^{-2}
Surface of the Earth	0.5×10^{-4}
Inside human brain (due to nerve impulses)	10^{-13}

Example 29.1 **An Electron Moving in a Magnetic Field**

An electron in a television picture tube moves toward the front of the tube with a speed of 8.0×10^6 m/s along the x axis (Fig. 29.5). Surrounding the neck of the tube are coils of wire that create a magnetic field of magnitude 0.025 T, directed at an angle of 60° to the x axis and lying in the xy plane.

(A) Calculate the magnetic force on the electron using Equation 29.2.

Solution Using Equation 29.2, we find the magnitude of the magnetic force:

$$F_B = |q|vB \sin \theta$$
$$= (1.6 \times 10^{-19} \text{ C})(8.0 \times 10^6 \text{ m/s})(0.025 \text{ T})(\sin 60°)$$
$$= \boxed{2.8 \times 10^{-14} \text{ N}}$$

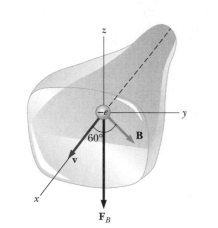

Figure 29.5 (Example 29.1) The magnetic force $\mathbf{F}_B$ acting on the electron is in the negative z direction when $\mathbf{v}$ and $\mathbf{B}$ lie in the xy plane.

Because $\mathbf{v} \times \mathbf{B}$ is in the positive z direction (from the right-hand rule) and the charge is negative, $\mathbf{F}_B$ is in the negative z direction.

(B) Find a vector expression for the magnetic force on the electron using Equation 29.1.

Solution We begin by writing a vector expression for the velocity of the electron:

$$\mathbf{v} = (8.0 \times 10^6 \,\hat{\mathbf{i}}) \text{ m/s}$$

and one for the magnetic field:

$$\mathbf{B} = (0.025 \cos 60° \,\hat{\mathbf{i}} + 0.025 \sin 60° \,\hat{\mathbf{j}}) \text{T}$$
$$= (0.013 \,\hat{\mathbf{i}} + 0.022 \,\hat{\mathbf{j}}) \text{T}$$

The force on the electron, using Equation 29.1, is

$$\mathbf{F}_B = q\mathbf{v} \times \mathbf{B}$$
$$= (-e)[(8.0 \times 10^6 \,\hat{\mathbf{i}}) \text{ m/s}] \times [(0.013 \,\hat{\mathbf{i}} + 0.022 \,\hat{\mathbf{j}}) \text{T}]$$
$$= (-e)[(8.0 \times 10^6 \,\hat{\mathbf{i}}) \text{ m/s}] \times [(0.013 \,\hat{\mathbf{i}}) \text{T}]$$
$$\quad + (-e)[(8.0 \times 10^6 \,\hat{\mathbf{i}}) \text{ m/s}] \times [(0.022 \,\hat{\mathbf{j}}) \text{T}]$$
$$= (-e)(8.0 \times 10^6 \text{ m/s})(0.013 \text{ T})(\hat{\mathbf{i}} \times \hat{\mathbf{i}})$$
$$\quad + (-e)(8.0 \times 10^6 \text{ m/s})(0.022 \text{ T})(\hat{\mathbf{i}} \times \hat{\mathbf{j}})$$
$$= (-1.6 \times 10^{-19} \text{ C})(8.0 \times 10^6 \text{ m/s})(0.022 \text{ T})\,\hat{\mathbf{k}}$$

where we have used Equations 11.7a and 11.7b to evaluate $\hat{\mathbf{i}} \times \hat{\mathbf{i}}$ and $\hat{\mathbf{i}} \times \hat{\mathbf{j}}$. Carrying out the multiplication, we find,

$$\mathbf{F}_B = \boxed{(-2.8 \times 10^{-14} \text{ N})\,\hat{\mathbf{k}}}$$

This expression agrees with the result in part (A). The magnitude is the same as we found there, and the force vector is in the negative z direction.

29.2 Magnetic Force Acting on a Current-Carrying Conductor

If a magnetic force is exerted on a single charged particle when the particle moves through a magnetic field, it should not surprise you that a current-carrying wire also experiences a force when placed in a magnetic field. This follows from the fact that the current is a collection of many charged particles in motion; hence, the resultant force exerted by the field on the wire is the vector sum of the individual forces exerted on all the charged particles making up the current. The force exerted on the particles is transmitted to the wire when the particles collide with the atoms making up the wire.

Before we continue our discussion, some explanation of the notation used in this book is in order. To indicate the direction of $\mathbf{B}$ in illustrations, we sometimes present perspective views, such as those in Figure 29.5. If $\mathbf{B}$ lies in the plane of the page or is present in a perspective drawing, we use blue vectors or blue field lines with arrowheads. In non-perspective illustrations, we depict a magnetic field perpendicular to and directed out of the page with a series of blue dots, which represent the tips of arrows coming toward you (see Fig. 29.6a). In this case, we label the field $\mathbf{B}_{out}$. If $\mathbf{B}$ is directed perpendicularly into the page, we use blue crosses, which represent the feathered tails of arrows fired away from you, as in Figure 29.6b. In this case, we label the field $\mathbf{B}_{in}$, where the subscript "in" indicates "into the page." The same notation with crosses and dots is also used for other quantities that might be perpendicular to the page, such as forces and current directions.

One can demonstrate the magnetic force acting on a current-carrying conductor by hanging a wire between the poles of a magnet, as shown in Figure 29.7a. For ease in visualization, part of the horseshoe magnet in part (a) is removed to show the end face of the south pole in parts (b), (c), and (d) of Figure 29.7. The magnetic field is directed into the page and covers the region within the shaded squares. When the current in the wire is zero, the wire remains vertical, as shown in Figure 29.7b. However, when the wire carries a current directed upward, as shown in Figure 29.7c, the wire deflects to the left. If we reverse the current, as shown in Figure 29.7d, the wire deflects to the right.

Let us quantify this discussion by considering a straight segment of wire of length L and cross-sectional area A, carrying a current I in a uniform magnetic field $\mathbf{B}$, as shown in Figure 29.8. The magnetic force exerted on a charge q moving with a drift velocity $\mathbf{v}_d$ is $q\mathbf{v}_d \times \mathbf{B}$. To find the total force acting on the wire, we multiply the force $q\mathbf{v}_d \times \mathbf{B}$ exerted on one charge by the number of charges in the segment. Because the volume of the segment is AL, the number of charges in the segment is nAL, where n is the number of charges per unit volume. Hence, the total magnetic force on the wire of length L is

$$\mathbf{F}_B = (q\mathbf{v}_d \times \mathbf{B})\,nAL$$

We can write this expression in a more convenient form by noting that, from Equation 27.4, the current in the wire is $I = nqv_dA$. Therefore,

$$\mathbf{F}_B = I\mathbf{L} \times \mathbf{B} \qquad (29.3)$$

where $\mathbf{L}$ is a vector that points in the direction of the current I and has a magnitude equal to the length L of the segment. Note that this expression applies only to a straight segment of wire in a uniform magnetic field.

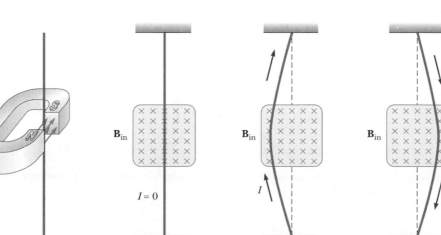

(a)

(b)

Figure 29.6 (a) Magnetic field lines coming out of the paper are indicated by dots, representing the tips of arrows coming outward. (b) Magnetic field lines going into the paper are indicated by crosses, representing the feathers of arrows going inward.

Force on a segment of current-carrying wire in a uniform magnetic field

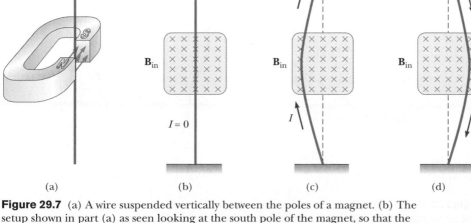

(a)   **(b)**   **(c)**   **(d)**

Figure 29.7 (a) A wire suspended vertically between the poles of a magnet. (b) The setup shown in part (a) as seen looking at the south pole of the magnet, so that the magnetic field (blue crosses) is directed into the page. When there is no current in the wire, it remains vertical. (c) When the current is upward, the wire deflects to the left. (d) When the current is downward, the wire deflects to the right.

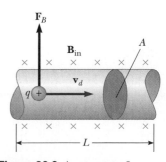

Figure 29.8 A segment of a current-carrying wire in a magnetic field $\mathbf{B}$. The magnetic force exerted on each charge making up the current is $q\mathbf{v}_d \times \mathbf{B}$ and the net force on the segment of length L is $I\mathbf{L} \times \mathbf{B}$.

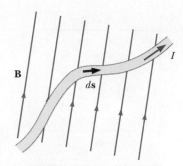

Figure 29.9 A wire segment of arbitrary shape carrying a current I in a magnetic field **B** experiences a magnetic force. The magnetic force on any segment $d\mathbf{s}$ is $I\,d\mathbf{s} \times \mathbf{B}$ and is directed out of the page. You should use the right-hand rule to confirm this force direction.

Now consider an arbitrarily shaped wire segment of uniform cross section in a magnetic field, as shown in Figure 29.9. It follows from Equation 29.3 that the magnetic force exerted on a small segment of vector length $d\mathbf{s}$ in the presence of a field **B** is

$$d\mathbf{F}_B = I\,d\mathbf{s} \times \mathbf{B} \qquad (29.4)$$

where $d\mathbf{F}_B$ is directed out of the page for the directions of **B** and $d\mathbf{s}$ in Figure 29.9. We can consider Equation 29.4 as an alternative definition of **B**. That is, we can define the magnetic field **B** in terms of a measurable force exerted on a current element, where the force is a maximum when **B** is perpendicular to the element and zero when **B** is parallel to the element.

To calculate the total force $\mathbf{F}_B$ acting on the wire shown in Figure 29.9, we integrate Equation 29.4 over the length of the wire:

$$\mathbf{F}_B = I\int_a^b d\mathbf{s} \times \mathbf{B} \qquad (29.5)$$

where a and b represent the end points of the wire. When this integration is carried out, the magnitude of the magnetic field and the direction the field makes with the vector $d\mathbf{s}$ may differ at different points.

We now treat two interesting special cases involving Equation 29.5. In both cases, the magnetic field is assumed to be uniform in magnitude and direction.

Case 1. A curved wire carries a current I and is located in a uniform magnetic field **B**, as shown in Figure 29.10a. Because the field is uniform, we can take **B** outside the integral in Equation 29.5, and we obtain

$$\mathbf{F}_B = I\left(\int_a^b d\mathbf{s}\right) \times \mathbf{B} \qquad (29.6)$$

But the quantity $\int_a^b d\mathbf{s}$ represents the *vector sum* of all the length elements from a to b. From the law of vector addition, the sum equals the vector $\mathbf{L}'$, directed from a to b. Therefore, Equation 29.6 reduces to

$$\mathbf{F}_B = I\mathbf{L}' \times \mathbf{B} \qquad (29.7)$$

From this we conclude that **the magnetic force on a curved current-carrying wire in a uniform magnetic field is equal to that on a straight wire connecting the end points and carrying the same current.**

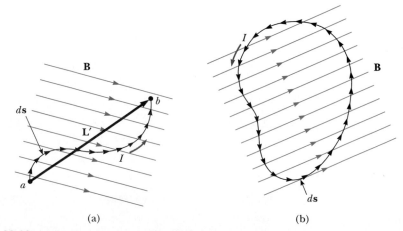

Figure 29.10 (a) A curved wire carrying a current I in a uniform magnetic field. The total magnetic force acting on the wire is equivalent to the force on a straight wire of length L' running between the ends of the curved wire. (b) A current-carrying loop of arbitrary shape in a uniform magnetic field. The net magnetic force on the loop is zero.

Case 2.   An arbitrarily shaped closed loop carrying a current I is placed in a uniform magnetic field, as shown in Figure 29.10b. We can again express the magnetic force acting on the loop in the form of Equation 29.6, but this time we must take the vector sum of the length elements $d\mathbf{s}$ over the entire loop:

$$\mathbf{F}_B = I \left(\oint d\mathbf{s} \right) \times \mathbf{B}$$

Because the set of length elements forms a closed polygon, the vector sum must be zero. This follows from the procedure for adding vectors by the graphical method. Because $\oint d\mathbf{s} = 0$, we conclude that $\mathbf{F}_B = 0$; that is, **the net magnetic force acting on any closed current loop in a uniform magnetic field is zero.**

Quick Quiz 29.4   The four wires shown in Figure 29.11 all carry the same current from point A to point B through the same magnetic field. In all four parts of the figure, the points A and B are 10 cm apart. Rank the wires according to the magnitude of the magnetic force exerted on them, from greatest to least.

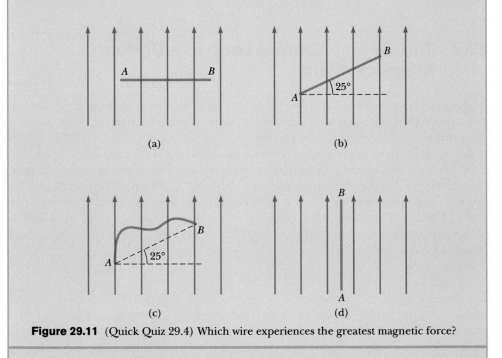

Figure 29.11 (Quick Quiz 29.4) Which wire experiences the greatest magnetic force?

Quick Quiz 29.5   A wire carries current in the plane of this paper toward the top of the page. The wire experiences a magnetic force toward the right edge of the page. The direction of the magnetic field causing this force is (a) in the plane of the page and toward the left edge, (b) in the plane of the page and toward the bottom edge, (c) upward out of the page, (d) downward into the page.

Example 29.2 Force on a Semicircular Conductor

A wire bent into a semicircle of radius R forms a closed circuit and carries a current I. The wire lies in the xy plane, and a uniform magnetic field is directed along the positive y axis, as shown in Figure 29.12. Find the magnitude and direction of the magnetic force acting

on the straight portion of the wire and on the curved portion.

Solution The magnetic force $\mathbf{F}_1$ acting on the straight portion has a magnitude $F_1 = ILB = 2IRB$ because $L = 2R$ and

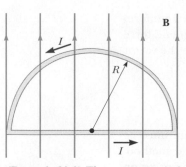

Figure 29.12 (Example 29.2) The net magnetic force acting on a closed current loop in a uniform magnetic field is zero. In the setup shown here, the magnetic force on the straight portion of the loop is $2IRB$ and directed out of the page, and the magnetic force on the curved portion is $2IRB$ directed into the page.

the wire is oriented perpendicular to **B**. The direction of $\mathbf{F}_1$ is out of the page based on the right-hand rule for the cross product $\mathbf{L} \times \mathbf{B}$.

To find the magnetic force $\mathbf{F}_2$ acting on the curved part, we use the results of Case 1. The magnetic force on the curved portion is the same as that on a straight wire of length $2R$ carrying current I to the left. Thus, $F_2 = ILB = 2IRB$. The direction of $\mathbf{F}_2$ is into the page based on the right-hand rule for the cross product $\mathbf{L} \times \mathbf{B}$.

Because the wire lies in the xy plane, the two forces on the loop can be expressed as

$$\mathbf{F}_1 = \boxed{2IRB\hat{\mathbf{k}}}$$

$$\mathbf{F}_2 = \boxed{-2IRB\hat{\mathbf{k}}}$$

The net magnetic force on the loop is

$$\sum \mathbf{F} = \mathbf{F}_1 + \mathbf{F}_2 = 2IRB\hat{\mathbf{k}} - 2IRB\hat{\mathbf{k}} = 0$$

Note that this is consistent with Case 2, because the wire forms a closed loop in a uniform magnetic field.

29.3 Torque on a Current Loop in a Uniform Magnetic Field

In the preceding section, we showed how a magnetic force is exerted on a current-carrying conductor placed in a magnetic field. With this as a starting point, we now show that a torque is exerted on a current loop placed in a magnetic field. The results of this analysis will be of great value when we discuss motors in Chapter 31.

Consider a rectangular loop carrying a current I in the presence of a uniform magnetic field directed parallel to the plane of the loop, as shown in Figure 29.13a. No magnetic forces act on sides ① and ③ because these wires are parallel to the field; hence, $\mathbf{L} \times \mathbf{B} = 0$ for these sides. However, magnetic forces do act on sides ② and ④ because these sides are oriented perpendicular to the field. The magnitude of these forces is, from Equation 29.3,

$$F_2 = F_4 = IaB$$

The direction of $\mathbf{F}_2$, the magnetic force exerted on wire ②, is out of the page in the view shown in Figure 29.13a, and that of $\mathbf{F}_4$, the magnetic force exerted on wire ④, is into the page in the same view. If we view the loop from side ③ and sight along sides ② and ④, we see the view shown in Figure 29.13b, and the two magnetic forces $\mathbf{F}_2$ and $\mathbf{F}_4$ are directed as shown. Note that the two forces point in opposite directions but are *not* directed along the same line of action. If the loop is pivoted so that it can rotate about point O, these two forces produce about O a torque that rotates the loop clockwise. The magnitude of this torque τ_{max} is

$$\tau_{\text{max}} = F_2 \frac{b}{2} + F_4 \frac{b}{2} = (IaB)\frac{b}{2} + (IaB)\frac{b}{2} = IabB$$

where the moment arm about O is $b/2$ for each force. Because the area enclosed by the loop is $A = ab$, we can express the maximum torque as

$$\tau_{\text{max}} = IAB \tag{29.8}$$

This maximum-torque result is valid only when the magnetic field is parallel to the plane of the loop. The sense of the rotation is clockwise when viewed from side ③, as indicated in Figure 29.13b. If the current direction were reversed, the force directions would also reverse, and the rotational tendency would be counterclockwise.

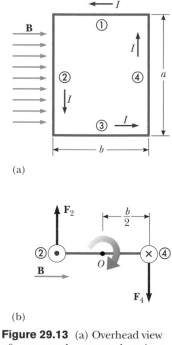

Figure 29.13 (a) Overhead view of a rectangular current loop in a uniform magnetic field. No magnetic forces are acting on sides ① and ③ because these sides are parallel to **B**. Forces are acting on sides ② and ④, however. (b) Edge view of the loop sighting down sides ② and ④ shows that the magnetic forces $\mathbf{F}_2$ and $\mathbf{F}_4$ exerted on these sides create a torque that tends to twist the loop clockwise. The purple dot in the left circle represents current in wire ② coming toward you; the purple cross in the right circle represents current in wire ④ moving away from you.

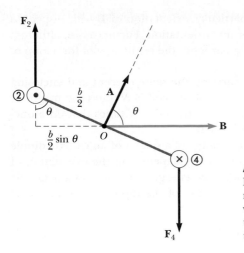

Active Figure 29.14 An end view of the loop in Figure 29.13b rotated through an angle with respect to the magnetic field. If **B** is at an angle θ with respect to vector **A**, which is perpendicular to the plane of the loop, the torque is $IAB \sin \theta$ where the magnitude of **A** is A, the area of the loop.

At the Active Figures link at http://www.pse6.com, *you can choose the current in the loop, the magnetic field, and the initial orientation of the loop and observe the subsequent motion.*

Now suppose that the uniform magnetic field makes an angle $\theta < 90°$ with a line perpendicular to the plane of the loop, as in Figure 29.14. For convenience, we assume that **B** is perpendicular to sides ② and ④. In this case, the magnetic forces $\mathbf{F}_1$ and $\mathbf{F}_3$ exerted on sides ① and ③ cancel each other and produce no torque because they pass through a common origin. However, the magnetic forces $\mathbf{F}_2$ and $\mathbf{F}_4$ acting on sides ② and ④ produce a torque about *any point*. Referring to the end view shown in Figure 29.14, we note that the moment arm of $\mathbf{F}_2$ about the point O is equal to $(b/2) \sin \theta$. Likewise, the moment arm of $\mathbf{F}_4$ about O is also $(b/2) \sin \theta$. Because $F_2 = F_4 = IaB$, the magnitude of the net torque about O is

$$\tau = F_2 \frac{b}{2} \sin \theta + F_4 \frac{b}{2} \sin \theta$$

$$= IaB \left(\frac{b}{2} \sin \theta \right) + IaB \left(\frac{b}{2} \sin \theta \right) = IabB \sin \theta$$

$$= IAB \sin \theta$$

where $A = ab$ is the area of the loop. This result shows that the torque has its maximum value IAB when the field is perpendicular to the normal to the plane of the loop ($\theta = 90°$), as we saw when discussing Figure 29.13, and is zero when the field is parallel to the normal to the plane of the loop ($\theta = 0$).

A convenient expression for the torque exerted on a loop placed in a uniform magnetic field **B** is

$$\tau = I\mathbf{A} \times \mathbf{B} \qquad (29.9)$$

where **A**, the vector shown in Figure 29.14, is perpendicular to the plane of the loop and has a magnitude equal to the area of the loop. We determine the direction of **A** using the right-hand rule described in Figure 29.15. When you curl the fingers of your right hand in the direction of the current in the loop, your thumb points in the direction of **A**. As we see in Figure 29.14, the loop tends to rotate in the direction of decreasing values of θ (that is, such that the area vector **A** rotates toward the direction of the magnetic field).

The product $I\mathbf{A}$ is defined to be the **magnetic dipole moment** μ (often simply called the "magnetic moment") of the loop:

$$\mu = I\mathbf{A} \qquad (29.10)$$

The SI unit of magnetic dipole moment is ampere-meter^2 (A·m^2). Using this definition, we can express the torque exerted on a current-carrying loop in a magnetic field **B** as

$$\tau = \mu \times \mathbf{B} \qquad (29.11)$$

Note that this result is analogous to Equation 26.18, $\tau = \mathbf{p} \times \mathbf{E}$, for the torque exerted on an electric dipole in the presence of an electric field **E**, where **p** is the electric dipole moment.

Figure 29.15 Right-hand rule for determining the direction of the vector **A**. The direction of the magnetic moment μ is the same as the direction of **A**.

Torque on a current loop in a magnetic field

Magnetic dipole moment of a current loop

Torque on a magnetic moment in a magnetic field

Although we obtained the torque for a particular orientation of **B** with respect to the loop, the equation $\boldsymbol{\tau} = \boldsymbol{\mu} \times \mathbf{B}$ is valid for any orientation. Furthermore, although we derived the torque expression for a rectangular loop, the result is valid for a loop of any shape.

If a coil consists of N turns of wire, each carrying the same current and enclosing the same area, the total magnetic dipole moment of the coil is N times the magnetic dipole moment for one turn. The torque on an N-turn coil is N times that on a one-turn coil. Thus, we write $\boldsymbol{\tau} = N\boldsymbol{\mu}_{\text{loop}} \times \mathbf{B} = \boldsymbol{\mu}_{\text{coil}} \times \mathbf{B}$.

In Section 26.6, we found that the potential energy of a system of an electric dipole in an electric field is given by $U = -\mathbf{p} \cdot \mathbf{E}$. This energy depends on the orientation of the dipole in the electric field. Likewise, the potential energy of a system of a magnetic dipole in a magnetic field depends on the orientation of the dipole in the magnetic field and is given by

Potential energy of a system of a magnetic moment in a magnetic field

$$U = -\boldsymbol{\mu} \cdot \mathbf{B} \tag{29.12}$$

From this expression, we see that the system has its lowest energy $U_{\text{min}} = -\mu B$ when $\boldsymbol{\mu}$ points in the same direction as **B**. The system has its highest energy $U_{\text{max}} = +\mu B$ when $\boldsymbol{\mu}$ points in the direction opposite **B**.

Quick Quiz 29.6 Rank the magnitudes of the torques acting on the rectangular loops shown edge-on in Figure 29.16, from highest to lowest. All loops are identical and carry the same current.

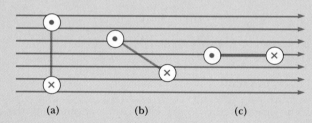

(a)　　　　　(b)　　　　　(c)

Figure 29.16 (Quick Quiz 29.6) Which current loop (seen edge-on) experiences the greatest torque? (Quick Quiz 29.7) Which current loop (seen edge-on) experiences the greatest net force?

Quick Quiz 29.7 Rank the magnitudes of the net forces acting on the rectangular loops shown in Figure 29.16, from highest to lowest. All loops are identical and carry the same current.

Example 29.3 The Magnetic Dipole Moment of a Coil

A rectangular coil of dimensions 5.40 cm × 8.50 cm consists of 25 turns of wire and carries a current of 15.0 mA. A 0.350-T magnetic field is applied parallel to the plane of the loop.

(A) Calculate the magnitude of its magnetic dipole moment.

Solution Because the coil has 25 turns, we modify Equation 29.10 to obtain

$$\mu_{\text{coil}} = NIA = (25)(15.0 \times 10^{-3}\,\text{A})(0.054\,0\,\text{m})(0.085\,0\,\text{m})$$

$$= 1.72 \times 10^{-3}\,\text{A} \cdot \text{m}^2$$

(B) What is the magnitude of the torque acting on the loop?

Solution Because **B** is perpendicular to $\boldsymbol{\mu}_{\text{coil}}$, Equation 29.11 gives

$$\tau = \mu_{\text{coil}}B = (1.72 \times 10^{-3}\,\text{A} \cdot \text{m}^2)(0.350\,\text{T})$$

$$= 6.02 \times 10^{-4}\,\text{N} \cdot \text{m}$$

Example 29.4   Satellite Attitude Control

Many satellites use coils called *torquers* to adjust their orientation. These devices interact with the Earth's magnetic field to create a torque on the spacecraft in the x, y, or z direction. The major advantage of this type of attitude-control system is that it uses solar-generated electricity and so does not consume any thruster fuel.

If a typical device has a magnetic dipole moment of $250 \, A \cdot m^2$, what is the maximum torque applied to a satellite when its torquer is turned on at an altitude where the magnitude of the Earth's magnetic field is 3.0×10^{-5} T?

Solution We once again apply Equation 29.11, recognizing that the maximum torque is obtained when the magnetic dipole moment of the torquer is perpendicular to the Earth's magnetic field:

$$\tau_{max} = \mu B = (250 \, A \cdot m^2)(3.0 \times 10^{-5} \, T)$$

$$= \boxed{7.5 \times 10^{-3} \, N \cdot m}$$

Example 29.5   The D'Arsonval Galvanometer

An end view of a D'Arsonval galvanometer (see Section 28.5) is shown in Figure 29.17. When the turns of wire making up the coil carry a current, the magnetic field created by the magnet exerts on the coil a torque that turns it (along with its attached pointer) against the spring. Show that the angle of deflection of the pointer is directly proportional to the current in the coil.

Solution We can use Equation 29.11 to find the torque τ_m that the magnetic field exerts on the coil. If we assume that the magnetic field through the coil is perpendicular to the normal to the plane of the coil, Equation 29.11 becomes

$$\tau_m = \mu B$$

(This is a reasonable assumption because the circular cross section of the magnet ensures radial magnetic field lines.) This magnetic torque is opposed by the torque due to the spring, which is given by the rotational version of Hooke's law, $\tau_s = -\kappa\phi$, where κ is the torsional spring constant and ϕ is the angle through which the spring turns. Because the coil does not have an angular acceleration when the pointer is at rest, the sum of these torques must be zero:

$$(1) \qquad \tau_m + \tau_s = \mu B - \kappa\phi = 0$$

Equation 29.10 allows us to relate the magnetic moment of the N turns of wire to the current through them:

$$\mu = NIA$$

We can substitute this expression for μ in Equation (1) to obtain

$$(NIA)B - \kappa\phi = 0$$

$$\phi = \boxed{\frac{NAB}{\kappa} I}$$

Thus, the angle of deflection of the pointer is directly proportional to the current in the loop. The factor NAB/κ tells us that deflection also depends on the design of the meter.

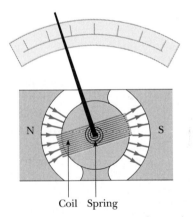

Figure 29.17 (Example 29.5) Structure of a moving-coil galvanometer.

29.4 Motion of a Charged Particle in a Uniform Magnetic Field

In Section 29.1 we found that the magnetic force acting on a charged particle moving in a magnetic field is perpendicular to the velocity of the particle and that consequently the work done by the magnetic force on the particle is zero. Now consider the special case of a positively charged particle moving in a uniform magnetic field with the initial velocity vector of the particle perpendicular to the field. Let us assume that the direction of the magnetic field is into the page, as in Figure 29.18. As the particle changes the direction of its velocity in response to the magnetic force, the magnetic force remains perpendicular to the velocity. As we found in Section 6.1, if the force is always perpendicular to the velocity, the path of

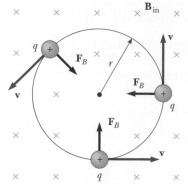

Active Figure 29.18 When the velocity of a charged particle is perpendicular to a uniform magnetic field, the particle moves in a circular path in a plane perpendicular to **B**. The magnetic force **F**$_B$ acting on the charge is always directed toward the center of the circle.

At the Active Figures link at http://www.pse6.com, you can adjust the mass, speed, and charge of the particle and the magnitude of the magnetic field to observe the resulting circular motion.

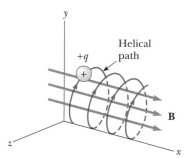

Active Figure 29.19 A charged particle having a velocity vector that has a component parallel to a uniform magnetic field moves in a helical path.

At the Active Figures link at http://www.pse6.com, you can adjust the x component of the velocity of the particle and observe the resulting helical motion.

the particle is a circle! Figure 29.18 shows the particle moving in a circle in a plane perpendicular to the magnetic field.

The particle moves in a circle because the magnetic force **F**$_B$ is perpendicular to **v** and **B** and has a constant magnitude qvB. As Figure 29.18 illustrates, the rotation is counterclockwise for a positive charge. If q were negative, the rotation would be clockwise. We can use Equation 6.1 to equate this magnetic force to the product of the particle mass and the centripetal acceleration:

$$\sum F = ma_c$$

$$F_B = qvB = \frac{mv^2}{r}$$

$$r = \frac{mv}{qB} \tag{29.13}$$

That is, the radius of the path is proportional to the linear momentum mv of the particle and inversely proportional to the magnitude of the charge on the particle and to the magnitude of the magnetic field. The angular speed of the particle (from Eq. 10.10) is

$$\omega = \frac{v}{r} = \frac{qB}{m} \tag{29.14}$$

The period of the motion (the time interval the particle requires to complete one revolution) is equal to the circumference of the circle divided by the linear speed of the particle:

$$T = \frac{2\pi r}{v} = \frac{2\pi}{\omega} = \frac{2\pi m}{qB} \tag{29.15}$$

These results show that the angular speed of the particle and the period of the circular motion do not depend on the linear speed of the particle or on the radius of the orbit. The angular speed ω is often referred to as the **cyclotron frequency** because charged particles circulate at this angular frequency in the type of accelerator called a *cyclotron*, which is discussed in Section 29.5.

If a charged particle moves in a uniform magnetic field with its velocity at some arbitrary angle with respect to **B**, its path is a helix. For example, if the field is directed in the x direction, as shown in Figure 29.19, there is no component of force in the x direction. As a result, $a_x = 0$, and the x component of velocity remains constant. However, the magnetic force $q\mathbf{v} \times \mathbf{B}$ causes the components v_y and v_z to change in time, and the resulting motion is a helix whose axis is parallel to the magnetic field. The projection of the path onto the yz plane (viewed along the x axis) is a circle. (The projections of the path onto the xy and xz planes are sinusoids!) Equations 29.13 to 29.15 still apply provided that v is replaced by $v_\perp = \sqrt{v_y^2 + v_z^2}$.

Quick Quiz 29.8 A charged particle is moving perpendicular to a magnetic field in a circle with a radius r. An identical particle enters the field, with **v** perpendicular to **B**, but with a higher speed v than the first particle. Compared to the radius of the circle for the first particle, the radius of the circle for the second particle is (a) smaller (b) larger (c) equal in size.

Quick Quiz 29.9 A charged particle is moving perpendicular to a magnetic field in a circle with a radius r. The magnitude of the magnetic field is increased. Compared to the initial radius of the circular path, the radius of the new path is (a) smaller (b) larger (c) equal in size.

Example 29.6   A Proton Moving Perpendicular to a Uniform Magnetic Field

A proton is moving in a circular orbit of radius 14 cm in a uniform 0.35-T magnetic field perpendicular to the velocity of the proton. Find the linear speed of the proton.

Solution   From Equation 29.13, we have

$$v = \frac{qBr}{m_p} = \frac{(1.60 \times 10^{-19}\,\text{C})\,(0.35\,\text{T})\,(0.14\,\text{m})}{1.67 \times 10^{-27}\,\text{kg}}$$

$$= \quad 4.7 \times 10^6\,\text{m/s}$$

What If?   What if an electron, rather than a proton, moves in a direction perpendicular to the same magnetic field with this same linear speed? Will the radius of its orbit be different?

Answer   An electron has a much smaller mass than a proton, so the magnetic force should be able to change its velocity much easier than for the proton. Thus, we should expect the radius to be smaller. Looking at Equation 29.13, we see that r is proportional to m with q, B, and v the same for the electron as for the proton. Consequently, the radius will be smaller by the same factor as the ratio of masses m_e/m_p.

Example 29.7   Bending an Electron Beam   Interactive

In an experiment designed to measure the magnitude of a uniform magnetic field, electrons are accelerated from rest through a potential difference of 350 V. The electrons travel along a curved path because of the magnetic force exerted on them, and the radius of the path is measured to be 7.5 cm. (Fig. 29.20 shows such a curved beam of electrons.) If the magnetic field is perpendicular to the beam,

(A) what is the magnitude of the field?

Solution   Conceptualize the circular motion of the electrons with the help of Figures 29.18 and 29.20. We categorize this problem as one involving both uniform circular motion and a magnetic force. Looking at Equation 29.13, we see that we need the speed v of the electron if we are to find the magnetic field magnitude, and v is not given. Consequently, we must find the speed of the electron based on the potential difference through which it is accelerated. Therefore, we also categorize this as a problem in conservation of mechanical energy for an isolated system. To begin analyzing the problem, we find the electron speed. For the isolated electron–electric field system, the loss of potential energy as the electron moves through the 350-V potential difference appears as an increase in the kinetic energy of the electron. Because $K_i = 0$ and $K_f = \frac{1}{2}m_e v^2$, we have

$$\Delta K + \Delta U = 0 \quad \longrightarrow \quad \tfrac{1}{2}m_e v^2 + (-e)\,\Delta V = 0$$

$$v = \sqrt{\frac{2e\,\Delta V}{m_e}} = \sqrt{\frac{2(1.60 \times 10^{-19}\,\text{C})\,(350\,\text{V})}{9.11 \times 10^{-31}\,\text{kg}}}$$

$$= 1.11 \times 10^7\,\text{m/s}$$

Now, using Equation 29.13, we find

$$B = \frac{m_e v}{er} = \frac{(9.11 \times 10^{-31}\,\text{kg})\,(1.11 \times 10^7\,\text{m/s})}{(1.60 \times 10^{-19}\,\text{C})\,(0.075\,\text{m})}$$

$$= \quad 8.4 \times 10^{-4}\,\text{T}$$

(B)   What is the angular speed of the electrons?

Solution   Using Equation 29.14, we find that

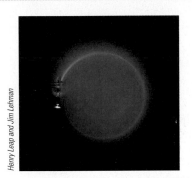

Henry Leap and Jim Lehman

Figure 29.20   (Example 29.7) The bending of an electron beam in a magnetic field.

$$\omega = \frac{v}{r} = \frac{1.11 \times 10^7\,\text{m/s}}{0.075\,\text{m}} = \quad 1.5 \times 10^8\,\text{rad/s}$$

To finalize this problem, note that the angular speed can be represented as $\omega = (1.5 \times 10^8\,\text{rad/s})\,(1\,\text{rev}/2\pi\,\text{rad}) = 2.4 \times 10^7\,\text{rev/s}$. The electrons travel around the circle 24 million times per second! This is consistent with the very high speed that we found in part (A).

What If?   What if a sudden voltage surge causes the accelerating voltage to increase to 400 V? How does this affect the angular speed of the electrons, assuming that the magnetic field remains constant?

Answer   The increase in accelerating voltage ΔV will cause the electrons to enter the magnetic field with a higher speed v. This will cause them to travel in a circle with a larger radius r. The angular speed is the ratio of v to r. Both v and r increase by the same factor, so that the effects cancel and the angular speed remains the same. Equation 29.14 is an expression for the cyclotron frequency, which is the same as the angular speed of the electrons. The cyclotron frequency depends only on the charge q, the magnetic field B, and the mass m_e, none of which have changed. Thus, the voltage surge has no effect on the angular speed. (However, in reality, the voltage surge may also increase the magnetic field if the magnetic field is powered by the same source as the accelerating voltage. In this case, the angular speed will increase according to Equation 29.14.)

At the Interactive Worked Example link at **http://www.pse6.com,** *you can investigate the relationship between the radius of the circular path of the electrons and the magnetic field.*

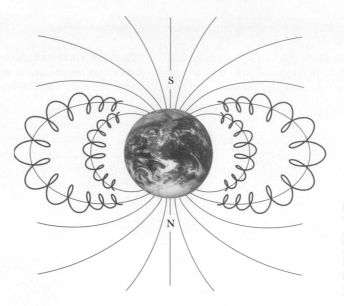

Figure 29.22 The Van Allen belts are made up of charged particles trapped by the Earth's nonuniform magnetic field. The magnetic field lines are in blue and the particle paths in red.

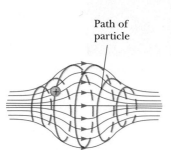

Figure 29.21 A charged particle moving in a nonuniform magnetic field (a magnetic bottle) spirals about the field and oscillates between the end points. The magnetic force exerted on the particle near either end of the bottle has a component that causes the particle to spiral back toward the center.

When charged particles move in a nonuniform magnetic field, the motion is complex. For example, in a magnetic field that is strong at the ends and weak in the middle, such as that shown in Figure 29.21, the particles can oscillate back and forth between two positions. A charged particle starting at one end spirals along the field lines until it reaches the other end, where it reverses its path and spirals back. This configuration is known as a *magnetic bottle* because charged particles can be trapped within it. The magnetic bottle has been used to confine a *plasma,* a gas consisting of ions and electrons. Such a plasma-confinement scheme could fulfill a crucial role in the control of nuclear fusion, a process that could supply us with an almost endless source of energy. Unfortunately, the magnetic bottle has its problems. If a large number of particles are trapped, collisions between them cause the particles to eventually leak from the system.

The Van Allen radiation belts consist of charged particles (mostly electrons and protons) surrounding the Earth in doughnut-shaped regions (Fig. 29.22). The particles, trapped by the Earth's nonuniform magnetic field, spiral around the field lines from pole to pole, covering the distance in just a few seconds. These particles originate mainly from the Sun, but some come from stars and other heavenly objects. For this reason, the particles are called *cosmic rays.* Most cosmic rays are deflected by the Earth's magnetic field and never reach the atmosphere. However, some of the particles become trapped; it is these particles that make up the Van Allen belts. When the particles are located over the poles, they sometimes collide with atoms in the atmosphere, causing the atoms to emit visible light. Such collisions are the origin of the beautiful Aurora Borealis, or Northern Lights, in the northern hemisphere and the Aurora Australis in the southern hemisphere. Auroras are usually confined to the polar regions because the Van Allen belts are nearest the Earth's surface there. Occasionally, though, solar activity causes larger numbers of charged particles to enter the belts and significantly distort the normal magnetic field lines associated with the Earth. In these situations an aurora can sometimes be seen at lower latitudes.

29.5 Applications Involving Charged Particles Moving in a Magnetic Field

A charge moving with a velocity **v** in the presence of both an electric field **E** and a magnetic field **B** experiences both an electric force $q\mathbf{E}$ and a magnetic force $q\mathbf{v} \times \mathbf{B}$. The total force (called the Lorentz force) acting on the charge is

Lorentz force

$$\mathbf{F} = q\mathbf{E} + q\mathbf{v} \times \mathbf{B} \qquad (29.16)$$

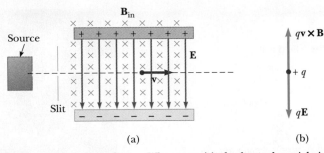

Active Figure 29.23 (a) A velocity selector. When a positively charged particle is moving with velocity **v** in the presence of a magnetic field directed into the page and an electric field directed downward, it experiences a downward electric force $q\mathbf{E}$ and an upward magnetic force $q\mathbf{v} \times \mathbf{B}$. (b) When these forces balance, the particle moves in a horizontal line through the fields.

At the Active Figures link at http://www.pse6.com, *you can adjust the electric and magnetic fields to try to achieve straight line motion for the charge.*

Velocity Selector

In many experiments involving moving charged particles, it is important that the particles all move with essentially the same velocity. This can be achieved by applying a combination of an electric field and a magnetic field oriented as shown in Figure 29.23. A uniform electric field is directed vertically downward (in the plane of the page in Fig. 29.23a), and a uniform magnetic field is applied in the direction perpendicular to the electric field (into the page in Fig. 29.23a). If q is positive and the velocity **v** is to the right, the magnetic force $q\mathbf{v} \times \mathbf{B}$ is upward and the electric force $q\mathbf{E}$ is downward. When the magnitudes of the two fields are chosen so that $qE = qvB$, the particle moves in a straight horizontal line through the region of the fields. From the expression $qE = qvB$, we find that

$$v = \frac{E}{B} \tag{29.17}$$

Only those particles having speed v pass undeflected through the mutually perpendicular electric and magnetic fields. The magnetic force exerted on particles moving at speeds greater than this is stronger than the electric force, and the particles are deflected upward. Those moving at speeds less than this are deflected downward.

The Mass Spectrometer

A **mass spectrometer** separates ions according to their mass-to-charge ratio. In one version of this device, known as the *Bainbridge mass spectrometer,* a beam of ions first passes through a velocity selector and then enters a second uniform magnetic field $\mathbf{B}_0$ that has the same direction as the magnetic field in the selector (Fig. 29.24). Upon entering the second magnetic field, the ions move in a semicircle of radius r before striking a detector array at P. If the ions are positively charged, the beam deflects upward, as Figure 29.24 shows. If the ions are negatively charged, the beam deflects

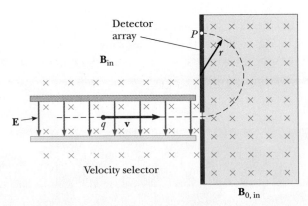

Active Figure 29.24 A mass spectrometer. Positively charged particles are sent first through a velocity selector and then into a region where the magnetic field $\mathbf{B}_0$ causes the particles to move in a semicircular path and strike a detector array at P.

At the Active Figures link at http://www.pse6.com, *you can predict where particles will strike the detector array.*

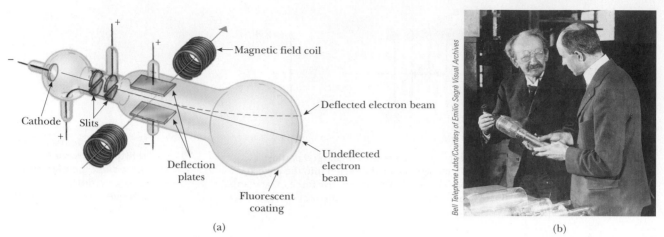

(a)

(b)

Figure 29.25 (a) Thomson's apparatus for measuring e/m_e. Electrons are accelerated from the cathode, pass through two slits, and are deflected by both an electric field and a magnetic field (directed perpendicular to the electric field). The beam of electrons then strikes a fluorescent screen. (b) J. J. Thomson (*left*) in the Cavendish Laboratory, University of Cambridge. The man on the right, Frank Baldwin Jewett, is a distant relative of John W. Jewett, Jr., co-author of this text.

downward. From Equation 29.13, we can express the ratio m/q as

$$\frac{m}{q} = \frac{rB_0}{v}$$

Using Equation 29.17, we find that

$$\frac{m}{q} = \frac{rB_0 B}{E} \tag{29.18}$$

Therefore, we can determine m/q by measuring the radius of curvature and knowing the field magnitudes B, B_0, and E. In practice, one usually measures the masses of various isotopes of a given ion, with the ions all carrying the same charge q. In this way, the mass ratios can be determined even if q is unknown.

A variation of this technique was used by J. J. Thomson (1856–1940) in 1897 to measure the ratio e/m_e for electrons. Figure 29.25a shows the basic apparatus he used. Electrons are accelerated from the cathode and pass through two slits. They then drift into a region of perpendicular electric and magnetic fields. The magnitudes of the two fields are first adjusted to produce an undeflected beam. When the magnetic field is turned off, the electric field produces a measurable beam deflection that is recorded on the fluorescent screen. From the size of the deflection and the measured values of E and B, the charge-to-mass ratio can be determined. The results of this crucial experiment represent the discovery of the electron as a fundamental particle of nature.

Quick Quiz 29.10 Three types of particles enter a mass spectrometer like the one shown in Figure 29.24. Figure 29.26 shows where the particles strike the detector array. Rank the particles that arrive at a, b, and c by speed and m/q ratio.

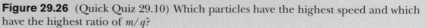

Gap for particles
from velocity
selector

a b c

Figure 29.26 (Quick Quiz 29.10) Which particles have the highest speed and which have the highest ratio of m/q?

The Cyclotron

A **cyclotron** is a device that can accelerate charged particles to very high speeds. The energetic particles produced are used to bombard atomic nuclei and thereby produce nuclear reactions of interest to researchers. A number of hospitals use cyclotron facilities to produce radioactive substances for diagnosis and treatment.

Both electric and magnetic forces have a key role in the operation of a cyclotron. A schematic drawing of a cyclotron is shown in Figure 29.27a. The charges move inside two semicircular containers D_1 and D_2, referred to as *dees*, because of their shape like the letter D. A high-frequency alternating potential difference is applied to the dees, and a uniform magnetic field is directed perpendicular to them. A positive ion released at P near the center of the magnet in one dee moves in a semicircular path (indicated by the dashed red line in the drawing) and arrives back at the gap in a time interval $T/2$, where T is the time interval needed to make one complete trip around the two dees, given by Equation 29.15. The frequency of the applied potential difference is adjusted so that the polarity of the dees is reversed in the same time interval during which the ion travels around one dee. If the applied potential difference is adjusted such that D_2 is at a lower electric potential than D_1 by an amount ΔV, the ion accelerates across the gap to D_2 and its kinetic energy increases by an amount $q\,\Delta V$. It then moves around D_2 in a semicircular path of greater radius (because its speed has increased). After a time interval $T/2$, it again arrives at the gap between the dees. By this time, the polarity across the dees has again been reversed, and the ion is given another "kick" across the gap. The motion continues so that for each half-circle trip around one dee, the ion gains additional kinetic energy equal to $q\,\Delta V$. When the radius of its path is nearly that of the dees, the energetic ion leaves the system through the exit slit. Note that the operation of the cyclotron is based on the fact that T is independent of the speed of the ion and of the radius of the circular path (Eq. 29.15).

We can obtain an expression for the kinetic energy of the ion when it exits the cyclotron in terms of the radius R of the dees. From Equation 29.13 we know that $v = qBR/m$. Hence, the kinetic energy is

$$K = \tfrac{1}{2}mv^2 = \frac{q^2 B^2 R^2}{2m} \tag{29.19}$$

When the energy of the ions in a cyclotron exceeds about 20 MeV, relativistic effects come into play. (Such effects are discussed in Chapter 39.) We observe that T increases and that the moving ions do not remain in phase with the applied potential

PITFALL PREVENTION

29.1 The Cyclotron Is Not State-of-the-Art Technology

The cyclotron is important historically because it was the first particle accelerator to achieve very high particle speeds. Cyclotrons are still in use in medical applications, but most accelerators currently in research use are not cyclotrons. Research accelerators work on a different principle and are generally called *synchrotrons*.

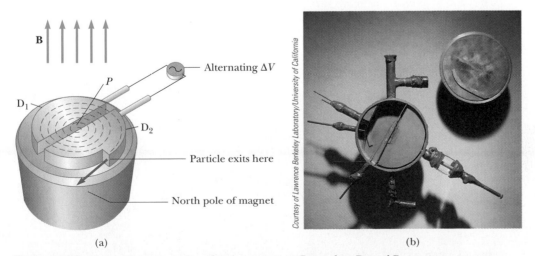

(a)   (b)

Figure 29.27 (a) A cyclotron consists of an ion source at P, two dees D_1 and D_2 across which an alternating potential difference is applied, and a uniform magnetic field. (The south pole of the magnet is not shown.) The red dashed curved lines represent the path of the particles. (b) The first cyclotron, invented by E. O. Lawrence and M. S. Livingston in 1934.

difference. Some accelerators overcome this problem by modifying the period of the applied potential difference so that it remains in phase with the moving ions.

29.6 The Hall Effect

When a current-carrying conductor is placed in a magnetic field, a potential difference is generated in a direction perpendicular to both the current and the magnetic field. This phenomenon, first observed by Edwin Hall (1855–1938) in 1879, is known as the *Hall effect*. It arises from the deflection of charge carriers to one side of the conductor as a result of the magnetic force they experience. The Hall effect gives information regarding the sign of the charge carriers and their density; it can also be used to measure the magnitude of magnetic fields.

The arrangement for observing the Hall effect consists of a flat conductor carrying a current I in the x direction, as shown in Figure 29.28. A uniform magnetic field $\mathbf{B}$ is applied in the y direction. If the charge carriers are electrons moving in the negative x direction with a drift velocity $\mathbf{v}_d$, they experience an upward magnetic force $\mathbf{F}_B = q\mathbf{v}_d \times \mathbf{B}$, are deflected upward, and accumulate at the upper edge of the flat conductor, leaving an excess of positive charge at the lower edge (Fig. 29.29a). This accumulation of charge at the edges establishes an electric field in the conductor and increases until the electric force on carriers remaining in the bulk of the conductor balances the magnetic force acting on the carriers. When this equilibrium condition is reached, the electrons are no longer deflected upward. A sensitive voltmeter or potentiometer connected across the sample, as shown in Figure 29.29, can measure the potential difference—known as the **Hall voltage** ΔV_{H}—generated across the conductor.

If the charge carriers are positive and hence move in the positive x direction (for rightward current), as shown in Figures 29.28 and 29.29b, they also experience an upward magnetic force $q\mathbf{v}_d \times \mathbf{B}$. This produces a buildup of positive charge on the upper edge and leaves an excess of negative charge on the lower edge. Hence, the sign of the Hall voltage generated in the sample is opposite the sign of the Hall voltage resulting from the deflection of electrons. The sign of the charge carriers can therefore be determined from a measurement of the polarity of the Hall voltage.

In deriving an expression for the Hall voltage, we first note that the magnetic force exerted on the carriers has magnitude qv_dB. In equilibrium, this force is balanced by the electric force qE_{H}, where E_{H} is the magnitude of the electric field due to the charge separation (sometimes referred to as the *Hall field*). Therefore,

$$qv_dB = qE_{\mathrm{H}}$$
$$E_{\mathrm{H}} = v_dB$$

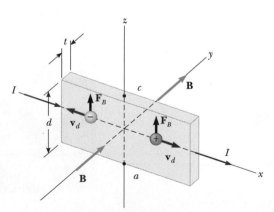

Figure 29.28 To observe the Hall effect, a magnetic field is applied to a current-carrying conductor. When I is in the x direction and $\mathbf{B}$ in the y direction, both positive and negative charge carriers are deflected upward in the magnetic field. The Hall voltage is measured between points a and c.

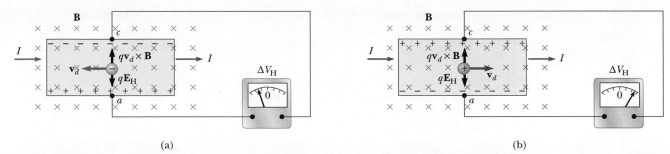

(a)   (b)

Figure 29.29 (a) When the charge carriers in a Hall-effect apparatus are negative, the upper edge of the conductor becomes negatively charged, and c is at a lower electric potential than a. (b) When the charge carriers are positive, the upper edge becomes positively charged, and c is at a higher potential than a. In either case, the charge carriers are no longer deflected when the edges become sufficiently charged that there is a balance on the charge carriers between the electrostatic force qE_H and the magnetic deflection force qvB.

If d is the width of the conductor, the Hall voltage is

$$\Delta V_H = E_H d = v_d B d \qquad (29.20)$$

Thus, the measured Hall voltage gives a value for the drift speed of the charge carriers if d and B are known.

We can obtain the charge carrier density n by measuring the current in the sample. From Equation 27.4, we can express the drift speed as

$$v_d = \frac{I}{nqA} \qquad (29.21)$$

where A is the cross-sectional area of the conductor. Substituting Equation 29.21 into Equation 29.20, we obtain

$$\Delta V_H = \frac{IBd}{nqA} \qquad (29.22)$$

Because $A = td$, where t is the thickness of the conductor, we can also express Equation 29.22 as

$$\Delta V_H = \frac{IB}{nqt} = \frac{R_H IB}{t} \qquad (29.23) \qquad \textbf{The Hall voltage}$$

where $R_H = 1/nq$ is the **Hall coefficient.** This relationship shows that a properly calibrated conductor can be used to measure the magnitude of an unknown magnetic field.

Because all quantities in Equation 29.23 other than nq can be measured, a value for the Hall coefficient is readily obtainable. The sign and magnitude of R_H give the sign of the charge carriers and their number density. In most metals, the charge carriers are electrons, and the charge-carrier density determined from Hall-effect measurements is in good agreement with calculated values for such metals as lithium (Li), sodium (Na), copper (Cu), and silver (Ag), whose atoms each give up one electron to act as a current carrier. In this case, n is approximately equal to the number of conducting electrons per unit volume. However, this classical model is not valid for metals such as iron (Fe), bismuth (Bi), and cadmium (Cd) or for semiconductors. These discrepancies can be explained only by using a model based on the quantum nature of solids.

An interesting medical application related to the Hall effect is the electromagnetic blood flowmeter, first developed in the 1950s and continually improved since then. Imagine that we replace the conductor in Figure 29.29 with an artery carrying blood. The blood contains charged ions that experience electric and magnetic forces like the charge carriers in the conductor. The speed of flow of these ions can be related to the volume rate of flow of blood. Solving Equation 29.20 for the speed v_d of the ions in the blood, we obtain

$$v_d = \frac{\Delta V_H}{Bd}$$

Thus, by measuring the voltage across the artery, the diameter of the artery, and the applied magnetic field, the speed of the blood can be calculated.

Example 29.8   The Hall Effect for Copper

A rectangular copper strip 1.5 cm wide and 0.10 cm thick carries a current of 5.0 A. Find the Hall voltage for a 1.2-T magnetic field applied in a direction perpendicular to the strip.

Solution If we assume that one electron per atom is available for conduction, we can take the charge carrier density to be 8.49×10^{28} electrons/m³ (see Example 27.1). Substituting this value and the given data into Equation 29.23 gives

$$\Delta V_H = \frac{IB}{nqt}$$

$$= \frac{(5.0 \text{ A})(1.2 \text{ T})}{(8.49 \times 10^{28} \text{ m}^{-3})(1.6 \times 10^{-19} \text{ C})(0.001\,0 \text{ m})}$$

$$\Delta V_H = \boxed{0.44 \ \mu\text{V}}$$

Such an extremely small Hall voltage is expected in good conductors. (Note that the width of the conductor is not needed in this calculation.)

What If? What if the strip has the same dimensions but is made of a semiconductor? Will the Hall voltage be smaller or larger?

Answer In semiconductors, n is much smaller than it is in metals that contribute one electron per atom to the current; hence, the Hall voltage is usually larger because it varies as the inverse of n. Currents on the order of 0.1 mA are generally used for such materials. Consider a piece of silicon that has the same dimensions as the copper strip in this example and whose value for n is 1.0×10^{20} electrons/m³. Taking $B = 1.2$ T and $I = 0.10$ mA, we find that $\Delta V_H = 7.5$ mV. A potential difference of this magnitude is readily measured.

SUMMARY

Take a practice test for this chapter by clicking on the Practice Test link at http://www.pse6.com.

The magnetic force that acts on a charge q moving with a velocity $\mathbf{v}$ in a magnetic field $\mathbf{B}$ is

$$\mathbf{F}_B = q\mathbf{v} \times \mathbf{B} \qquad (29.1)$$

The direction of this magnetic force is perpendicular both to the velocity of the particle and to the magnetic field. The magnitude of this force is

$$F_B = |q|vB \sin \theta \qquad (29.2)$$

where θ is the smaller angle between $\mathbf{v}$ and $\mathbf{B}$. The SI unit of $\mathbf{B}$ is the **tesla** (T), where $1 \text{ T} = 1 \text{ N/A} \cdot \text{m}$.

When a charged particle moves in a magnetic field, the work done by the magnetic force on the particle is zero because the displacement is always perpendicular to the direction of the force. The magnetic field can alter the direction of the particle's velocity vector, but it cannot change its speed.

If a straight conductor of length L carries a current I, the force exerted on that conductor when it is placed in a uniform magnetic field $\mathbf{B}$ is

$$\mathbf{F}_B = I\mathbf{L} \times \mathbf{B} \qquad (29.3)$$

where the direction of $\mathbf{L}$ is in the direction of the current and $|\mathbf{L}| = L$.

If an arbitrarily shaped wire carrying a current I is placed in a magnetic field, the magnetic force exerted on a very small segment $d\mathbf{s}$ is

$$d\mathbf{F}_B = I\,d\mathbf{s} \times \mathbf{B} \qquad (29.4)$$

To determine the total magnetic force on the wire, one must integrate Equation 29.4, keeping in mind that both $\mathbf{B}$ and $d\mathbf{s}$ may vary at each point. Integration gives for the force exerted on a current-carrying conductor of arbitrary shape in a uniform magnetic field

$$\mathbf{F}_B = I\mathbf{L}' \times \mathbf{B} \tag{29.7}$$

where $\mathbf{L}'$ is a vector directed from one end of the conductor to the opposite end. Because integration of Equation 29.4 for a closed loop yields a zero result, the net magnetic force on any closed loop carrying a current in a uniform magnetic field is zero.

The **magnetic dipole moment** $\boldsymbol{\mu}$ of a loop carrying a current I is

$$\boldsymbol{\mu} = I\mathbf{A} \tag{29.10}$$

where the area vector $\mathbf{A}$ is perpendicular to the plane of the loop and $|\mathbf{A}|$ is equal to the area of the loop. The SI unit of $\boldsymbol{\mu}$ is $\mathrm{A \cdot m^2}$.

The torque $\boldsymbol{\tau}$ on a current loop placed in a uniform magnetic field $\mathbf{B}$ is

$$\boldsymbol{\tau} = \boldsymbol{\mu} \times \mathbf{B} \tag{29.11}$$

The potential energy of the system of a magnetic dipole in a magnetic field is

$$U = -\boldsymbol{\mu} \cdot \mathbf{B} \tag{29.12}$$

If a charged particle moves in a uniform magnetic field so that its initial velocity is perpendicular to the field, the particle moves in a circle, the plane of which is perpendicular to the magnetic field. The radius of the circular path is

$$r = \frac{mv}{qB} \tag{29.13}$$

where m is the mass of the particle and q is its charge. The angular speed of the charged particle is

$$\omega = \frac{qB}{m} \tag{29.14}$$

QUESTIONS

1. At a given instant, a proton moves in the positive x direction through a magnetic field in the negative z direction. What is the direction of the magnetic force? Does the proton continue to move in the positive x direction? Explain.

2. Two charged particles are projected into a magnetic field perpendicular to their velocities. If the charges are deflected in opposite directions, what can you say about them?

3. If a charged particle moves in a straight line through some region of space, can you say that the magnetic field in that region is zero?

4. Suppose an electron is chasing a proton up this page when they suddenly enter a magnetic field perpendicular to the page. What happens to the particles?

5. How can the motion of a moving charged particle be used to distinguish between a magnetic field and an electric field? Give a specific example to justify your argument.

6. List several similarities and differences between electric and magnetic forces.

7. Justify the following statement: "It is impossible for a constant (in other words, a time-independent) magnetic field to alter the speed of a charged particle."

8. In view of your answer to Question 7, what is the role of a magnetic field in a cyclotron?

9. The electron beam in Figure Q29.9 is projected to the right. The beam deflects downward in the presence of a magnetic field produced by a pair of current-carrying coils. (a) What is the direction of the magnetic field? (b) What would happen to the beam if the magnetic field were reversed in direction?

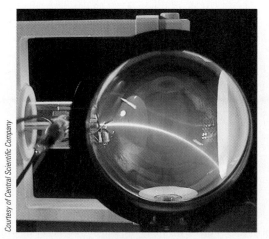

Courtesy of Central Scientific Company

Figure Q29.9

10. A current-carrying conductor experiences no magnetic force when placed in a certain manner in a uniform magnetic field. Explain.

11. Is it possible to orient a current loop in a uniform magnetic field such that the loop does not tend to rotate? Explain.

12. Explain why it is not possible to determine the charge and the mass of a charged particle separately by measuring accelerations produced by electric and magnetic forces on the particle.

13. How can a current loop be used to determine the presence of a magnetic field in a given region of space?

14. Charged particles from outer space, called cosmic rays, strike the Earth more frequently near the poles than near the equator. Why?

15. What is the net force on a compass needle in a uniform magnetic field?

16. What type of magnetic field is required to exert a resultant force on a magnetic dipole? What is the direction of the resultant force?

17. A proton moving horizontally enters a uniform magnetic field perpendicular to the proton's velocity, as shown in Figure Q29.17. Describe the subsequent motion of the proton. How would an electron behave under the same circumstances?

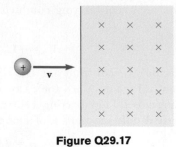

Figure Q29.17

18. In the cyclotron, why do particles having different speeds take the same amount of time to complete a one-half circle trip around one dee?

19. The *bubble chamber* is a device used for observing tracks of particles that pass through the chamber, which is immersed in a magnetic field. If some of the tracks are spirals and others are straight lines, what can you say about the particles?

20. Can a constant magnetic field set into motion an electron initially at rest? Explain your answer.

21. You are designing a magnetic probe that uses the Hall effect to measure magnetic fields. Assume that you are restricted to using a given material and that you have already made the probe as thin as possible. What, if anything, can be done to increase the Hall voltage produced for a given magnitude of magnetic field?

PROBLEMS

1, 2, 3 = straightforward, intermediate, challenging   ☐ = full solution available in the *Student Solutions Manual and Study Guide*

🌀 = coached solution with hints available at http://www.pse6.com   💻 = computer useful in solving problem

▨ = paired numerical and symbolic problems

Section 29.1   Magnetic Fields and Forces

1. 🌀 Determine the initial direction of the deflection of charged particles as they enter the magnetic fields as shown in Figure P29.1.

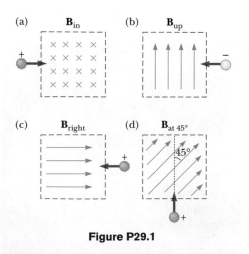

Figure P29.1

2. Consider an electron near the Earth's equator. In which direction does it tend to deflect if its velocity is directed (a) downward, (b) northward, (c) westward, or (d) southeastward?

3. An electron moving along the positive x axis perpendicular to a magnetic field experiences a magnetic deflection in the negative y direction. What is the direction of the magnetic field?

4. A proton travels with a speed of 3.00×10^6 m/s at an angle of $37.0°$ with the direction of a magnetic field of 0.300 T in the $+y$ direction. What are (a) the magnitude of the magnetic force on the proton and (b) its acceleration?

5. A proton moves perpendicular to a uniform magnetic field **B** at 1.00×10^7 m/s and experiences an acceleration of 2.00×10^{13} m/s^2 in the $+x$ direction when its velocity is in the $+z$ direction. Determine the magnitude and direction of the field.

6. An electron is accelerated through 2 400 V from rest and then enters a uniform 1.70-T magnetic field. What are (a) the maximum and (b) the minimum values of the magnetic force this charge can experience?

7. A proton moving at 4.00×10^6 m/s through a magnetic field of 1.70 T experiences a magnetic force of magnitude 8.20×10^{-13} N. What is the angle between the proton's velocity and the field?

8. At the equator, near the surface of the Earth, the magnetic field is approximately 50.0 μT northward, and the electric field is about 100 N/C downward in fair weather. Find the gravitational, electric, and magnetic forces on an electron in this environment, assuming the electron has an instantaneous velocity of 6.00×10^6 m/s directed to the east.

9. A proton moves with a velocity of $\mathbf{v} = (2\hat{\mathbf{i}} - 4\hat{\mathbf{j}} + \hat{\mathbf{k}})$ m/s in a region in which the magnetic field is $\mathbf{B} = (\hat{\mathbf{i}} + 2\hat{\mathbf{j}} - 3\hat{\mathbf{k}})$ T. What is the magnitude of the magnetic force this charge experiences?

10. An electron has a velocity of 1.20×10^4 m/s (in the positive x direction), and an acceleration of 2.00×10^{12} m/s^2 (in the positive z direction) in a uniform electric and magnetic field. If the electric field has a magnitude of 20.0 N/C (in the positive z direction), what can you determine about the magnetic field in the region? What can you not determine?

Section 29.2 Magnetic Force Acting on a Current-Carrying Conductor

11. A wire having a mass per unit length of 0.500 g/cm carries a 2.00-A current horizontally to the south. What are the direction and magnitude of the minimum magnetic field needed to lift this wire vertically upward?

12. A wire carries a steady current of 2.40 A. A straight section of the wire is 0.750 m long and lies along the x axis within a uniform magnetic field, $\mathbf{B} = 1.60\hat{\mathbf{k}}$ T. If the current is in the $+x$ direction, what is the magnetic force on the section of wire?

13. A wire 2.80 m in length carries a current of 5.00 A in a region where a uniform magnetic field has a magnitude of 0.390 T. Calculate the magnitude of the magnetic force on the wire assuming the angle between the magnetic field and the current is (a) 60.0°, (b) 90.0°, (c) 120°.

14. A conductor suspended by two flexible wires as shown in Figure P29.14 has a mass per unit length of 0.040 0 kg/m. What current must exist in the conductor in order for the tension in the supporting wires to be zero when the magnetic field is 3.60 T into the page? What is the required direction for the current?

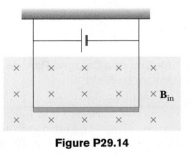

Figure P29.14

15. **Review Problem.** A rod of mass 0.720 kg and radius 6.00 cm rests on two parallel rails (Fig. P29.15) that are $d = 12.0$ cm apart and $L = 45.0$ cm long. The rod carries a current of $I = 48.0$ A (in the direction shown) and rolls along the rails without slipping. A uniform magnetic field

of magnitude 0.240 T is directed perpendicular to the rod and the rails. If it starts from rest, what is the speed of the rod as it leaves the rails?

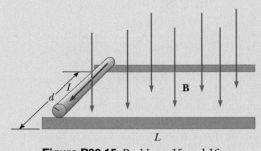

Figure P29.15 Problems 15 and 16.

16. **Review Problem.** A rod of mass m and radius R rests on two parallel rails (Fig. P29.15) that are a distance d apart and have a length L. The rod carries a current I (in the direction shown) and rolls along the rails without slipping. A uniform magnetic field B is directed perpendicular to the rod and the rails. If it starts from rest, what is the speed of the rod as it leaves the rails?

17. *A nonuniform magnetic field exerts a net force on a magnetic dipole.* A strong magnet is placed under a horizontal conducting ring of radius r that carries current I as shown in Figure P29.17. If the magnetic field $\mathbf{B}$ makes an angle θ with the vertical at the ring's location, what are the magnitude and direction of the resultant force on the ring?

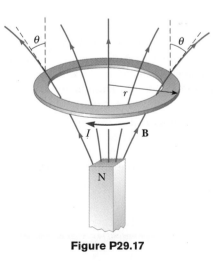

Figure P29.17

18. In Figure P29.18, the cube is 40.0 cm on each edge. Four straight segments of wire—ab, bc, cd, and da—form a closed loop that carries a current $I = 5.00$ A, in the direction shown. A uniform magnetic field of magnitude $B = 0.020\,0$ T is in the positive y direction. Determine the magnitude and direction of the magnetic force on each segment.

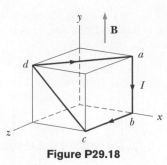

Figure P29.18

19. Assume that in Atlanta, Georgia, the Earth's magnetic field is 52.0 μT northward at 60.0° below the horizontal. A tube in a neon sign carries current 35.0 mA, between two diagonally opposite corners of a shop window, which lies in a north–south vertical plane. The current enters the tube at the bottom south corner of the window. It exits at the opposite corner, which is 1.40 m farther north and 0.850 m higher up. Between these two points, the glowing tube spells out DONUTS. Use the theorem proved as Case 1 in the text to determine the total vector magnetic force on the tube.

Section 29.3   Torque on a Current Loop in a Uniform Magnetic Field

20. A current of 17.0 mA is maintained in a single circular loop of 2.00 m circumference. A magnetic field of 0.800 T is directed parallel to the plane of the loop. (a) Calculate the magnetic moment of the loop. (b) What is the magnitude of the torque exerted by the magnetic field on the loop?

21. A small bar magnet is suspended in a uniform 0.250-T magnetic field. The maximum torque experienced by the bar magnet is 4.60×10^{-3} N·m. Calculate the magnetic moment of the bar magnet.

22. A long piece of wire with a mass of 0.100 kg and a total length of 4.00 m is used to make a square coil with a side of 0.100 m. The coil is hinged along a horizontal side, carries a 3.40-A current, and is placed in a vertical magnetic field with a magnitude of 0.010 0 T. (a) Determine the angle that the plane of the coil makes with the vertical when the coil is in equilibrium. (b) Find the torque acting on the coil due to the magnetic force at equilibrium.

23. A rectangular coil consists of $N = 100$ closely wrapped turns and has dimensions $a = 0.400$ m and $b = 0.300$ m. The coil is hinged along the y axis, and its plane makes an angle $\theta = 30.0°$ with the x axis (Fig. P29.23). What is the

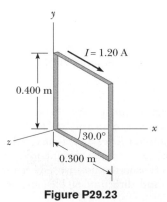

Figure P29.23

magnitude of the torque exerted on the coil by a uniform magnetic field $B = 0.800$ T directed along the x axis when the current is $I = 1.20$ A in the direction shown? What is the expected direction of rotation of the coil?

24. A 40.0-cm length of wire carries a current of 20.0 A. It is bent into a loop and placed with its normal perpendicular to a magnetic field with a magnitude of 0.520 T. What is the torque on the loop if it is bent into (a) an equilateral triangle? **What If?** What is the torque if the loop is (b) a square or (c) a circle? (d) Which torque is greatest?

25. A current loop with magnetic dipole moment $\boldsymbol{\mu}$ is placed in a uniform magnetic field **B**, with its moment making angle θ with the field. With the arbitrary choice of $U = 0$ for $\theta = 90°$, prove that the potential energy of the dipole–field system is $U = -\boldsymbol{\mu} \cdot \mathbf{B}$. You may imitate the discussion in Chapter 26 of the potential energy of an electric dipole in an electric field.

26. The needle of a magnetic compass has magnetic moment 9.70 mA·m². At its location, the Earth's magnetic field is 55.0 μT north at 48.0° below the horizontal. (a) Identify the orientations of the compass needle that represent minimum potential energy and maximum potential energy of the needle–field system. (b) How much work must be done on the needle to move it from the former to the latter orientation?

27. A wire is formed into a circle having a diameter of 10.0 cm and placed in a uniform magnetic field of 3.00 mT. The wire carries a current of 5.00 A. Find (a) the maximum torque on the wire and (b) the range of potential energies of the wire–field system for different orientations of the circle.

28. The rotor in a certain electric motor is a flat rectangular coil with 80 turns of wire and dimensions 2.50 cm by 4.00 cm. The rotor rotates in a uniform magnetic field of 0.800 T. When the plane of the rotor is perpendicular to the direction of the magnetic field, it carries a current of 10.0 mA. In this orientation, the magnetic moment of the rotor is directed opposite the magnetic field. The rotor then turns through one-half revolution. This process is repeated to cause the rotor to turn steadily at 3 600 rev/min. (a) Find the maximum torque acting on the rotor. (b) Find the peak power output of the motor. (c) Determine the amount of work performed by the magnetic field on the rotor in every full revolution. (d) What is the average power of the motor?

Section 29.4   Motion of a Charged Particle in a Uniform Magnetic Field

29. The magnetic field of the Earth at a certain location is directed vertically downward and has a magnitude of 50.0 μT. A proton is moving horizontally toward the west in this field with a speed of 6.20×10^6 m/s. (a) What are the direction and magnitude of the magnetic force the field exerts on this charge? (b) What is the radius of the circular arc followed by this proton?

30. A singly charged positive ion has a mass of 3.20×10^{-26} kg. After being accelerated from rest through a potential difference of 833 V, the ion enters a magnetic field of 0.920 T along a direction perpendicular to the direction

of the field. Calculate the radius of the path of the ion in the field.

31. **Review Problem.** One electron collides elastically with a second electron initially at rest. After the collision, the radii of their trajectories are 1.00 cm and 2.40 cm. The trajectories are perpendicular to a uniform magnetic field of magnitude 0.044 0 T. Determine the energy (in keV) of the incident electron.

32. A proton moving in a circular path perpendicular to a constant magnetic field takes 1.00 μs to complete one revolution. Determine the magnitude of the magnetic field.

33. A proton (charge $+ e$, mass m_p), a deuteron (charge $+ e$, mass $2m_p$), and an alpha particle (charge $+ 2e$, mass $4m_p$) are accelerated through a common potential difference ΔV. Each of the particles enters a uniform magnetic field $\mathbf{B}$, with its velocity in a direction perpendicular to $\mathbf{B}$. The proton moves in a circular path of radius r_p. Determine the radii of the circular orbits for the deuteron, r_d, and the alpha particle, r_α, in terms of r_p.

34. **Review Problem.** An electron moves in a circular path perpendicular to a constant magnetic field of magnitude 1.00 mT. The angular momentum of the electron about the center of the circle is 4.00×10^{-25} J·s. Determine (a) the radius of the circular path and (b) the speed of the electron.

35. Calculate the cyclotron frequency of a proton in a magnetic field of magnitude 5.20 T.

36. A singly charged ion of mass m is accelerated from rest by a potential difference ΔV. It is then deflected by a uniform magnetic field (perpendicular to the ion's velocity) into a semicircle of radius R. Now a doubly charged ion of mass m' is accelerated through the same potential difference and deflected by the same magnetic field into a semicircle of radius $R' = 2R$. What is the ratio of the masses of the ions?

37. A cosmic-ray proton in interstellar space has an energy of 10.0 MeV and executes a circular orbit having a radius equal to that of Mercury's orbit around the Sun (5.80 $\times$ 10^{10} m). What is the magnetic field in that region of space?

38. Figure 29.21 shows a charged particle traveling in a nonuniform magnetic field forming a magnetic bottle. (a) Explain why the positively charged particle in the figure must be moving clockwise. The particle travels along a helix whose radius decreases and whose pitch decreases as the particle moves into a stronger magnetic field. If the particle is moving to the right along the x axis, its velocity in this direction will be reduced to zero and it will be reflected from the right-hand side of the bottle, acting as a "magnetic mirror." The particle ends up bouncing back and forth between the ends of the bottle. (b) Explain qualitatively why the axial velocity is reduced to zero as the particle moves into the region of strong magnetic field at the end of the bottle. (c) Explain why the tangential velocity increases as the particle approaches the end of the bottle. (d) Explain why the orbiting particle has a magnetic dipole moment. (e) Sketch the magnetic moment and use the result of Problem 17 to explain again how the nonuniform magnetic field exerts a force on the orbiting particle along the x axis.

39. A singly charged positive ion moving at 4.60×10^5 m/s leaves a circular track of radius 7.94 mm along a direction perpendicular to the 1.80-T magnetic field of a bubble chamber. Compute the mass (in atomic mass units) of this ion, and, from that value, identify it.

Section 29.5 Applications Involving Charged Particles Moving in a Magnetic Field

40. A velocity selector consists of electric and magnetic fields described by the expressions $\mathbf{E} = E\hat{\mathbf{k}}$ and $\mathbf{B} = B\hat{\mathbf{j}}$, with $B = 15.0$ mT. Find the value of E such that a 750-eV electron moving along the positive x axis is undeflected.

41. Singly charged uranium-238 ions are accelerated through a potential difference of 2.00 kV and enter a uniform magnetic field of 1.20 T directed perpendicular to their velocities. (a) Determine the radius of their circular path. (b) Repeat for uranium-235 ions. **What If?** How does the ratio of these path radii depend on the accelerating voltage and on the magnitude of the magnetic field?

42. Consider the mass spectrometer shown schematically in Figure 29.24. The magnitude of the electric field between the plates of the velocity selector is 2 500 V/m, and the magnetic field in both the velocity selector and the deflection chamber has a magnitude of 0.035 0 T. Calculate the radius of the path for a singly charged ion having a mass $m = 2.18 \times 10^{-26}$ kg.

43. A cyclotron designed to accelerate protons has a magnetic field of magnitude 0.450 T over a region of radius 1.20 m. What are (a) the cyclotron frequency and (b) the maximum speed acquired by the protons?

44. What is the required radius of a cyclotron designed to accelerate protons to energies of 34.0 MeV using a magnetic field of 5.20 T?

45. A cyclotron designed to accelerate protons has an outer radius of 0.350 m. The protons are emitted nearly at rest from a source at the center and are accelerated through 600 V each time they cross the gap between the dees. The dees are between the poles of an electromagnet where the field is 0.800 T. (a) Find the cyclotron frequency. (b) Find the speed at which protons exit the cyclotron and (c) their maximum kinetic energy. (d) How many revolutions does a proton make in the cyclotron? (e) For what time interval does one proton accelerate?

46. At the Fermilab accelerator in Batavia, Illinois, protons having momentum 4.80×10^{-16} kg·m/s are held in a circular orbit of radius 1.00 km by an upward magnetic field. What is the magnitude of this field?

47. The picture tube in a television uses magnetic deflection coils rather than electric deflection plates. Suppose an electron beam is accelerated through a 50.0-kV potential difference and then through a region of uniform magnetic field 1.00 cm wide. The screen is located 10.0 cm from the center of the coils and is 50.0 cm wide. When the field is turned off, the electron beam hits the center of the screen. What field magnitude is necessary to deflect the beam to the side of the screen? Ignore relativistic corrections.

Section 29.6 The Hall Effect

48. A flat ribbon of silver having a thickness $t = 0.200$ mm is used in a Hall-effect measurement of a uniform magnetic field perpendicular to the ribbon, as shown in Figure P29.48. The Hall coefficient for silver is $R_H = 0.840 \times 10^{-10}$ m^3/C. (a) What is the density of charge carriers in silver? (b) If a current $I = 20.0$ A produces a Hall voltage $\Delta V_H = 15.0$ μV, what is the magnitude of the applied magnetic field?

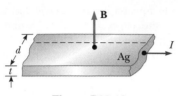

Figure P29.48

49. A flat copper ribbon 0.330 mm thick carries a steady current of 50.0 A and is located in a uniform 1.30-T magnetic field directed perpendicular to the plane of the ribbon. If a Hall voltage of 9.60 μV is measured across the ribbon, what is the charge density of the free electrons? What effective number of free electrons per atom does this result indicate?

50. A Hall-effect probe operates with a 120-mA current. When the probe is placed in a uniform magnetic field of magnitude 0.080 0 T, it produces a Hall voltage of 0.700 μV. (a) When it is measuring an unknown magnetic field, the Hall voltage is 0.330 μV. What is the magnitude of the unknown field? (b) The thickness of the probe in the direction of **B** is 2.00 mm. Find the density of the charge carriers, each of which has charge of magnitude e.

51. In an experiment that is designed to measure the Earth's magnetic field using the Hall effect, a copper bar 0.500 cm thick is positioned along an east–west direction. If a current of 8.00 A in the conductor results in a Hall voltage of 5.10×10^{-12} V, what is the magnitude of the Earth's magnetic field? (Assume that $n = 8.49 \times 10^{28}$ electrons/m^3 and that the plane of the bar is rotated to be perpendicular to the direction of **B**.)

Additional Problems

52. Assume that the region to the right of a certain vertical plane contains a vertical magnetic field of magnitude 1.00 mT, and the field is zero in the region to the left of the plane. An electron, originally traveling perpendicular to the boundary plane, passes into the region of the field. (a) Determine the time interval required for the electron to leave the "field-filled" region, noting that its path is a semicircle. (b) Find the kinetic energy of the electron if the maximum depth of penetration into the field is 2.00 cm.

53. Sodium melts at 99°C. Liquid sodium, an excellent thermal conductor, is used in some nuclear reactors to cool the reactor core. The liquid sodium is moved through pipes by pumps that exploit the force on a moving charge in a magnetic field. The principle is as follows. Assume the liquid metal to be in an electrically insulating pipe having a rectangular cross section of width w and height h. A uniform magnetic field perpendicular to the pipe affects a section of length L (Fig. P29.53). An electric current directed perpendicular to the pipe and to the magnetic field produces a current density J in the liquid sodium. (a) Explain why this arrangement produces on the liquid a force that is directed along the length of the pipe. (b) Show that the section of liquid in the magnetic field experiences a pressure increase JLB.

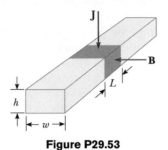

Figure P29.53

54. A 0.200-kg metal rod carrying a current of 10.0 A glides on two horizontal rails 0.500 m apart. What vertical magnetic field is required to keep the rod moving at a constant speed if the coefficient of kinetic friction between the rod and rails is 0.100?

55. Protons having a kinetic energy of 5.00 MeV are moving in the positive x direction and enter a magnetic field $\mathbf{B} = 0.050\ 0\hat{\mathbf{k}}$ T directed out of the plane of the page and extending from $x = 0$ to $x = 1.00$ m, as shown in Figure P29.55. (a) Calculate the y component of the protons' momentum as they leave the magnetic field. (b) Find the angle α between the initial velocity vector of the proton beam and the velocity vector after the beam emerges from the field. Ignore relativistic effects and note that 1 eV $= 1.60 \times 10^{-19}$ J.

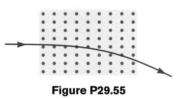

Figure P29.55

56. (a) A proton moving in the $+x$ direction with velocity $\mathbf{v} = v_i\hat{\mathbf{i}}$ experiences a magnetic force $\mathbf{F} = F_i\hat{\mathbf{j}}$ in the $+y$ direction. Explain what you can and cannot infer about **B** from this information. (b) **What If?** In terms of F_i, what would be the force on a proton in the same field moving with velocity $\mathbf{v} = -v_i\hat{\mathbf{i}}$? (c) What would be the force on an electron in the same field moving with velocity $\mathbf{v} = v_i\hat{\mathbf{i}}$?

57. A positive charge $q = 3.20 \times 10^{-19}$ C moves with a velocity $\mathbf{v} = (2\hat{\mathbf{i}} + 3\hat{\mathbf{j}} - \hat{\mathbf{k}})$ m/s through a region where both a uniform magnetic field and a uniform electric field exist. (a) Calculate the total force on the moving charge (in unit-vector notation), taking $\mathbf{B} = (2\hat{\mathbf{i}} + 4\hat{\mathbf{j}} + \hat{\mathbf{k}})$ T and $\mathbf{E} = (4\hat{\mathbf{i}} - \hat{\mathbf{j}} - 2\hat{\mathbf{k}})$ V/m. (b) What angle does the force vector make with the positive x axis?

58. **Review Problem.** A wire having a linear mass density of 1.00 g/cm is placed on a horizontal surface that has a coefficient of kinetic friction of 0.200. The wire carries a current of 1.50 A toward the east and slides horizontally to the north. What are the magnitude and direction of the smallest magnetic field that enables the wire to move in this fashion?

59. Electrons in a beam are accelerated from rest through a potential difference ΔV. The beam enters an experimental chamber through a small hole. As shown in Figure P29.59, the electron velocity vectors lie within a narrow cone of half angle ϕ oriented along the beam axis. We wish to use a uniform magnetic field directed parallel to the axis to focus the beam, so that all of the electrons can pass through a small exit port on the opposite side of the chamber after they travel the length d of the chamber. What is the required magnitude of the magnetic field? *Hint:* Because every electron passes through the same potential difference and the angle ϕ is small, they all require the same time interval to travel the axial distance d.

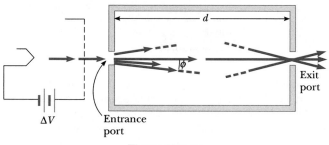

Figure P29.59

60. **Review Problem.** A proton is at rest at the plane vertical boundary of a region containing a uniform vertical magnetic field B. An alpha particle moving horizontally makes a head-on elastic collision with the proton. Immediately after the collision, both particles enter the magnetic field, moving perpendicular to the direction of the field. The radius of the proton's trajectory is R. Find the radius of the alpha particle's trajectory. The mass of the alpha particle is four times that of the proton, and its charge is twice that of the proton.

61. The circuit in Figure P29.61 consists of wires at the top and bottom and identical metal springs in the left and right sides. The upper portion of the circuit is fixed. The wire at the bottom has a mass of 10.0 g and is 5.00 cm

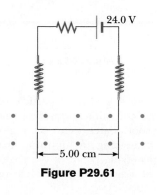

Figure P29.61

long. The springs stretch 0.500 cm under the weight of the wire and the circuit has a total resistance of 12.0 Ω. When a magnetic field is turned on, directed out of the page, the springs stretch an additional 0.300 cm. What is the magnitude of the magnetic field?

62. A hand-held electric mixer contains an electric motor. Model the motor as a single flat compact circular coil carrying electric current in a region where a magnetic field is produced by an external permanent magnet. You need consider only one instant in the operation of the motor. (We will consider motors again in Chapter 31.) The coil moves because the magnetic field exerts torque on the coil, as described in Section 29.3. Make order-of-magnitude estimates of the magnetic field, the torque on the coil, the current in it, its area, and the number of turns in the coil, so that they are related according to Equation 29.11. Note that the input power to the motor is electric, given by $\mathcal{P} = I \Delta V$, and the useful output power is mechanical, $\mathcal{P} = \tau \omega$.

63. A nonconducting sphere has mass 80.0 g and radius 20.0 cm. A flat compact coil of wire with 5 turns is wrapped tightly around it, with each turn concentric with the sphere. As shown in Figure P29.63, the sphere is placed on an inclined plane that slopes downward to the left, making an angle θ with the horizontal, so that the coil is parallel to the inclined plane. A uniform magnetic field of 0.350 T vertically upward exists in the region of the sphere. What current in the coil will enable the sphere to rest in equilibrium on the inclined plane? Show that the result does not depend on the value of θ.

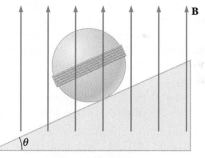

Figure P29.63

64. A metal rod having a mass per unit length λ carries a current I. The rod hangs from two vertical wires in a uniform vertical magnetic field as shown in Figure P29.64. The wires make an angle θ with the vertical when in equilibrium. Determine the magnitude of the magnetic field.

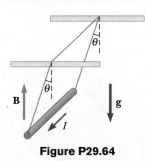

Figure P29.64

65. A cyclotron is sometimes used for carbon dating, as described in Chapter 44. Carbon-14 and carbon-12 ions are obtained from a sample of the material to be dated, and accelerated in the cyclotron. If the cyclotron has a magnetic field of magnitude 2.40 T, what is the difference in cyclotron frequencies for the two ions?

66. A uniform magnetic field of magnitude 0.150 T is directed along the positive x axis. A positron moving at 5.00×10^6 m/s enters the field along a direction that makes an angle of 85.0° with the x axis (Fig. P29.66). The motion of the particle is expected to be a helix, as described in Section 29.4. Calculate (a) the pitch p and (b) the radius r of the trajectory.

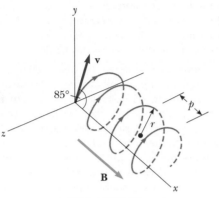

Figure P29.66

67. Consider an electron orbiting a proton and maintained in a fixed circular path of radius $R = 5.29 \times 10^{-11}$ m by the Coulomb force. Treating the orbiting charge as a current loop, calculate the resulting torque when the system is in a magnetic field of 0.400 T directed perpendicular to the magnetic moment of the electron.

68. A singly charged ion completes five revolutions in a uniform magnetic field of magnitude 5.00×10^{-2} T in 1.50 ms. Calculate the mass of the ion in kilograms.

69. A proton moving in the plane of the page has a kinetic energy of 6.00 MeV. A magnetic field of magnitude $B = 1.00$ T is directed into the page. The proton enters the magnetic field with its velocity vector at an angle $\theta = 45.0°$ to the linear boundary of the field as shown in Figure P29.69. (a) Find x, the distance from the point of entry to where the proton will leave the field. (b) Determine θ', the angle between the boundary and the proton's velocity vector as it leaves the field.

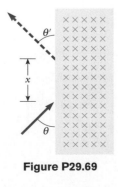

Figure P29.69

70. 💻 Table P29.70 shows measurements of a Hall voltage and corresponding magnetic field for a probe used to measure magnetic fields. (a) Plot these data, and deduce a relationship between the two variables. (b) If the measurements were taken with a current of 0.200 A and the sample is made from a material having a charge-carrier density of 1.00×10^{26}/m³, what is the thickness of the sample?

Table P29.70

ΔV_H (μV)	B (T)
0	0.00
11	0.10
19	0.20
28	0.30
42	0.40
50	0.50
61	0.60
68	0.70
79	0.80
90	0.90
102	1.00

71. A heart surgeon monitors the flow rate of blood through an artery using an electromagnetic flowmeter (Fig. P29.71). Electrodes A and B make contact with the outer surface of the blood vessel, which has interior diameter 3.00 mm. (a) For a magnetic field magnitude of 0.040 0 T, an emf of 160 μV appears between the electrodes. Calculate the speed of the blood. (b) Verify that electrode A is positive, as shown. Does the sign of the emf depend on whether the mobile ions in the blood are predominantly positively or negatively charged? Explain.

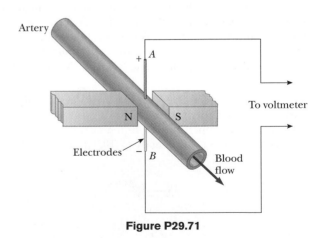

Figure P29.71

72. As shown in Figure P29.72, a particle of mass m having positive charge q is initially traveling with velocity $v\hat{\mathbf{j}}$. At the origin of coordinates it enters a region between $y = 0$ and $y = h$ containing a uniform magnetic field $B\hat{\mathbf{k}}$ directed perpendicularly out of the page. (a) What is the critical value of v such that the particle just reaches $y = h$?

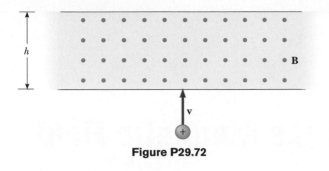

Figure P29.72

Describe the path of the particle under this condition, and predict its final velocity. (b) Specify the path the particle takes and its final velocity, if v is less than the critical value. (c) **What If?** Specify the path the particle takes and its final velocity if v is greater than the critical value.

Answers to Quick Quizzes

29.1 (c). The magnetic force exerted by a magnetic field on a charge is proportional to the charge's velocity relative to the field. If the charge is stationary, as in this situation, there is no magnetic force.

29.2 (b). The maximum value of $\sin \theta$ occurs for $\theta = 90°$.

29.3 (e). The right-hand rule gives the direction. Be sure to account for the negative charge on the electron.

29.4 (a), (b) = (c), (d). The magnitude of the force depends on the value of $\sin \theta$. The maximum force occurs when the wire is perpendicular to the field (a), and there is zero force when the wire is parallel (d). Choices (b) and (c) represent the same force because Case 1 tells us that a straight wire between A and B will have the same force on it as the curved wire.

29.5 (c). Use the right-hand rule to determine the direction of the magnetic field.

29.6 (c), (b), (a). Because all loops enclose the same area and carry the same current, the magnitude of $\boldsymbol{\mu}$ is the same for all. For (c), $\boldsymbol{\mu}$ points upward and is perpendicular to the magnetic field and $\tau = \mu B$, the maximum torque possible. For the loop in (a), $\boldsymbol{\mu}$ points along the direction of **B** and the torque is zero. For (b), the torque is intermediate between zero and the maximum value.

29.7 (a) = (b) = (c). Because the magnetic field is uniform, there is zero net force on all three loops.

29.8 (b). The magnetic force on the particle increases in proportion to v, but the centripetal acceleration increases according to the square of v. The result is a larger radius, as we can see from Equation 29.13.

29.9 (a). The magnetic force on the particle increases in proportion to B. The result is a smaller radius, as we can see from Equation 29.13.

29.10 Speed: (a) = (b) = (c). m/q ratio, from greatest to least: (c), (b), (a). The velocity selector ensures that all three types of particles have the same speed. We cannot determine individual masses or charges, but we can rank the particles by m/q ratio. Equation 29.18 indicates that those particles traveling through the circle of greatest radius have the greatest m/q ratio.

Chapter 30

Sources of the Magnetic Field

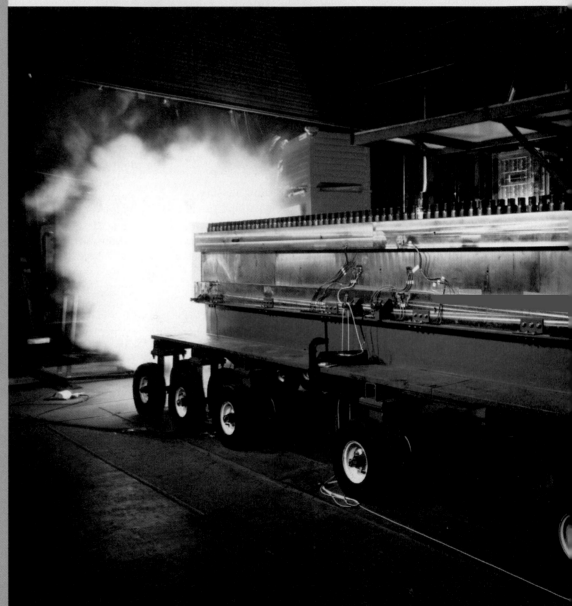

▲ A proposed method for launching future payloads into space is the use of rail guns, in which projectiles are accelerated by means of magnetic forces. This photo shows the firing of a projectile at a speed of over 3 km/s from an experimental rail gun at Sandia National Research Laboratories, Albuquerque, New Mexico. (Defense Threat Reduction Agency [DTRA])

In the preceding chapter, we discussed the magnetic force exerted on a charged particle moving in a magnetic field. To complete the description of the magnetic interaction, this chapter explores the origin of the magnetic field—moving charges. We begin by showing how to use the law of Biot and Savart to calculate the magnetic field produced at some point in space by a small current element. Using this formalism and the principle of superposition, we then calculate the total magnetic field due to various current distributions. Next, we show how to determine the force between two current-carrying conductors, which leads to the definition of the ampere. We also introduce Ampère's law, which is useful in calculating the magnetic field of a highly symmetric configuration carrying a steady current.

This chapter is also concerned with the complex processes that occur in magnetic materials. All magnetic effects in matter can be explained on the basis of atomic magnetic moments, which arise both from the orbital motion of electrons and from an intrinsic property of electrons known as spin.

30.1 The Biot–Savart Law

Shortly after Oersted's discovery in 1819 that a compass needle is deflected by a current-carrying conductor, Jean-Baptiste Biot (1774–1862) and Félix Savart (1791–1841) performed quantitative experiments on the force exerted by an electric current on a nearby magnet. From their experimental results, Biot and Savart arrived at a mathematical expression that gives the magnetic field at some point in space in terms of the current that produces the field. That expression is based on the following experimental observations for the magnetic field $d\mathbf{B}$ at a point P associated with a length element $d\mathbf{s}$ of a wire carrying a steady current I (Fig. 30.1):

- The vector $d\mathbf{B}$ is perpendicular both to $d\mathbf{s}$ (which points in the direction of the current) and to the unit vector $\hat{\mathbf{r}}$ directed from $d\mathbf{s}$ toward P.
- The magnitude of $d\mathbf{B}$ is inversely proportional to r^2, where r is the distance from $d\mathbf{s}$ to P.
- The magnitude of $d\mathbf{B}$ is proportional to the current and to the magnitude ds of the length element $d\mathbf{s}$.
- The magnitude of $d\mathbf{B}$ is proportional to $\sin \theta$, where θ is the angle between the vectors $d\mathbf{s}$ and $\hat{\mathbf{r}}$.

These observations are summarized in the mathematical expression known today as the **Biot–Savart law:**

$$d\mathbf{B} = \frac{\mu_0}{4\pi} \frac{I\, d\mathbf{s} \times \hat{\mathbf{r}}}{r^2}$$

(30.1)

Figure 30.1 The magnetic field $d\mathbf{B}$ at a point due to the current I through a length element $d\mathbf{s}$ is given by the Biot–Savart law. The direction of the field is out of the page at P and into the page at P'.

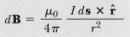 **PITFALL PREVENTION**

30.1 The Biot–Savart Law

The magnetic field described by the Biot–Savart law is the field *due to* a given current-carrying conductor. Do not confuse this field with any *external* field that may be applied to the conductor from some other source.

Biot–Savart law

where μ_0 is a constant called the **permeability of free space:**

$$\mu_0 = 4\pi \times 10^{-7}\ \text{T}\cdot\text{m/A} \tag{30.2}$$

Note that the field $d\mathbf{B}$ in Equation 30.1 is the field created by the current in only a small length element $d\mathbf{s}$ of the conductor. To find the *total* magnetic field $\mathbf{B}$ created at some point by a current of finite size, we must sum up contributions from all current elements $I\ d\mathbf{s}$ that make up the current. That is, we must evaluate $\mathbf{B}$ by integrating Equation 30.1:

$$\mathbf{B} = \frac{\mu_0 I}{4\pi} \int \frac{d\mathbf{s} \times \hat{\mathbf{r}}}{r^2} \tag{30.3}$$

where the integral is taken over the entire current distribution. This expression must be handled with special care because the integrand is a cross product and therefore a vector quantity. We shall see one case of such an integration in Example 30.1.

Although we developed the Biot–Savart law for a current-carrying wire, it is also valid for a current consisting of charges flowing through space, such as the electron beam in a television set. In that case, $d\mathbf{s}$ represents the length of a small segment of space in which the charges flow.

Interesting similarities exist between Equation 30.1 for the magnetic field due to a current element and Equation 23.9 for the electric field due to a point charge. The magnitude of the magnetic field varies as the inverse square of the distance from the source, as does the electric field due to a point charge. However, the directions of the two fields are quite different. The electric field created by a point charge is radial, but the magnetic field created by a current element is perpendicular to both the length element $d\mathbf{s}$ and the unit vector $\hat{\mathbf{r}}$, as described by the cross product in Equation 30.1. Hence, if the conductor lies in the plane of the page, as shown in Figure 30.1, $d\mathbf{B}$ points out of the page at P and into the page at P'.

Another difference between electric and magnetic fields is related to the source of the field. An electric field is established by an isolated electric charge. The Biot–Savart law gives the magnetic field of an isolated current element at some point, but such an isolated current element cannot exist the way an isolated electric charge can. A current element *must* be part of an extended current distribution because we must have a complete circuit in order for charges to flow. Thus, the Biot–Savart law (Eq. 30.1) is only the first step in a calculation of a magnetic field; it must be followed by an integration over the current distribution, as in Equation 30.3.

Quick Quiz 30.1 Consider the current in the length of wire shown in Figure 30.2. Rank the points A, B, and C, in terms of magnitude of the magnetic field due to the current in the length element shown, from greatest to least.

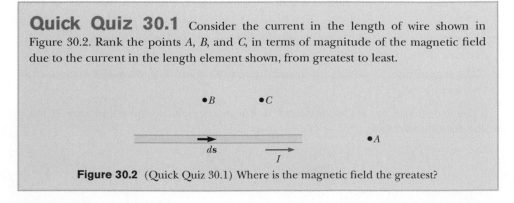

Figure 30.2 (Quick Quiz 30.1) Where is the magnetic field the greatest?

Example 30.1   Magnetic Field Surrounding a Thin, Straight Conductor   Interactive

Consider a thin, straight wire carrying a constant current I and placed along the x axis as shown in Figure 30.3. Determine the magnitude and direction of the magnetic field at point P due to this current.

Solution From the Biot–Savart law, we expect that the magnitude of the field is proportional to the current in the wire and decreases as the distance a from the wire to point P increases. We start by considering a length element $d\mathbf{s}$ located a distance r from P. The direction of the magnetic field at point P due to the current in this element is out of the page because $d\mathbf{s} \times \hat{\mathbf{r}}$ is out of the page. In fact, because *all* of the current elements $I\,d\mathbf{s}$ lie in the plane of the page, they all produce a magnetic field directed out of the page at point P. Thus, we have the direction of the magnetic field at point P, and we need only find the magnitude. Taking the origin at O and letting point P be along the positive y axis, with $\hat{\mathbf{k}}$ being a unit vector pointing out of the page, we see that

$$d\mathbf{s} \times \hat{\mathbf{r}} = |d\mathbf{s} \times \hat{\mathbf{r}}|\,\hat{\mathbf{k}} = (dx \sin \theta)\,\hat{\mathbf{k}}$$

where $|d\mathbf{s} \times \hat{\mathbf{r}}|$ represents the magnitude of $d\mathbf{s} \times \hat{\mathbf{r}}$. Because $\hat{\mathbf{r}}$ is a unit vector, the magnitude of the cross

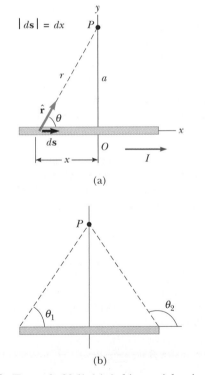

(a)

(b)

Figure 30.3 (Example 30.1) (a) A thin, straight wire carrying a current I. The magnetic field at point P due to the current in each element $d\mathbf{s}$ of the wire is out of the page, so the net field at point P is also out of the page. (b) The angles θ_1 and θ_2 used for determining the net field. When the wire is infinitely long, $\theta_1 = 0$ and $\theta_2 = 180°$.

product is simply the magnitude of $d\mathbf{s}$, which is the length dx. Substitution into Equation 30.1 gives

$$d\mathbf{B} = (dB)\hat{\mathbf{k}} = \frac{\mu_0 I}{4\pi}\frac{dx \sin \theta}{r^2}\,\hat{\mathbf{k}}$$

Because all current elements produce a magnetic field in the $\hat{\mathbf{k}}$ direction, let us restrict our attention to the magnitude of the field due to one current element, which is

$$(1) \qquad dB = \frac{\mu_0 I}{4\pi}\frac{dx \sin \theta}{r^2}$$

To integrate this expression, we must relate the variables θ, x, and r. One approach is to express x and r in terms of θ. From the geometry in Figure 30.3a, we have

$$(2) \qquad r = \frac{a}{\sin \theta} = a \csc \theta$$

Because $\tan \theta = a/(-x)$ from the right triangle in Figure 30.3a (the negative sign is necessary because $d\mathbf{s}$ is located at a negative value of x), we have

$$x = -a \cot \theta$$

Taking the derivative of this expression gives

$$(3) \qquad dx = a \csc^2 \theta\, d\theta$$

Substitution of Equations (2) and (3) into Equation (1) gives

$$(4) \qquad dB = \frac{\mu_0 I}{4\pi}\frac{a \csc^2 \theta \sin \theta\, d\theta}{a^2 \csc^2 \theta} = \frac{\mu_0 I}{4\pi a} \sin \theta\, d\theta$$

an expression in which the only variable is θ. We now obtain the magnitude of the magnetic field at point P by integrating Equation (4) over all elements, where the subtending angles range from θ_1 to θ_2 as defined in Figure 30.3b:

$$B = \frac{\mu_0 I}{4\pi a}\int_{\theta_1}^{\theta_2} \sin \theta\, d\theta = \frac{\mu_0 I}{4\pi a}(\cos \theta_1 - \cos \theta_2) \qquad (30.4)$$

We can use this result to find the magnetic field of *any* straight current-carrying wire if we know the geometry and hence the angles θ_1 and θ_2. Consider the special case of an infinitely long, straight wire. If we let the wire in Figure 30.3b become infinitely long, we see that $\theta_1 = 0$ and $\theta_2 = \pi$ for length elements ranging between positions $x = -\infty$ and $x = +\infty$. Because $(\cos \theta_1 - \cos \theta_2) = (\cos 0 - \cos \pi) = 2$, Equation 30.4 becomes

$$B = \frac{\mu_0 I}{2\pi a} \qquad (30.5)$$

Equations 30.4 and 30.5 both show that the magnitude of the magnetic field is proportional to the current and decreases with increasing distance from the wire, as we expected. Notice that Equation 30.5 has the same mathematical form as the expression for the magnitude of the electric field due to a long charged wire (see Eq. 24.7).

At the Interactive Worked Example link at **http://www.pse6.com,** *you can explore the field for different lengths of wire.*

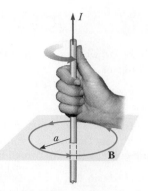

Figure 30.4 The right-hand rule for determining the direction of the magnetic field surrounding a long, straight wire carrying a current. Note that the magnetic field lines form circles around the wire.

The result of Example 30.1 is important because a current in the form of a long, straight wire occurs often. Figure 30.4 is a perspective view of the magnetic field surrounding a long, straight current-carrying wire. Because of the symmetry of the wire, the magnetic field lines are circles concentric with the wire and lie in planes perpendicular to the wire. The magnitude of **B** is constant on any circle of radius a and is given by Equation 30.5. A convenient rule for determining the direction of **B** is to grasp the wire with the right hand, positioning the thumb along the direction of the current. The four fingers wrap in the direction of the magnetic field.

Another observation we can make in Figure 30.4 is that the magnetic field line shown has no beginning and no end. It forms a closed loop. This is a major difference between magnetic field lines and electric field lines, which begin on positive charges and end on negative charges. We will explore this feature of magnetic field lines further in Section 30.6.

Example 30.2   Magnetic Field Due to a Curved Wire Segment

Calculate the magnetic field at point O for the current-carrying wire segment shown in Figure 30.5. The wire consists of two straight portions and a circular arc of radius R, which subtends an angle θ. The arrowheads on the wire indicate the direction of the current.

Solution The magnetic field at O due to the current in the straight segments AA' and CC' is zero because $d\mathbf{s}$ is parallel to $\hat{\mathbf{r}}$ along these paths; this means that $d\mathbf{s} \times \hat{\mathbf{r}} = 0$. Each length element $d\mathbf{s}$ along path AC is at the same distance R from O, and the current in each contributes a field element $d\mathbf{B}$ directed into the page at O. Furthermore, at every point on AC, $d\mathbf{s}$ is perpendicular to $\hat{\mathbf{r}}$; hence, $|d\mathbf{s} \times \hat{\mathbf{r}}| = ds$. Using this information and Equation 30.1, we can find the magnitude of the field at O due to the current in an ele-

ment of length ds:

$$dB = \frac{\mu_0 I}{4\pi} \frac{ds}{R^2}$$

Because I and R are constants in this situation, we can easily integrate this expression over the curved path AC:

$$B = \frac{\mu_0 I}{4\pi R^2} \int ds = \frac{\mu_0 I}{4\pi R^2} s = \frac{\mu_0 I}{4\pi R} \theta \qquad (30.6)$$

where we have used the fact that $s = R\theta$ with θ measured in radians. The direction of **B** is into the page at O because $d\mathbf{s} \times \hat{\mathbf{r}}$ is into the page for every length element.

What If? What if you were asked to find the magnetic field at the center of a circular wire loop of radius R that carries a current I? Can we answer this question at this point in our understanding of the source of magnetic fields?

Answer Yes, we can. We argued that the straight wires in Figure 30.5 do not contribute to the magnetic field. The only contribution is from the curved segment. If we imagine increasing the angle θ, the curved segment will become a full circle when $\theta = 2\pi$. Thus, we can find the magnetic field at the center of a wire loop by letting $\theta = 2\pi$ in Equation 30.6:

$$B = \frac{\mu_0 I}{4\pi R} 2\pi = \frac{\mu_0 I}{2R}$$

We will confirm this result as a limiting case of a more general result in Example 30.3.

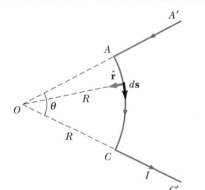

Figure 30.5 (Example 30.2) The magnetic field at O due to the current in the curved segment AC is into the page. The contribution to the field at O due to the current in the two straight segments is zero.

Example 30.3   Magnetic Field on the Axis of a Circular Current Loop   `Interactive`

Consider a circular wire loop of radius R located in the yz plane and carrying a steady current I, as in Figure 30.6. Calculate the magnetic field at an axial point P a distance x from the center of the loop.

Solution In this situation, every length element $d\mathbf{s}$ is perpendicular to the vector $\hat{\mathbf{r}}$ at the location of the element. Thus, for any element, $|d\mathbf{s} \times \hat{\mathbf{r}}| = (ds)(1)\sin 90° = ds$. Furthermore, all length elements around the loop are at the

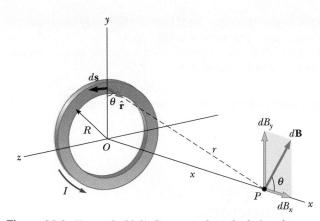

Figure 30.6 (Example 30.3) Geometry for calculating the magnetic field at a point P lying on the axis of a current loop. By symmetry, the total field **B** is along this axis.

same distance r from P, where $r^2 = x^2 + R^2$. Hence, the magnitude of $d\mathbf{B}$ due to the current in any length element $d\mathbf{s}$ is

$$dB = \frac{\mu_0 I}{4\pi} \frac{|d\mathbf{s} \times \hat{\mathbf{r}}|}{r^2} = \frac{\mu_0 I}{4\pi} \frac{ds}{(x^2 + R^2)}$$

The direction of $d\mathbf{B}$ is perpendicular to the plane formed by $\hat{\mathbf{r}}$ and $d\mathbf{s}$, as shown in Figure 30.6. We can resolve this vector into a component dB_x along the x axis and a component dB_y perpendicular to the x axis. When the components dB_y are summed over all elements around the loop, the resultant component is zero. That is, by symmetry the current in any element on one side of the loop sets up a perpendicular component of $d\mathbf{B}$ that cancels the perpendicular component set up by the current through the element diametrically opposite it. Therefore, *the resultant field at P must be along the x axis* and we can find it by integrating the components $dB_x = dB \cos \theta$. That is,

$\mathbf{B} = B_x \hat{\mathbf{i}}$ where

$$B_x = \oint dB \cos \theta = \frac{\mu_0 I}{4\pi} \oint \frac{ds \cos \theta}{x^2 + R^2}$$

and we must take the integral over the entire loop. Because θ, x, and R are constants for all elements of the loop and because $\cos \theta = R/(x^2 + R^2)^{1/2}$, we obtain

$$B_x = \frac{\mu_0 I R}{4\pi (x^2 + R^2)^{3/2}} \oint ds = \frac{\mu_0 I R^2}{2(x^2 + R^2)^{3/2}} \quad (30.7)$$

where we have used the fact that $\oint ds = 2\pi R$ (the circumference of the loop).

To find the magnetic field at the center of the loop, we set $x = 0$ in Equation 30.7. At this special point, therefore,

$$B = \frac{\mu_0 I}{2R} \quad \text{(at } x = 0) \quad (30.8)$$

which is consistent with the result of the **What If?** feature in Example 30.2.

The pattern of magnetic field lines for a circular current loop is shown in Figure 30.7a. For clarity, the lines are drawn for only one plane—one that contains the axis of the loop. Note that the field-line pattern is axially symmetric and looks like the pattern around a bar magnet, shown in Figure 30.7c.

What If? What if we consider points on the x axis very far from the loop? How does the magnetic field behave at these distant points?

Answer In this case, in which $x \gg R$, we can neglect the term R^2 in the denominator of Equation 30.7 and obtain

$$B \approx \frac{\mu_0 I R^2}{2x^3} \quad \text{(for } x \gg R) \quad (30.9)$$

Because the magnitude of the magnetic moment μ of the loop is defined as the product of current and loop area (see

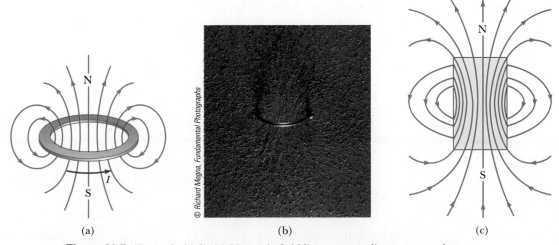

(a)   (b)   (c)

© Richard Megna, Fundamental Photographs

Figure 30.7 (Example 30.3) (a) Magnetic field lines surrounding a current loop. (b) Magnetic field lines surrounding a current loop, displayed with iron filings. (c) Magnetic field lines surrounding a bar magnet. Note the similarity between this line pattern and that of a current loop.

Eq. 29.10), $\mu = I(\pi R^2)$ for our circular loop. We can express Equation 30.9 as

$$B \approx \frac{\mu_0}{2\pi} \frac{\mu}{x^3} \qquad (30.10)$$

This result is similar in form to the expression for the electric field due to an electric dipole, $E = k_e(2qa/y^3)$ (see Example 23.6), where $2qa = p$ is the electric dipole moment as defined in Equation 26.16.

At the Interactive Worked Example link at **http://www.pse6.com,** *you can explore the field for different loop radii.*

30.2 The Magnetic Force Between Two Parallel Conductors

In Chapter 29 we described the magnetic force that acts on a current-carrying conductor placed in an external magnetic field. Because a current in a conductor sets up its own magnetic field, it is easy to understand that two current-carrying conductors exert magnetic forces on each other. Such forces can be used as the basis for defining the ampere and the coulomb.

Consider two long, straight, parallel wires separated by a distance a and carrying currents I_1 and I_2 in the same direction, as in Figure 30.8. We can determine the force exerted on one wire due to the magnetic field set up by the other wire. Wire 2, which carries a current I_2 and is identified arbitrarily as the source wire, creates a magnetic field $\mathbf{B}_2$ at the location of wire 1, the test wire. The direction of $\mathbf{B}_2$ is perpendicular to wire 1, as shown in Figure 30.8. According to Equation 29.3, the magnetic force on a length ℓ of wire 1 is $\mathbf{F}_1 = I_1\boldsymbol{\ell} \times \mathbf{B}_2$. Because $\boldsymbol{\ell}$ is perpendicular to $\mathbf{B}_2$ in this situation, the magnitude of $\mathbf{F}_1$ is $F_1 = I_1\ell B_2$. Because the magnitude of $\mathbf{B}_2$ is given by Equation 30.5, we see that

$$F_1 = I_1\ell B_2 = I_1\ell \left(\frac{\mu_0 I_2}{2\pi a}\right) = \frac{\mu_0 I_1 I_2}{2\pi a}\ell \qquad (30.11)$$

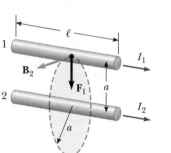

Active Figure 30.8 Two parallel wires that each carry a steady current exert a magnetic force on each other. The field $\mathbf{B}_2$ due to the current in wire 2 exerts a magnetic force of magnitude $F_1 = I_1\ell B_2$ on wire 1. The force is attractive if the currents are parallel (as shown) and repulsive if the currents are antiparallel.

At the Active Figures link at **http://www.pse6.com,** *you can adjust the currents in the wires and the distance between them to see the effect on the force.*

The direction of $\mathbf{F}_1$ is toward wire 2 because $\boldsymbol{\ell} \times \mathbf{B}_2$ is in that direction. If the field set up at wire 2 by wire 1 is calculated, the force $\mathbf{F}_2$ acting on wire 2 is found to be equal in magnitude and opposite in direction to $\mathbf{F}_1$. This is what we expect because Newton's third law must be obeyed.[1] When the currents are in opposite directions (that is, when one of the currents is reversed in Fig. 30.8), the forces are reversed and the wires repel each other. Hence, **parallel conductors carrying currents in the same direction attract each other, and parallel conductors carrying currents in opposite directions repel each other.**

Because the magnitudes of the forces are the same on both wires, we denote the magnitude of the magnetic force between the wires as simply F_B. We can rewrite this magnitude in terms of the force per unit length:

$$\frac{F_B}{\ell} = \frac{\mu_0 I_1 I_2}{2\pi a} \qquad (30.12)$$

The force between two parallel wires is used to define the **ampere** as follows:

Definition of the ampere

When the magnitude of the force per unit length between two long parallel wires that carry identical currents and are separated by 1 m is 2×10^{-7} N/m, the current in each wire is defined to be 1 A.

[1] Although the total force exerted on wire 1 is equal in magnitude and opposite in direction to the total force exerted on wire 2, Newton's third law does not apply when one considers two small elements of the wires that are not exactly opposite each other. This apparent violation of Newton's third law and of the law of conservation of momentum is described in more advanced treatments on electricity and magnetism.

The value 2×10^{-7} N/m is obtained from Equation 30.12 with $I_1 = I_2 = 1$ A and $a = 1$ m. Because this definition is based on a force, a mechanical measurement can be used to standardize the ampere. For instance, the National Institute of Standards and Technology uses an instrument called a *current balance* for primary current measurements. The results are then used to standardize other, more conventional instruments, such as ammeters.

The SI unit of charge, the **coulomb,** is defined in terms of the ampere:

> When a conductor carries a steady current of 1 A, the quantity of charge that flows through a cross section of the conductor in 1 s is 1 C.

In deriving Equations 30.11 and 30.12, we assumed that both wires are long compared with their separation distance. In fact, only one wire needs to be long. The equations accurately describe the forces exerted on each other by a long wire and a straight parallel wire of limited length ℓ.

Quick Quiz 30.2 For $I_1 = 2$ A and $I_2 = 6$ A in Figure 30.8, which is true: (a) $F_1 = 3F_2$, (b) $F_1 = F_2/3$, (c) $F_1 = F_2$?

Quick Quiz 30.3 A loose spiral spring carrying no current is hung from the ceiling. When a switch is thrown so that a current exists in the spring, do the coils move (a) closer together, (b) farther apart, or (c) do they not move at all?

30.3 Ampère's Law

Oersted's 1819 discovery about deflected compass needles demonstrates that a current-carrying conductor produces a magnetic field. Figure 30.9a shows how this effect can be demonstrated in the classroom. Several compass needles are placed in a horizontal plane near a long vertical wire. When no current is

Andre-Marie Ampère
French Physicist (1775–1836)

Ampère is credited with the discovery of electromagnetism—the relationship between electric currents and magnetic fields. Ampère's genius, particularly in mathematics, became evident by the time he was 12 years old; his personal life, however, was filled with tragedy. His father, a wealthy city official, was guillotined during the French Revolution, and his wife died young, in 1803. Ampère died at the age of 61 of pneumonia. His judgment of his life is clear from the epitaph he chose for his gravestone: *Tandem Felix* (Happy at Last). *(Leonard de Selva/CORBIS)*

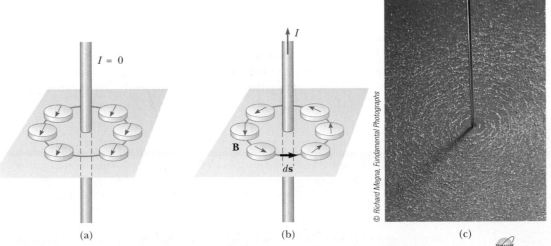

Active Figure 30.9 (a) When no current is present in the wire, all compass needles point in the same direction (toward the Earth's north pole). (b) When the wire carries a strong current, the compass needles deflect in a direction tangent to the circle, which is the direction of the magnetic field created by the current. (c) Circular magnetic field lines surrounding a current-carrying conductor, displayed with iron filings.

At the Active Figures link at http://www.pse6.com, you can change the value of the current to see the effect on the compasses.

present in the wire, all the needles point in the same direction (that of the Earth's magnetic field), as expected. When the wire carries a strong, steady current, the needles all deflect in a direction tangent to the circle, as in Figure 30.9b. These observations demonstrate that the direction of the magnetic field produced by the current in the wire is consistent with the right-hand rule described in Figure 30.4. When the current is reversed, the needles in Figure 30.9b also reverse.

Because the compass needles point in the direction of **B**, we conclude that the lines of **B** form circles around the wire, as discussed in the preceding section. By symmetry, the magnitude of **B** is the same everywhere on a circular path centered on the wire and lying in a plane perpendicular to the wire. By varying the current and distance a from the wire, we find that B is proportional to the current and inversely proportional to the distance from the wire, as Equation 30.5 describes.

Now let us evaluate the product $\mathbf{B} \cdot d\mathbf{s}$ for a small length element $d\mathbf{s}$ on the circular path defined by the compass needles, and sum the products for all elements over the closed circular path.[2] Along this path, the vectors $d\mathbf{s}$ and $\mathbf{B}$ are parallel at each point (see Fig. 30.9b), so $\mathbf{B} \cdot d\mathbf{s} = B\,ds$. Furthermore, the magnitude of **B** is constant on this circle and is given by Equation 30.5. Therefore, the sum of the products $B\,ds$ over the closed path, which is equivalent to the line integral of $\mathbf{B} \cdot d\mathbf{s}$, is

$$\oint \mathbf{B} \cdot d\mathbf{s} = B \oint ds = \frac{\mu_0 I}{2\pi r}(2\pi r) = \mu_0 I$$

where $\oint ds = 2\pi r$ is the circumference of the circular path. Although this result was calculated for the special case of a circular path surrounding a wire, it holds for a closed path of *any* shape (an *amperian loop*) surrounding a current that exists in an unbroken circuit. The general case, known as **Ampère's law,** can be stated as follows:

> The line integral of $\mathbf{B} \cdot d\mathbf{s}$ around any closed path equals $\mu_0 I$, where I is the total steady current passing through any surface bounded by the closed path.

$$\oint \mathbf{B} \cdot d\mathbf{s} = \mu_0 I \tag{30.13}$$

Ampère's law describes the creation of magnetic fields by all continuous current configurations, but at our mathematical level it is useful only for calculating the magnetic field of current configurations having a high degree of symmetry. Its use is similar to that of Gauss's law in calculating electric fields for highly symmetric charge distributions.

Quick Quiz 30.4 Rank the magnitudes of $\oint \mathbf{B} \cdot d\mathbf{s}$ for the closed paths in Figure 30.10, from least to greatest.

---

[2] You may wonder why we would choose to do this. The origin of Ampère's law is in nineteenth century science, in which a "magnetic charge" (the supposed analog to an isolated electric charge) was imagined to be moved around a circular field line. The work done on the charge was related to $\mathbf{B} \cdot d\mathbf{s}$, just as the work done moving an electric charge in an electric field is related to $\mathbf{E} \cdot d\mathbf{s}$. Thus, Ampère's law, a valid and useful principle, arose from an erroneous and abandoned work calculation!

▲ PITFALL PREVENTION

30.2 Avoiding Problems with Signs

When using Ampère's law, apply the following right-hand rule. Point your thumb in the direction of the current through the amperian loop. Your curled fingers then point in the direction that you should integrate around the loop in order to avoid having to define the current as negative.

Ampère's law

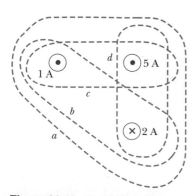

Figure 30.10 (Quick Quiz 30.4) Four closed paths around three current-carrying wires.

Quick Quiz 30.5 Rank the magnitudes of $\oint \mathbf{B} \cdot d\mathbf{s}$ for the closed paths in Figure 30.11, from least to greatest.

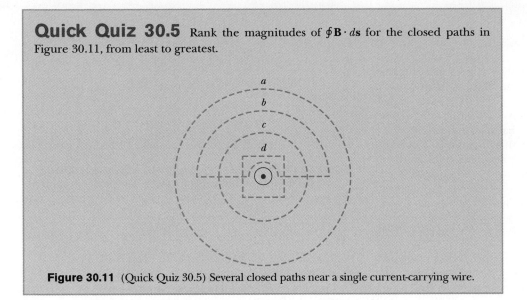

Figure 30.11 (Quick Quiz 30.5) Several closed paths near a single current-carrying wire.

Example 30.4   The Magnetic Field Created by a Long Current-Carrying Wire

A long, straight wire of radius R carries a steady current I that is uniformly distributed through the cross section of the wire (Fig. 30.12). Calculate the magnetic field a distance r from the center of the wire in the regions $r \geq R$ and $r < R$.

Solution Figure 30.12 helps us to conceptualize the wire and the current. Because the wire has a high degree of symmetry, we categorize this as an Ampère's law problem. For the $r \geq R$ case, we should arrive at the same result we obtained in Example 30.1, in which we applied the Biot–Savart law to the same situation. To analyze the problem, let us choose for our path of integration circle 1 in Figure 30.12. From symmetry, $\mathbf{B}$ must be constant in magnitude and parallel to $d\mathbf{s}$ at every point on this circle. Because the total current passing through the plane of the

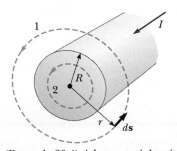

Figure 30.12 (Example 30.4) A long, straight wire of radius R carrying a steady current I uniformly distributed across the cross section of the wire. The magnetic field at any point can be calculated from Ampère's law using a circular path of radius r, concentric with the wire.

circle is I, Ampère's law gives

$$\oint \mathbf{B} \cdot d\mathbf{s} = B \oint ds = B(2\pi r) = \mu_0 I$$

$$B = \boxed{\frac{\mu_0 I}{2\pi r}} \qquad \text{(for } r \geq R\text{)} \qquad (30.14)$$

which is identical in form to Equation 30.5. Note how much easier it is to use Ampère's law than to use the Biot–Savart law. This is often the case in highly symmetric situations.

Now consider the interior of the wire, where $r < R$. Here the current I' passing through the plane of circle 2 is less than the total current I. Because the current is uniform over the cross section of the wire, the fraction of the current enclosed by circle 2 must equal the ratio of the area πr^2 enclosed by circle 2 to the cross-sectional area πR^2 of the wire:[3]

$$\frac{I'}{I} = \frac{\pi r^2}{\pi R^2}$$

$$I' = \frac{r^2}{R^2} I$$

Following the same procedure as for circle 1, we apply Ampère's law to circle 2:

$$\oint \mathbf{B} \cdot d\mathbf{s} = B(2\pi r) = \mu_0 I' = \mu_0 \left(\frac{r^2}{R^2} I \right)$$

[3] Another way to look at this problem is to realize that the current enclosed by circle 2 must equal the product of the current density $J = I/\pi R^2$ and the area πr^2 of this circle.

$$B = \left(\frac{\mu_0 I}{2\pi R^2}\right) r \qquad \text{(for } r < R) \qquad (30.15)$$

To finalize this problem, note that this result is similar in form to the expression for the electric field inside a uniformly charged sphere (see Example 24.5). The magnitude of the magnetic field versus r for this configuration is plotted in Figure 30.13. Note that inside the wire, $B \rightarrow 0$ as $r \rightarrow 0$. Furthermore, we see that Equations 30.14 and 30.15 give the same value of the magnetic field at $r = R$, demonstrating that the magnetic field is continuous at the surface of the wire.

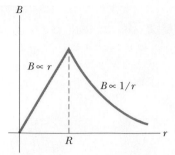

Figure 30.13 (Example 30.4) Magnitude of the magnetic field versus r for the wire shown in Figure 30.12. The field is proportional to r inside the wire and varies as $1/r$ outside the wire.

Example 30.5 The Magnetic Field Created by a Toroid

A device called a *toroid* (Fig. 30.14) is often used to create an almost uniform magnetic field in some enclosed area. The device consists of a conducting wire wrapped around a ring (a *torus*) made of a nonconducting material. For a toroid having N closely spaced turns of wire, calculate the magnetic field in the region occupied by the torus, a distance r from the center.

Solution To calculate this field, we must evaluate $\oint \mathbf{B} \cdot d\mathbf{s}$ over the circular amperian loop of radius r in the plane of Figure 30.14. By symmetry, we see that the magnitude of the field is constant on this circle and tangent to it, so $\mathbf{B} \cdot d\mathbf{s} = B \, ds$. Furthermore, the wire passes through the loop N times,

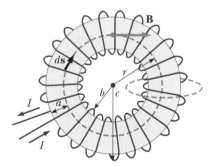

Figure 30.14 (Example 30.5) A toroid consisting of many turns of wire. If the turns are closely spaced, the magnetic field in the interior of the torus (the gold-shaded region) is tangent to the dashed circle and varies as $1/r$. The dimension a is the cross-sectional radius of the torus. The field outside the toroid is very small and can be described by using the amperian loop at the right side, perpendicular to the page.

so that the total current through the loop is NI. Therefore, the right side of Equation 30.13 is $\mu_0 NI$ in this case.

Ampère's law applied to the circle gives

$$\oint \mathbf{B} \cdot d\mathbf{s} = B \oint ds = B(2\pi r) = \mu_0 NI$$

$$B = \frac{\mu_0 NI}{2\pi r} \qquad (30.16)$$

This result shows that B varies as $1/r$ and hence is *nonuniform* in the region occupied by the torus. However, if r is very large compared with the cross-sectional radius a of the torus, then the field is approximately uniform inside the torus.

For an ideal toroid, in which the turns are closely spaced, the external magnetic field is close to zero. It is not exactly zero, however. In Figure 30.14, imagine the radius r of the amperian loop to be either smaller than b or larger than c. In either case, the loop encloses zero net current, so $\oint \mathbf{B} \cdot d\mathbf{s} = 0$. We might be tempted to claim that this proves that $\mathbf{B} = 0$, but it does not. Consider the amperian loop on the right side of the toroid in Figure 30.14. The plane of this loop is perpendicular to the page, and the toroid passes through the loop. As charges enter the toroid as indicated by the current directions in Figure 30.14, they work their way counterclockwise around the toroid. Thus, a current passes through the perpendicular amperian loop! This current is small, but it is not zero. As a result, the toroid acts as a current loop and produces a weak external field of the form shown in Figure 30.7. The reason that $\oint \mathbf{B} \cdot d\mathbf{s} = 0$ for the amperian loops of radius $r < b$ and $r > c$ in the plane of the page is that the field lines are perpendicular to $d\mathbf{s}$, *not* because $\mathbf{B} = 0$.

Example 30.6 Magnetic Field Created by an Infinite Current Sheet

So far we have imagined currents carried by wires of small cross section. Let us now consider an example in which a current exists in an extended object. A thin, infinitely large sheet lying in the yz plane carries a current of linear current density $\mathbf{J}_s$. The current is in the y direction, and J_s represents the current per unit length measured along the z axis. Find the magnetic field near the sheet.

Solution This situation is similar to those involving Gauss's law (see Example 24.8). You may recall that the electric field

due to an infinite sheet of charge does not depend on distance from the sheet. Thus, we might expect a similar result here for the magnetic field.

To evaluate the line integral in Ampère's law, we construct a rectangular path through the sheet, as in Figure 30.15. The rectangle has dimensions ℓ and w, with the sides of length ℓ parallel to the sheet surface. The net current in the plane of the rectangle is $J_s \ell$. We apply Ampère's law over the rectangle and note that the two sides of length w do not contribute to the line integral because the component of $\mathbf{B}$

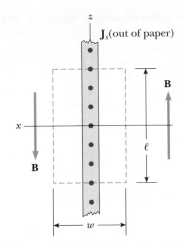

Figure 30.15 (Example 30.6) End view of an infinite current sheet lying in the yz plane, where the current is in the y direction (out of the page). This view shows the direction of **B** on both sides of the sheet.

along the direction of these paths is zero. By symmetry, the magnetic field is constant over the sides of length ℓ because every point on the infinitely large sheet is equivalent, and

hence the field should not vary from point to point. The only choices of field direction that are reasonable in this situation are either perpendicular or parallel to the sheet. However, a perpendicular field would pass *through* the current, which is inconsistent with the Biot–Savart law. Assuming a field that is constant in magnitude and parallel to the plane of the sheet, we obtain

$$\oint \mathbf{B} \cdot d\mathbf{s} = \mu_0 I = \mu_0 J_s \ell$$

$$2B\ell = \mu_0 J_s \ell$$

$$B = \boxed{\mu_0 \frac{J_s}{2}}$$

This result shows that the magnetic field is independent of distance from the current sheet, as we suspected. The expression for the magnitude of the magnetic field is similar in form to that for the magnitude of the electric field due to an infinite sheet of charge (Example 24.8):

$$E = \frac{\sigma}{2\epsilon_0}$$

Example 30.7   The Magnetic Force on a Current Segment

Wire 1 in Figure 30.16 is oriented along the y axis and carries a steady current I_1. A rectangular loop located to the right of the wire and in the xy plane carries a current I_2. Find the magnetic force exerted by wire 1 on the top wire of length b in the loop, labeled "Wire 2" in the figure.

Solution You may be tempted to use Equation 30.12 to obtain the force exerted on a small segment of length dx of wire 2. However, this equation applies only to two *parallel* wires and cannot be used here. The correct approach is to consider the force exerted by wire 1 on a small segment $d\mathbf{s}$ of wire 2 by using Equation 29.4. This force is given by $d\mathbf{F}_B = I \, d\mathbf{s} \times \mathbf{B}$, where $I = I_2$ and **B** is the magnetic field created by the current in wire 1 at the position of $d\mathbf{s}$. From Ampère's law, the field at a distance x

from wire 1 (see Eq. 30.14) is

$$\mathbf{B} = \frac{\mu_0 I_1}{2\pi x} \, (-\hat{\mathbf{k}})$$

where the unit vector $-\hat{\mathbf{k}}$ is used to indicate that the field due to the current in wire 1 at the position of $d\mathbf{s}$ points into the page. Because wire 2 is along the x axis, $d\mathbf{s} = dx\,\hat{\mathbf{i}}$, and we find that

$$d\mathbf{F}_B = \frac{\mu_0 I_1 I_2}{2\pi x} \, [\hat{\mathbf{i}} \times (-\hat{\mathbf{k}})] \, dx = \frac{\mu_0 I_1 I_2}{2\pi} \frac{dx}{x} \, \hat{\mathbf{j}}$$

Integrating over the limits $x = a$ to $x = a + b$ gives

$$\mathbf{F}_B = \frac{\mu_0 I_1 I_2}{2\pi} \, \ln x \Big]_a^{a+b} \hat{\mathbf{j}}$$

(1) $$\mathbf{F}_B = \boxed{\frac{\mu_0 I_1 I_2}{2\pi} \ln \left(1 + \frac{b}{a} \right) \hat{\mathbf{j}}}$$

The force on wire 2 points in the positive y direction, as indicated by the unit vector $\hat{\mathbf{j}}$ and as shown in Figure 30.16.

What If? What if the wire loop is moved to the left in Figure 30.16 until $a = 0$? What happens to the magnitude of the force on the wire?

Answer The force should become stronger because the loop is moving into a region of stronger magnetic field. Equation (1) shows that the force not only becomes stronger but the magnitude of the force becomes *infinite* as $a \rightarrow 0$! Thus, as the loop is moved to the left in Figure 30.16, the loop should be torn apart by the infinite upward force on the top side and the corresponding downward force on the bottom side! Furthermore, the force on the left side is

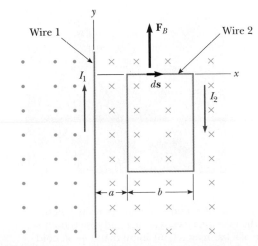

Figure 30.16 (Example 30.7) A wire on one side of a rectangular loop lying near a current-carrying wire experiences a force.

toward the left and should also become infinite. This is larger than the force toward the right on the right side because this side is still far from the wire, so the loop should be pulled into the wire with infinite force!

Does this really happen? In reality, it is impossible for $a \to 0$ because both wire 1 and wire 2 have finite sizes, so that the separation of the centers of the two wires is at least the sum of their radii.

A similar situation occurs when we re-examine the magnetic field due to a long straight wire, given by Equation 30.5. If we could move our observation point infinitesimally close to the wire, the magnetic field would become infinite! But in reality, the wire has a radius, and as soon as we enter the wire, the magnetic field starts to fall off as described by Equation 30.15—approaching zero as we approach the center of the wire.

30.4 The Magnetic Field of a Solenoid

A **solenoid** is a long wire wound in the form of a helix. With this configuration, a reasonably uniform magnetic field can be produced in the space surrounded by the turns of wire—which we shall call the *interior* of the solenoid—when the solenoid carries a current. When the turns are closely spaced, each can be approximated as a circular loop, and the net magnetic field is the vector sum of the fields resulting from all the turns.

Figure 30.17 shows the magnetic field lines surrounding a loosely wound solenoid. Note that the field lines in the interior are nearly parallel to one another, are uniformly distributed, and are close together, indicating that the field in this space is strong and almost uniform.

If the turns are closely spaced and the solenoid is of finite length, the magnetic field lines are as shown in Figure 30.18a. This field line distribution is similar to that surrounding a bar magnet (see Fig. 30.18b). Hence, one end of the solenoid behaves like the north pole of a magnet, and the opposite end behaves like the south pole. As the length of the solenoid increases, the interior field becomes more uniform and the exterior field becomes weaker. An *ideal solenoid* is approached when the turns are closely spaced and the length is much greater than the radius of the turns. Figure 30.19 shows a longitudinal cross section of part of such a solenoid carrying a current I. In this case, the external field is close to zero, and the interior field is uniform over a great volume.

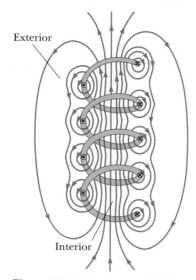

Exterior

Interior

Figure 30.17 The magnetic field lines for a loosely wound solenoid.

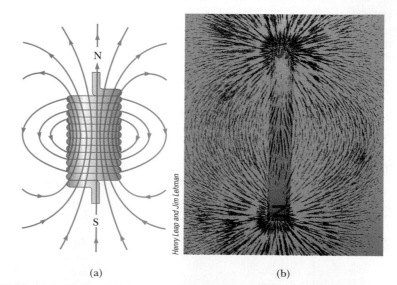

N

S

(a)

Henry Leap and Jim Lehman

(b)

Figure 30.18 (a) Magnetic field lines for a tightly wound solenoid of finite length, carrying a steady current. The field in the interior space is strong and nearly uniform. Note that the field lines resemble those of a bar magnet, meaning that the solenoid effectively has north and south poles. (b) The magnetic field pattern of a bar magnet, displayed with small iron filings on a sheet of paper.

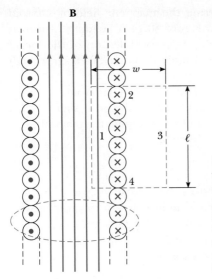

Figure 30.19 Cross-sectional view of an ideal solenoid, where the interior magnetic field is uniform and the exterior field is close to zero. Ampère's law applied to the circular path near the bottom whose plane is perpendicular to the page can be used to show that there is a weak field outside the solenoid. Ampère's law applied to the rectangular dashed path in the plane of the page can be used to calculate the magnitude of the interior field.

If we consider the amperian loop perpendicular to the page in Figure 30.19, surrounding the ideal solenoid, we see that it encloses a small current as the charges in the wire move coil by coil along the length of the solenoid. Thus, there is a nonzero magnetic field outside the solenoid. It is a weak field, with circular field lines, like those due to a line of current as in Figure 30.4. For an ideal solenoid, this is the only field external to the solenoid. We can eliminate this field in Figure 30.19 by adding a second layer of turns of wire outside the first layer, with the current carried along the axis of the solenoid in the opposite direction compared to the first layer. Then the net current along the axis is zero.

We can use Ampère's law to obtain a quantitative expression for the interior magnetic field in an ideal solenoid. Because the solenoid is ideal, **B** in the interior space is uniform and parallel to the axis, and the magnetic field lines in the exterior space form circles around the solenoid. The planes of these circles are perpendicular to the page. Consider the rectangular path of length ℓ and width w shown in Figure 30.19. We can apply Ampère's law to this path by evaluating the integral of $\mathbf{B} \cdot d\mathbf{s}$ over each side of the rectangle. The contribution along side 3 is zero because the magnetic field lines are perpendicular to the path in this region. The contributions from sides 2 and 4 are both zero, again because **B** is perpendicular to $d\mathbf{s}$ along these paths, both inside and outside the solenoid. Side 1 gives a contribution to the integral because along this path **B** is uniform and parallel to $d\mathbf{s}$. The integral over the closed rectangular path is therefore

$$\oint \mathbf{B} \cdot d\mathbf{s} = \int_{\text{path 1}} \mathbf{B} \cdot d\mathbf{s} = B \int_{\text{path 1}} ds = B\ell$$

The right side of Ampère's law involves the total current I through the area bounded by the path of integration. In this case, the total current through the rectangular path equals the current through each turn multiplied by the number of turns. If N is the number of turns in the length ℓ, the total current through the rectangle is NI. Therefore, Ampère's law applied to this path gives

$$\oint \mathbf{B} \cdot d\mathbf{s} = B\ell = \mu_0 NI$$

$$B = \mu_0 \frac{N}{\ell} I = \mu_0 nI \qquad (30.17) \qquad \textbf{Magnetic field inside a solenoid}$$

where $n = N/\ell$ is the number of turns per unit length.

We also could obtain this result by reconsidering the magnetic field of a toroid (see Example 30.5). If the radius r of the torus in Figure 30.14 containing N turns is much greater than the toroid's cross-sectional radius a, a short section of the toroid approximates a solenoid for which $n = N/2\pi r$. In this limit, Equation 30.16 agrees with Equation 30.17.

Equation 30.17 is valid only for points near the center (that is, far from the ends) of a very long solenoid. As you might expect, the field near each end is smaller than the value given by Equation 30.17. At the very end of a long solenoid, the magnitude of the field is half the magnitude at the center (see Problem 32).

> **Quick Quiz 30.6** Consider a solenoid that is very long compared to the radius. Of the following choices, the most effective way to increase the magnetic field in the interior of the solenoid is to (a) double its length, keeping the number of turns per unit length constant, (b) reduce its radius by half, keeping the number of turns per unit length constant, (c) overwrapping the entire solenoid with an additional layer of current-carrying wire.

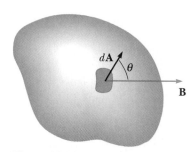

Figure 30.20 The magnetic flux through an area element dA is $\mathbf{B} \cdot d\mathbf{A} = B\,dA \cos\theta$, where $d\mathbf{A}$ is a vector perpendicular to the surface.

Definition of magnetic flux

30.5 Magnetic Flux

The flux associated with a magnetic field is defined in a manner similar to that used to define electric flux (see Eq. 24.3). Consider an element of area dA on an arbitrarily shaped surface, as shown in Figure 30.20. If the magnetic field at this element is $\mathbf{B}$, the magnetic flux through the element is $\mathbf{B} \cdot d\mathbf{A}$, where $d\mathbf{A}$ is a vector that is perpendicular to the surface and has a magnitude equal to the area dA. Therefore, the total magnetic flux Φ_B through the surface is

$$\Phi_B = \int \mathbf{B} \cdot d\mathbf{A} \tag{30.18}$$

Consider the special case of a plane of area A in a uniform field $\mathbf{B}$ that makes an angle θ with $d\mathbf{A}$. The magnetic flux through the plane in this case is

$$\Phi_B = BA \cos\theta \tag{30.19}$$

If the magnetic field is parallel to the plane, as in Figure 30.21a, then $\theta = 90°$ and the flux through the plane is zero. If the field is perpendicular to the plane, as in Figure 30.21b, then $\theta = 0$ and the flux through the plane is BA (the maximum value).

The unit of magnetic flux is $\text{T} \cdot \text{m}^2$, which is defined as a *weber* (Wb); $1\,\text{Wb} = 1\,\text{T} \cdot \text{m}^2$.

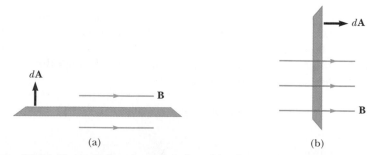

(a)   (b)

Active Figure 30.21 Magnetic flux through a plane lying in a magnetic field. (a) The flux through the plane is zero when the magnetic field is parallel to the plane surface. (b) The flux through the plane is a maximum when the magnetic field is perpendicular to the plane.

At the Active Figures link at http://www.pse6.com, you can rotate the plane and change the value of the field to see the effect on the flux.

Example 30.8   Magnetic Flux Through a Rectangular Loop

A rectangular loop of width a and length b is located near a long wire carrying a current I (Fig. 30.22). The distance between the wire and the closest side of the loop is c. The wire is parallel to the long side of the loop. Find the total magnetic flux through the loop due to the current in the wire.

Solution From Equation 30.14, we know that the magnitude of the magnetic field created by the wire at a distance r from the wire is

$$B = \frac{\mu_0 I}{2\pi r}$$

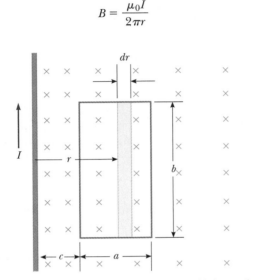

Figure 30.22 (Example 30.8) The magnetic field due to the wire carrying a current I is not uniform over the rectangular loop.

The factor $1/r$ indicates that the field varies over the loop, and Figure 30.22 shows that the field is directed into the page at the location of the loop. Because **B** is parallel to $d\mathbf{A}$ at any point within the loop, the magnetic flux through an area element dA is

$$\Phi_B = \int B\, dA = \int \frac{\mu_0 I}{2\pi r}\, dA$$

To integrate, we first express the area element (the tan region in Fig. 30.22) as $dA = b\, dr$. Because r is now the only variable in the integral, we have

$$\Phi_B = \frac{\mu_0 I b}{2\pi} \int_{c}^{a+c} \frac{dr}{r} = \frac{\mu_0 I b}{2\pi} \ln r \Big]_{c}^{a+c}$$

$$(1) \qquad = \frac{\mu_0 I b}{2\pi} \ln\left(\frac{a+c}{c}\right) = \frac{\mu_0 I b}{2\pi} \ln\left(1 + \frac{a}{c}\right)$$

What If? Suppose we move the loop in Figure 30.22 very far away from the wire. What happens to the magnetic flux?

Answer The flux should become smaller as the loop moves into weaker and weaker fields.

As the loop moves far away, the value of c is much larger than that of a, so that $a/c \rightarrow 0$. Thus, the natural logarithm in Equation (1) approaches the limit

$$\ln\left(1 + \frac{a}{c}\right) \longrightarrow \ln(1+0) = \ln(1) = 0$$

and we find that $\Phi_B \rightarrow 0$ as we expected.

At the Interactive Worked Example link at **http://www.pse6.com,** *you can investigate the flux as the loop parameters change.*

30.6   Gauss's Law in Magnetism

In Chapter 24 we found that the electric flux through a closed surface surrounding a net charge is proportional to that charge (Gauss's law). In other words, the number of electric field lines leaving the surface depends only on the net charge within it. This property is based on the fact that electric field lines originate and terminate on electric charges.

The situation is quite different for magnetic fields, which are continuous and form closed loops. In other words, magnetic field lines do not begin or end at any point—as illustrated in Figures 30.4 and 30.23. Figure 30.23 shows the magnetic field lines of a bar magnet. Note that for any closed surface, such as the one outlined by the dashed line in Figure 30.23, the number of lines entering the surface equals the number leaving the surface; thus, the net magnetic flux is zero. In contrast, for a closed surface surrounding one charge of an electric dipole (Fig. 30.24), the net electric flux is not zero.

Gauss's law in magnetism states that

the net magnetic flux through any closed surface is always zero:

$$\oint \mathbf{B} \cdot d\mathbf{A} = 0 \qquad\qquad (30.20)$$ **Gauss's law in magnetism**

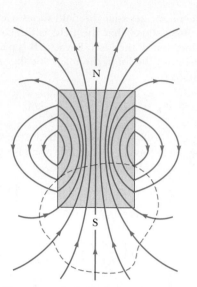

Figure 30.23 The magnetic field lines of a bar magnet form closed loops. Note that the net magnetic flux through a closed surface surrounding one of the poles (or any other closed surface) is zero. (The dashed line represents the intersection of the surface with the page.)

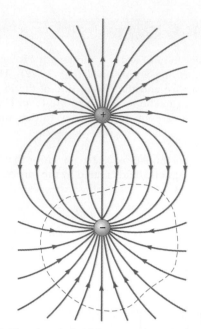

Figure 30.24 The electric field lines surrounding an electric dipole begin on the positive charge and terminate on the negative charge. The electric flux through a closed surface surrounding one of the charges is not zero.

This statement is based on the experimental fact, mentioned in the opening of Chapter 29, that isolated magnetic poles (monopoles) have never been detected and perhaps do not exist. Nonetheless, scientists continue the search because certain theories that are otherwise successful in explaining fundamental physical behavior suggest the possible existence of monopoles.

30.7 Displacement Current and the General Form of Ampère's Law

We have seen that charges in motion produce magnetic fields. When a current-carrying conductor has high symmetry, we can use Ampère's law to calculate the magnetic field it creates. In Equation 30.13, $\oint \mathbf{B} \cdot d\mathbf{s} = \mu_0 I$, the line integral is over any closed path through which the conduction current passes, where the conduction current is defined by the expression $I = dq/dt$. (In this section we use the term *conduction current* to refer to the current carried by the wire, to distinguish it from a new type of current that we shall introduce shortly.) We now show that **Ampère's law in this form is valid only if any electric fields present are constant in time.** Maxwell recognized this limitation and modified Ampère's law to include time-varying electric fields.

We can understand the problem by considering a capacitor that is being charged as illustrated in Figure 30.25. When a conduction current is present, the charge on the positive plate changes but *no conduction current exists in the gap between the plates.* Now consider the two surfaces S_1 and S_2 in Figure 30.25, bounded by the same path P. Ampère's law states that $\oint \mathbf{B} \cdot d\mathbf{s}$ around this path must equal $\mu_0 I$, where I is the total current through *any* surface bounded by the path P.

When the path P is considered as bounding S_1, $\oint \mathbf{B} \cdot d\mathbf{s} = \mu_0 I$ because the conduction current passes through S_1. When the path is considered as bounding S_2, however, $\oint \mathbf{B} \cdot d\mathbf{s} = 0$ because no conduction current passes through S_2. Thus, we have a contradictory situation that arises from the discontinuity of the current! Maxwell solved this problem by postulating an additional term on the right side

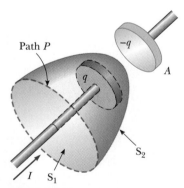

Figure 30.25 Two surfaces S_1 and S_2 near the plate of a capacitor are bounded by the same path P. The conduction current in the wire passes only through S_1. This leads to a contradiction in Ampère's law that is resolved only if one postulates a displacement current through S_2.

of Equation 30.13, which includes a factor called the **displacement current** I_d, defined as[4]

$$I_d \equiv \epsilon_0 \frac{d\Phi_E}{dt} \qquad (30.21)$$

where ϵ_0 is the permittivity of free space (see Section 23.3) and $\Phi_E = \int \mathbf{E} \cdot d\mathbf{A}$ is the electric flux (see Eq. 24.3).

As the capacitor is being charged (or discharged), the changing electric field between the plates may be considered equivalent to a current that acts as a continuation of the conduction current in the wire. When the expression for the displacement current given by Equation 30.21 is added to the conduction current on the right side of Ampère's law, the difficulty represented in Figure 30.25 is resolved. No matter which surface bounded by the path P is chosen, either a conduction current or a displacement current passes through it. With this new term I_d, we can express the general form of Ampère's law (sometimes called the **Ampère–Maxwell law**) as[5]

$$\oint \mathbf{B} \cdot d\mathbf{s} = \mu_0(I + I_d) = \mu_0 I + \mu_0 \epsilon_0 \frac{d\Phi_E}{dt} \qquad (30.22)$$

We can understand the meaning of this expression by referring to Figure 30.26. The electric flux through surface S_2 is $\Phi_E = \int \mathbf{E} \cdot d\mathbf{A} = EA$, where A is the area of the capacitor plates and E is the magnitude of the uniform electric field between the plates. If q is the charge on the plates at any instant, then $E = q/(\epsilon_0 A)$. (See Section 26.2.) Therefore, the electric flux through S_2 is simply

$$\Phi_E = EA = \frac{q}{\epsilon_0}$$

Hence, the displacement current through S_2 is

$$I_d = \epsilon_0 \frac{d\Phi_E}{dt} = \frac{dq}{dt} \qquad (30.23)$$

That is, the displacement current I_d through S_2 is precisely equal to the conduction current I through S_1!

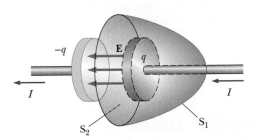

Figure 30.26 Because it exists only in the wires attached to the capacitor plates, the conduction current $I = dq/dt$ passes through S_1 but not through S_2. Only the displacement current $I_d = \epsilon_0 d\Phi_E/dt$ passes through S_2. The two currents must be equal for continuity.

[4]   *Displacement* in this context does not have the meaning it does in Chapter 2. Despite the inaccurate implications, the word is historically entrenched in the language of physics, so we continue to use it.

[5]   Strictly speaking, this expression is valid only in a vacuum. If a magnetic material is present, one must change μ_0 and ϵ_0 on the right-hand side of Equation 30.22 to the permeability μ_m (see Section 30.8) and permittivity ϵ characteristic of the material. Alternatively, one may include a magnetizing current I_m on the right hand side of Equation 30.22 to make Ampère's law fully general. On a microscopic scale, I_m is as real as I.

By considering surface S_2, we can identify the displacement current as the source of the magnetic field on the surface boundary. The displacement current has its physical origin in the time-varying electric field. The central point of this formalism is that

> magnetic fields are produced both by conduction currents and by time-varying electric fields.

This result was a remarkable example of theoretical work by Maxwell, and it contributed to major advances in the understanding of electromagnetism.

> **Quick Quiz 30.7** In an *RC* circuit, the capacitor begins to discharge. During the discharge, in the region of space between the plates of the capacitor, there is (a) conduction current but no displacement current, (b) displacement current but no conduction current, (c) both conduction and displacement current, (d) no current of any type.

> **Quick Quiz 30.8** The capacitor in an *RC* circuit begins to discharge. During the discharge, in the region of space between the plates of the capacitor, there is (a) an electric field but no magnetic field, (b) a magnetic field but no electric field, (c) both electric and magnetic fields, (d) no fields of any type.

Example 30.9 Displacement Current in a Capacitor

A sinusoidally varying voltage is applied across an 8.00-μF capacitor. The frequency of the voltage is 3.00 kHz, and the voltage amplitude is 30.0 V. Find the displacement current in the capacitor.

Solution The angular frequency of the source, from Equation 15.12, is given by $\omega = 2\pi f = 2\pi(3.00 \times 10^3 \text{ Hz}) = 1.88 \times 10^4 \text{ s}^{-1}$. Hence, the voltage across the capacitor in terms of t is

$$\Delta V = \Delta V_{max} \sin \omega t = (30.0 \text{ V}) \sin(1.88 \times 10^4 t)$$

We can use Equation 30.23 and the fact that the charge on the capacitor is $q = C\Delta V$ to find the displacement current:

$$I_d = \frac{dq}{dt} = \frac{d}{dt}(C\Delta V) = C\frac{d}{dt}(\Delta V)$$

$$= (8.00 \times 10^{-6} \text{ F})\frac{d}{dt}[(30.0 \text{ V})\sin(1.88 \times 10^4 t)]$$

$$= (4.52 \text{ A})\cos(1.88 \times 10^4 t)$$

The displacement current varies sinusoidally with time and has a maximum value of 4.52 A.

30.8 Magnetism in Matter

The magnetic field produced by a current in a coil of wire gives us a hint as to what causes certain materials to exhibit strong magnetic properties. Earlier we found that a coil like the one shown in Figure 30.18 has a north pole and a south pole. In general, *any* current loop has a magnetic field and thus has a magnetic dipole moment, including the atomic-level current loops described in some models of the atom.

The Magnetic Moments of Atoms

We begin our discussion with a classical model of the atom in which electrons move in circular orbits around the much more massive nucleus. In this model, an orbiting electron constitutes a tiny current loop (because it is a moving charge),

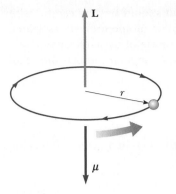

Figure 30.27 An electron moving in the direction of the gray arrow in a circular orbit of radius r has an angular momentum **L** in one direction and a magnetic moment **μ** in the opposite direction. Because the electron carries a negative charge, the direction of the current due to its motion about the nucleus is opposite the direction of that motion.

and the magnetic moment of the electron is associated with this orbital motion. Although this model has many deficiencies, some of its predictions are in good agreement with the correct theory, which is expressed in terms of quantum physics.

In our classical model, we assume that an electron moves with constant speed v in a circular orbit of radius r about the nucleus, as in Figure 30.27. Because the electron travels a distance of $2\pi r$ (the circumference of the circle) in a time interval T, its orbital speed is $v = 2\pi r/T$. The current I associated with this orbiting electron is its charge e divided by T. Using $T = 2\pi/\omega$ and $\omega = v/r$, we have

$$I = \frac{e}{T} = \frac{e\omega}{2\pi} = \frac{ev}{2\pi r}$$

The magnitude of the magnetic moment associated with this current loop is $\mu = IA$, where $A = \pi r^2$ is the area enclosed by the orbit. Therefore,

$$\mu = IA = \left(\frac{ev}{2\pi r}\right)\pi r^2 = \tfrac{1}{2}evr \tag{30.24}$$

Because the magnitude of the orbital angular momentum of the electron is $L = m_e vr$ (Eq. 11.12 with $\phi = 90°$), the magnetic moment can be written as

$$\mu = \left(\frac{e}{2m_e}\right)L \tag{30.25}$$

Orbital magnetic moment

This result demonstrates that **the magnetic moment of the electron is proportional to its orbital angular momentum.** Because the electron is negatively charged, the vectors **μ** and **L** point in *opposite* directions. Both vectors are perpendicular to the plane of the orbit, as indicated in Figure 30.27.

A fundamental outcome of quantum physics is that orbital angular momentum is quantized and is equal to multiples of $\hbar = h/2\pi = 1.05 \times 10^{-34}$ J·s, where h is Planck's constant (introduced in Section 11.6). The smallest nonzero value of the electron's magnetic moment resulting from its orbital motion is

$$\mu = \sqrt{2}\,\frac{e}{2m_e}\,\hbar \tag{30.26}$$

We shall see in Chapter 42 how expressions such as Equation 30.26 arise.

Because all substances contain electrons, you may wonder why most substances are not magnetic. The main reason is that in most substances, the magnetic moment of one electron in an atom is canceled by that of another electron orbiting in the opposite direction. The net result is that, for most materials, **the magnetic effect produced by the orbital motion of the electrons is either zero or very small.**

In addition to its orbital magnetic moment, an electron (as well as protons, neutrons, and other particles) has an intrinsic property called **spin** that also contributes to its magnetic moment. Classically, the electron might be viewed as

30.3 The Electron Does Not Spin

Do not be misled; the electron is *not* physically spinning. It has an intrinsic angular momentum *as if it were spinning*, but the notion of rotation for a point particle is meaningless. Rotation applies only to a *rigid object*, with an extent in space, as in Chapter 10. Spin angular momentum is actually a relativistic effect.

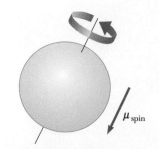

μ_{spin}

Figure 30.28 Classical model of a spinning electron. We can adopt this model to remind ourselves that electrons have an intrinsic angular momentum. The model should not be pushed too far, however—it gives an incorrect magnitude for the magnetic moment, incorrect quantum numbers, and too many degrees of freedom.

Table 30.1

Magnetic Moments of Some Atoms and Ions	
Atom or Ion	Magnetic Moment (10^{-24} J/T)
H	9.27
He	0
Ne	0
Ce^{3+}	19.8
Yb^{3+}	37.1

Magnetization vector M

spinning about its axis as shown in Figure 30.28, but you should be very careful with the classical interpretation. The magnitude of the angular momentum **S** associated with spin is on the same order of magnitude as the magnitude of the angular momentum **L** due to the orbital motion. The magnitude of the spin angular momentum of an electron predicted by quantum theory is

$$S = \frac{\sqrt{3}}{2}\,\hbar$$

The magnetic moment characteristically associated with the spin of an electron has the value

$$\mu_{\text{spin}} = \frac{e\hbar}{2m_e} \tag{30.27}$$

This combination of constants is called the **Bohr magneton μ_B:**

$$\mu_B = \frac{e\hbar}{2m_e} = 9.27 \times 10^{-24}\ \text{J/T} \tag{30.28}$$

Thus, atomic magnetic moments can be expressed as multiples of the Bohr magneton. (Note that $1\ \text{J/T} = 1\ \text{A}\cdot\text{m}^2$.)

In atoms containing many electrons, the electrons usually pair up with their spins opposite each other; thus, the spin magnetic moments cancel. However, atoms containing an odd number of electrons must have at least one unpaired electron and therefore some spin magnetic moment. The total magnetic moment of an atom is the vector sum of the orbital and spin magnetic moments, and a few examples are given in Table 30.1. Note that helium and neon have zero moments because their individual spin and orbital moments cancel.

The nucleus of an atom also has a magnetic moment associated with its constituent protons and neutrons. However, the magnetic moment of a proton or neutron is much smaller than that of an electron and can usually be neglected. We can understand this by inspecting Equation 30.28 and replacing the mass of the electron with the mass of a proton or a neutron. Because the masses of the proton and neutron are much greater than that of the electron, their magnetic moments are on the order of 10^3 times smaller than that of the electron.

Magnetization Vector and Magnetic Field Strength

The magnetic state of a substance is described by a quantity called the **magnetization vector M. The magnitude of this vector is defined as the magnetic moment per unit volume of the substance.** As you might expect, the total magnetic field **B** at a point within a substance depends on both the applied (external) field **B_0** and the magnetization of the substance.

Consider a region in which a magnetic field **B_0** is produced by a current-carrying conductor. If we now fill that region with a magnetic substance, the total magnetic field **B** in the region is $\mathbf{B} = \mathbf{B}_0 + \mathbf{B}_m$, where **$B_m$** is the field produced by the magnetic substance.

Let us determine the relationship between **B_m** and **M**. Imagine that the field **B_m** is created by a solenoid rather than by the magnetic material. Then, $B_m = \mu_0 nI$, where I is the current in the imaginary solenoid and n is the number of turns per unit length. Let us manipulate this expression as follows:

$$B_m = \mu_0 nI = \mu_0 \frac{N}{\ell} I = \mu_0 \frac{NIA}{\ell A}$$

where N is the number of turns in length ℓ, and we have multiplied the numerator and denominator by A, the cross sectional area of the solenoid in the last step. We recognize the numerator NIA as the total magnetic moment of all the loops in length ℓ and the denominator ℓA as the volume of the solenoid associated with this length:

$$B_m = \mu_0 \frac{\mu}{V}$$

The ratio of total magnetic moment to volume is what we have defined as magnetization in the case where the field is due to a material rather than a solenoid. Thus, we can express the contribution $\mathbf{B}_m$ to the total field in terms of the magnetization vector of the substance as $\mathbf{B}_m = \mu_0\mathbf{M}$. When a substance is placed in a magnetic field, the total magnetic field in the region is expressed as

$$\mathbf{B} = \mathbf{B}_0 + \mu_0\mathbf{M} \tag{30.29}$$

When analyzing magnetic fields that arise from magnetization, it is convenient to introduce a field quantity called the **magnetic field strength H** within the substance. The magnetic field strength is related to the magnetic field due to the conduction currents in wires. To emphasize the distinction between the field strength $\mathbf{H}$ and the field $\mathbf{B}$, the latter is often called the *magnetic flux density* or the *magnetic induction*. The magnetic field strength is the magnetic moment per unit volume due to currents; thus, it is similar to the vector $\mathbf{M}$ and has the same units.

Magnetic field strength H

Recognizing the similarity between $\mathbf{M}$ and $\mathbf{H}$, we can define $\mathbf{H}$ as $\mathbf{H} \equiv \mathbf{B}_0/\mu_0$. Thus, Equation 30.29 can be written

$$\mathbf{B} = \mu_0(\mathbf{H} + \mathbf{M}) \tag{30.30}$$

The quantities $\mathbf{H}$ and $\mathbf{M}$ have the same units. Because $\mathbf{M}$ is magnetic moment per unit volume, its SI units are (ampere)(meter)^2/(meter)^3, or amperes per meter.

To better understand these expressions, consider the torus region of a toroid that carries a current I. If this region is a vacuum, $\mathbf{M} = 0$ (because no magnetic material is present), the total magnetic field is that arising from the current alone, and $\mathbf{B} = \mathbf{B}_0 = \mu_0\mathbf{H}$. Because $B_0 = \mu_0 nI$ in the torus region, where n is the number of turns per unit length of the toroid, $H = B_0/\mu_0 = \mu_0 nI/\mu_0$ or

$$H = nI \tag{30.31}$$

In this case, the magnetic field in the torus region is due only to the current in the windings of the toroid.

If the torus is now made of some substance and the current I is kept constant, $\mathbf{H}$ in the torus region remains unchanged (because it depends on the current only) and has magnitude nI. The total field $\mathbf{B}$, however, is different from that when the torus region was a vacuum. From Equation 30.30, we see that part of $\mathbf{B}$ arises from the term $\mu_0\mathbf{H}$ associated with the current in the toroid, and part arises from the term $\mu_0\mathbf{M}$ due to the magnetization of the substance of which the torus is made.

Classification of Magnetic Substances

Substances can be classified as belonging to one of three categories, depending on their magnetic properties. **Paramagnetic** and **ferromagnetic** materials are those made of atoms that have permanent magnetic moments. **Diamagnetic** materials are those made of atoms that do not have permanent magnetic moments.

For paramagnetic and diamagnetic substances, the magnetization vector $\mathbf{M}$ is proportional to the magnetic field strength $\mathbf{H}$. For these substances placed in an external magnetic field, we can write

$$\mathbf{M} = \chi\mathbf{H} \tag{30.32}$$

where χ (Greek letter chi) is a dimensionless factor called the **magnetic susceptibility.** It can be considered a measure of how *susceptible* a material is to being magnetized. For paramagnetic substances, χ is positive and $\mathbf{M}$ is in the same direction as $\mathbf{H}$. For

Magnetic susceptibility χ

Table 30.2

Magnetic Susceptibilities of Some Paramagnetic and Diamagnetic Substances at 300 K			
Paramagnetic Substance	χ	Diamagnetic Substance	χ
Aluminum	2.3×10^{-5}	Bismuth	-1.66×10^{-5}
Calcium	1.9×10^{-5}	Copper	-9.8×10^{-6}
Chromium	2.7×10^{-4}	Diamond	-2.2×10^{-5}
Lithium	2.1×10^{-5}	Gold	-3.6×10^{-5}
Magnesium	1.2×10^{-5}	Lead	-1.7×10^{-5}
Niobium	2.6×10^{-4}	Mercury	-2.9×10^{-5}
Oxygen	2.1×10^{-6}	Nitrogen	-5.0×10^{-9}
Platinum	2.9×10^{-4}	Silver	-2.6×10^{-5}
Tungsten	6.8×10^{-5}	Silicon	-4.2×10^{-6}

diamagnetic substances, χ is negative and **M** is opposite **H**. The susceptibilities of some substances are given in Table 30.2.

Substituting Equation 30.32 for **M** into Equation 30.30 gives

$$\mathbf{B} = \mu_0(\mathbf{H} + \mathbf{M}) = \mu_0(\mathbf{H} + \chi\mathbf{H}) = \mu_0(1 + \chi)\mathbf{H}$$

or

$$\mathbf{B} = \mu_m\mathbf{H} \qquad (30.33)$$

Magnetic permeability

where the constant μ_m is called the **magnetic permeability** of the substance and is related to the susceptibility by

$$\mu_m = \mu_0(1 + \chi) \qquad (30.34)$$

Substances may be classified in terms of how their magnetic permeability μ_m compares with μ_0 (the permeability of free space), as follows:

$$\text{Paramagnetic} \qquad \mu_m > \mu_0$$

$$\text{Diamagnetic} \qquad \mu_m < \mu_0$$

Because χ is very small for paramagnetic and diamagnetic substances (see Table 30.2), μ_m is nearly equal to μ_0 for these substances. For ferromagnetic substances, however, μ_m is typically several thousand times greater than μ_0 (meaning that χ is very large for ferromagnetic substances).

Although Equation 30.33 provides a simple relationship between **B** and **H**, we must interpret it with care when dealing with ferromagnetic substances. We find that **M** is not a linear function of **H** for ferromagnetic substances. This is because the value of μ_m is not only a characteristic of the ferromagnetic substance but also depends on the previous state of the substance and on the process it underwent as it moved from its previous state to its present one. We shall investigate this more deeply after the following example.

Example 30.10   An Iron-Filled Toroid

A toroid wound with 60.0 turns/m of wire carries a current of 5.00 A. The torus is iron, which has a magnetic permeability of $\mu_m = 5\,000\mu_0$ under the given conditions. Find H and B inside the iron.

Solution Using Equations 30.31 and 30.33, we obtain

$$H = nI = (60.0 \text{ turns/m})(5.00 \text{ A}) = \boxed{300 \text{ A} \cdot \text{turns/m}}$$

$$B = \mu_m H = 5\,000\mu_0 H$$
$$= 5\,000(4\pi \times 10^{-7} \text{ T} \cdot \text{m/A})(300 \text{ A} \cdot \text{turns/m})$$
$$= \boxed{1.88 \text{ T}}$$

This value of B is 5 000 times the value in the absence of iron!

Ferromagnetism

A small number of crystalline substances exhibit strong magnetic effects called **ferromagnetism.** Some examples of ferromagnetic substances are iron, cobalt, nickel, gadolinium, and dysprosium. These substances contain permanent atomic magnetic moments that tend to align parallel to each other even in a weak external magnetic field. Once the moments are aligned, the substance remains magnetized after the external field is removed. This permanent alignment is due to a strong coupling between neighboring moments, a coupling that can be understood only in quantum-mechanical terms.

All ferromagnetic materials are made up of microscopic regions called **domains,** regions within which all magnetic moments are aligned. These domains have volumes of about 10^{-12} to 10^{-8} m^3 and contain 10^{17} to 10^{21} atoms. The boundaries between the various domains having different orientations are called **domain walls.** In an unmagnetized sample, the magnetic moments in the domains are randomly oriented so that the net magnetic moment is zero, as in Figure 30.29a. When the sample is placed in an external magnetic field $\mathbf{B}_0$, the size of those domains with magnetic moments aligned with the field grows, which results in a magnetized sample, as in Figure 30.29b. As the external field becomes very strong, as in Figure 30.29c, the domains in which the magnetic moments are not aligned with the field become very small. When the external field is removed, the sample may retain a net magnetization in the direction of the original field. At ordinary temperatures, thermal agitation is not sufficient to disrupt this preferred orientation of magnetic moments.

A typical experimental arrangement that is used to measure the magnetic properties of a ferromagnetic material consists of a torus made of the material wound with N turns of wire, as shown in Figure 30.30, where the windings are represented in black and are referred to as the *primary coil.* This apparatus is sometimes referred to as a **Rowland ring.** A *secondary coil* (the red wires in Fig. 30.30) connected to a galvanometer is used to measure the total magnetic flux through the torus. The magnetic field **B** in the torus is measured by increasing the current in the toroid from zero to I. As the current changes, the magnetic flux through the secondary coil changes by an amount BA, where A is the cross-sectional area of the toroid. As shown in Chapter 31, because of this changing flux, an emf that is proportional to the rate of change in magnetic flux is induced in the secondary coil. If the galvanometer is properly calibrated, a value for **B** corresponding to any value of the current in the primary coil can be obtained. The magnetic field **B** is measured first in the absence of the torus and then with the torus in place. The magnetic properties of the torus material are then obtained from a comparison of the two measurements.

Now consider a torus made of unmagnetized iron. If the current in the primary coil is increased from zero to some value I, the magnitude of the magnetic field strength H increases linearly with I according to the expression $H = nI$. Furthermore,

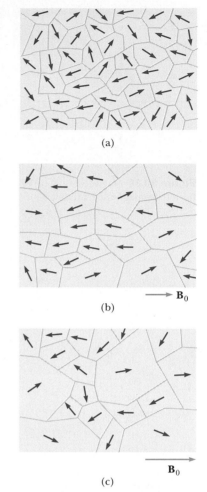

(a)

(b) $\longrightarrow \mathbf{B}_0$

(c) $\longrightarrow \mathbf{B}_0$

Figure 30.29 (a) Random orientation of atomic magnetic dipoles in the domains of an unmagnetized substance. (b) When an external field $\mathbf{B}_0$ is applied, the domains with components of magnetic moment in the same direction as $\mathbf{B}_0$ grow larger, giving the sample a net magnetization. (c) As the field is made even stronger, the domains with magnetic moment vectors not aligned with the external field become very small.

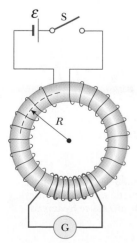

Figure 30.30 A toroidal winding arrangement used to measure the magnetic properties of a material. The torus is made of the material under study, and the circuit containing the galvanometer measures the magnetic flux.

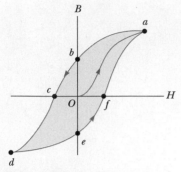

Figure 30.31 Magnetization curve for a ferromagnetic material.

the magnitude of the total field B also increases with increasing current, as shown by the curve from point O to point a in Figure 30.31. At point O, the domains in the iron are randomly oriented, corresponding to $B_m = 0$. As the increasing current in the primary coil causes the external field $\mathbf{B}_0$ to increase, the aligned domains grow in size until nearly all magnetic moments are aligned at point a. At this point the iron core is approaching *saturation*, which is the condition in which all magnetic moments in the iron are aligned.

Next, suppose that the current is reduced to zero, and the external field is consequently eliminated. The B-versus-H curve, called a **magnetization curve,** now follows the path ab in Figure 30.31. Note that at point b, $\mathbf{B}$ is not zero even though the external field $\mathbf{B}_0$ is zero. The reason is that the iron is now magnetized due to the alignment of a large number of its magnetic moments (that is, $\mathbf{B} = \mathbf{B}_m$). At this point, the iron is said to have a *remanent* magnetization.

If the current in the primary coil is reversed so that the direction of the external magnetic field is reversed, the magnetic moments reorient until the sample is again unmagnetized at point c, where $B = 0$. An increase in the reverse current causes the iron to be magnetized in the opposite direction, approaching saturation at point d in Figure 30.31. A similar sequence of events occurs as the current is reduced to zero and then increased in the original (positive) direction. In this case the magnetization curve follows the path def. If the current is increased sufficiently, the magnetization curve returns to point a, where the sample again has its maximum magnetization.

The effect just described, called **magnetic hysteresis,** shows that the magnetization of a ferromagnetic substance depends on the history of the substance as well as on the magnitude of the applied field. (The word *hysteresis* means "lagging behind.") It is often said that a ferromagnetic substance has a "memory" because it remains magnetized after the external field is removed. The closed loop in Figure 30.31 is referred to as a hysteresis loop. Its shape and size depend on the properties of the ferromagnetic substance and on the strength of the maximum applied field. The hysteresis loop for "hard" ferromagnetic materials is characteristically wide like the one shown in Figure 30.32a, corresponding to a large remanent magnetization. Such materials cannot be easily demagnetized by an external field. "Soft" ferromagnetic materials, such as iron, have a very narrow hysteresis loop and a small remanent magnetization (Fig. 30.32b.) Such materials are easily magnetized and demagnetized. An ideal soft ferromagnet would exhibit no hysteresis and hence would have no remanent magnetization. A ferromagnetic substance can be demagnetized by carrying it through successive hysteresis loops, due to a decreasing applied magnetic field, as shown in Figure 30.33.

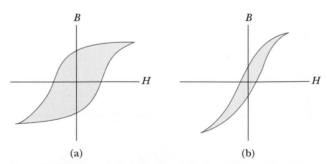

(a) (b)

Figure 30.32 Hysteresis loops for (a) a hard ferromagnetic material and (b) a soft ferromagnetic material.

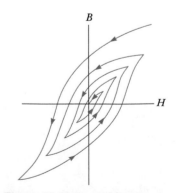

Figure 30.33 Demagnetizing a ferromagnetic material by carrying it through successive hysteresis loops.

The magnetization curve is useful for another reason: **the area enclosed by the magnetization curve represents the energy input required to take the material through the hysteresis cycle.** The energy acquired by the material in the magnetization process originates from the source of the external field—that is, the emf in the circuit of the toroidal coil. When the magnetization cycle is repeated, dissipative processes within the material due to realignment of the magnetic moments result in an increase in internal energy, made evident by an increase in the temperature of the substance. For this reason, devices subjected to alternating fields (such as AC adapters for cell phones, power tools, and so on) use cores made of soft ferromagnetic substances, which have narrow hysteresis loops and correspondingly little energy loss per cycle.

Magnetic computer disks store information by alternating the direction of **B** for portions of a thin layer of ferromagnetic material. Floppy disks have the layer on a circular sheet of plastic. Hard disks have several rigid platters with magnetic coatings on each side. Audio tapes and videotapes work the same way as floppy disks except that the ferromagnetic material is on a very long strip of plastic. Tiny coils of wire in a recording head are placed close to the magnetic material (which is moving rapidly past the head). Varying the current in the coils creates a magnetic field that magnetizes the recording material. To retrieve the information, the magnetized material is moved past a playback coil. The changing magnetism of the material induces a current in the coil, as shown in Chapter 31. This current is then amplified by audio or video equipment, or it is processed by computer circuitry.

When the temperature of a ferromagnetic substance reaches or exceeds a critical temperature called the **Curie temperature,** the substance loses its residual magnetization and becomes paramagnetic (Fig. 30.34). Below the Curie temperature, the magnetic moments are aligned and the substance is ferromagnetic. Above the Curie temperature, the thermal agitation is great enough to cause a random orientation of the moments, and the substance becomes paramagnetic. Curie temperatures for several ferromagnetic substances are given in Table 30.3.

Paramagnetism

Paramagnetic substances have a small but positive magnetic susceptibility ($0 < \chi \ll 1$) resulting from the presence of atoms (or ions) that have permanent magnetic moments. These moments interact only weakly with each other and are randomly oriented in the absence of an external magnetic field. When a paramagnetic substance is placed in an external magnetic field, its atomic moments tend to line up with the field. However, this alignment process must compete with thermal motion, which tends to randomize the magnetic moment orientations.

Pierre Curie (1859–1906) and others since him have found experimentally that, under a wide range of conditions, the magnetization of a paramagnetic substance is proportional to the applied magnetic field and inversely proportional to the absolute temperature:

$$M = C\,\frac{B_0}{T} \tag{30.35}$$

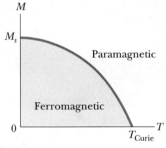

Figure 30.34 Magnetization versus absolute temperature for a ferromagnetic substance. The magnetic moments are aligned below the Curie temperature T_{Curie}, where the substance is ferromagnetic. The substance becomes paramagnetic (magnetic moments unaligned) above T_{Curie}.

Table 30.3

Curie Temperatures for Several Ferromagnetic Substance	
Substance	$T_{\text{Curie}}(\text{K})$
Iron	1 043
Cobalt	1 394
Nickel	631
Gadolinium	317
Fe_2O_3	893

This relationship is known as **Curie's law** after its discoverer, and the constant C is called **Curie's constant.** The law shows that when $B_0 = 0$, the magnetization is zero, corresponding to a random orientation of magnetic moments. As the ratio of magnetic field to temperature becomes great, the magnetization approaches its saturation value, corresponding to a complete alignment of its moments, and Equation 30.35 is no longer valid.

Diamagnetism

When an external magnetic field is applied to a diamagnetic substance, a weak magnetic moment is induced in the direction opposite the applied field. This causes diamagnetic substances to be weakly repelled by a magnet. Although diamagnetism is present in all matter, its effects are much smaller than those of paramagnetism or ferromagnetism, and are evident only when those other effects do not exist.

We can attain some understanding of diamagnetism by considering a classical model of two atomic electrons orbiting the nucleus in opposite directions but with the same speed. The electrons remain in their circular orbits because of the attractive electrostatic force exerted by the positively charged nucleus. Because the magnetic moments of the two electrons are equal in magnitude and opposite in direction, they cancel each other, and the magnetic moment of the atom is zero. When an external magnetic field is applied, the electrons experience an additional magnetic force $q\mathbf{v} \times \mathbf{B}$. This added magnetic force combines with the electrostatic force to increase the orbital speed of the electron whose magnetic moment is antiparallel to the field and to decrease the speed of the electron whose magnetic moment is parallel to the field. As a result, the two magnetic moments of the electrons no longer cancel, and the substance acquires a net magnetic moment that is opposite the applied field.

As you recall from Chapter 27, a superconductor is a substance in which the electrical resistance is zero below some critical temperature. Certain types of superconductors also exhibit perfect diamagnetism in the superconducting state. As a result, an applied magnetic field is expelled by the superconductor so that the field is zero in its interior. This phenomenon is known as the **Meissner effect.** If a permanent magnet is brought near a superconductor, the two objects repel each other. This is illustrated in Figure 30.35, which shows a small permanent magnet levitated above a superconductor maintained at 77 K.

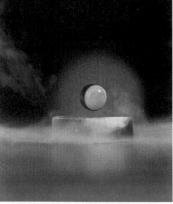

Photo courtesy Argonne National Laboratory

Figure 30.35 An illustration of the Meissner effect, shown by this magnet suspended above a cooled ceramic superconductor disk, has become our most visual image of high-temperature superconductivity. Superconductivity is the loss of all resistance to electrical current, and is a key to more efficient energy use. In the Meissner effect, the magnet induces superconducting current in the disk, which is cooled to $-321°\text{F}$ (77 K). The currents create a magnetic force that repels and levitates the disk.

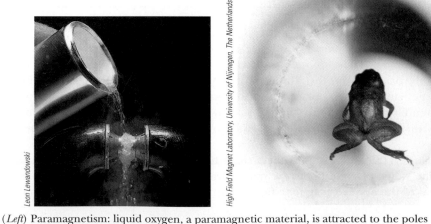

Leon Lewandowski

High Field Magnet Laboratory, University of Nijmegen, The Netherlands.

(*Left*) Paramagnetism: liquid oxygen, a paramagnetic material, is attracted to the poles of a magnet. (*Right*) Diamagnetism: a frog is levitated in a 16-T magnetic field at the Nijmegen High Field Magnet Laboratory, Netherlands. The levitation force is exerted on the diamagnetic water molecules in the frog's body. The frog suffered no ill effects from the levitation experience.

Example 30.11   Saturation Magnetization

Estimate the saturation magnetization in a long cylinder of iron, assuming one unpaired electron spin per atom.

Solution The saturation magnetization is obtained when all the magnetic moments in the sample are aligned. If the sample contains n atoms per unit volume, then the saturation magnetization M_s has the value

$$M_s = n\mu$$

where μ is the magnetic moment per atom. Because the molar mass of iron is 55 g/mol and its density is 7.9 g/cm^3,

the value of n for iron is 8.6×10^{28} atoms/m^3. Assuming that each atom contributes one Bohr magneton (due to one unpaired spin) to the magnetic moment, we obtain

$$M_s = (8.6 \times 10^{28} \text{ atoms/m}^3)(9.27 \times 10^{-24} \text{ A·m}^2/\text{atom})$$

$$= \boxed{8.0 \times 10^5 \text{ A/m}}$$

This is about half the experimentally determined saturation magnetization for iron, which indicates that actually two unpaired electron spins are present per atom.

30.9   The Magnetic Field of the Earth

When we speak of a compass magnet having a north pole and a south pole, we should say more properly that it has a "north-seeking" pole and a "south-seeking" pole. By this we mean that one pole of the magnet seeks, or points to, the north geographic pole of the Earth. Because the north pole of a magnet is attracted toward the north geographic pole of the Earth, we conclude that **the Earth's south magnetic pole is located near the north geographic pole, and the Earth's north magnetic pole is located near the south geographic pole.** In fact, the configuration of the Earth's magnetic field, pictured in Figure 30.36, is very much like the one that would be achieved by burying a gigantic bar magnet deep in the interior of the Earth.

If a compass needle is suspended in bearings that allow it to rotate in the vertical plane as well as in the horizontal plane, the needle is horizontal with respect to the Earth's surface only near the equator. As the compass is moved northward, the needle rotates so that it points more and more toward the surface of the Earth. Finally, at a point near Hudson Bay in Canada, the north pole of the needle points directly downward. This site, first found in 1832, is considered to be the location of the south magnetic pole of the Earth. It is approximately 1 300 mi from the Earth's geographic North Pole, and its exact position varies slowly with time. Similarly, the north magnetic pole of the Earth is about 1 200 mi away from the Earth's geographic South Pole.

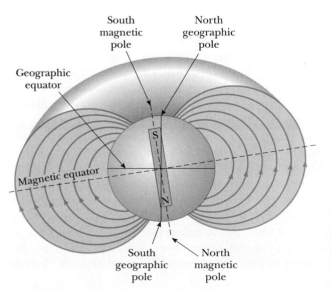

Figure 30.36 The Earth's magnetic field lines. Note that a south magnetic pole is near the north geographic pole, and a north magnetic pole is near the south geographic pole.

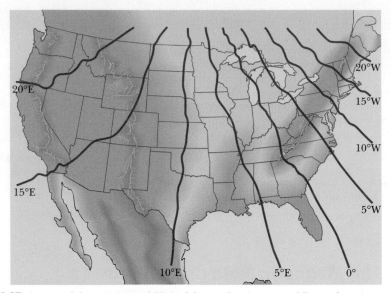

Figure 30.37 A map of the continental United States showing several lines of constant magnetic declination.

Because of this distance between the north geographic and south magnetic poles, it is only approximately correct to say that a compass needle points north. The difference between true north, defined as the geographic North Pole, and north indicated by a compass varies from point to point on the Earth, and the difference is referred to as *magnetic declination*. For example, along a line through Florida and the Great Lakes, a compass indicates true north, whereas in the state of Washington, it aligns 25° east of true north. Figure 30.37 shows some representative values of the magnetic declination for the continental United States.

Quick Quiz 30.10 If we wanted to cancel the Earth's magnetic field by running an enormous current loop around the equator, which way would the current have to to be directed: (a) east to west or (b) west to east?

Although the magnetic field pattern of the Earth is similar to the one that would be set up by a bar magnet deep within the Earth, it is easy to understand why the source of the Earth's magnetic field cannot be large masses of permanently magnetized material. The Earth does have large deposits of iron ore deep beneath its surface, but the high temperatures in the Earth's core prevent the iron from retaining any permanent magnetization. Scientists consider it more likely that the true source of the Earth's magnetic field is convection currents in the Earth's core. Charged ions or electrons circulating in the liquid interior could produce a magnetic field just as a current loop does. There is also strong evidence that the magnitude of a planet's magnetic field is related to the planet's rate of rotation. For example, Jupiter rotates faster than the Earth, and space probes indicate that Jupiter's magnetic field is stronger than ours. Venus, on the other hand, rotates more slowly than the Earth, and its magnetic field is found to be weaker. Investigation into the cause of the Earth's magnetism is ongoing.

There is an interesting sidelight concerning the Earth's magnetic field. It has been found that the direction of the field has been reversed several times during the last million years. Evidence for this is provided by basalt, a type of rock that contains iron and that forms from material spewed forth by volcanic activity on the ocean floor. As the lava cools, it solidifies and retains a picture of the Earth's magnetic field direction. The rocks are dated by other means to provide a timeline for these periodic reversals of the magnetic field.

SUMMARY

Take a practice test for this chapter by clicking on the Practice Test link at http://www.pse6.com.

The **Biot–Savart law** says that the magnetic field $d\mathbf{B}$ at a point P due to a length element $d\mathbf{s}$ that carries a steady current I is

$$d\mathbf{B} = \frac{\mu_0}{4\pi} \frac{I\, d\mathbf{s} \times \hat{\mathbf{r}}}{r^2} \qquad (30.1)$$

where μ_0 is the **permeability of free space,** r is the distance from the element to the point P, and $\hat{\mathbf{r}}$ is a unit vector pointing from $d\mathbf{s}$ toward point P. We find the total field at P by integrating this expression over the entire current distribution.

The magnetic force per unit length between two parallel wires separated by a distance a and carrying currents I_1 and I_2 has a magnitude

$$\frac{F_B}{\ell} = \frac{\mu_0 I_1 I_2}{2\pi a} \qquad (30.12)$$

The force is attractive if the currents are in the same direction and repulsive if they are in opposite directions.

Ampère's law says that the line integral of $\mathbf{B} \cdot d\mathbf{s}$ around any closed path equals $\mu_0 I$, where I is the total steady current through any surface bounded by the closed path:

$$\oint \mathbf{B} \cdot d\mathbf{s} = \mu_0 I \qquad (30.13)$$

Using Ampère's law, one finds that the magnitude of the magnetic field at a distance r from a long, straight wire carrying an electric current I is

$$B = \frac{\mu_0 I}{2\pi r} \qquad (30.14)$$

The field lines are circles concentric with the wire.

The magnitudes of the fields inside a toroid and solenoid are

$$B = \frac{\mu_0 N I}{2\pi r} \qquad \text{(toroid)} \qquad (30.16)$$

$$B = \mu_0 \frac{N}{\ell} I = \mu_0 n I \qquad \text{(solenoid)} \qquad (30.17)$$

where N is the total number of turns.

The **magnetic flux** Φ_B through a surface is defined by the surface integral

$$\Phi_B = \int \mathbf{B} \cdot d\mathbf{A} \qquad (30.18)$$

Gauss's law of magnetism states that the net magnetic flux through any closed surface is zero.

The general form of Ampère's law, which is also called the **Ampère–Maxwell law,** is

$$\oint \mathbf{B} \cdot d\mathbf{s} = \mu_0 I + \mu_0 \epsilon_0 \frac{d\Phi_E}{dt} \qquad (30.22)$$

This law describes the fact that magnetic fields are produced both by conduction currents and by changing electric fields.

When a substance is placed in an external magnetic field $\mathbf{B}_0$, the total magnetic field $\mathbf{B}$ is a combination of the external field and a magnetic field due to magnetic moments of atoms and electrons within the substance:

$$\mathbf{B} = \mathbf{B}_0 + \mu_0 \mathbf{M} \qquad (30.29)$$

where **M** is the **magnetization vector.** The magnetization vector is the magnetic moment per unit volume in the substance.

The effect of external currents on the magnetic field in a substance is described by the **magnetic field strength H** = $\mathbf{B}_0/\mu_0$. The magnetization vector is related to the magnetic field strength as follows:

$$\mathbf{M} = \chi\mathbf{H} \tag{30.32}$$

where χ is the **magnetic susceptibility.**

Substances can be classified into one of three categories that describe their magnetic behavior. **Diamagnetic** substances are those in which the magnetization is weak and opposite the field $\mathbf{B}_0$, so that the susceptibility is negative. **Paramagnetic** substances are those in which the magnetization is weak and in the same direction as the field $\mathbf{B}_0$, so that the susceptibility is positive. In **ferromagnetic** substances, interactions between atoms cause magnetic moments to align and create a strong magnetization that remains after the external field is removed.

QUESTIONS

1. Is the magnetic field created by a current loop uniform? Explain.

2. A current in a conductor produces a magnetic field that can be calculated using the Biot–Savart law. Because current is defined as the rate of flow of charge, what can you conclude about the magnetic field produced by stationary charges? What about that produced by moving charges?

3. Explain why two parallel wires carrying currents in opposite directions repel each other.

4. Parallel current-carrying wires exert magnetic forces on each other. What about perpendicular wires? Imagine two such wires oriented perpendicular to each other, and almost touching. Does a magnetic force exist between the wires?

5. Is Ampère's law valid for all closed paths surrounding a conductor? Why is it not useful for calculating **B** for all such paths?

6. Compare Ampère's law with the Biot–Savart law. Which is more generally useful for calculating **B** for a current-carrying conductor?

7. Is the magnetic field inside a toroid uniform? Explain.

8. Describe the similarities between Ampère's law in magnetism and Gauss's law in electrostatics.

9. A hollow copper tube carries a current along its length. Why is **B** = 0 inside the tube? Is **B** nonzero outside the tube?

10. Describe the change in the magnetic field in the space enclosed by a solenoid carrying a steady current I if (a) the length of the solenoid is doubled but the number of turns remains the same and (b) the number of turns is doubled but the length remains the same.

11. A flat conducting loop is located in a uniform magnetic field directed along the x axis. For what orientation of the loop is the flux through it a maximum? A minimum?

12. What new concept did Maxwell's generalized form of Ampère's law include?

13. Many loops of wire are wrapped around a nail and the ends of the wire are connected to a battery. Identify the source of **M**, of **H**, and of **B**.

14. A magnet attracts a piece of iron. The iron can then attract another piece of iron. On the basis of domain alignment, explain what happens in each piece of iron.

15. Why does hitting a magnet with a hammer cause the magnetism to be reduced?

16. A Hindu ruler once suggested that he be entombed in a magnetic coffin with the polarity arranged so that he would be forever suspended between heaven and Earth. Is such magnetic levitation possible? Discuss.

17. Why is **M** = 0 in a vacuum? What is the relationship between **B** and **H** in a vacuum?

18. Explain why some atoms have permanent magnetic dipole moments and others do not.

19. What factors contribute to the total magnetic dipole moment of an atom?

20. Why is the susceptibility of a diamagnetic substance negative?

21. Why can the effect of diamagnetism be neglected in a paramagnetic substance?

22. Explain the significance of the Curie temperature for a ferromagnetic substance.

23. Discuss the difference among ferromagnetic, paramagnetic, and diamagnetic substances.

24. A current in a solenoid having air in the interior creates a magnetic field **B** = μ_0**H**. Describe qualitatively what happens to the magnitude of **B** as (a) aluminum, (b) copper, and (c) iron are placed in the interior.

25. What is the difference between hard and soft ferromagnetic materials?

26. Should the surface of a computer disk be made from a hard or a soft ferromagnetic substance?

27. Explain why it is desirable to use hard ferromagnetic materials to make permanent magnets.

28. Would you expect the tape from a tape recorder to be attracted to a magnet? (Try it, but not with a recording you wish to save.)

29. Given only a strong magnet and a screwdriver, how would you first magnetize and then demagnetize the screwdriver?

30. Which way would a compass point if you were at the north magnetic pole of the Earth?

31. Figure Q30.31 shows two permanent magnets, each having a hole through its center. Note that the upper magnet is levitated above the lower one. (a) How does this occur? (b) What purpose does the pencil serve? (c) What can you say about the poles of the magnets from this observation? (d) If the upper magnet were inverted, what do you suppose would happen?

Figure Q30.31

PROBLEMS

1, 2, 3 = straightforward, intermediate, challenging   ☐ = full solution available in the *Student Solutions Manual and Study Guide*

🌐 = coached solution with hints available at http://www.pse6.com   🖥 = computer useful in solving problem

▨ = paired numerical and symbolic problems

Section 30.1 The Biot–Savart Law

1. In Niels Bohr's 1913 model of the hydrogen atom, an electron circles the proton at a distance of 5.29×10^{-11} m with a speed of 2.19×10^6 m/s. Compute the magnitude of the magnetic field that this motion produces at the location of the proton.

2. A lightning bolt may carry a current of 1.00×10^4 A for a short period of time. What is the resulting magnetic field 100 m from the bolt? Suppose that the bolt extends far above and below the point of observation.

3. (a) A conductor in the shape of a square loop of edge length $\ell = 0.400$ m carries a current $I = 10.0$ A as in Fig. P30.3. Calculate the magnitude and direction of the magnetic field at the center of the square. (b) **What If?** If this conductor is formed into a single circular turn and carries the same current, what is the value of the magnetic field at the center?

4. Calculate the magnitude of the magnetic field at a point 100 cm from a long, thin conductor carrying a current of 1.00 A.

5. 🌐 Determine the magnetic field at a point P located a distance x from the corner of an infinitely long wire bent at a right angle, as shown in Figure P30.5. The wire carries a steady current I.

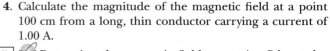

Figure P30.5

6. A conductor consists of a circular loop of radius R and two straight, long sections, as shown in Figure P30.6. The wire

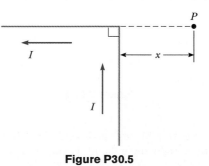

Figure P30.6

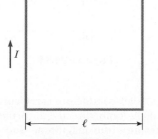

Figure P30.3

lies in the plane of the paper and carries a current I. Find an expression for the vector magnetic field at the center of the loop.

7. The segment of wire in Figure P30.7 carries a current of $I = 5.00$ A, where the radius of the circular arc is $R = 3.00$ cm. Determine the magnitude and direction of the magnetic field at the origin.

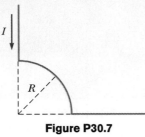

Figure P30.7

8. 🖥 Consider a flat circular current loop of radius R carrying current I. Choose the x axis to be along the axis of the loop, with the origin at the center of the loop. Plot a graph of the ratio of the magnitude of the magnetic field at coordinate x to that at the origin, for $x = 0$ to $x = 5R$. It may be useful to use a programmable calculator or a computer to solve this problem.

9. Two very long, straight, parallel wires carry currents that are directed perpendicular to the page, as in Figure P30.9. Wire 1 carries a current I_1 into the page (in the $-z$ direction) and passes through the x axis at $x = +a$. Wire 2 passes through the x axis at $x = -2a$ and carries an unknown current I_2. The total magnetic field at the origin due to the current-carrying wires has the magnitude $2\mu_0 I_1/(2\pi a)$. The current I_2 can have either of two possible values. (a) Find the value of I_2 with the smaller magnitude, stating it in terms of I_1 and giving its direction. (b) Find the other possible value of I_2.

Figure P30.9

10. A very long straight wire carries current I. In the middle of the wire a right-angle bend is made. The bend forms

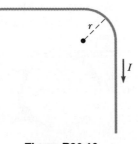

Figure P30.10

an arc of a circle of radius r, as shown in Figure P30.10. Determine the magnetic field at the center of the arc.

11. One very long wire carries current 30.0 A to the left along the x axis. A second very long wire carries current 50.0 A to the right along the line $(y = 0.280$ m, $z = 0)$. (a) Where in the plane of the two wires is the total magnetic field equal to zero? (b) A particle with a charge of -2.00 μC is moving with a velocity of $150\hat{\mathbf{i}}$ Mm/s along the line $(y = 0.100$ m, $z = 0)$. Calculate the vector magnetic force acting on the particle. (c) **What If?** A uniform electric field is applied to allow this particle to pass through this region undeflected. Calculate the required vector electric field.

12. Consider the current-carrying loop shown in Figure P30.12, formed of radial lines and segments of circles whose centers are at point P. Find the magnitude and direction of **B** at P.

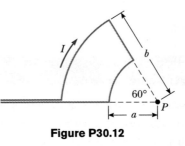

Figure P30.12

13. A wire carrying a current I is bent into the shape of an equilateral triangle of side L. (a) Find the magnitude of the magnetic field at the center of the triangle. (b) At a point halfway between the center and any vertex, is the field stronger or weaker than at the center?

14. Determine the magnetic field (in terms of I, a, and d) at the origin due to the current loop in Figure P30.14.

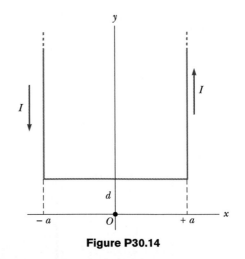

Figure P30.14

15. Two long, parallel conductors carry currents $I_1 = 3.00$ A and $I_2 = 3.00$ A, both directed into the page in Figure P30.15. Determine the magnitude and direction of the resultant magnetic field at P.

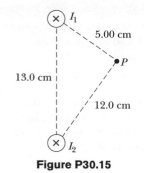

Figure P30.15

Section 30.2   The Magnetic Force Between Two Parallel Conductors

16. Two long, parallel conductors, separated by 10.0 cm, carry currents in the same direction. The first wire carries current $I_1 = 5.00$ A and the second carries $I_2 = 8.00$ A. (a) What is the magnitude of the magnetic field created by I_1 at the location of I_2? (b) What is the force per unit length exerted by I_1 on I_2? (c) What is the magnitude of the magnetic field created by I_2 at the location of I_1? (d) What is the force per length exerted by I_2 on I_1?

17. In Figure P30.17, the current in the long, straight wire is $I_1 = 5.00$ A and the wire lies in the plane of the rectangular loop, which carries the current $I_2 = 10.0$ A. The dimensions are $c = 0.100$ m, $a = 0.150$ m, and $\ell = 0.450$ m. Find the magnitude and direction of the net force exerted on the loop by the magnetic field created by the wire.

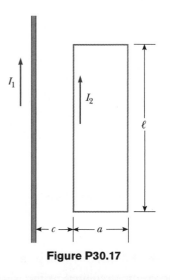

Figure P30.17

18. Two long, parallel wires are attracted to each other by a force per unit length of 320 μN/m when they are separated by a vertical distance of 0.500 m. The current in the upper wire is 20.0 A to the right. Determine the location of the line in the plane of the two wires along which the total magnetic field is zero.

19. Three long wires (wire 1, wire 2, and wire 3) hang vertically. The distance between wire 1 and wire 2 is 20.0 cm. On the left, wire 1 carries an upward current of 1.50 A. To the right, wire 2 carries a downward current of 4.00 A.

Wire 3 is located such that when it carries a certain current, each wire experiences no net force. Find (a) the position of wire 3, and (b) the magnitude and direction of the current in wire 3.

20. The unit of magnetic flux is named for Wilhelm Weber. The practical-size unit of magnetic field is named for Johann Karl Friedrich Gauss. Both were scientists at Göttingen, Germany. Along with their individual accomplishments, together they built a telegraph in 1833. It consisted of a battery and switch, at one end of a transmission line 3 km long, operating an electromagnet at the other end. (André Ampère suggested electrical signaling in 1821; Samuel Morse built a telegraph line between Baltimore and Washington in 1844.) Suppose that Weber and Gauss's transmission line was as diagrammed in Figure P30.20. Two long, parallel wires, each having a mass per unit length of 40.0 g/m, are supported in a horizontal plane by strings 6.00 cm long. When both wires carry the same current I, the wires repel each other so that the angle θ between the supporting strings is 16.0°. (a) Are the currents in the same direction or in opposite directions? (b) Find the magnitude of the current.

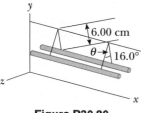

Figure P30.20

Section 30.3   Ampère's Law

21. Four long, parallel conductors carry equal currents of $I = 5.00$ A. Figure P30.21 is an end view of the conductors. The current direction is into the page at points A and B (indicated by the crosses) and out of the page at C and D (indicated by the dots). Calculate the magnitude and direction of the magnetic field at point P, located at the center of the square of edge length 0.200 m.

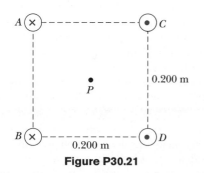

Figure P30.21

22. A long straight wire lies on a horizontal table and carries a current of 1.20 μA. In a vacuum, a proton moves parallel to the wire (opposite the current) with a constant speed of 2.30×10^4 m/s at a distance d above the wire. Determine the value of d. You may ignore the magnetic field due to the Earth.

23. Figure P30.23 is a cross-sectional view of a coaxial cable. The center conductor is surrounded by a rubber layer, which is surrounded by an outer conductor, which is surrounded by another rubber layer. In a particular application, the current in the inner conductor is 1.00 A out of the page and the current in the outer conductor is 3.00 A into the page. Determine the magnitude and direction of the magnetic field at points *a* and *b*.

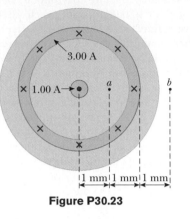

Figure P30.23

24. The magnetic field 40.0 cm away from a long straight wire carrying current 2.00 A is 1.00 μT. (a) At what distance is it 0.100 μT? (b) **What If?** At one instant, the two conductors in a long household extension cord carry equal 2.00-A currents in opposite directions. The two wires are 3.00 mm apart. Find the magnetic field 40.0 cm away from the middle of the straight cord, in the plane of the two wires. (c) At what distance is it one tenth as large? (d) The center wire in a coaxial cable carries current 2.00 A in one direction and the sheath around it carries current 2.00 A in the opposite direction. What magnetic field does the cable create at points outside?

25. A packed bundle of 100 long, straight, insulated wires forms a cylinder of radius $R = 0.500$ cm. (a) If each wire carries 2.00 A, what are the magnitude and direction of the magnetic force per unit length acting on a wire located 0.200 cm from the center of the bundle? (b) **What If?** Would a wire on the outer edge of the bundle experience a force greater or smaller than the value calculated in part (a)?

26. The magnetic coils of a tokamak fusion reactor are in the shape of a toroid having an inner radius of 0.700 m and an outer radius of 1.30 m. The toroid has 900 turns of large-diameter wire, each of which carries a current of 14.0 kA. Find the magnitude of the magnetic field inside the toroid along (a) the inner radius and (b) the outer radius.

27. Consider a column of electric current passing through plasma (ionized gas). Filaments of current within the column are magnetically attracted to one another. They can crowd together to yield a very great current density and a very strong magnetic field in a small region. Sometimes the current can be cut off momentarily by this *pinch effect*. (In a metallic wire a pinch effect is not important, because the current-carrying electrons repel one another with electric forces.) The pinch effect can be demonstrated by making an empty aluminum can carry a large current parallel to its axis. Let R represent the radius of the can and I the upward current, uniformly distributed over its curved wall. Determine the magnetic field (a) just inside the wall and (b) just outside. (c) Determine the pressure on the wall.

28. Niobium metal becomes a superconductor when cooled below 9 K. Its superconductivity is destroyed when the surface magnetic field exceeds 0.100 T. Determine the maximum current a 2.00-mm-diameter niobium wire can carry and remain superconducting, in the absence of any external magnetic field.

29. A long cylindrical conductor of radius R carries a current I as shown in Figure P30.29. The current density J, however, is not uniform over the cross section of the conductor but is a function of the radius according to $J = br$, where b is a constant. Find an expression for the magnetic field B (a) at a distance $r_1 < R$ and (b) at a distance $r_2 > R$, measured from the axis.

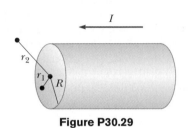

Figure P30.29

30. In Figure P30.30, both currents in the infinitely long wires are in the negative x direction. (a) Sketch the magnetic field pattern in the yz plane. (b) At what distance d along the z axis is the magnetic field a maximum?

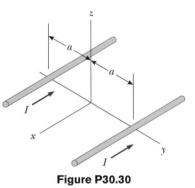

Figure P30.30

Section 30.4   The Magnetic Field of a Solenoid

31. What current is required in the windings of a long solenoid that has 1 000 turns uniformly distributed over a length of 0.400 m, to produce at the center of the solenoid a magnetic field of magnitude 1.00×10^{-4} T?

32. Consider a solenoid of length ℓ and radius R, containing N closely spaced turns and carrying a steady current I. (a) In terms of these parameters, find the magnetic field at a point along the axis as a function of distance a from the end of the solenoid. (b) Show that as ℓ becomes very long, B approaches $\mu_0 NI/2\ell$ at each end of the solenoid.

33. A single-turn square loop of wire, 2.00 cm on each edge, carries a clockwise current of 0.200 A. The loop is inside a solenoid, with the plane of the loop perpendicular to the magnetic field of the solenoid. The solenoid has 30 turns/cm and carries a clockwise current of 15.0 A. Find the force on each side of the loop and the torque acting on the loop.

Section 30.5   Magnetic Flux

34. Consider the hemispherical closed surface in Figure P30.34. The hemisphere is in a uniform magnetic field that makes an angle θ with the vertical. Calculate the magnetic flux through (a) the flat surface S_1 and (b) the hemispherical surface S_2.

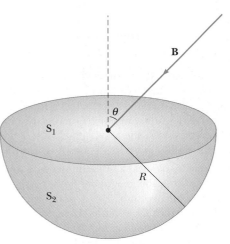

Figure P30.34

35. A cube of edge length $\ell = 2.50$ cm is positioned as shown in Figure P30.35. A uniform magnetic field given by $\mathbf{B} = (5\hat{\mathbf{i}} + 4\hat{\mathbf{j}} + 3\hat{\mathbf{k}})$ T exists throughout the region. (a) Calculate the flux through the shaded face. (b) What is the total flux through the six faces?

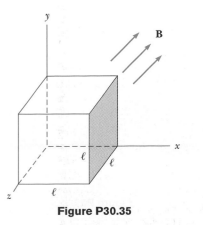

Figure P30.35

36. A solenoid 2.50 cm in diameter and 30.0 cm long has 300 turns and carries 12.0 A. (a) Calculate the flux through the surface of a disk of radius 5.00 cm that is positioned perpendicular to and centered on the axis of the solenoid, as shown in Figure P30.36a. (b) Figure P30.36b shows an enlarged end view of the same solenoid. Calculate the flux through the blue area, which is defined by an annulus that has an inner radius of 0.400 cm and outer radius of 0.800 cm.

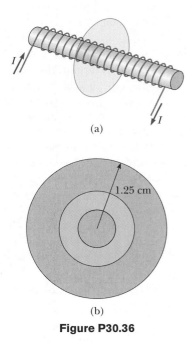

Figure P30.36

Section 30.7   Displacement Current and the General Form of Ampère's Law

37. A 0.100-A current is charging a capacitor that has square plates 5.00 cm on each side. The plate separation is 4.00 mm. Find (a) the time rate of change of electric flux between the plates and (b) the displacement current between the plates.

38. A 0.200-A current is charging a capacitor that has circular plates 10.0 cm in radius. If the plate separation is 4.00 mm, (a) what is the time rate of increase of electric field between the plates? (b) What is the magnetic field between the plates 5.00 cm from the center?

Section 30.8   Magnetism in Matter

39. In Bohr's 1913 model of the hydrogen atom, the electron is in a circular orbit of radius 5.29×10^{-11} m and its speed is 2.19×10^6 m/s. (a) What is the magnitude of the magnetic moment due to the electron's motion? (b) If the electron moves in a horizontal circle, counterclockwise as seen from above, what is the direction of this magnetic moment vector?

40. A magnetic field of 1.30 T is to be set up in an iron-core toroid. The toroid has a mean radius of 10.0 cm, and magnetic permeability of 5 000 μ_0. What current is required if the winding has 470 turns of wire? The thickness of the iron ring is small compared to 10 cm, so the field in the material is nearly uniform.

41. A toroid with a mean radius of 20.0 cm and 630 turns (see Fig. 30.30) is filled with powdered steel whose magnetic susceptibility χ is 100. The current in the windings is 3.00 A. Find B (assumed uniform) inside the toroid.

42. A particular paramagnetic substance achieves 10.0% of its saturation magnetization when placed in a magnetic field of 5.00 T at a temperature of 4.00 K. The density of magnetic atoms in the sample is 8.00×10^{27} atoms/m^3, and the magnetic moment per atom is 5.00 Bohr magnetons. Calculate the Curie constant for this substance.

43. Calculate the magnetic field strength H of a magnetized substance in which the magnetization is 0.880×10^6 A/m and the magnetic field has magnitude 4.40 T.

44. At *saturation*, when nearly all of the atoms have their magnetic moments aligned, the magnetic field in a sample of iron can be 2.00 T. If each electron contributes a magnetic moment of 9.27×10^{-24} A·m^2 (one Bohr magneton), how many electrons per atom contribute to the saturated field of iron? Iron contains approximately 8.50×10^{28} atoms/m^3.

45. (a) Show that Curie's law can be stated in the following way: The magnetic susceptibility of a paramagnetic substance is inversely proportional to the absolute temperature, according to $\chi = C\mu_0/T$, where C is Curie's constant. (b) Evaluate Curie's constant for chromium.

Section 30.9   The Magnetic Field of the Earth

46. A circular coil of 5 turns and a diameter of 30.0 cm is oriented in a vertical plane with its axis perpendicular to the horizontal component of the Earth's magnetic field. A horizontal compass placed at the center of the coil is made to deflect 45.0° from magnetic north by a current of 0.600 A in the coil. (a) What is the horizontal component of the Earth's magnetic field? (b) The current in the coil is switched off. A "dip needle" is a magnetic compass mounted so that it can rotate in a vertical north–south plane. At this location a dip needle makes an angle of 13.0° from the vertical. What is the total magnitude of the Earth's magnetic field at this location?

47. The magnetic moment of the Earth is approximately 8.00×10^{22} A·m^2. (a) If this were caused by the complete magnetization of a huge iron deposit, how many unpaired electrons would this correspond to? (b) At two unpaired electrons per iron atom, how many kilograms of iron would this correspond to? (Iron has a density of 7 900 kg/m^3, and approximately 8.50×10^{28} iron atoms/m^3.)

Additional Problems

48. The magnitude of the Earth's magnetic field at either pole is approximately 7.00×10^{-5} T. Suppose that the field fades away, before its next reversal. Scouts, sailors, and conservative politicians around the world join together in a program to replace the field. One plan is to use a current loop around the equator, without relying on magnetization of any materials inside the Earth. Determine the current that would generate such a field if this plan were carried out. (Take the radius of the Earth as $R_E = 6.37 \times 10^6$ m.)

49. A very long, thin strip of metal of width w carries a current I along its length as shown in Figure P30.49. Find the magnetic field at the point P in the diagram. The point P is in the plane of the strip at distance b away from it.

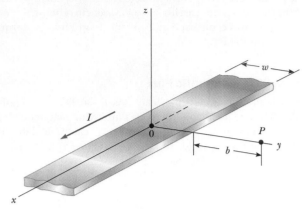

Figure P30.49

50. Suppose you install a compass on the center of the dashboard of a car. Compute an order-of-magnitude estimate for the magnetic field at this location produced by the current when you switch on the headlights. How does it compare with the Earth's magnetic field? You may suppose the dashboard is made mostly of plastic.

51. For a research project, a student needs a solenoid that produces an interior magnetic field of 0.030 0 T. She decides to use a current of 1.00 A and a wire 0.500 mm in diameter. She winds the solenoid in layers on an insulating form 1.00 cm in diameter and 10.0 cm long. Determine the number of layers of wire needed and the total length of the wire.

52. A thin copper bar of length $\ell = 10.0$ cm is supported horizontally by two (nonmagnetic) contacts. The bar carries current $I_1 = 100$ A in the $-x$ direction, as shown in Figure P30.52. At a distance $h = 0.500$ cm below one end of the bar, a long straight wire carries a current $I_2 = 200$ A in the z direction. Determine the magnetic force exerted on the bar.

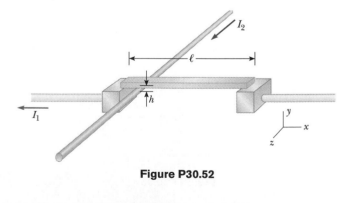

Figure P30.52

53. A nonconducting ring of radius 10.0 cm is uniformly charged with a total positive charge 10.0 μC. The ring rotates at a constant angular speed 20.0 rad/s about an

axis through its center, perpendicular to the plane of the ring. What is the magnitude of the magnetic field on the axis of the ring 5.00 cm from its center?

54. A nonconducting ring of radius R is uniformly charged with a total positive charge q. The ring rotates at a constant angular speed ω about an axis through its center, perpendicular to the plane of the ring. What is the magnitude of the magnetic field on the axis of the ring a distance $R/2$ from its center?

55. Two circular coils of radius R, each with N turns, are perpendicular to a common axis. The coil centers are a distance R apart. Each coil carries a steady current I in the same direction, as shown in Figure P30.55. (a) Show that the magnetic field on the axis at a distance x from the center of one coil is

$$B = \frac{N\mu_0 IR^2}{2}\left[\frac{1}{(R^2 + x^2)^{3/2}} + \frac{1}{(2R^2 + x^2 - 2Rx)^{3/2}}\right]$$

(b) Show that dB/dx and d^2B/dx^2 are both zero at the point midway between the coils. This means the magnetic field in the region midway between the coils is uniform. Coils in this configuration are called *Helmholtz coils*.

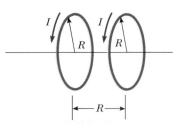

Figure P30.55 Problems 55 and 56.

56. Two identical, flat, circular coils of wire each have 100 turns and a radius of 0.500 m. The coils are arranged as a set of Helmholtz coils (see Fig. P30.55), parallel and with separation 0.500 m. Each coil carries a current of 10.0 A. Determine the magnitude of the magnetic field at a point on the common axis of the coils and halfway between them.

57. We have seen that a long solenoid produces a uniform magnetic field directed along the axis of a cylindrical region. However, to produce a uniform magnetic field directed parallel to a *diameter* of a cylindrical region, one can use the *saddle coils* illustrated in Figure P30.57. The loops are wrapped over a somewhat flattened tube. Assume the straight sections of wire are very long. The end view of the tube shows how the windings are applied. The overall current distribution is the superposition of two overlapping circular cylinders of uniformly distributed current, one toward you and one away from you. The current density J is the same for each cylinder. The position of the axis of one cylinder is described by a position vector **a** relative to the other cylinder. Prove that the magnetic field inside the hollow tube is $\mu_0 Ja/2$ downward. *Suggestion:* The use of vector methods simplifies the calculation.

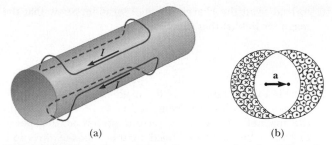

(a)   (b)

Figure P30.57 (a) General view of one turn of each saddle coil. (b) End view of the coils carrying current into the paper on the left and out of the paper on the right.

58. A very large parallel-plate capacitor carries charge with uniform charge per unit area $+\sigma$ on the upper plate and $-\sigma$ on the lower plate. The plates are horizontal and both move horizontally with speed v to the right. (a) What is the magnetic field between the plates? (b) What is the magnetic field close to the plates but outside of the capacitor? (c) What is the magnitude and direction of the magnetic force per unit area on the upper plate? (d) At what extrapolated speed v will the magnetic force on a plate balance the electric force on the plate? Calculate this speed numerically.

59. Two circular loops are parallel, coaxial, and almost in contact, 1.00 mm apart (Fig. P30.59). Each loop is 10.0 cm in radius. The top loop carries a clockwise current of 140 A. The bottom loop carries a counterclockwise current of 140 A. (a) Calculate the magnetic force exerted by the bottom loop on the top loop. (b) The upper loop has a mass of 0.021 0 kg. Calculate its acceleration, assuming that the only forces acting on it are the force in part (a) and the gravitational force. *Suggestion:* Think about how one loop looks to a bug perched on the other loop.

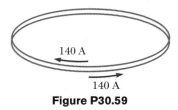

140 A

140 A

Figure P30.59

60. What objects experience a force in an electric field? Chapter 23 gives the answer: any electric charge, stationary or moving, other than the charge that created the field. What creates an electric field? Any electric charge, stationary or moving, as you studied in Chapter 23. What objects experience a force in a magnetic field? An electric current or a moving electric charge, other than the current or charge that created the field, as discussed in Chapter 29. What creates a magnetic field? An electric current, as you studied in Section 30.1, or a moving electric charge, as shown in this problem. (a) To display how a moving charge creates a magnetic field, consider a charge q moving with velocity **v**. Define the vector $\mathbf{r} = r\hat{\mathbf{r}}$

to lead from the charge to some location. Show that the magnetic field at that location is

$$\mathbf{B} = \frac{\mu_0}{4\pi}\frac{q\mathbf{v}\times\hat{\mathbf{r}}}{r^2}$$

(b) Find the magnitude of the magnetic field 1.00 mm to the side of a proton moving at 2.00×10^7 m/s. (c) Find the magnetic force on a second proton at this point, moving with the same speed in the opposite direction. (d) Find the electric force on the second proton.

61. *Rail guns* have been suggested for launching projectiles into space without chemical rockets, and for ground-to-air antimissile weapons of war. A tabletop model rail gun (Fig. P30.61) consists of two long parallel horizontal rails 3.50 cm apart, bridged by a bar *BD* of mass 3.00 g. The bar is originally at rest at the midpoint of the rails and is free to slide without friction. When the switch is closed, electric current is quickly established in the circuit *ABCDEA*. The rails and bar have low electric resistance, and the current is limited to a constant 24.0 A by the power supply. (a) Find the magnitude of the magnetic field 1.75 cm from a single very long straight wire carrying current 24.0 A. (b) Find the magnitude and direction of the magnetic field at point *C* in the diagram, the midpoint of the bar, immediately after the switch is closed. *Suggestion:* Consider what conclusions you can draw from the Biot–Savart law. (c) At other points along the bar *BD*, the field is in the same direction as at point *C*, but larger in magnitude. Assume that the average effective magnetic field along *BD* is five times larger than the field at *C*. With this assumption, find the magnitude and direction of the force on the bar. (d) Find the acceleration of the bar when it is in motion. (e) Does the bar move with constant acceleration? (f) Find the velocity of the bar after it has traveled 130 cm to the end of the rails.

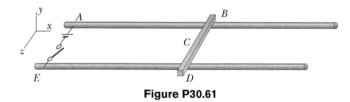

Figure P30.61

62. 🖳 Fifty turns of insulated wire 0.100 cm in diameter are tightly wound to form a flat spiral. The spiral fills a disk surrounding a circle of radius 5.00 cm and extending to a radius 10.00 cm at the outer edge. Assume the wire carries current *I* at the center of its cross section. Approximate each turn of wire as a circle. Then a loop of current exists at radius 5.05 cm, another at 5.15 cm, and so on. Numerically calculate the magnetic field at the center of the coil.

63. Two long, parallel conductors carry currents in the same direction as shown in Figure P30.63. Conductor A carries a current of 150 A and is held firmly in position. Conductor B carries a current I_B and is allowed to slide freely up and down (parallel to A) between a set of nonconducting guides. If the mass per unit length of conductor B

is 0.100 g/cm, what value of current I_B will result in equilibrium when the distance between the two conductors is 2.50 cm?

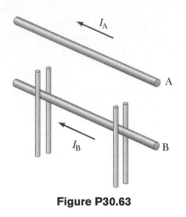

Figure P30.63

64. Charge is sprayed onto a large nonconducting belt above the left-hand roller in Figure P30.64. The belt carries the charge with a uniform surface charge density σ as it moves with a speed v between the rollers as shown. The charge is removed by a wiper at the right-hand roller. Consider a point just above the surface of the moving belt. (a) Find an expression for the magnitude of the magnetic field **B** at this point. (b) If the belt is positively charged, what is the direction of **B**? (Note that the belt may be considered as an infinite sheet.)

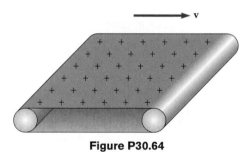

Figure P30.64

65. An infinitely long straight wire carrying a current I_1 is partially surrounded by a loop as shown in Figure P30.65.

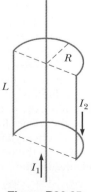

Figure P30.65

The loop has a length L, radius R, and carries a current I_2. The axis of the loop coincides with the wire. Calculate the force exerted on the loop.

66. Measurements of the magnetic field of a large tornado were made at the Geophysical Observatory in Tulsa, Oklahoma, in 1962. The tornado's field was measured to be $B = 1.50 \times 10^{-8}$ T pointing north when the tornado was 9.00 km east of the observatory. What current was carried up or down the funnel of the tornado, modeled as a long straight wire?

67. A wire is formed into the shape of a square of edge length L (Fig. P30.67). Show that when the current in the loop is I, the magnetic field at point P, a distance x from the center of the square along its axis is

$$B = \frac{\mu_0 I L^2}{2\pi (x^2 + L^2/4)\sqrt{x^2 + L^2/2}}$$

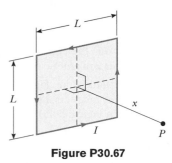

Figure P30.67

68. The force on a magnetic dipole $\boldsymbol{\mu}$ aligned with a nonuniform magnetic field in the x direction is given by $F_x = |\boldsymbol{\mu}|\,dB/dx$. Suppose that two flat loops of wire each have radius R and carry current I. (a) The loops are arranged coaxially and separated by a variable distance x, large compared to R. Show that the magnetic force between them varies as $1/x^4$. (b) Evaluate the magnitude of this force if $I = 10.0$ A, $R = 0.500$ cm, and $x = 5.00$ cm.

69. A wire carrying a current I is bent into the shape of an exponential spiral, $r = e^\theta$, from $\theta = 0$ to $\theta = 2\pi$ as suggested in Figure P30.69. To complete a loop, the ends of the spiral are connected by a straight wire along the x axis. Find the magnitude and direction of $\mathbf{B}$ at the origin. *Suggestions:* Use the Biot–Savart law. The angle β between a radial line and its tangent line at any point on the curve $r = f(\theta)$ is related to the function in the following way:

$$\tan \beta = \frac{r}{dr/d\theta}$$

Thus in this case $r = e^\theta$, $\tan \beta = 1$ and $\beta = \pi/4$. Therefore, the angle between $d\mathbf{s}$ and $\hat{\mathbf{r}}$ is $\pi - \beta = 3\pi/4$. Also

$$ds = \frac{dr}{\sin(\pi/4)} = \sqrt{2}\,dr$$

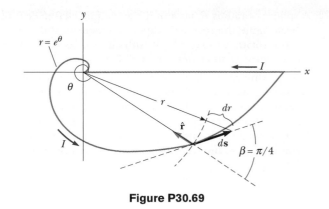

Figure P30.69

70. Table P30.70 contains data taken for a ferromagnetic material. (a) Construct a magnetization curve from the data. Remember that $\mathbf{B} = \mathbf{B}_0 + \mu_0 \mathbf{M}$. (b) Determine the ratio B/B_0 for each pair of values of B and B_0, and construct a graph of B/B_0 versus B_0. (The fraction B/B_0 is called the relative permeability, and it is a measure of the induced magnetic field.)

Table P30.70

B (T)	B_0 (T)
0.2	4.8×10^{-5}
0.4	7.0×10^{-5}
0.6	8.8×10^{-5}
0.8	1.2×10^{-4}
1.0	1.8×10^{-4}
1.2	3.1×10^{-4}
1.4	8.7×10^{-4}
1.6	3.4×10^{-3}
1.8	1.2×10^{-1}

71. A sphere of radius R has a uniform volume charge density ρ. Determine the magnetic field at the center of the sphere when it rotates as a rigid object with angular speed ω about an axis through its center (Fig. P30.71).

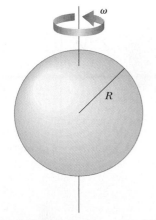

Figure P30.71 Problems 71 and 72.

72. A sphere of radius R has a uniform volume charge density ρ. Determine the magnetic dipole moment of the sphere when it rotates as a rigid body with angular speed ω about an axis through its center (Fig. P30.71).

73. A long cylindrical conductor of radius a has two cylindrical cavities of diameter a through its entire length, as shown in Figure P30.73. A current I is directed out of the page and is uniform through a cross section of the conductor. Find the magnitude and direction of the magnetic field in terms of μ_0, I, r, and a at (a) point P_1 and (b) point P_2.

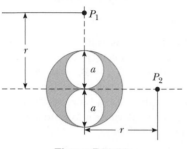

Figure P30.73

Answers to Quick Quizzes

30.1 B, C, A. Point B is closest to the current element. Point C is farther away and the field is further reduced by the $\sin \theta$ factor in the cross product $d\mathbf{s} \times \hat{\mathbf{r}}$. The field at A is zero because $\theta = 0$.

30.2 (c). $F_1 = F_2$ as required by Newton's third law. Another way to arrive at this answer is to realize that Equation 30.11 gives the same result whether the multiplication of currents is $(2\,\text{A})(6\,\text{A})$ or $(6\,\text{A})(2\,\text{A})$.

30.3 (a). The coils act like wires carrying parallel currents in the same direction and hence attract one another.

30.4 b, d, a, c. Equation 30.13 indicates that the value of the line integral depends only on the net current through each closed path. Path b encloses 1 A, path d encloses 3 A, path a encloses 4 A, and path c encloses 6 A.

30.5 b, then $a = c = d$. Paths a, c, and d all give the same nonzero value $\mu_0 I$ because the size and shape of the paths do not matter. Path b does not enclose the current, and hence its line integral is zero.

30.6 (c). The magnetic field in a very long solenoid is independent of its length or radius. Overwrapping with an additional layer of wire increases the number of turns per unit length.

30.7 (b). There can be no conduction current because there is no conductor between the plates. There is a time-varying electric field because of the decreasing charge on the plates, and the time-varying electric flux represents a displacement current.

30.8 (c). There is a time-varying electric field because of the decreasing charge on the plates. This time-varying electric field produces a magnetic field.

30.9 (a). The loop that looks like Figure 30.32a is better because the remanent magnetization at the point corresponding to point b in Figure 30.31 is greater.

30.10 (b). The lines of the Earth's magnetic field enter the planet in Hudson Bay and emerge from Antarctica; thus, the field lines resulting from the current would have to go in the opposite direction. Compare Figure 30.7a with Figure 30.36.

Calvin and Hobbes   by Bill Watterson

Chapter 31

Faraday's Law

▲ In a commercial electric power plant, large generators produce energy that is transferred out of the plant by electrical transmission. These generators use magnetic induction to generate a potential difference when coils of wire in the generator are rotated in a magnetic field. The source of energy to rotate the coils might be falling water, burning fossil fuels, or a nuclear reaction. (Michael Melford/Getty Images)

Michael Faraday
British Physicist and Chemist (1791–1867)

Faraday is often regarded as the greatest experimental scientist of the 1800s. His many contributions to the study of electricity include the invention of the electric motor, electric generator, and transformer, as well as the discovery of electromagnetic induction and the laws of electrolysis. Greatly influenced by religion, he refused to work on the development of poison gas for the British military. *(By kind permission of the President and Council of the Royal Society)*

The focus of our studies in electricity and magnetism so far has been the electric fields produced by stationary charges and the magnetic fields produced by moving charges. This chapter explores the effects produced by magnetic fields that vary in time.

Experiments conducted by Michael Faraday in England in 1831 and independently by Joseph Henry in the United States that same year showed that an emf can be induced in a circuit by a changing magnetic field. The results of these experiments led to a very basic and important law of electromagnetism known as *Faraday's law of induction*. An emf (and therefore a current as well) can be induced in various processes that involve a change in a magnetic flux.

With the treatment of Faraday's law, we complete our introduction to the fundamental laws of electromagnetism. These laws can be summarized in a set of four equations called *Maxwell's equations*. Together with the *Lorentz force law*, they represent a complete theory for describing the interaction of charged objects.

31.1 Faraday's Law of Induction

To see how an emf can be induced by a changing magnetic field, consider a loop of wire connected to a sensitive ammeter, as illustrated in Figure 31.1. When a magnet is moved toward the loop, the galvanometer needle deflects in one direction, arbitrarily shown to the right in Figure 31.1a. When the magnet is brought to rest and held stationary relative to the loop (Fig. 31.1b), no deflection is observed. When the magnet is moved away from the loop, the needle deflects in the opposite direction, as shown in Figure 31.1c. Finally, if the magnet is held stationary and the loop is moved either toward or away from it, the needle deflects. From these observations, we conclude that the loop detects that the magnet is moving relative to it and we relate this detection to a change in magnetic field. Thus, it seems that a relationship exists between current and changing magnetic field.

These results are quite remarkable in view of the fact that **a current is set up even though no batteries are present in the circuit!** We call such a current an *induced current* and say that it is produced by an *induced emf*.

Now let us describe an experiment conducted by Faraday and illustrated in Figure 31.2. A primary coil is connected to a switch and a battery. The coil is wrapped around an iron ring, and a current in the coil produces a magnetic field when the switch is closed. A secondary coil also is wrapped around the ring and is connected to a sensitive ammeter. No battery is present in the secondary circuit, and the secondary coil is not electrically connected to the primary coil. Any current detected in the secondary circuit must be induced by some external agent.

Initially, you might guess that no current is ever detected in the secondary circuit. However, something quite amazing happens when the switch in the primary circuit is either opened or thrown closed. At the instant the switch is closed, the galvanometer needle deflects in one direction and then returns to zero. At the instant the switch is opened, the needle deflects in the opposite direction and again returns to zero.

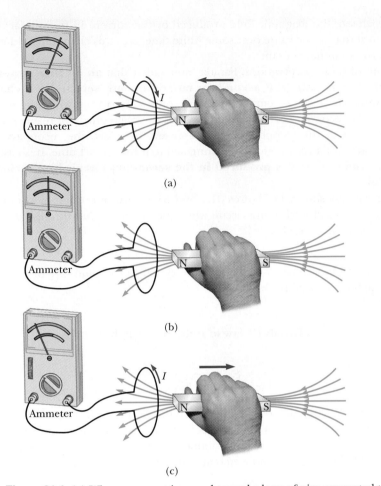

(a)

(b)

(c)

Active Figure 31.1 (a) When a magnet is moved toward a loop of wire connected to a sensitive ammeter, the ammeter deflects as shown, indicating that a current is induced in the loop. (b) When the magnet is held stationary, there is no induced current in the loop, even when the magnet is inside the loop. (c) When the magnet is moved away from the loop, the ammeter deflects in the opposite direction, indicating that the induced current is opposite that shown in part (a). Changing the direction of the magnet's motion changes the direction of the current induced by that motion.

At the Active Figures link at http://www.pse6.com, you can move the magnet and observe the current in the ammeter.

Finally, the galvanometer reads zero when there is either a steady current or no current in the primary circuit. The key to understanding what happens in this experiment is to note first that when the switch is closed, the current in the primary circuit produces a magnetic field that penetrates the secondary circuit. Furthermore, when

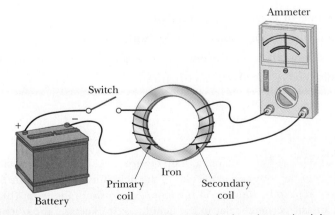

Active Figure 31.2 Faraday's experiment. When the switch in the primary circuit is closed, the ammeter in the secondary circuit deflects momentarily. The emf induced in the secondary circuit is caused by the changing magnetic field through the secondary coil.

At the Active Figures link at http://www.pse6.com, you can open and close the switch and observe the current in the ammeter.

the switch is closed, the magnetic field produced by the current in the primary circuit changes from zero to some value over some finite time, and this changing field induces a current in the secondary circuit.

As a result of these observations, Faraday concluded that **an electric current can be induced in a circuit (the secondary circuit in our setup) by a changing magnetic field.** The induced current exists for only a short time while the magnetic field through the secondary coil is changing. Once the magnetic field reaches a steady value, the current in the secondary coil disappears. In effect, the secondary circuit behaves as though a source of emf were connected to it for a short time. It is customary to say that **an induced emf is produced in the secondary circuit by the changing magnetic field.**

The experiments shown in Figures 31.1 and 31.2 have one thing in common: in each case, an emf is induced in the circuit when the magnetic flux through the circuit changes with time. In general,

> The emf induced in a circuit is directly proportional to the time rate of change of the magnetic flux through the circuit.

This statement, known as **Faraday's law of induction,** can be written

$$\mathcal{E} = -\frac{d\Phi_B}{dt} \tag{31.1}$$

where $\Phi_B = \int \mathbf{B} \cdot d\mathbf{A}$ is the magnetic flux through the circuit. (See Section 30.5.)

If the circuit is a coil consisting of N loops all of the same area and if Φ_B is the magnetic flux through one loop, an emf is induced in every loop. The loops are in series, so their emfs add; thus, the total induced emf in the coil is given by the expression

$$\mathcal{E} = -N\frac{d\Phi_B}{dt} \tag{31.2}$$

The negative sign in Equations 31.1 and 31.2 is of important physical significance, as discussed in Section 31.3.

Suppose that a loop enclosing an area A lies in a uniform magnetic field $\mathbf{B}$, as in Figure 31.3. The magnetic flux through the loop is equal to $BA \cos\theta$; hence, the induced emf can be expressed as

$$\mathcal{E} = -\frac{d}{dt}(BA \cos\theta) \tag{31.3}$$

From this expression, we see that an emf can be induced in the circuit in several ways:

- The magnitude of $\mathbf{B}$ can change with time.
- The area enclosed by the loop can change with time.
- The angle θ between $\mathbf{B}$ and the normal to the loop can change with time.
- Any combination of the above can occur.

Faraday's law

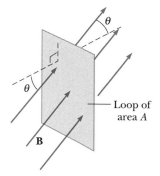

Figure 31.3 A conducting loop that encloses an area A in the presence of a uniform magnetic field $\mathbf{B}$. The angle between $\mathbf{B}$ and the normal to the loop is θ.

> **Quick Quiz 31.1** A circular loop of wire is held in a uniform magnetic field, with the plane of the loop perpendicular to the field lines. Which of the following will *not* cause a current to be induced in the loop? (a) crushing the loop; (b) rotating the loop about an axis perpendicular to the field lines; (c) keeping the orientation of the loop fixed and moving it along the field lines; (d) pulling the loop out of the field.

Quick Quiz 31.2 Figure 31.4 shows a graphical representation of the field magnitude versus time for a magnetic field that passes through a fixed loop and is oriented perpendicular to the plane of the loop. The magnitude of the magnetic field at any time is uniform over the area of the loop. Rank the magnitudes of the emf generated in the loop at the five instants indicated, from largest to smallest.

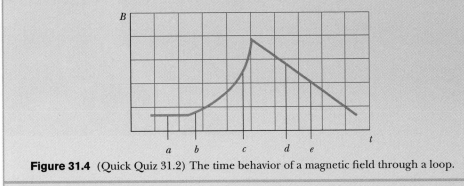

Figure 31.4 (Quick Quiz 31.2) The time behavior of a magnetic field through a loop.

Quick Quiz 31.3 Suppose you would like to steal power for your home from the electric company by placing a loop of wire near a transmission cable, so as to induce an emf in the loop (an illegal procedure). Should you (a) place your loop so that the transmission cable passes through your loop, or (b) simply place your loop near the transmission cable?

Some Applications of Faraday's Law

The ground fault interrupter (GFI) is an interesting safety device that protects users of electrical appliances against electric shock. Its operation makes use of Faraday's law. In the GFI shown in Figure 31.5, wire 1 leads from the wall outlet to the appliance to be protected, and wire 2 leads from the appliance back to the wall outlet. An iron ring surrounds the two wires, and a sensing coil is wrapped around part of the ring. Because the currents in the wires are in opposite directions, the net magnetic flux through the sensing coil due to the currents is zero. However, if the return current in wire 2 changes, the net magnetic flux through the sensing coil is no longer zero. (This can happen, for example, if the appliance becomes wet, enabling current to leak to ground.) Because household current is alternating (meaning that its direction keeps reversing), the magnetic flux through the sensing coil changes with time, inducing an emf in the coil. This induced emf is used to trigger a circuit breaker, which stops the current before it is able to reach a harmful level.

Another interesting application of Faraday's law is the production of sound in an electric guitar (Fig. 31.6). The coil in this case, called the *pickup coil*, is placed near the vibrating guitar string, which is made of a metal that can be magnetized. A permanent

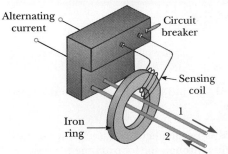

Figure 31.5 Essential components of a ground fault interrupter.

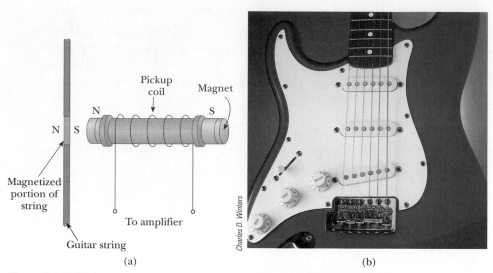

(a)   (b)

Figure 31.6 (a) In an electric guitar, a vibrating magnetized string induces an emf in a pickup coil. (b) The pickups (the circles beneath the metallic strings) of this electric guitar detect the vibrations of the strings and send this information through an amplifier and into speakers. (A switch on the guitar allows the musician to select which set of six pickups is used.)

magnet inside the coil magnetizes the portion of the string nearest the coil. When the string vibrates at some frequency, its magnetized segment produces a changing magnetic flux through the coil. The changing flux induces an emf in the coil that is fed to an amplifier. The output of the amplifier is sent to the loudspeakers, which produce the sound waves we hear.

Example 31.1 One Way to Induce an emf in a Coil

A coil consists of 200 turns of wire. Each turn is a square of side 18 cm, and a uniform magnetic field directed perpendicular to the plane of the coil is turned on. If the field changes linearly from 0 to 0.50 T in 0.80 s, what is the magnitude of the induced emf in the coil while the field is changing?

Solution The area of one turn of the coil is $(0.18 \text{ m})^2 = 0.032\,4 \text{ m}^2$. The magnetic flux through the coil at $t = 0$ is zero because $B = 0$ at that time. At $t = 0.80$ s, the magnetic flux through one turn is $\Phi_B = BA = (0.50 \text{ T})(0.032\,4 \text{ m}^2) = 0.016\,2 \text{ T·m}^2$. Therefore, the magnitude of the induced emf is, from Equation 31.2,

$$|\mathcal{E}| = N \frac{\Delta \Phi_B}{\Delta t} = 200 \frac{(0.016\,2 \text{ T·m}^2 - 0)}{0.80 \text{ s}}$$

$$= 4.1 \text{ T·m}^2/\text{s} = \boxed{4.1 \text{ V}}$$

You should be able to show that $1 \text{ T·m}^2/\text{s} = 1 \text{ V}$.

What If? What if you were asked to find the magnitude of the induced current in the coil while the field is changing? Can you answer this question?

Answer If the ends of the coil are not connected to a circuit, the answer to this question is easy—the current is zero! (Charges will move within the wire of the coil, but they cannot move into or out of the ends of the coil.) In order for a steady current to exist, the ends of the coil must be connected to an external circuit. Let us assume that the coil is connected to a circuit and that the total resistance of the coil and the circuit is 2.0 Ω. Then, the current in the coil is

$$I = \frac{\mathcal{E}}{R} = \frac{4.1 \text{ V}}{2.0 \text{ Ω}} = 2.0 \text{ A}$$

Example 31.2 An Exponentially Decaying B Field

A loop of wire enclosing an area A is placed in a region where the magnetic field is perpendicular to the plane of the loop. The magnitude of **B** varies in time according to the expression $B = B_{max}e^{-at}$, where a is some constant. That is, at $t = 0$ the field is B_{max}, and for $t > 0$, the field decreases

exponentially (Fig. 31.7). Find the induced emf in the loop as a function of time.

Solution Because **B** is perpendicular to the plane of the loop, the magnetic flux through the loop at time $t > 0$ is

$$\Phi_B = BA \cos 0 = AB_{max}e^{-at}$$

Because AB_{max} and a are constants, the induced emf calculated from Equation 31.1 is

$$\mathcal{E} = -\frac{d\Phi_B}{dt} = -AB_{max}\frac{d}{dt}e^{-at}$$

$$= aAB_{max}e^{-at}$$

This expression indicates that the induced emf decays exponentially in time. Note that the maximum emf occurs at $t = 0$, where $\mathcal{E}_{max} = aAB_{max}$. The plot of $\mathcal{E}$ versus t is similar to the B-versus-t curve shown in Figure 31.7.

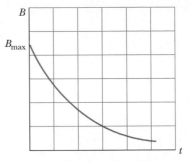

Figure 31.7 (Example 31.2) Exponential decrease in the magnitude of the magnetic field with time. The induced emf and induced current vary with time in the same way.

Conceptual Example 31.3   Which Bulb Is Shorted Out?

Two bulbs are connected to opposite sides of a circular loop of wire, as shown in Figure 31.8a. A changing magnetic field (confined to the smaller circular area shown in the figure) induces an emf in the loop that causes the two bulbs to light. When the switch is closed, the resistance-free wires connected to the switch short out bulb 2 and it goes out. What happens if the wires containing the closed switch remain connected at points a and b, but the switch and the wires are lifted up and moved to the other side of the field, as in Figure 3.18b? The wire is still connected to bulb 2 as it was before, so does it continue to stay dark?

Solution When the wire is moved to the other side, even though the connections have not changed, bulb 1 goes out and bulb 2 glows. The bulb that is shorted depends on which side of the changing field the switch is positioned! In Figure 31.8a, because the branch containing bulb 2 is infinitely more resistant than the branch containing the resistance-free switch, we can imagine removing the branch with the bulb without altering the circuit. Then we have a simple loop containing only bulb 1, which glows.

When the wire is moved, as in Figure 31.8b, there are two possible paths for current below points a and b. We can imagine removing the branch with bulb 1, leaving only a single loop with bulb 2.

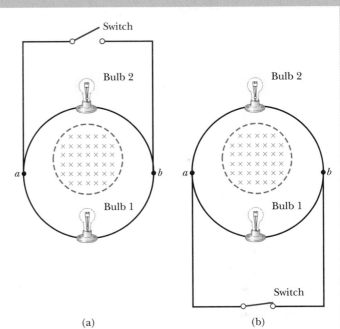

(a)   (b)

Figure 31.8 (Conceptual Example 31.3) (a) When the wire with the switch is located as shown, bulb 2 goes out when the switch is closed. (b) What happens when the switch and the wires are moved to the other side of the magnetic field?

31.2 Motional emf

In Examples 31.1 and 31.2, we considered cases in which an emf is induced in a stationary circuit placed in a magnetic field when the field changes with time. In this section we describe what is called **motional emf,** which is the emf induced in a conductor moving through a constant magnetic field.

The straight conductor of length ℓ shown in Figure 31.9 is moving through a uniform magnetic field directed into the page. For simplicity, we assume that the conductor is moving in a direction perpendicular to the field with constant velocity under the influence of some external agent. The electrons in the conductor experience a force $\mathbf{F}_B = q\mathbf{v} \times \mathbf{B}$ that is directed along the length ℓ, perpendicular to both $\mathbf{v}$ and $\mathbf{B}$ (Eq. 29.1). Under the influence of this force, the electrons move to the lower end of the conductor and accumulate there, leaving a net positive charge at the upper end. As a result of this charge separation, an electric field $\mathbf{E}$ is produced

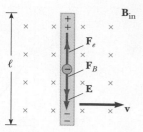

Figure 31.9 A straight electrical conductor of length ℓ moving with a velocity **v** through a uniform magnetic field **B** directed perpendicular to **v**. Due to the magnetic force on electrons, the ends of the conductor become oppositely charged. This establishes an electric field in the conductor. In steady state, the electric and magnetic forces on an electron in the wire are balanced.

inside the conductor. The charges accumulate at both ends until the downward magnetic force qvB on charges remaining in the conductor is balanced by the upward electric force qE. At this point, electrons move only with random thermal motion. The condition for equilibrium requires that

$$qE = qvB \quad \text{or} \quad E = vB$$

The electric field produced in the conductor is related to the potential difference across the ends of the conductor according to the relationship $\Delta V = E\ell$ (Eq. 25.6). Thus, for the equilibrium condition,

$$\Delta V = E\ell = B\ell v \tag{31.4}$$

where the upper end of the conductor in Figure 31.9 is at a higher electric potential than the lower end. Thus, **a potential difference is maintained between the ends of the conductor as long as the conductor continues to move through the uniform magnetic field.** If the direction of the motion is reversed, the polarity of the potential difference is also reversed.

A more interesting situation occurs when the moving conductor is part of a closed conducting path. This situation is particularly useful for illustrating how a changing magnetic flux causes an induced current in a closed circuit. Consider a circuit consisting of a conducting bar of length ℓ sliding along two fixed parallel conducting rails, as shown in Figure 31.10a.

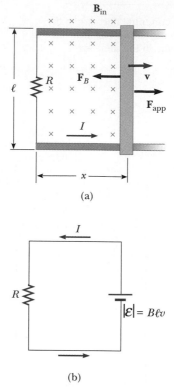

(a)

(b)

Active Figure 31.10 (a) A conducting bar sliding with a velocity **v** along two conducting rails under the action of an applied force **F**$_{app}$. The magnetic force **F**$_B$ opposes the motion, and a counterclockwise current I is induced in the loop. (b) The equivalent circuit diagram for the setup shown in part (a).

At the **Active Figures link** at http://www.pse6.com, you can adjust the applied force, the magnetic field, and the resistance to see the effects on the motion of the bar.

For simplicity, we assume that the bar has zero resistance and that the stationary part of the circuit has a resistance R. A uniform and constant magnetic field **B** is applied perpendicular to the plane of the circuit. As the bar is pulled to the right with a velocity **v** under the influence of an applied force **F**$_{app}$, free charges in the bar experience a magnetic force directed along the length of the bar. This force sets up an induced current because the charges are free to move in the closed conducting path. In this case, the rate of change of magnetic flux through the loop and the corresponding induced motional emf across the moving bar are proportional to the change in area of the loop. If the bar is pulled to the right with a constant velocity, the work done by the applied force appears as internal energy in the resistor R. (See Section 27.6.)

Because the area enclosed by the circuit at any instant is ℓx, where x is the position of the bar, the magnetic flux through that area is

$$\Phi_B = B\ell x$$

Using Faraday's law, and noting that x changes with time at a rate $dx/dt = v$, we find that the induced motional emf is

$$\mathcal{E} = -\frac{d\Phi_B}{dt} = -\frac{d}{dt}(B\ell x) = -B\ell\frac{dx}{dt}$$

$$\mathcal{E} = -B\ell v \tag{31.5}$$

Motional emf

Because the resistance of the circuit is R, the magnitude of the induced current is

$$I = \frac{|\mathcal{E}|}{R} = \frac{B\ell v}{R} \tag{31.6}$$

The equivalent circuit diagram for this example is shown in Figure 31.10b.

Let us examine the system using energy considerations. Because no battery is in the circuit, we might wonder about the origin of the induced current and the energy delivered to the resistor. We can understand the source of this current and energy by noting that the applied force does work on the conducting bar, thereby moving charges through a magnetic field. Their movement through the field causes the charges to move along the bar with some average drift velocity, and hence a current is established. The change in energy in the system during some time interval must be equal to the transfer of energy into the system by work, consistent with the general principle of conservation of energy described by Equation 7.17.

Let us verify this mathematically. As the bar moves through the uniform magnetic field **B**, it experiences a magnetic force $\mathbf{F}_B$ of magnitude $I\ell B$ (see Section 29.2). The direction of this force is opposite the motion of the bar, to the left in Figure 31.10a. Because the bar moves with constant velocity, the applied force must be equal in magnitude and opposite in direction to the magnetic force, or to the right in Figure 31.10a. (If $\mathbf{F}_B$ acted in the direction of motion, it would cause the bar to accelerate, violating the principle of conservation of energy.) Using Equation 31.6 and the fact that $F_{app} = I\ell B$, we find that the power delivered by the applied force is

$$\mathcal{P} = F_{app}v = (I\ell B)v = \frac{B^2\ell^2 v^2}{R} = \frac{\mathcal{E}^2}{R} \tag{31.7}$$

From Equation 27.23, we see that this power input is equal to the rate at which energy is delivered to the resistor, so that Equation 7.17 is confirmed in this situation.

Quick Quiz 31.4 As an airplane flies from Los Angeles to Seattle, it passes through the Earth's magnetic field. As a result, a motional emf is developed between the wingtips. Which wingtip is positively charged? (a) the left wing (b) the right wing.

Quick Quiz 31.5 In Figure 31.10, a given applied force of magnitude F_{app} results in a constant speed v and a power input $\mathcal{P}$. Imagine that the force is increased so that the constant speed of the bar is doubled to $2v$. Under these conditions, the new force and the new power input are (a) $2F$ and $2\mathcal{P}$ (b) $4F$ and $2\mathcal{P}$ (c) $2F$ and $4\mathcal{P}$ (d) $4F$ and $4\mathcal{P}$.

Quick Quiz 31.6 You wish to move a rectangular loop of wire into a region of uniform magnetic field at a given speed so as to induce an emf in the loop. The plane of the loop remains perpendicular to the magnetic field lines. In which orientation should you hold the loop while you move it into the region of magnetic field in order to generate the largest emf? (a) with the long dimension of the loop parallel to the velocity vector (b) with the short dimension of the loop parallel to the velocity vector (c) either way—the emf is the same regardless of orientation.

Example 31.4   Motional emf Induced in a Rotating Bar   `Interactive`

A conducting bar of length ℓ rotates with a constant angular speed ω about a pivot at one end. A uniform magnetic field **B** is directed perpendicular to the plane of rotation, as shown in Figure 31.11. Find the motional emf induced between the ends of the bar.

Solution Consider a segment of the bar of length dr having a velocity **v**. According to Equation 31.5, the magnitude of

the emf induced in this segment is

$$d\mathcal{E} = Bv\, dr$$

Because every segment of the bar is moving perpendicular to **B**, an emf $d\mathcal{E}$ of the same form is generated across each segment. Summing the emfs induced across all segments, which are in series, gives the total emf between the ends

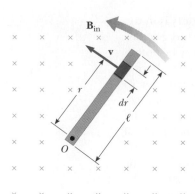

Figure 31.11 (Example 31.4) A conducting bar rotating around a pivot at one end in a uniform magnetic field that is perpendicular to the plane of rotation. A motional emf is induced across the ends of the bar.

of the bar:

$$\mathcal{E} = \int Bv\, dr$$

To integrate this expression, note that the linear speed v of an element is related to the angular speed ω through the relationship $v = r\omega$ (Eq. 10.10). Therefore, because B and ω are constants, we find that

$$\mathcal{E} = B\int v\, dr = B\omega \int_0^{\ell} r\, dr = \boxed{\tfrac{1}{2}B\omega\ell^2}$$

What If? Suppose, after reading through this example, you come up with a brilliant idea. A Ferris wheel has radial metallic spokes between the hub and the circular rim. These spokes move in the magnetic field of the Earth, so each spoke acts like the bar in Figure 31.11. You plan to use the emf generated by the rotation of the Ferris wheel to power the lightbulbs on the wheel! Will this idea work?

Answer The fact that this is not done in practice suggests that others may have thought of this idea and rejected it. Let us estimate the emf that is generated in this situation. We know the magnitude of the magnetic field of the Earth from Table 29.1, $B = 0.5 \times 10^{-4}$ T. A typical spoke on a Ferris wheel might have a length on the order of 10 m. Suppose the period of rotation is on the order of 10 s. This gives an angular speed of

$$\omega = \frac{2\pi}{T} = \frac{2\pi}{10\text{ s}} = 0.63\text{ s}^{-1} \sim 1\text{ s}^{-1}$$

Assuming that the magnetic field lines of the Earth are horizontal at the location of the Ferris wheel and perpendicular to the spokes, the emf generated is

$$\mathcal{E} = \tfrac{1}{2}B\omega\ell^2 = \tfrac{1}{2}(0.5 \times 10^{-4}\text{ T})(1\text{ s}^{-1})(10\text{ m})^2$$

$$= 2.5 \times 10^{-3}\text{ V} \sim 1\text{ mV}$$

This is a tiny emf, far smaller than that required to operate lightbulbs.

An additional difficulty is related to energy. Assuming you could find lightbulbs that operate using a potential difference on the order of millivolts, a spoke must be part of a circuit in order to provide a voltage to the bulbs. Consequently, the spoke must carry a current. Because this current-carrying spoke is in a magnetic field, a magnetic force is exerted on the spoke and the direction of the force is opposite to its direction of motion. As a result, the motor of the Ferris wheel must supply more energy to perform work against this magnetic drag force. The motor must ultimately provide the energy that is operating the lightbulbs and you have not gained anything for free!

At the Interactive Worked Example link at **http://www.pse6.com,** *you can explore the induced emf for different angular speeds and field magnitudes.*

Example 31.5   Magnetic Force Acting on a Sliding Bar   `Interactive`

The conducting bar illustrated in Figure 31.12 moves on two frictionless parallel rails in the presence of a uniform magnetic field directed into the page. The bar has mass m and its length is ℓ. The bar is given an initial velocity $\mathbf{v}_i$ to the right and is released at $t = 0$.

(A) Using Newton's laws, find the velocity of the bar as a function of time.

(B) Show that the same result is reached by using an energy approach.

Solution (A) Conceptualize this situation as follows. As the bar slides to the right in Figure 31.12, a counterclockwise current is established in the circuit consisting of the bar, the rails, and the resistor. The upward current in the bar results in a magnetic force to the left on the bar as shown in the figure. As a result, the bar will slow down, so our mathematical solution should demonstrate this. The text of part (A) already categorizes this as a problem in using Newton's laws. To analyze the problem, we determine from

Equation 29.3 that the magnetic force is $F_B = -I\ell B$, where the negative sign indicates that the retarding force is to the left. Because this is the *only* horizontal force acting on the bar, Newton's second law applied to motion in the

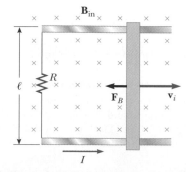
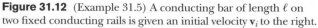

Figure 31.12 (Example 31.5) A conducting bar of length ℓ on two fixed conducting rails is given an initial velocity $\mathbf{v}_i$ to the right.

horizontal direction gives

$$F_x = ma = m \frac{dv}{dt} = -I\ell B$$

From Equation 31.6, we know that $I = B\ell v/R$, and so we can write this expression as

$$m \frac{dv}{dt} = -\frac{B^2\ell^2}{R} v$$

$$\frac{dv}{v} = -\left(\frac{B^2\ell^2}{mR}\right) dt$$

Integrating this equation using the initial condition that $v = v_i$ at $t = 0$, we find that

$$\int_{v_i}^{v} \frac{dv}{v} = \frac{-B^2\ell^2}{mR} \int_{0}^{t} dt$$

$$\ln\left(\frac{v}{v_i}\right) = -\left(\frac{B^2\ell^2}{mR}\right) t = -\frac{t}{\tau}$$

where the constant $\tau = mR/B^2\ell^2$. From this result, we see that the velocity can be expressed in the exponential form

$$(1) \qquad v = v_i e^{-t/\tau}$$

To finalize the problem, note that this expression for v indicates that the velocity of the bar decreases with time under the action of the magnetic retarding force, as we expect from our conceptualization of the problem.

(B) The text of part (B) immediately categorizes this as a problem in energy conservation. Consider the sliding bar as one system possessing kinetic energy, which decreases because energy is transferring *out* of the system by electrical transmission through the rails. The resistor is another system possessing internal energy, which rises because energy is transferring *into* this system. Because energy is not leaving the combination of two systems, the rate of energy transfer out of the bar equals the rate of energy transfer into the resistor. Thus,

$$\mathcal{P}_{resistor} = -\mathcal{P}_{bar}$$

where the negative sign is necessary because energy is leaving the bar and $\mathcal{P}_{bar}$ is a negative number. Substituting for the electrical power delivered to the resistor and the

time rate of change of kinetic energy for the bar, we have

$$I^2 R = -\frac{d}{dt}\left(\tfrac{1}{2} mv^2\right)$$

Using Equation 31.6 for the current and carrying out the derivative, we find

$$\frac{B^2\ell^2 v^2}{R} = -mv \frac{dv}{dt}$$

Rearranging terms gives

$$\frac{dv}{v} = -\left(\frac{B^2\ell^2}{mR}\right) dt$$

To finalize this part of the problem, note that this is the same expression that we obtained in part (A).

What If? Suppose you wished to increase the distance through which the bar moves between the time when it is initially projected and the time when it essentially comes to rest. You can do this by changing one of three variables: v_i, R, or B, by a factor of 2 or $\frac{1}{2}$. Which variable should you change in order to maximize the distance, and would you double it or halve it?

Answer Increasing v_i would make the bar move farther. Increasing R would decrease the current and, therefore, the magnetic force, making the bar move farther. Decreasing B would decrease the magnetic force and make the bar move farther. But which is most effective?

We use Equation (1) to find the distance that the bar moves by integration:

$$v = \frac{dx}{dt} = v_i e^{-t/\tau}$$

$$x = \int_{0}^{\infty} v_i e^{-t/\tau} dt = -v_i \tau e^{-t/\tau} \Big|_{0}^{\infty}$$

$$= -v_i \tau(0 - 1) = v_i \tau = v_i \left(\frac{mR}{B^2\ell^2}\right)$$

From this expression, we see that doubling v_i or R will double the distance. But changing B by a factor of $\frac{1}{2}$ causes the distance to be four times as great!

At the *Interactive Worked Example* link at **http://www.pse6.com,** *you can study the motion of the bar after it is released.*

31.3 Lenz's Law

Faraday's law (Eq. 31.1) indicates that the induced emf and the change in flux have opposite algebraic signs. This has a very real physical interpretation that has come to be known as **Lenz's law**[1]:

> The induced current in a loop is in the direction that creates a magnetic field that opposes the change in magnetic flux through the area enclosed by the loop.

Lenz's law

---

[1] Developed by the German physicist Heinrich Lenz (1804–1865).

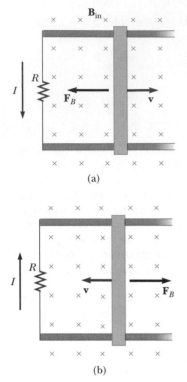

(a)

(b)

Figure 31.13 (a) As the conducting bar slides on the two fixed conducting rails, the magnetic flux due to the external magnetic field into the page through the area enclosed by the loop increases in time. By Lenz's law, the induced current must be counterclockwise so as to produce a counteracting magnetic field directed out of the page. (b) When the bar moves to the left, the induced current must be clockwise. Why?

That is, the induced current tends to keep the original magnetic flux through the circuit from changing. We shall show that this law is a consequence of the law of conservation of energy.

To understand Lenz's law, let us return to the example of a bar moving to the right on two parallel rails in the presence of a uniform magnetic field (the *external* magnetic field, Fig. 31.13a.) As the bar moves to the right, the magnetic flux through the area enclosed by the circuit increases with time because the area increases. Lenz's law states that the induced current must be directed so that the magnetic field it produces opposes the change in the external magnetic flux. Because the magnetic flux due to an external field directed into the page is increasing, the induced current, if it is to oppose this change, must produce a field directed out of the page. Hence, the induced current must be directed counterclockwise when the bar moves to the right. (Use the right-hand rule to verify this direction.) If the bar is moving to the left, as in Figure 31.13b, the external magnetic flux through the area enclosed by the loop decreases with time. Because the field is directed into the page, the direction of the induced current must be clockwise if it is to produce a field that also is directed into the page. In either case, the induced current tends to maintain the original flux through the area enclosed by the current loop.

Let us examine this situation using energy considerations. Suppose that the bar is given a slight push to the right. In the preceding analysis, we found that this motion sets up a counterclockwise current in the loop. What happens if we assume that the

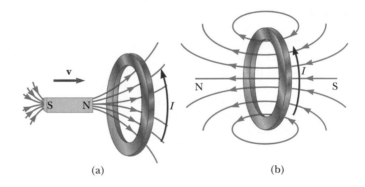

(a)   **(b)**

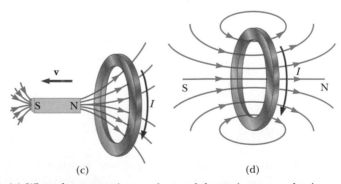

(c)   **(d)**

Figure 31.14 (a) When the magnet is moved toward the stationary conducting loop, a current is induced in the direction shown. The magnetic field lines shown are those due to the bar magnet. (b) This induced current produces its own magnetic field directed to the left that counteracts the increasing external flux. The magnetic field lines shown are those due to the induced current in the ring. (c) When the magnet is moved away from the stationary conducting loop, a current is induced in the direction shown. The magnetic field lines shown are those due to the bar magnet. (d) This induced current produces a magnetic field directed to the right and so counteracts the decreasing external flux. The magnetic field lines shown are those due to the induced current in the ring.

current is clockwise, such that the direction of the magnetic force exerted on the bar is to the right? This force would accelerate the rod and increase its velocity. This, in turn, would cause the area enclosed by the loop to increase more rapidly; this would result in an increase in the induced current, which would cause an increase in the force, which would produce an increase in the current, and so on. In effect, the system would acquire energy with no input of energy. This is clearly inconsistent with all experience and violates the law of conservation of energy. Thus, we are forced to conclude that the current must be counterclockwise.

Let us consider another situation, one in which a bar magnet moves toward a stationary metal loop, as in Figure 31.14a. As the magnet moves to the right toward the loop, the external magnetic flux through the loop increases with time. To counteract this increase in flux due to a field toward the right, the induced current produces its own magnetic field to the left, as illustrated in Figure 31.14b; hence, the induced current is in the direction shown. Knowing that like magnetic poles repel each other, we conclude that the left face of the current loop acts like a north pole and that the right face acts like a south pole.

If the magnet moves to the left, as in Figure 31.14c, its flux through the area enclosed by the loop decreases in time. Now the induced current in the loop is in the direction shown in Figure 31.14d because this current direction produces a magnetic field in the same direction as the external field. In this case, the left face of the loop is a south pole and the right face is a north pole.

Quick Quiz 31.7   Figure 31.15 shows a magnet being moved in the vicinity of a solenoid connected to a sensitive ammeter. The south pole of the magnet is the pole nearest the solenoid, and the ammeter indicates a clockwise (viewed from above) current in the solenoid. Is the person (a) inserting the magnet or (b) pulling it out?

Quick Quiz 31.8   Figure 31.16 shows a circular loop of wire being dropped toward a wire carrying a current to the left. The direction of the induced current in the loop of wire is (a) clockwise (b) counterclockwise (c) zero (d) impossible to determine.

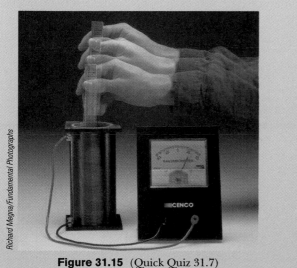

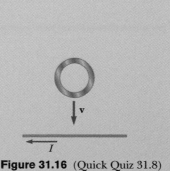

Figure 31.15 (Quick Quiz 31.7)   **Figure 31.16** (Quick Quiz 31.8)

Conceptual Example 31.6 Application of Lenz's Law

A metal ring is placed near a solenoid, as shown in Figure 31.17a. Find the direction of the induced current in the ring

(A) at the instant the switch in the circuit containing the solenoid is thrown closed,

(B) after the switch has been closed for several seconds, and

(C) at the instant the switch is thrown open.

Solution (A) At the instant the switch is thrown closed, the situation changes from one in which no magnetic flux exists in the ring to one in which flux exists and the magnetic field is to the left as shown in Figure 31.17b. To counteract this change in the flux, the current induced in the ring must set up a magnetic field directed from left to right in Figure 31.17b. This requires a current directed as shown.

(B) After the switch has been closed for several seconds, no change in the magnetic flux through the loop occurs; hence, the induced current in the ring is zero.

(C) Opening the switch changes the situation from one in which magnetic flux exists in the ring to one in which there is no magnetic flux. The direction of the induced current is as shown in Figure 31.17c because current in this direction

produces a magnetic field that is directed right to left and so counteracts the decrease in the flux produced by the solenoid.

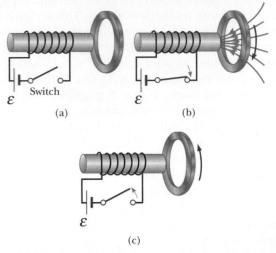

Figure 31.17 (Example 31.6) A current is induced in a metal ring near a solenoid when the switch is opened or thrown closed.

Conceptual Example 31.7 A Loop Moving Through a Magnetic Field

A rectangular metallic loop of dimensions ℓ and w and resistance R moves with constant speed v to the right, as in Figure 31.18a. The loop passes through a uniform magnetic field **B** directed into the page and extending a distance $3w$ along the x axis. Defining x as the position of the right side of the loop along the x axis, plot as functions of x

(A) the magnetic flux through the area enclosed by the loop,

(B) the induced motional emf, and

(C) the external applied force necessary to counter the magnetic force and keep v constant.

Solution (A) Figure 31.18b shows the flux through the area enclosed by the loop as a function of x. Before the loop enters the field, the flux is zero. As the loop enters the field, the flux increases linearly with position until the left edge of

the loop is just inside the field. Finally, the flux through the loop decreases linearly to zero as the loop leaves the field.

(B) Before the loop enters the field, no motional emf is induced in it because no field is present (Fig. 31.18c). As the right side of the loop enters the field, the magnetic flux directed into the page increases. Hence, according to Lenz's law, the induced current is counterclockwise because it must produce its own magnetic field directed out of the page. The motional emf $-B\ell v$ (from Eq. 31.5) arises from the magnetic force experienced by charges in the right side of the loop. When the loop is entirely in the field, the change in magnetic flux is zero, and hence the motional emf vanishes. This happens because, once the left side of the loop enters the field, the motional emf induced in it cancels the motional emf present in the right side of the loop. As the right side of the loop leaves the field, the flux begins to decrease, a clockwise

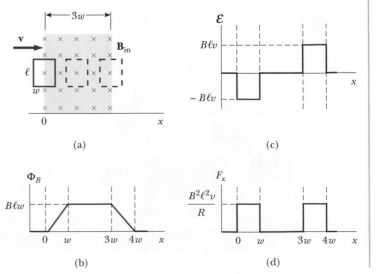

Figure 31.18 (Conceptual Example 31.7) (a) A conducting rectangular loop of width w and length ℓ moving with a velocity **v** through a uniform magnetic field extending a distance $3w$. (b) Magnetic flux through the area enclosed by the loop as a function of loop position. (c) Induced emf as a function of loop position. (d) Applied force required for constant velocity as a function of loop position.

current is induced, and the induced emf is $B\ell v$. As soon as the left side leaves the field, the emf decreases to zero.

(C) The external force that must be applied to the loop to maintain this motion is plotted in Figure 31.18d. Before the loop enters the field, no magnetic force acts on it; hence, the applied force must be zero if v is constant. When the right side of the loop enters the field, the applied force necessary to maintain constant speed must be equal in magnitude and opposite in direction to the magnetic force exerted on that side. When the loop is entirely in the field, the flux through the loop is not changing with time. Hence, the net emf induced in

the loop is zero, and the current also is zero. Therefore, no external force is needed to maintain the motion. Finally, as the right side leaves the field, the applied force must be equal in magnitude and opposite in direction to the magnetic force acting on the left side of the loop.

From this analysis, we conclude that power is supplied only when the loop is either entering or leaving the field. Furthermore, this example shows that the motional emf induced in the loop can be zero even when there is motion through the field! A motional emf is induced *only* when the magnetic flux through the loop *changes in time*.

31.4 Induced emf and Electric Fields

We have seen that a changing magnetic flux induces an emf and a current in a conducting loop. In our study of electricity, we related a current to an electric field that applies electric forces on charged particles. In the same way, we can relate an induced current in a conducting loop to an electric field by claiming that **an electric field is created in the conductor as a result of the changing magnetic flux.**

We also noted in our study of electricity that the existence of an electric field is independent of the presence of any test charges. This suggests that even in the absence of a conducting loop, a changing magnetic field would still generate an electric field in empty space.

This induced electric field is *nonconservative*, unlike the electrostatic field produced by stationary charges. We can illustrate this point by considering a conducting loop of radius r situated in a uniform magnetic field that is perpendicular to the plane of the loop, as in Figure 31.19. If the magnetic field changes with time, then, according to Faraday's law (Eq. 31.1), an emf $\mathcal{E} = -\,d\Phi_B/dt$ is induced in the loop. The induction of a current in the loop implies the presence of an induced electric field **E**, which must be tangent to the loop because this is the direction in which the charges in the wire move in response to the electric force. The work done by the electric field in moving a test charge q once around the loop is equal to $q\mathcal{E}$. Because the electric force acting on the charge is $q\mathbf{E}$, the work done by the electric field in moving the charge once around the loop is $qE(2\pi r)$, where $2\pi r$ is the circumference of the loop. These two expressions for the work done must be equal; therefore, we see that

$$q\mathcal{E} = qE(2\pi r)$$

$$E = \frac{\mathcal{E}}{2\pi r}$$

Using this result, along with Equation 31.1 and the fact that $\Phi_B = BA = \pi r^2 B$ for a circular loop, we find that the induced electric field can be expressed as

$$E = -\frac{1}{2\pi r}\frac{d\Phi_B}{dt} = -\frac{r}{2}\frac{dB}{dt} \qquad (31.8)$$

If the time variation of the magnetic field is specified, we can easily calculate the induced electric field from Equation 31.8.

The emf for any closed path can be expressed as the line integral of $\mathbf{E} \cdot d\mathbf{s}$ over that path: $\mathcal{E} = \oint \mathbf{E} \cdot d\mathbf{s}$. In more general cases, E may not be constant, and the path may not be a circle. Hence, Faraday's law of induction, $\mathcal{E} = -\,d\Phi_B/dt$, can be written in the general form

$$\oint \mathbf{E} \cdot d\mathbf{s} = -\frac{d\Phi_B}{dt} \qquad (31.9)$$

The induced electric field E in Equation 31.9 is a nonconservative field that is generated by a changing magnetic field. The field **E** that satisfies Equation 31.9

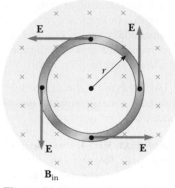

Figure 31.19 A conducting loop of radius r in a uniform magnetic field perpendicular to the plane of the loop. If **B** changes in time, an electric field is induced in a direction tangent to the circumference of the loop.

▲ **PITFALL PREVENTION**

31.2 Induced Electric Fields

The changing magnetic field does *not* need to be in existence at the location of the induced electric field. In Figure 31.19, even a loop outside the region of magnetic field will experience an induced electric field. For another example, consider Figure 31.8. The light bulbs glow (if the switch is open) even though the wires are outside the region of the magnetic field.

Faraday's law in general form

cannot possibly be an electrostatic field because if the field were electrostatic, and hence conservative, the line integral of $\mathbf{E} \cdot d\mathbf{s}$ over a closed loop would be zero (Section 25.1); this would be in contradiction to Equation 31.9.

Quick Quiz 31.9 In a region of space, the magnetic field increases at a constant rate. This changing magnetic field induces an electric field that (a) increases in time (b) is conservative (c) is in the direction of the magnetic field (d) has a constant magnitude.

Example 31.8   Electric Field Induced by a Changing Magnetic Field in a Solenoid

A long solenoid of radius R has n turns of wire per unit length and carries a time-varying current that varies sinusoidally as $I = I_{max} \cos \omega t$, where I_{max} is the maximum current and ω is the angular frequency of the alternating current source (Fig. 31.20).

(A) Determine the magnitude of the induced electric field outside the solenoid at a distance $r > R$ from its long central axis.

Solution First let us consider an external point and take the path for our line integral to be a circle of radius r centered on the solenoid, as illustrated in Figure 31.20. By symmetry we see that the magnitude of $\mathbf{E}$ is constant on this path and that $\mathbf{E}$ is tangent to it. The magnetic flux through the area enclosed by this path is $BA = B\pi R^2$; hence, Equation 31.9 gives

$$\oint \mathbf{E} \cdot d\mathbf{s} = -\frac{d}{dt}(B\pi R^2) = -\pi R^2 \frac{dB}{dt}$$

$$(1) \qquad \oint \mathbf{E} \cdot d\mathbf{s} = E(2\pi r) = -\pi R^2 \frac{dB}{dt}$$

The magnetic field inside a long solenoid is given by Equation 30.17, $B = \mu_0 nI$. When we substitute the expression $I = I_{max} \cos \omega t$ into this equation for B and then substitute the result into Equation (1), we find that

$$E(2\pi r) = -\pi R^2 \mu_0 nI_{max} \frac{d}{dt}(\cos \omega t)$$

$$= \pi R^2 \mu_0 nI_{max} \omega \sin \omega t$$

$$(2) \qquad E = \frac{\mu_0 nI_{max}\omega R^2}{2r} \sin \omega t \qquad \text{(for } r > R)$$

Hence, the amplitude of the electric field outside the solenoid falls off as $1/r$ and varies sinusoidally with time.

(B) What is the magnitude of the induced electric field inside the solenoid, a distance r from its axis?

Solution For an interior point $(r < R)$, the flux through an integration loop is given by $B\pi r^2$. Using the same procedure as in part (A), we find that

$$E(2\pi r) = -\pi r^2 \frac{dB}{dt} = \pi r^2 \mu_0 nI_{max} \omega \sin \omega t$$

$$(3) \qquad E = \frac{\mu_0 nI_{max}\omega}{2} r \sin \omega t \qquad \text{(for } r < R)$$

This shows that the amplitude of the electric field induced inside the solenoid by the changing magnetic flux through the solenoid increases linearly with r and varies sinusoidally with time.

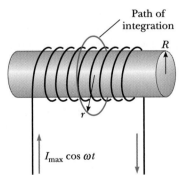

Figure 31.20 (Example 31.8) A long solenoid carrying a time-varying current given by $I = I_{max} \cos \omega t$. An electric field is induced both inside and outside the solenoid.

31.5   Generators and Motors

Electric generators take in energy by work and transfer it out by electrical transmission. To understand how they operate, let us consider the **alternating current** (AC) **generator**. In its simplest form, it consists of a loop of wire rotated by some external means in a magnetic field (Fig. 31.21a).

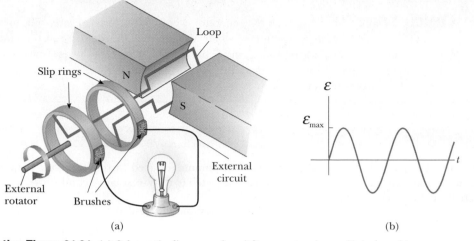

(a)   (b)

Active Figure 31.21 (a) Schematic diagram of an AC generator. An emf is induced in a loop that rotates in a magnetic field. (b) The alternating emf induced in the loop plotted as a function of time.

At the *Active Figures link* at http://www.pse6.com, *you can adjust the speed of rotation and the strength of the field to see the effects on the emf generated.*

In commercial power plants, the energy required to rotate the loop can be derived from a variety of sources. For example, in a hydroelectric plant, falling water directed against the blades of a turbine produces the rotary motion; in a coal-fired plant, the energy released by burning coal is used to convert water to steam, and this steam is directed against the turbine blades. As a loop rotates in a magnetic field, the magnetic flux through the area enclosed by the loop changes with time; this induces an emf and a current in the loop according to Faraday's law. The ends of the loop are connected to slip rings that rotate with the loop. Connections from these slip rings, which act as output terminals of the generator, to the external circuit are made by stationary brushes in contact with the slip rings.

Suppose that, instead of a single turn, the loop has N turns (a more practical situation), all of the same area A, and rotates in a magnetic field with a constant angular speed ω. If θ is the angle between the magnetic field and the normal to the plane of the loop, as in Figure 31.22, then the magnetic flux through the loop at any time t is

$$\Phi_B = BA \cos \theta = BA \cos \omega t$$

where we have used the relationship $\theta = \omega t$ between angular position and angular speed (see Eq. 10.3). (We have set the clock so that $t = 0$ when $\theta = 0$.) Hence, the induced emf in the coil is

$$\mathcal{E} = -N \frac{d\Phi_B}{dt} = -NAB \frac{d}{dt}(\cos \omega t) = NAB\omega \sin \omega t \qquad (31.10)$$

This result shows that the emf varies sinusoidally with time, as plotted in Figure 31.21b. From Equation 31.10 we see that the maximum emf has the value

$$\mathcal{E}_{max} = NAB\omega \qquad (31.11)$$

which occurs when $\omega t = 90°$ or $270°$. In other words, $\mathcal{E} = \mathcal{E}_{max}$ when the magnetic field is in the plane of the coil and the time rate of change of flux is a maximum. Furthermore, the emf is zero when $\omega t = 0$ or $180°$, that is, when **B** is perpendicular to the plane of the coil and the time rate of change of flux is zero.

The frequency for commercial generators in the United States and Canada is 60 Hz, whereas in some European countries it is 50 Hz. (Recall that $\omega = 2\pi f$, where f is the frequency in hertz.)

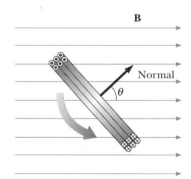

Figure 31.22 A loop enclosing an area A and containing N turns, rotating with constant angular speed ω in a magnetic field. The emf induced in the loop varies sinusoidally in time.

Example 31.9   emf Induced in a Generator

An AC generator consists of 8 turns of wire, each of area $A = 0.090\ 0\ \text{m}^2$, and the total resistance of the wire is $12.0\ \Omega$. The loop rotates in a 0.500-T magnetic field at a constant frequency of 60.0 Hz.

(A) Find the maximum induced emf.

Solution First, note that $\omega = 2\pi f = 2\pi(60.0\ \text{Hz}) = 377\ \text{s}^{-1}$. Thus, Equation 31.11 gives

$$\mathcal{E}_{\text{max}} = NAB\omega = 8(0.090\ 0\ \text{m}^2)(0.500\ \text{T})(377\ \text{s}^{-1})$$

$$= \boxed{136\ \text{V}}$$

(B) What is the maximum induced current when the output terminals are connected to a low-resistance conductor?

Solution From Equation 27.8 and the results to part (A), we have

$$I_{\text{max}} = \frac{\mathcal{E}_{\text{max}}}{R} = \frac{136\ \text{V}}{12.0\ \Omega} = \boxed{11.3\ \text{A}}$$

The **direct current** (DC) **generator** is illustrated in Figure 31.23a. Such generators are used, for instance, in older cars to charge the storage batteries. The components are essentially the same as those of the AC generator except that the contacts to the rotating loop are made using a split ring called a *commutator.*

In this configuration, the output voltage always has the same polarity and pulsates with time, as shown in Figure 31.23b. We can understand the reason for this by noting that the contacts to the split ring reverse their roles every half cycle. At the same time, the polarity of the induced emf reverses; hence, the polarity of the split ring (which is the same as the polarity of the output voltage) remains the same.

A pulsating DC current is not suitable for most applications. To obtain a more steady DC current, commercial DC generators use many coils and commutators distributed so that the sinusoidal pulses from the various coils are out of phase. When these pulses are superimposed, the DC output is almost free of fluctuations.

Motors are devices into which energy is transferred by electrical transmission while energy is transferred out by work. Essentially, a motor is a generator operating

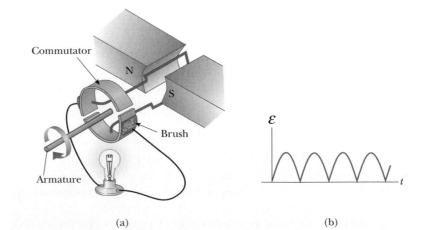

(a)   (b)

At the Active Figures link at http://www.pse6.com, you can adjust the speed of rotation and the strength of the field to see the effects on the emf generated.

Active Figure 31.23 (a) Schematic diagram of a DC generator. (b) The magnitude of the emf varies in time but the polarity never changes.

in reverse. Instead of generating a current by rotating a coil, a current is supplied to the coil by a battery, and the torque acting on the current-carrying coil causes it to rotate.

Useful mechanical work can be done by attaching the rotating coil to some external device. However, as the coil rotates in a magnetic field, the changing magnetic flux induces an emf in the coil; this induced emf always acts to reduce the current in the coil. If this were not the case, Lenz's law would be violated. The back emf increases in magnitude as the rotational speed of the coil increases. (The phrase *back emf* is used to indicate an emf that tends to reduce the supplied current.) Because the voltage available to supply current equals the difference between the supply voltage and the back emf, the current in the rotating coil is limited by the back emf.

When a motor is turned on, there is initially no back emf; thus, the current is very large because it is limited only by the resistance of the coil. As the coil begins to rotate, the induced back emf opposes the applied voltage, and the current in the coil is reduced. If the mechanical load increases, the motor slows down; this causes the back emf to decrease. This reduction in the back emf increases the current in the coil and therefore also increases the power needed from the external voltage source. For this reason, the power requirements for starting a motor and for running it are greater for heavy loads than for light ones. If the motor is allowed to run under no mechanical load, the back emf reduces the current to a value just large enough to overcome energy losses due to internal energy and friction. If a very heavy load jams the motor so that it cannot rotate, the lack of a back emf can lead to dangerously high current in the motor's wire. This is a dangerous situation, and is explored in the **What If?** section of Example 31.10.

A current application of motors in automobiles is seen in the development of *hybrid drive systems*. In these automobiles, a gasoline engine and an electric motor are combined to increase the fuel economy of the vehicle and reduce its emissions. Figure 31.24 shows the engine compartment of the Toyota Prius, which is one of a small number of hybrids available in the United States. In this automobile, power to the wheels can come from either the gasoline engine or the electric motor. In normal driving, the electric motor accelerates the vehicle from rest until it is moving at a speed of about 15 mi/h (24 km/h). During this acceleration period, the engine is not running, so that gasoline is not used and there is no emission. When a hybrid vehicle brakes, the motor acts as a generator and returns some of the kinetic energy of the vehicle back to the battery as stored energy. In a normal vehicle, this kinetic energy is simply lost as it is transformed to internal energy in the brakes and roadway.

Figure 31.24 The engine compartment of the Toyota Prius, a hybrid vehicle.

Example 31.10 The Induced Current in a Motor

Assume that a motor in which the coil has a total resistance of 10 Ω is supplied by a voltage of 120 V. When the motor is running at its maximum speed, the back emf is 70 V. Find the current in the coil

(A) when the motor is turned on and

(B) when it has reached maximum speed.

Solution (A) When the motor is first turned on, the back emf is zero (because the coil is motionless). Thus, the current in the coil is a maximum and equal to

$$I = \frac{\mathcal{E}}{R} = \frac{120 \text{ V}}{10 \ \Omega} = \boxed{12 \text{ A}}$$

(B) At the maximum speed, the back emf has its maximum value. Thus, the effective supply voltage is that of the external source minus the back emf. Hence, the current is reduced to

$$I = \frac{\mathcal{E} - \mathcal{E}_{\text{back}}}{R} = \frac{120 \text{ V} - 70 \text{ V}}{10 \ \Omega} = \frac{50 \text{ V}}{10 \ \Omega} = \boxed{5.0 \text{ A}}$$

What If? Suppose that this motor is in a circular saw. You are operating the saw and the blade becomes jammed in a piece of wood so that the motor cannot turn. By what percentage does the power input to the motor increase when it is jammed?

Answer You may have everyday experiences with motors becoming warm when they are prevented from turning. This is due to the increased power input to the motor. The higher rate of energy transfer results in an increase in internal energy of the coil, an undesirable effect. When the motor is jammed, the current is that given in part (A). Let us set up the ratio of power input to the motor when jammed to that when it is not jammed:

$$\frac{\mathcal{P}_{\text{jammed}}}{\mathcal{P}_{\text{not jammed}}} = \frac{I_{(A)}^2 R}{I_{(B)}^2 R} = \frac{I_{(A)}^2}{I_{(B)}^2}$$

where the subscripts (A) and (B) refer to the currents in parts (A) and (B) of the example. Substituting these values,

$$\frac{\mathcal{P}_{\text{jammed}}}{\mathcal{P}_{\text{not jammed}}} = \frac{(12 \text{ A})^2}{(5.0 \text{ A})^2} = 5.76$$

This represents a 476% increase in the input power! Such a high power input can cause the coil to become so hot that it is damaged.

31.6 Eddy Currents

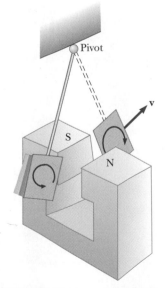

Figure 31.25 Formation of eddy currents in a conducting plate moving through a magnetic field. As the plate enters or leaves the field, the changing magnetic flux induces an emf, which causes eddy currents in the plate.

As we have seen, an emf and a current are induced in a circuit by a changing magnetic flux. In the same manner, circulating currents called **eddy currents** are induced in bulk pieces of metal moving through a magnetic field. This can easily be demonstrated by allowing a flat copper or aluminum plate attached at the end of a rigid bar to swing back and forth through a magnetic field (Fig. 31.25). As the plate enters the field, the changing magnetic flux induces an emf in the plate, which in turn causes the free electrons in the plate to move, producing the swirling eddy currents. According to Lenz's law, the direction of the eddy currents is such that they create magnetic fields that oppose the change that causes the currents. For this reason, the eddy currents must produce effective magnetic poles on the plate, which are repelled by the poles of the magnet; this gives rise to a repulsive force that opposes the motion of the plate. (If the opposite were true, the plate would accelerate and its energy would increase after each swing, in violation of the law of conservation of energy.)

As indicated in Figure 31.26a, with **B** directed into the page, the induced eddy current is counterclockwise as the swinging plate enters the field at position 1. This is because the flux due to the external magnetic field into the page through the plate is increasing, and hence by Lenz's law the induced current must provide its own magnetic field out of the page. The opposite is true as the plate leaves the field at position 2, where the current is clockwise. Because the induced eddy current always produces a magnetic retarding force $\mathbf{F}_B$ when the plate enters or leaves the field, the swinging plate eventually comes to rest.

If slots are cut in the plate, as shown in Figure 31.26b, the eddy currents and the corresponding retarding force are greatly reduced. We can understand this

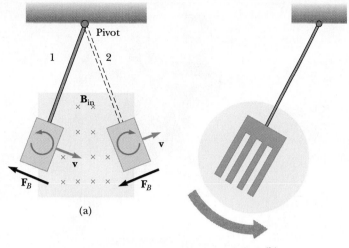

Active Figure 31.26 (a) As the conducting plate enters the field (position 1), the eddy currents are counterclockwise. As the plate leaves the field (position 2), the currents are clockwise. In either case, the force on the plate is opposite the velocity, and eventually the plate comes to rest. (b) When slots are cut in the conducting plate, the eddy currents are reduced and the plate swings more freely through the magnetic field.

Choose to let a solid or a slotted plate swing through the magnetic field and observe the effect at the Active Figures link at http://www.pse6.com.

by realizing that the cuts in the plate prevent the formation of any large current loops.

The braking systems on many subway and rapid-transit cars make use of electromagnetic induction and eddy currents. An electromagnet attached to the train is positioned near the steel rails. (An electromagnet is essentially a solenoid with an iron core.) The braking action occurs when a large current is passed through the electromagnet. The relative motion of the magnet and rails induces eddy currents in the rails, and the direction of these currents produces a drag force on the moving train. Because the eddy currents decrease steadily in magnitude as the train slows down, the braking effect is quite smooth. As a safety measure, some power tools use eddy currents to stop rapidly spinning blades once the device is turned off.

Eddy currents are often undesirable because they represent a transformation of mechanical energy to internal energy. To reduce this energy loss, conducting parts are often laminated—that is, they are built up in thin layers separated by a nonconducting material such as lacquer or a metal oxide. This layered structure increases the resistance of eddy current paths and effectively confines the currents to individual layers. Such a laminated structure is used in transformer cores (see Section 33.8) and motors to minimize eddy currents and thereby increase the efficiency of these devices.

Quick Quiz 31.11 In equal-arm balances from the early twentieth century (Fig. 31.27), it is sometimes observed that an aluminum sheet hangs from one of the arms and passes between the poles of a magnet. This causes the oscillations of the equal-arm balance to decay rapidly. In the absence of such magnetic braking, the oscillation might continue for a very long time, so that the experimenter would have to wait to take a reading. The oscillations decay because (a) the aluminum sheet is attracted to the magnet; (b) currents in the aluminum sheet set up a magnetic field that opposes the oscillations; (c) aluminum is paramagnetic.

John W. Jewett, Jr.

Figure 31.27 (Quick Quiz 31.11) In an old-fashioned equal-arm balance, an aluminum sheet hangs between the poles of a magnet.

31.7 Maxwell's Equations

We conclude this chapter by presenting four equations that are regarded as the basis of all electrical and magnetic phenomena. These equations, developed by James Clerk Maxwell, are as fundamental to electromagnetic phenomena as Newton's laws are to mechanical phenomena. In fact, the theory that Maxwell developed was more far-reaching than even he imagined because it turned out to be in agreement with the special theory of relativity, as Einstein showed in 1905.

Maxwell's equations represent the laws of electricity and magnetism that we have already discussed, but they have additional important consequences. In Chapter 34 we shall show that these equations predict the existence of electromagnetic waves (traveling patterns of electric and magnetic fields), which travel with a speed $c = 1/\sqrt{\mu_0 \epsilon_0} = 3.00 \times 10^8$ m/s, the speed of light. Furthermore, the theory shows that such waves are radiated by accelerating charges.

For simplicity, we present **Maxwell's equations** as applied to free space, that is, in the absence of any dielectric or magnetic material. The four equations are

Gauss's law

$$\oint_S \mathbf{E} \cdot d\mathbf{A} = \frac{q}{\epsilon_0} \qquad (31.12)$$

$$\oint_S \mathbf{B} \cdot d\mathbf{A} = 0 \tag{31.13}$$

$$\oint \mathbf{E} \cdot d\mathbf{s} = -\frac{d\Phi_B}{dt} \tag{31.14}$$

$$\oint \mathbf{B} \cdot d\mathbf{s} = \mu_0 I + \epsilon_0 \mu_0 \frac{d\Phi_E}{dt} \tag{31.15}$$

Equation 31.12 is Gauss's law: **the total electric flux through any closed surface equals the net charge inside that surface divided by ϵ_0.** This law relates an electric field to the charge distribution that creates it.

Equation 31.13, which can be considered Gauss's law in magnetism, states that **the net magnetic flux through a closed surface is zero.** That is, the number of magnetic field lines that enter a closed volume must equal the number that leave that volume. This implies that magnetic field lines cannot begin or end at any point. If they did, it would mean that isolated magnetic monopoles existed at those points. The fact that isolated magnetic monopoles have not been observed in nature can be taken as a confirmation of Equation 31.13.

Equation 31.14 is Faraday's law of induction, which describes the creation of an electric field by a changing magnetic flux. This law states that **the emf, which is the line integral of the electric field around any closed path, equals the rate of change of magnetic flux through any surface area bounded by that path.** One consequence of Faraday's law is the current induced in a conducting loop placed in a time-varying magnetic field.

Equation 31.15, usually called the Ampère–Maxwell law, is the generalized form of Ampère's law, and describes the creation of a magnetic field by an electric field and electric currents: **the line integral of the magnetic field around any closed path is the sum of μ_0 times the net current through that path and $\epsilon_0\mu_0$ times the rate of change of electric flux through any surface bounded by that path.**

Once the electric and magnetic fields are known at some point in space, the force acting on a particle of charge q can be calculated from the expression

$$\mathbf{F} = q\mathbf{E} + q\mathbf{v} \times \mathbf{B} \tag{31.16}$$

This relationship is called the **Lorentz force law.** (We saw this relationship earlier as Equation 29.16.) Maxwell's equations, together with this force law, completely describe all classical electromagnetic interactions.

It is interesting to note the symmetry of Maxwell's equations. Equations 31.12 and 31.13 are symmetric, apart from the absence of the term for magnetic monopoles in Equation 31.13. Furthermore, Equations 31.14 and 31.15 are symmetric in that the line integrals of $\mathbf{E}$ and $\mathbf{B}$ around a closed path are related to the rate of change of magnetic flux and electric flux, respectively. Maxwell's equations are of fundamental importance not only to electromagnetism but to all of science. Heinrich Hertz once wrote, "One cannot escape the feeling that these mathematical formulas have an independent existence and an intelligence of their own, that they are wiser than we are, wiser even than their discoverers, that we get more out of them than we put into them."

SUMMARY

Faraday's law of induction states that the emf induced in a circuit is directly proportional to the time rate of change of magnetic flux through the circuit:

$$\mathcal{E} = -\frac{d\Phi_B}{dt} \tag{31.1}$$

where $\Phi_B = \oint \mathbf{B} \cdot d\mathbf{A}$ is the magnetic flux.

Take a practice test for this chapter by clicking on the Practice Test link at http://www.pse6.com.

When a conducting bar of length ℓ moves at a velocity $\mathbf{v}$ through a magnetic field $\mathbf{B}$, where $\mathbf{B}$ is perpendicular to the bar and to $\mathbf{v}$, the **motional emf** induced in the bar is

$$\mathcal{E} = -B\ell v \tag{31.5}$$

Lenz's law states that the induced current and induced emf in a conductor are in such a direction as to set up a magnetic field that opposes the change that produced them.

A general form of **Faraday's law of induction** is

$$\mathcal{E} = \oint \mathbf{E} \cdot d\mathbf{s} = -\frac{d\Phi_B}{dt} \tag{31.9}$$

where $\mathbf{E}$ is the nonconservative electric field that is produced by the changing magnetic flux.

When used with the Lorentz force law, $\mathbf{F} = q\mathbf{E} + q\mathbf{v} \times \mathbf{B}$, **Maxwell's equations** describe all electromagnetic phenomena:

$$\oint_S \mathbf{E} \cdot d\mathbf{A} = \frac{q}{\epsilon_0} \tag{31.12}$$

$$\oint_S \mathbf{B} \cdot d\mathbf{A} = 0 \tag{31.13}$$

$$\oint \mathbf{E} \cdot d\mathbf{s} = -\frac{d\Phi_B}{dt} \tag{31.14}$$

$$\oint \mathbf{B} \cdot d\mathbf{s} = \mu_0 I + \epsilon_0 \mu_0 \frac{d\Phi_E}{dt} \tag{31.15}$$

QUESTIONS

1. What is the difference between magnetic flux and magnetic field?

2. A loop of wire is placed in a uniform magnetic field. For what orientation of the loop is the magnetic flux a maximum? For what orientation is the flux zero?

3. As the bar in Figure Q31.3 moves to the right, an electric field is set up directed downward in the bar. Explain why the electric field would be upward if the bar were moving to the left.

4. As the bar in Figure Q31.3 moves perpendicular to the field, is an external force required to keep it moving with constant speed?

5. The bar in Figure Q31.5 moves on rails to the right with a velocity $\mathbf{v}$, and the uniform, constant magnetic field is directed out of the page. Why is the induced current clockwise? If the bar were moving to the left, what would be the direction of the induced current?

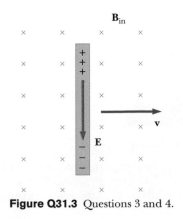

Figure Q31.3 Questions 3 and 4.

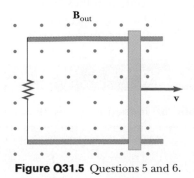

Figure Q31.5 Questions 5 and 6.

6. Explain why an applied force is necessary to keep the bar in Figure Q31.5 moving with a constant speed.

7. Wearing a metal bracelet in a region of strong magnetic field could be hazardous. Explain.

8. When a small magnet is moved toward a solenoid, an emf is induced in the coil. However, if the magnet is moved around inside a toroid, no measurable emf is induced. Explain.

9. How is energy produced in dams that is then transferred out by electrical transmission? (That is, how is the energy of motion of the water converted to energy that is transmitted by AC electricity?)

10. Will dropping a magnet down a long copper tube produce a current in the walls of the tube? Explain.

11. A piece of aluminum is dropped vertically downward between the poles of an electromagnet. Does the magnetic field affect the velocity of the aluminum?

12. What happens when the rotational speed of a generator coil is increased?

13. When the switch in Figure Q31.13a is closed, a current is set up in the coil and the metal ring springs upward (Fig. Q31.13b). Explain this behavior.

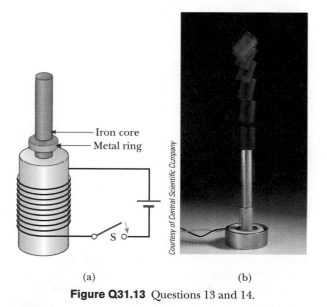

(a)   (b)

Figure Q31.13 Questions 13 and 14.

14. Assume that the battery in Figure Q31.13a is replaced by an AC source and the switch is held closed. If held down, the metal ring on top of the solenoid becomes hot. Why?

15. A bar magnet is held above a loop of wire in a horizontal plane, as shown in Figure Q31.15. The south end of the magnet is toward the loop of wire. The magnet is dropped toward the loop. Find the direction of the current through the resistor (a) while the magnet is falling toward the loop and (b) after the magnet has passed through the loop and moves away from it.

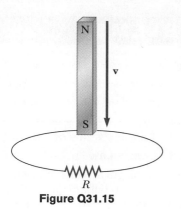

Figure Q31.15

16. Find the direction of the current in the resistor in Figure Q31.16 (a) at the instant the switch is closed, (b) after the switch has been closed for several minutes, and (c) at the instant the switch is opened.

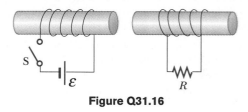

Figure Q31.16

17. Quick Quiz 31.4 describes the emf induced between the wingtips of an airplane by its motion in the Earth's magnetic field. Can this emf be used to power a light in the passenger compartment? Explain your answer.

18. Do Maxwell's equations allow for the existence of magnetic monopoles? Explain.

19. *Induction welding* has many important industrial applications. One example is the manufacture of airtight tubes, represented in Figure Q31.19. A sheet of metal is rolled into a cylinder and forced between compression rollers to bring its edges into contact. The tube then enters a coil carrying a time-varying current. The seam is welded when induced currents around the tube raise its temperature. Typically, a sinusoidal current with a frequency of 10 kHz is used. (a) What causes a current in the tube? (b) Why is a high frequency like 10 kHz chosen, rather than the 120 Hz commonly used for power transmission? (c) Why do the induced currents raise the temperature mainly of the seam, rather than all of the metal of the tube? (d) Why is it necessary to bring the edges of the sheet together with the compression rollers before the seam can be welded?

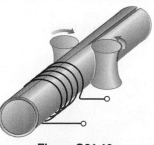

Figure Q31.19

PROBLEMS

1, 2, 3 = straightforward, intermediate, challenging   ☐ = full solution available in the *Student Solutions Manual and Study Guide*

🌀 = coached solution with hints available at http://www.pse.com   💻 = computer useful in solving problem

▒ = paired numerical and symbolic problems

Section 31.1   Faraday's Law of Induction
Section 31.3   Lenz's Law

1. A 50-turn rectangular coil of dimensions 5.00 cm × 10.0 cm is allowed to fall from a position where $B = 0$ to a new position where $B = 0.500$ T and the magnetic field is directed perpendicular to the plane of the coil. Calculate the magnitude of the average emf that is induced in the coil if the displacement occurs in 0.250 s.

2. A flat loop of wire consisting of a single turn of cross-sectional area 8.00 cm² is perpendicular to a magnetic field that increases uniformly in magnitude from 0.500 T to 2.50 T in 1.00 s. What is the resulting induced current if the loop has a resistance of 2.00 Ω?

3. A 25-turn circular coil of wire has diameter 1.00 m. It is placed with its axis along the direction of the Earth's magnetic field of 50.0 μT, and then in 0.200 s it is flipped 180°. An average emf of what magnitude is generated in the coil?

4. A rectangular loop of area A is placed in a region where the magnetic field is perpendicular to the plane of the loop. The magnitude of the field is allowed to vary in time according to $B = B_{max}e^{-t/\tau}$, where B_{max} and τ are constants. The field has the constant value B_{max} for $t < 0$. (a) Use Faraday's law to show that the emf induced in the loop is given by

$$\mathcal{E} = \frac{AB_{max}}{\tau}e^{-t/\tau}$$

(b) Obtain a numerical value for $\mathcal{E}$ at $t = 4.00$ s when $A = 0.160$ m², $B_{max} = 0.350$ T, and $\tau = 2.00$ s. (c) For the values of A, B_{max}, and τ given in (b), what is the maximum value of $\mathcal{E}$?

5. 🌀 A strong electromagnet produces a uniform magnetic field of 1.60 T over a cross-sectional area of 0.200 m². We place a coil having 200 turns and a total resistance of 20.0 Ω around the electromagnet. We then smoothly reduce the current in the electromagnet until it reaches zero in 20.0 ms. What is the current induced in the coil?

6. A magnetic field of 0.200 T exists within a solenoid of 500 turns and a diameter of 10.0 cm. How rapidly (that is, within what period of time) must the field be reduced to zero, if the average induced emf within the coil during this time interval is to be 10.0 kV?

7. 🌀 An aluminum ring of radius 5.00 cm and resistance 3.00×10^{-4} Ω is placed on top of a long air-core solenoid with 1 000 turns per meter and radius 3.00 cm, as shown in Figure P31.7. Over the area of the end of the solenoid, assume that the axial component of the field produced by the solenoid is half as strong as at the center of the solenoid. Assume the solenoid produces negligible field outside its cross-sectional area. The current in the solenoid is increasing at a rate of 270 A/s. (a) What is the induced current in the ring? At the center of the ring, what are (b) the magnitude and (c) the direction of the magnetic field produced by the induced current in the ring?

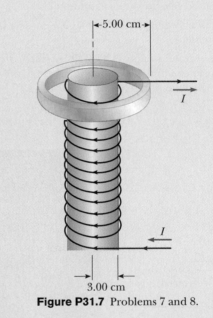

Figure P31.7 Problems 7 and 8.

8. An aluminum ring of radius r_1 and resistance R is placed around the top of a long air-core solenoid with n turns per meter and smaller radius r_2 as shown in Figure P31.7. Assume that the axial component of the field produced by the solenoid over the area of the end of the solenoid is half as strong as at the center of the solenoid. Assume that the solenoid produces negligible field outside its cross-sectional area. The current in the solenoid is increasing at a rate of $\Delta I/\Delta t$. (a) What is the induced current in the ring? (b) At the center of the ring, what is the magnetic field produced by the induced current in the ring? (c) What is the direction of this field?

9. (a) A loop of wire in the shape of a rectangle of width w and length L and a long, straight wire carrying a current I lie on a tabletop as shown in Figure P31.9. (a) Determine the magnetic flux through the loop due to the current I. (b) Suppose the current is changing with time according to $I = a + bt$, where a and b are constants. Determine the emf that is induced in the loop if $b = 10.0$ A/s, $h = 1.00$ cm, $w = 10.0$ cm, and $L = 100$ cm. What is the direction of the induced current in the rectangle?

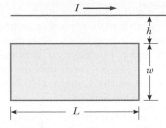

Figure P31.9 Problems 9 and 71.

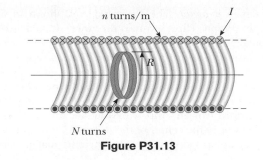

Figure P31.13

10. A coil of 15 turns and radius 10.0 cm surrounds a long solenoid of radius 2.00 cm and 1.00×10^3 turns/meter (Fig. P31.10). The current in the solenoid changes as $I = (5.00 \text{ A}) \sin(120t)$. Find the induced emf in the 15-turn coil as a function of time.

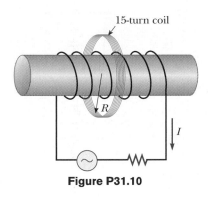

Figure P31.10

11. Find the current through section PQ of length $a = 65.0$ cm in Figure P31.11. The circuit is located in a magnetic field whose magnitude varies with time according to the expression $B = (1.00 \times 10^{-3} \text{ T/s}) t$. Assume the resistance per length of the wire is 0.100 Ω/m.

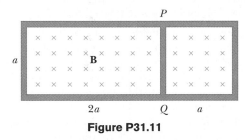

Figure P31.11

12. A 30-turn circular coil of radius 4.00 cm and resistance 1.00 Ω is placed in a magnetic field directed perpendicular to the plane of the coil. The magnitude of the magnetic field varies in time according to the expression $B = 0.010\,0t + 0.040\,0t^2$, where t is in seconds and B is in tesla. Calculate the induced emf in the coil at $t = 5.00$ s.

13. A long solenoid has $n = 400$ turns per meter and carries a current given by $I = (30.0 \text{ A})(1 - e^{-1.60t})$. Inside the solenoid and coaxial with it is a coil that has a radius of 6.00 cm and consists of a total of $N = 250$ turns of fine wire (Fig. P31.13). What emf is induced in the coil by the changing current?

14. An instrument based on induced emf has been used to measure projectile speeds up to 6 km/s. A small magnet is imbedded in the projectile, as shown in Figure P31.14. The projectile passes through two coils separated by a distance d. As the projectile passes through each coil a pulse of emf is induced in the coil. The time interval between pulses can be measured accurately with an oscilloscope, and thus the speed can be determined. (a) Sketch a graph of ΔV versus t for the arrangement shown. Consider a current that flows counterclockwise as viewed from the starting point of the projectile as positive. On your graph, indicate which pulse is from coil 1 and which is from coil 2. (b) If the pulse separation is 2.40 ms and $d = 1.50$ m, what is the projectile speed?

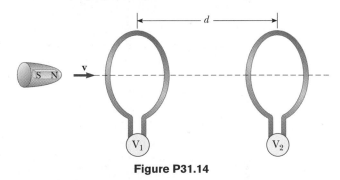

Figure P31.14

15. A coil formed by wrapping 50 turns of wire in the shape of a square is positioned in a magnetic field so that the normal to the plane of the coil makes an angle of 30.0° with the direction of the field. When the magnetic field is increased uniformly from 200 μT to 600 μT in 0.400 s, an emf of magnitude 80.0 mV is induced in the coil. What is the total length of the wire?

16. When a wire carries an AC current with a known frequency, you can use a *Rogowski coil* to determine the amplitude I_{max} of the current without disconnecting the wire to shunt the

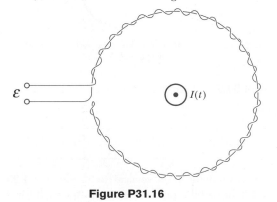

Figure P31.16

current in a meter. The Rogowski coil, shown in Figure P31.16, simply clips around the wire. It consists of a toroidal conductor wrapped around a circular return cord. The toroid has n turns per unit length and a cross-sectional area A. The current to be measured is given by $I(t) = I_{max} \sin \omega t$. (a) Show that the amplitude of the emf induced in the Rogowski coil is $\mathcal{E}_{max} = \mu_0 n A \omega I_{max}$. (b) Explain why the wire carrying the unknown current need not be at the center of the Rogowski coil, and why the coil will not respond to nearby currents that it does not enclose.

17. A toroid having a rectangular cross section ($a = 2.00$ cm by $b = 3.00$ cm) and inner radius $R = 4.00$ cm consists of 500 turns of wire that carries a sinusoidal current $I = I_{max} \sin \omega t$, with $I_{max} = 50.0$ A and a frequency $f = \omega/2\pi = 60.0$ Hz. A coil that consists of 20 turns of wire links with the toroid, as in Figure P31.17. Determine the emf induced in the coil as a function of time.

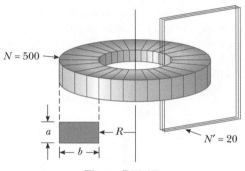

Figure P31.17

18. A piece of insulated wire is shaped into a figure 8, as in Figure P31.18. The radius of the upper circle is 5.00 cm and that of the lower circle is 9.00 cm. The wire has a uniform resistance per unit length of 3.00 Ω/m. A uniform magnetic field is applied perpendicular to the plane of the two circles, in the direction shown. The magnetic field is increasing at a constant rate of 2.00 T/s. Find the magnitude and direction of the induced current in the wire.

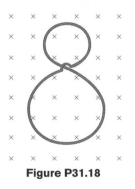

Figure P31.18

Section 31.2 Motional emf

Section 31.3 Lenz's Law

Problem 71 in Chapter 29 can be assigned with this section.

19. An automobile has a vertical radio antenna 1.20 m long. The automobile travels at 65.0 km/h on a horizontal road

where the Earth's magnetic field is 50.0 μT directed toward the north and downward at an angle of 65.0° below the horizontal. (a) Specify the direction that the automobile should move in order to generate the maximum motional emf in the antenna, with the top of the antenna positive relative to the bottom. (b) Calculate the magnitude of this induced emf.

20. Consider the arrangement shown in Figure P31.20. Assume that $R = 6.00$ Ω, $\ell = 1.20$ m, and a uniform 2.50-T magnetic field is directed into the page. At what speed should the bar be moved to produce a current of 0.500 A in the resistor?

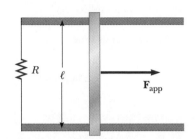

Figure P31.20 Problems 20, 21, and 22.

21. Figure P31.20 shows a top view of a bar that can slide without friction. The resistor is 6.00 Ω and a 2.50-T magnetic field is directed perpendicularly downward, into the paper. Let $\ell = 1.20$ m. (a) Calculate the applied force required to move the bar to the right at a constant speed of 2.00 m/s. (b) At what rate is energy delivered to the resistor?

22. A conducting rod of length ℓ moves on two horizontal, frictionless rails, as shown in Figure P31.20. If a constant force of 1.00 N moves the bar at 2.00 m/s through a magnetic field **B** that is directed into the page, (a) what is the current through the 8.00-Ω resistor R? (b) What is the rate at which energy is delivered to the resistor? (c) What is the mechanical power delivered by the force **F**$_{app}$?

23. Very large magnetic fields can be produced using a procedure called *flux compression*. A metallic cylindrical tube of radius R is placed coaxially in a long solenoid of somewhat larger radius. The space between the tube and the solenoid is filled with a highly explosive material. When the explosive is set off, it collapses the tube to a cylinder of radius $r < R$. If the collapse happens very rapidly, induced current in the tube maintains the magnetic flux nearly constant inside the tube. If the initial magnetic field in the solenoid is 2.50 T, and $R/r = 12.0$, what maximum value of magnetic field can be achieved?

24. The *homopolar generator*, also called the *Faraday disk*, is a low-voltage, high-current electric generator. It consists of a rotating conducting disk with one stationary brush (a sliding electrical contact) at its axle and another at a point on its circumference, as shown in Figure P31.24. A magnetic field is applied perpendicular to the plane of the disk. Assume the field is 0.900 T, the angular speed is 3 200 rev/min, and the radius of the disk is 0.400 m. Find the emf generated between the brushes. When superconducting coils are used to produce a large magnetic field, a homopolar generator can have a power output of several

megawatts. Such a generator is useful, for example, in purifying metals by electrolysis. If a voltage is applied to the output terminals of the generator, it runs in reverse as a *homopolar motor* capable of providing great torque, useful in ship propulsion.

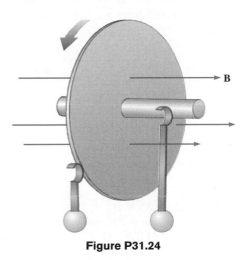

Figure P31.24

25. **Review problem.** A flexible metallic wire with linear density 3.00×10^{-3} kg/m is stretched between two fixed clamps 64.0 cm apart and held under tension 267 N. A magnet is placed near the wire as shown in Figure P31.25. Assume that the magnet produces a uniform field of 4.50 mT over a 2.00-cm length at the center of the wire, and a negligible field elsewhere. The wire is set vibrating at its fundamental (lowest) frequency. The section of the wire in the magnetic field moves with a uniform amplitude of 1.50 cm. Find (a) the frequency and (b) the amplitude of the electromotive force induced between the ends of the wire.

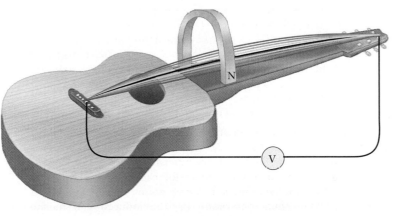

Figure P31.25

26. The square loop in Figure P31.26 is made of wires with total series resistance 10.0 Ω. It is placed in a uniform 0.100-T magnetic field directed perpendicularly into the plane of the paper. The loop, which is hinged at each corner, is pulled as shown until the separation between points A and B is 3.00 m. If this process takes 0.100 s, what is the average current generated in the loop? What is the direction of the current?

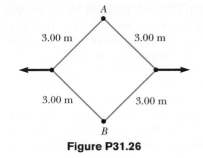

Figure P31.26

27. A helicopter (Figure P31.27) has blades of length 3.00 m, extending out from a central hub and rotating at 2.00 rev/s. If the vertical component of the Earth's magnetic field is 50.0 μT, what is the emf induced between the blade tip and the center hub?

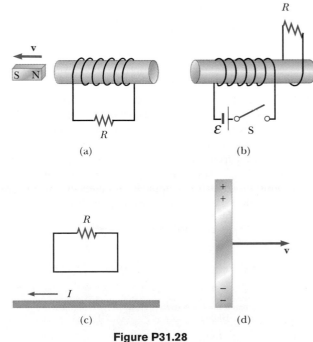

Figure P31.27

28. Use Lenz's law to answer the following questions concerning the direction of induced currents. (a) What is the direction of the induced current in resistor R in Figure P31.28a when the bar magnet is moved to the left? (b) What is the direction of the current induced in the resistor R immediately after the switch S in Figure P31.28b

Figure P31.28

is closed? (c) What is the direction of the induced current in R when the current I in Figure P31.28c decreases rapidly to zero? (d) A copper bar is moved to the right while its axis is maintained in a direction perpendicular to a magnetic field, as shown in Figure P31.28d. If the top of the bar becomes positive relative to the bottom, what is the direction of the magnetic field?

29. A rectangular coil with resistance R has N turns, each of length ℓ and width w as shown in Figure P31.29. The coil moves into a uniform magnetic field **B** with constant velocity **v**. What are the magnitude and direction of the total magnetic force on the coil (a) as it enters the magnetic field, (b) as it moves within the field, and (c) as it leaves the field?

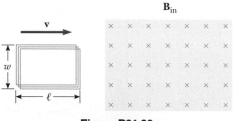

Figure P31.29

30. In Figure P31.30, the bar magnet is moved toward the loop. Is $V_a - V_b$ positive, negative, or zero? Explain.

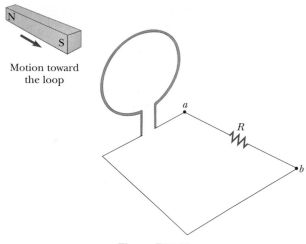

Figure P31.30

31. Two parallel rails with negligible resistance are 10.0 cm apart and are connected by a 5.00-Ω resistor. The circuit also contains two metal rods having resistances of 10.0 Ω and 15.0 Ω sliding along the rails (Fig. P31.31). The rods are pulled away from the resistor at constant speeds of 4.00 m/s and 2.00 m/s, respectively. A uniform magnetic field of magnitude 0.010 0 T is applied perpendicular to the plane of the rails. Determine the current in the 5.00-Ω resistor.

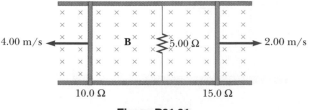

Figure P31.31

Section 31.4   Induced emf and Electric Fields

32. For the situation shown in Figure P31.32, the magnetic field changes with time according to the expression $B = (2.00t^3 - 4.00t^2 + 0.800)\,\text{T}$, and $r_2 = 2R = 5.00$ cm. (a) Calculate the magnitude and direction of the force exerted on an electron located at point P_2 when $t = 2.00$ s. (b) At what time is this force equal to zero?

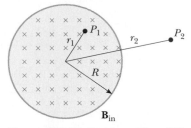

Figure P31.32 Problems 32 and 33.

33. A magnetic field directed into the page changes with time according to $B = (0.030\,0t^2 + 1.40)\,\text{T}$, where t is in seconds. The field has a circular cross section of radius $R = 2.50$ cm (Fig. P31.32). What are the magnitude and direction of the electric field at point P_1 when $t = 3.00$ s and $r_1 = 0.020\,0$ m?

34. A long solenoid with 1 000 turns per meter and radius 2.00 cm carries an oscillating current given by $I = (5.00\ \text{A})\sin(100\pi t)$. What is the electric field induced at a radius $r = 1.00$ cm from the axis of the solenoid? What is the direction of this electric field when the current is increasing counterclockwise in the coil?

Section 31.5   Generators and Motors

Problems 28 and 62 in Chapter 29 can be assigned with this section.

35. A coil of area 0.100 m^2 is rotating at 60.0 rev/s with the axis of rotation perpendicular to a 0.200-T magnetic field. (a) If the coil has 1 000 turns, what is the maximum emf generated in it? (b) What is the orientation of the coil with respect to the magnetic field when the maximum induced voltage occurs?

36. In a 250-turn automobile alternator, the magnetic flux in each turn is $\Phi_B = (2.50 \times 10^{-4}\ \text{Wb})\cos(\omega t)$, where ω is the angular speed of the alternator. The alternator is geared to rotate three times for each engine revolution. When the engine is running at an angular speed of 1 000 rev/min, determine (a) the induced emf in the alternator as a function of time and (b) the maximum emf in the alternator.

37. A long solenoid, with its axis along the x axis, consists of 200 turns per meter of wire that carries a steady current of 15.0 A. A coil is formed by wrapping 30 turns of thin wire around a circular frame that has a radius of 8.00 cm. The coil is placed inside the solenoid and mounted on an axis that is a diameter of the coil and coincides with the y axis. The coil is then rotated with an angular speed of 4.00π rad/s. (The plane of the coil is in the yz plane at $t = 0$.) Determine the emf generated in the coil as a function of time.

38. A bar magnet is spun at constant angular speed ω around an axis as shown in Figure P31.38. A stationary flat rectangular conducting loop surrounds the magnet, and at $t = 0$, the magnet is oriented as shown. Make a qualitative graph of the induced current in the loop as a function of time, plotting counterclockwise currents as positive and clockwise currents as negative.

Figure P31.38

39. A motor in normal operation carries a direct current of 0.850 A when connected to a 120-V power supply. The resistance of the motor windings is 11.8 Ω. While in normal operation, (a) what is the back emf generated by the motor? (b) At what rate is internal energy produced in the windings? (c) **What If?** Suppose that a malfunction stops the motor shaft from rotating. At what rate will internal energy be produced in the windings in this case? (Most motors have a thermal switch that will turn off the motor to prevent overheating when this occurs.)

40. A semicircular conductor of radius $R = 0.250$ m is rotated about the axis AC at a constant rate of 120 rev/min (Fig. P31.40). A uniform magnetic field in all of the lower half of the figure is directed out of the plane of rotation and has a magnitude of 1.30 T. (a) Calculate the maximum value of the emf induced in the conductor. (b) What is the value of the average induced emf for each complete rotation? (c) **What If?** How would the answers to (a) and (b) change if **B** were allowed to extend a distance R above the axis of rotation? Sketch the emf versus time (d) when the field is as drawn in Figure P31.40 and (e) when the field is extended as described in (c).

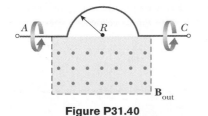

Figure P31.40

41. The rotating loop in an AC generator is a square 10.0 cm on a side. It is rotated at 60.0 Hz in a uniform field of 0.800 T. Calculate (a) the flux through the loop as a function of time, (b) the emf induced in the loop, (c) the

current induced in the loop for a loop resistance of 1.00 Ω, (d) the power delivered to the loop, and (e) the torque that must be exerted to rotate the loop.

Section 31.6 Eddy Currents

42. Figure P31.42 represents an electromagnetic brake that uses eddy currents. An electromagnet hangs from a railroad car near one rail. To stop the car, a large current is sent through the coils of the electromagnet. The moving electromagnet induces eddy currents in the rails, whose fields oppose the change in the field of the electromagnet. The magnetic fields of the eddy currents exert force on the current in the electromagnet, thereby slowing the car. The direction of the car's motion and the direction of the current in the electromagnet are shown correctly in the picture. Determine which of the eddy currents shown on the rails is correct. Explain your answer.

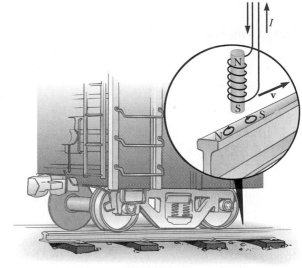

Figure P31.42

43. A conducting rectangular loop of mass M, resistance R, and dimensions w by ℓ falls from rest into a magnetic field **B** as shown in Figure P31.43. During the time interval

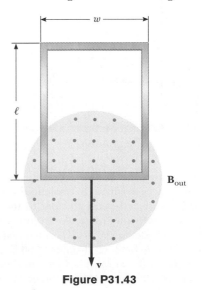

Figure P31.43

before the top edge of the loop reaches the field, the loop approaches a terminal speed v_T. (a) Show that

$$v_T = \frac{MgR}{B^2 w^2}$$

(b) Why is v_T proportional to R? (c) Why is it inversely proportional to B^2?

Section 31.7 Maxwell's Equations

44. An electron moves through a uniform electric field $\mathbf{E} = (2.50\hat{\mathbf{i}} + 5.00\hat{\mathbf{j}})$ V/m and a uniform magnetic field $\mathbf{B} = (0.400\hat{\mathbf{k}})$ T. Determine the acceleration of the electron when it has a velocity $\mathbf{v} = 10.0\hat{\mathbf{i}}$ m/s.

45. A proton moves through a uniform electric field given by $\mathbf{E} = 50.0\hat{\mathbf{j}}$ V/m and a uniform magnetic field $\mathbf{B} = (0.200\hat{\mathbf{i}} + 0.300\hat{\mathbf{j}} + 0.400\hat{\mathbf{k}})$ T. Determine the acceleration of the proton when it has a velocity $\mathbf{v} = 200\hat{\mathbf{i}}$ m/s.

Additional Problems

46. A steel guitar string vibrates (Figure 31.6). The component of magnetic field perpendicular to the area of a pickup coil nearby is given by

$$B = 50.0 \text{ mT} + (3.20 \text{ mT}) \sin(2\pi 523\, t/\text{s})$$

The circular pickup coil has 30 turns and radius 2.70 mm. Find the emf induced in the coil as a function of time.

47. Figure P31.47 is a graph of the induced emf versus time for a coil of N turns rotating with angular speed ω in a uniform magnetic field directed perpendicular to the axis of rotation of the coil. **What If?** Copy this sketch (on a larger scale), and on the same set of axes show the graph of emf versus t (a) if the number of turns in the coil is doubled; (b) if instead the angular speed is doubled; and (c) if the angular speed is doubled while the number of turns in the coil is halved.

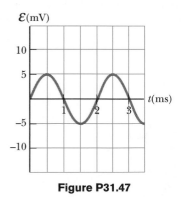

Figure P31.47

48. A technician wearing a brass bracelet enclosing area 0.005 00 m² places her hand in a solenoid whose magnetic field is 5.00 T directed perpendicular to the plane of the bracelet. The electrical resistance around the circumference of the bracelet is 0.020 0 Ω. An unexpected power failure causes the field to drop to 1.50 T in a time of 20.0 ms. Find (a) the current induced in the bracelet and (b) the power delivered to the bracelet. *Note:* As this

problem implies, you should not wear any metal objects when working in regions of strong magnetic fields.

49. Two infinitely long solenoids (seen in cross section) pass through a circuit as shown in Figure P31.49. The magnitude of **B** inside each is the same and is increasing at the rate of 100 T/s. What is the current in each resistor?

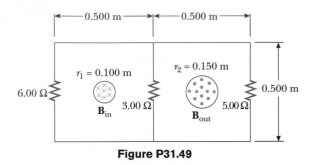

Figure P31.49

50. A conducting rod of length $\ell = 35.0$ cm is free to slide on two parallel conducting bars as shown in Figure P31.50. Two resistors $R_1 = 2.00$ Ω and $R_2 = 5.00$ Ω are connected across the ends of the bars to form a loop. A constant magnetic field $B = 2.50$ T is directed perpendicularly into the page. An external agent pulls the rod to the left with a constant speed of $v = 8.00$ m/s. Find (a) the currents in both resistors, (b) the total power delivered to the resistance of the circuit, and (c) the magnitude of the applied force that is needed to move the rod with this constant velocity.

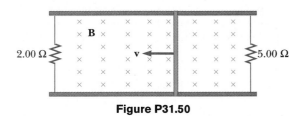

Figure P31.50

51. Suppose you wrap wire onto the core from a roll of cellophane tape to make a coil. Describe how you can use a bar magnet to produce an induced voltage in the coil. What is the order of magnitude of the emf you generate? State the quantities you take as data and their values.

52. A bar of mass m, length d, and resistance R slides without friction in a horizontal plane, moving on parallel rails as shown in Figure P31.52. A battery that maintains a constant emf $\mathcal{E}$ is connected between the rails, and a constant magnetic field **B** is directed perpendicularly to the plane of the page. Assuming the bar starts from rest, show that at time t it moves with a speed

$$v = \frac{\mathcal{E}}{Bd} (1 - e^{-B^2 d^2 t/mR})$$

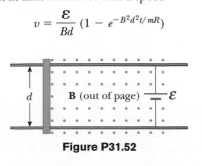

Figure P31.52

53. Review problem. A particle with a mass of 2.00×10^{-16} kg and a charge of 30.0 nC starts from rest, is accelerated by a strong electric field, and is fired from a small source inside a region of uniform constant magnetic field 0.600 T. The velocity of the particle is perpendicular to the field. The circular orbit of the particle encloses a magnetic flux of 15.0 μWb. (a) Calculate the speed of the particle. (b) Calculate the potential difference through which the particle accelerated inside the source.

54. An *induction furnace* uses electromagnetic induction to produce eddy currents in a conductor, thereby raising the conductor's temperature. Commercial units operate at frequencies ranging from 60 Hz to about 1 MHz and deliver powers from a few watts to several megawatts. Induction heating can be used for welding in a vacuum enclosure, to avoid oxidation and contamination of the metal. At high frequencies, induced currents occur only near the surface of the conductor—this is the "skin effect." By creating an induced current for a short time at an appropriately high frequency, one can heat a sample down to a controlled depth. For example, the surface of a farm tiller can be tempered to make it hard and brittle for effective cutting while keeping the interior metal soft and ductile to resist breakage.

To explore induction heating, consider a flat conducting disk of radius R, thickness b, and resistivity ρ. A sinusoidal magnetic field $B_{max} \cos \omega t$ is applied perpendicular to the disk. Assume that the frequency is so low that the skin effect is not important. Assume the eddy currents occur in circles concentric with the disk. (a) Calculate the average power delivered to the disk. (b) **What If?** By what factor does the power change when the amplitude of the field doubles? (c) When the frequency doubles? (d) When the radius of the disk doubles?

55. The plane of a square loop of wire with edge length $a = 0.200$ m is perpendicular to the Earth's magnetic field at a point where $B = 15.0$ μT, as shown in Figure P31.55. The total resistance of the loop and the wires connecting it to a sensitive ammeter is 0.500 Ω. If the loop is suddenly collapsed by horizontal forces as shown, what total charge passes through the ammeter?

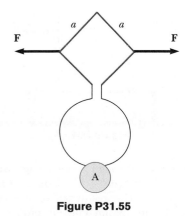

Figure P31.55

56. Magnetic field values are often determined by using a device known as a *search coil*. This technique depends on the measurement of the total charge passing through a coil in a time interval during which the magnetic flux linking the windings changes either because of the motion of the coil or because of a change in the value of B. (a) Show that as the flux through the coil changes from Φ_1 to Φ_2, the charge transferred through the coil will be given by $Q = N(\Phi_2 - \Phi_1)/R$, where R is the resistance of the coil and a sensitive ammeter connected across it and N is the number of turns. (b) As a specific example, calculate B when a 100-turn coil of resistance 200 Ω and cross-sectional area 40.0 cm^2 produces the following results. A total charge of 5.00×10^{-4} C passes through the coil when it is rotated in a uniform field from a position where the plane of the coil is perpendicular to the field to a position where the coil's plane is parallel to the field.

57. In Figure P31.57, the rolling axle, 1.50 m long, is pushed along horizontal rails at a constant speed $v = 3.00$ m/s. A resistor $R = 0.400$ Ω is connected to the rails at points a and b, directly opposite each other. (The wheels make good electrical contact with the rails, and so the axle, rails, and R form a closed-loop circuit. The only significant resistance in the circuit is R.) A uniform magnetic field $B = 0.080\,0$ T is vertically downward. (a) Find the induced current I in the resistor. (b) What horizontal force F is required to keep the axle rolling at constant speed? (c) Which end of the resistor, a or b, is at the higher electric potential? (d) **What If?** After the axle rolls past the resistor, does the current in R reverse direction? Explain your answer.

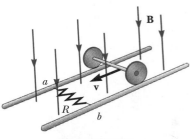

Figure P31.57

58. A conducting rod moves with a constant velocity **v** in a direction perpendicular to a long, straight wire carrying a current I as shown in Figure P31.58. Show that the magnitude of the emf generated between the ends of the rod is

$$|\mathcal{E}| = \frac{\mu_0 v I \ell}{2 \pi r}$$

In this case, note that the emf decreases with increasing r, as you might expect.

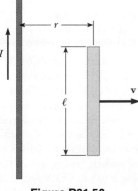

Figure P31.58

59. A circular loop of wire of radius r is in a uniform magnetic field, with the plane of the loop perpendicular to the direction of the field (Fig. P31.59). The magnetic field varies with time according to $B(t) = a + bt$, where a and b are constants. (a) Calculate the magnetic flux through the loop at $t = 0$. (b) Calculate the emf induced in the loop. (c) If the resistance of the loop is R, what is the induced current? (d) At what rate is energy being delivered to the resistance of the loop?

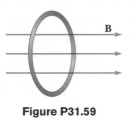

Figure P31.59

60. In Figure P31.60, a uniform magnetic field decreases at a constant rate $dB/dt = -K$, where K is a positive constant. A circular loop of wire of radius a containing a resistance R and a capacitance C is placed with its plane normal to the field. (a) Find the charge Q on the capacitor when it is fully charged. (b) Which plate is at the higher potential? (c) Discuss the force that causes the separation of charges.

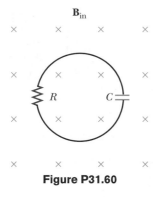

Figure P31.60

61. A rectangular coil of 60 turns, dimensions 0.100 m by 0.200 m and total resistance 10.0 Ω, rotates with angular speed 30.0 rad/s about the y axis in a region where a 1.00-T magnetic field is directed along the x axis. The rotation is initiated so that the plane of the coil is perpendicular to the direction of **B** at $t = 0$. Calculate (a) the maximum induced emf in the coil, (b) the maximum rate of change of magnetic flux through the coil, (c) the induced emf at $t = 0.050\,0$ s, and (d) the torque exerted by the magnetic field on the coil at the instant when the emf is a maximum.

62. A small circular washer of radius 0.500 cm is held directly below a long, straight wire carrying a current of 10.0 A. The washer is located 0.500 m above the top of a table (Fig. P31.62). (a) If the washer is dropped from rest, what is the magnitude of the average induced emf in the washer from the time it is released to the moment it hits the table-top? Assume that the magnetic field is nearly constant over the area of the washer, and equal to the magnetic field at the center of the washer. (b) What is the direction of the induced current in the washer?

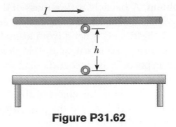

Figure P31.62

63. A conducting rod of length ℓ moves with velocity **v** parallel to a long wire carrying a steady current I. The axis of the rod is maintained perpendicular to the wire with the near end a distance r away, as shown in Figure P31.63. Show that the magnitude of the emf induced in the rod is

$$|\mathcal{E}| = \frac{\mu_0 I v}{2\pi} \ln\left(1 + \frac{\ell}{r}\right)$$

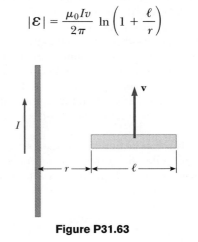

Figure P31.63

64. A rectangular loop of dimensions ℓ and w moves with a constant velocity **v** away from a long wire that carries a current I in the plane of the loop (Fig. P31.64). The total resistance of the loop is R. Derive an expression that gives the current in the loop at the instant the near side is a distance r from the wire.

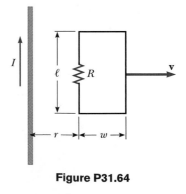

Figure P31.64

65. The magnetic flux through a metal ring varies with time t according to $\Phi_B = 3(at^3 - bt^2)$ T·m², with $a = 2.00$ s⁻³ and $b = 6.00$ s⁻². The resistance of the ring is 3.00 Ω. Determine the maximum current induced in the ring during the interval from $t = 0$ to $t = 2.00$ s.

66. **Review problem.** The bar of mass m in Figure P31.66 is pulled horizontally across parallel rails by a massless string that passes over an ideal pulley and is attached to a

suspended object of mass M. The uniform magnetic field has a magnitude B, and the distance between the rails is ℓ. The rails are connected at one end by a load resistor R. Derive an expression that gives the horizontal speed of the bar as a function of time, assuming that the suspended object is released with the bar at rest at $t = 0$. Assume no friction between rails and bar.

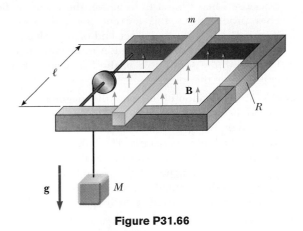

Figure P31.66

67. A solenoid wound with 2 000 turns/m is supplied with current that varies in time according to $I = (4\text{A}) \sin(120\pi t)$, where t is in seconds. A small coaxial circular coil of 40 turns and radius $r = 5.00$ cm is located inside the solenoid near its center. (a) Derive an expression that describes the manner in which the emf in the small coil varies in time. (b) At what average rate is energy delivered to the small coil if the windings have a total resistance of 8.00 Ω?

68. Figure P31.68 shows a stationary conductor whose shape is similar to the letter e. The radius of its circular portion is $a = 50.0$ cm. It is placed in a constant magnetic field of 0.500 T directed out of the page. A straight conducting rod, 50.0 cm long, is pivoted about point O and rotates with a constant angular speed of 2.00 rad/s. (a) Determine the induced emf in the loop POQ. Note that the area of the loop is $\theta a^2/2$. (b) If all of the conducting material has a resistance per length of 5.00 Ω/m, what is the induced current in the loop POQ at the instant 0.250 s after point P passes point Q?

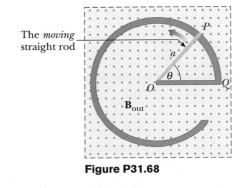

The *moving* straight rod

Figure P31.68

69. A *betatron* accelerates electrons to energies in the MeV range by means of electromagnetic induction. Electrons in a vacuum chamber are held in a circular orbit by a magnetic field perpendicular to the orbital plane. The magnetic field is gradually increased to induce an electric field around the orbit. (a) Show that the electric field is in the correct direction to make the electrons speed up. (b) Assume that the radius of the orbit remains constant. Show that the average magnetic field over the area enclosed by the orbit must be twice as large as the magnetic field at the circumference of the circle.

70. A wire 30.0 cm long is held parallel to and 80.0 cm above a long wire carrying 200 A and resting on the floor (Fig. P31.70). The 30.0-cm wire is released and falls, remaining parallel with the current-carrying wire as it falls. Assume that the falling wire accelerates at 9.80 m/s² and derive an equation for the emf induced in it. Express your result as a function of the time t after the wire is dropped. What is the induced emf 0.300 s after the wire is released?

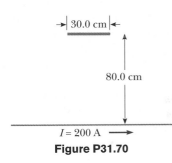

Figure P31.70

71. A long, straight wire carries a current that is given by $I = I_{\text{max}} \sin(\omega t + \phi)$ and lies in the plane of a rectangular coil of N turns of wire, as shown in Figure P31.9. The quantities I_{max}, ω, and ϕ are all constants. Determine the emf induced in the coil by the magnetic field created by the current in the straight wire. Assume $I_{\text{max}} = 50.0$ A, $\omega = 200\pi\,\text{s}^{-1}$, $N = 100$, $h = w = 5.00$ cm, and $L = 20.0$ cm.

72. A dime is suspended from a thread and hung between the poles of a strong horseshoe magnet as shown in Figure P31.72. The dime rotates at constant angular speed ω

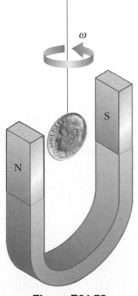

Figure P31.72

about a vertical axis. Letting θ represent the angle between the direction of **B** and the normal to the face of the dime, sketch a graph of the torque due to induced currents as a function of θ for $0 < \theta < 2\pi$.

Answers to Quick Quizzes

31.1 (c). In all cases except this one, there is a change in the magnetic flux through the loop.

31.2 $c, d = e, b, a$. The magnitude of the emf is proportional to the rate of change of the magnetic flux. For the situation described, the rate of change of magnetic flux is proportional to the rate of change of the magnetic field. This rate of change is the slope of the graph in Figure 31.4. The magnitude of the slope is largest at c. Points d and e are on a straight line, so the slope is the same at each point. Point b represents a point of relatively small slope, while a is at a point of zero slope because the curve is horizontal at that point.

31.3 (b). The magnetic field lines around the transmission cable will be circular, centered on the cable. If you place your loop around the cable, there are no field lines passing through the loop, so no emf is induced. The loop must be placed next to the cable, with the plane of the loop parallel to the cable to maximize the flux through its area.

31.4 (a). The Earth's magnetic field has a downward component in the northern hemisphere. As the plane flies north, the right-hand rule illustrated in Figure 29.4 indicates that positive charge experiences a force directed toward the west. Thus, the left wingtip becomes positively charged and the right wingtip negatively charged.

31.5 (c). The force on the wire is of magnitude $F_{app} = F_B = I\ell B$, with I given by Equation 31.6. Thus, the force is proportional to the speed and the force doubles. Because $\mathcal{P} = F_{app}v$, the doubling of the force *and* the speed results in the power being four times as large.

31.6 (b). According to Equation 31.5, because B and v are fixed, the emf depends only on the length of the wire moving in the magnetic field. Thus, you want the long dimension moving through the magnetic field lines so that it is perpendicular to the velocity vector. In this case, the short dimension is parallel to the velocity vector.

31.7 (a). Because the current induced in the solenoid is clockwise when viewed from above, the magnetic field lines produced by this current point downward in Figure 31.15. Thus, the upper end of the solenoid acts as a south pole. For this situation to be consistent with Lenz's law, the south pole of the bar magnet must be approaching the solenoid.

31.8 (b). At the position of the loop, the magnetic field lines due to the wire point into the page. The loop is entering a region of stronger magnetic field as it drops toward the wire, so the flux is increasing. The induced current must set up a magnetic field that opposes this increase. To do this, it creates a magnetic field directed out of the page. By the right-hand rule for current loops, this requires a counterclockwise current in the loop.

31.9 (d). The constant rate of change of B will result in a constant rate of change of the magnetic flux. According to Equation 31.9, if $d\Phi_B/dt$ is constant, **E** is constant in magnitude.

31.10 (a). While reducing the resistance may increase the current that the generator provides to a load, it does not alter the emf. Equation 31.11 shows that the emf depends on ω, B, and N, so all other choices increase the emf.

31.11 (b). When the aluminum sheet moves between the poles of the magnet, eddy currents are established in the aluminum. According to Lenz's law, these currents are in a direction so as to oppose the original change, which is the movement of the aluminum sheet in the magnetic field. The same principle is used in common laboratory triple-beam balances. See if you can find the magnet and the aluminum sheet the next time you use a triple-beam balance.

Inductance

▲ *An airport metal detector contains a large coil of wire around the frame. This coil has a property called inductance. When a passenger carries metal through the detector, the inductance of the coil changes, and the change in inductance signals an alarm to sound. (Jack Hollingsworth/Getty Images)*

In Chapter 31, we saw that an emf and a current are induced in a circuit when the magnetic flux through the area enclosed by the circuit changes with time. This phenomenon of electromagnetic induction has some practical consequences. In this chapter, we first describe an effect known as *self-induction,* in which a time-varying current in a circuit produces an induced emf opposing the emf that initially set up the time-varying current. Self-induction is the basis of the *inductor,* an electrical circuit element. We discuss the energy stored in the magnetic field of an inductor and the energy density associated with the magnetic field.

Next, we study how an emf is induced in a circuit as a result of a changing magnetic flux produced by a second circuit; this is the basic principle of *mutual induction.* Finally, we examine the characteristics of circuits that contain inductors, resistors, and capacitors in various combinations.

32.1 Self-Inductance

In this chapter, we need to distinguish carefully between emfs and currents that are caused by batteries or other sources and those that are induced by changing magnetic fields. When we use a term without an adjective (such as *emf* and *current*) we are describing the parameters associated with a physical source. We use the adjective *induced* to describe those emfs and currents caused by a changing magnetic field.

Consider a circuit consisting of a switch, a resistor, and a source of emf, as shown in Figure 32.1. When the switch is thrown to its closed position, the current does not immediately jump from zero to its maximum value $\mathcal{E}/R$. Faraday's law of electromagnetic induction (Eq. 31.1) can be used to describe this effect as follows: as the current increases with time, the magnetic flux through the circuit loop due to this current also increases with time. This increasing flux creates an induced emf in the circuit. The direction of the induced emf is such that it would cause an induced current in the loop (if the loop did not already carry a current), which would establish a magnetic field opposing the change in the original magnetic field. Thus, the direction of the induced emf is opposite the direction of the emf of the battery; this results in a gradual rather than instantaneous increase in the current to its final equilibrium value. Because of the direction of the induced emf, it is also called a *back emf,* similar to that in a motor, as discussed in Chapter 31. This effect is called **self-induction** because the changing flux through the circuit and the resultant induced emf arise from the circuit itself. The emf $\mathcal{E}_L$ set up in this case is called a **self-induced emf.**

As a second example of self-induction, consider Figure 32.2, which shows a coil wound on a cylindrical core. Assume that the current in the coil either increases or decreases with time. When the current is in the direction shown, a magnetic field directed from right to left is set up inside the coil, as seen in Figure 32.2a. As the current changes with time, the magnetic flux through the coil also changes and induces an emf in the coil. From Lenz's law, the polarity of this induced emf must be such that it opposes the change in the magnetic field from the current. If the current

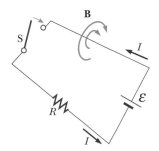

Figure 32.1 After the switch is closed, the current produces a magnetic flux through the area enclosed by the loop. As the current increases toward its equilibrium value, this magnetic flux changes in time and induces an emf in the loop.

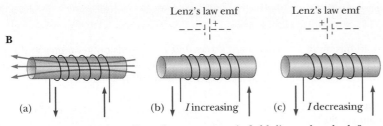

Figure 32.2 (a) A current in the coil produces a magnetic field directed to the left. (b) If the current increases, the increasing magnetic flux creates an induced emf in the coil having the polarity shown by the dashed battery. (c) The polarity of the induced emf reverses if the current decreases.

Joseph Henry
American Physicist (1797–1878)

Henry became the first director of the Smithsonian Institution and first president of the Academy of Natural Science. He improved the design of the electromagnet and constructed one of the first motors. He also discovered the phenomenon of self-induction but failed to publish his findings. The unit of inductance, the henry, is named in his honor. *(North Wind Picture Archives)*

is increasing, the polarity of the induced emf is as pictured in Figure 32.2b, and if the current is decreasing, the polarity of the induced emf is as shown in Figure 32.2c.

To obtain a quantitative description of self-induction, we recall from Faraday's law that the induced emf is equal to the negative of the time rate of change of the magnetic flux. The magnetic flux is proportional to the magnetic field due to the current, which in turn is proportional to the current in the circuit. Therefore, **a self-induced emf is always proportional to the time rate of change of the current.** For any coil, we find that

$$\mathcal{E}_L = -L\frac{dI}{dt} \tag{32.1}$$

where L is a proportionality constant—called the **inductance** of the coil—that depends on the geometry of the coil and other physical characteristics. Combining this expression with Faraday's law, $\mathcal{E}_L = -N\,d\Phi_B/dt$, we see that the inductance of a closely spaced coil of N turns (a toroid or an ideal solenoid) carrying a current I and containing N turns is

$$L = \frac{N\Phi_B}{I} \tag{32.2}$$

Inductance of an *N*-turn coil

where it is assumed that the same magnetic flux passes through each turn.

From Equation 32.1, we can also write the inductance as the ratio

$$L = -\frac{\mathcal{E}_L}{dI/dt} \tag{32.3}$$

Inductance

Recall that resistance is a measure of the opposition to current ($R = \Delta V/I$); in comparison, inductance is a measure of the opposition to a *change* in current.

The SI unit of inductance is the **henry** (H), which, as we can see from Equation 32.3, is 1 volt-second per ampere:

$$1\,\text{H} = 1\,\frac{\text{V}\cdot\text{s}}{\text{A}}$$

As shown in Examples 32.1 and 32.2, the inductance of a coil depends on its geometry. This is analogous to the capacitance of a capacitor depending on the geometry of its plates, as we found in Chapter 26. Inductance calculations can be quite difficult to perform for complicated geometries; however, the examples below involve simple situations for which inductances are easily evaluated.

Quick Quiz 32.1 A coil with zero resistance has its ends labeled *a* and *b*. The potential at *a* is higher than at *b*. Which of the following could be consistent with this situation? (a) The current is constant and is directed from *a* to *b*; (b) The current is constant and is directed from *b* to *a*; (c) The current is increasing and is directed from *a* to *b*; (d) The current is decreasing and is directed from *a* to *b*; (e) The current is increasing and is directed from *b* to *a*; (f) The current is decreasing and is directed from *b* to *a*.

Example 32.1 **Inductance of a Solenoid**

Find the inductance of a uniformly wound solenoid having N turns and length ℓ. Assume that ℓ is much longer than the radius of the windings and that the core of the solenoid is air.

Solution We can assume that the interior magnetic field due to the current is uniform and given by Equation 30.17:

$$B = \mu_0 nI = \mu_0 \frac{N}{\ell} I$$

where $n = N/\ell$ is the number of turns per unit length. The magnetic flux through each turn is

$$\Phi_B = BA = \mu_0 \frac{NA}{\ell} I$$

where A is the cross-sectional area of the solenoid. Using this expression and Equation 32.2, we find that

$$L = \frac{N\Phi_B}{I} = \boxed{\frac{\mu_0 N^2 A}{\ell}} \qquad (32.4)$$

This result shows that L depends on geometry and is proportional to the square of the number of turns. Because $N = n\ell$, we can also express the result in the form

$$L = \mu_0 \frac{(n\ell)^2}{\ell} A = \mu_0 n^2 A\ell = \mu_0 n^2 V \qquad (32.5)$$

where $V = A\ell$ is the interior volume of the solenoid.

What If? What would happen to the inductance if you inserted a ferromagnetic material inside the solenoid?

Answer The inductance would increase. For a given current, the magnetic flux in the solenoid is much greater because of the increase in the magnetic field originating from the magnetization of the ferromagnetic material. For example, if the material has a magnetic permeability of $500\mu_0$, the inductance increases by a factor of 500.

Example 32.2 **Calculating Inductance and emf**

(A) Calculate the inductance of an air-core solenoid containing 300 turns if the length of the solenoid is 25.0 cm and its cross-sectional area is 4.00 cm^2.

Solution Using Equation 32.4, we obtain

$$L = \frac{\mu_0 N^2 A}{\ell}$$

$$= \frac{(4\pi \times 10^{-7}\ \mathrm{T \cdot m/A})(300)^2(4.00 \times 10^{-4}\ \mathrm{m}^2)}{25.0 \times 10^{-2}\ \mathrm{m}}$$

$$= 1.81 \times 10^{-4}\ \mathrm{T \cdot m^2/A} = \boxed{0.181\ \mathrm{mH}}$$

(B) Calculate the self-induced emf in the solenoid if the current it carries is decreasing at the rate of 50.0 A/s.

Solution Using Equation 32.1 and given that $dI/dt = -50.0$ A/s, we obtain

$$\mathcal{E}_L = -L\frac{dI}{dt} = -(1.81 \times 10^{-4}\ \mathrm{H})(-50.0\ \mathrm{A/s})$$

$$= \boxed{9.05\ \mathrm{mV}}$$

32.2 *RL* Circuits

If a circuit contains a coil, such as a solenoid, the self-inductance of the coil prevents the current in the circuit from increasing or decreasing instantaneously. A circuit element that has a large self-inductance is called an **inductor** and has the circuit symbol ⎓⎓⎓⎓. We always assume that the self-inductance of the remainder of a circuit is negligible compared with that of the inductor. Keep in mind, however, that even a circuit without a coil has some self-inductance that can affect the behavior of the circuit.

Because the inductance of the inductor results in a back emf, **an inductor in a circuit opposes changes in the current in that circuit.** The inductor attempts to keep the current the same as it was before the change occurred. If the battery voltage in the circuit is increased so that the current rises, the inductor opposes this change, and the rise is not instantaneous. If the battery voltage is decreased, the presence of the inductor results in a slow drop in the current rather than an immediate drop. Thus, the inductor causes the circuit to be "sluggish" as it reacts to changes in the voltage.

Consider the circuit shown in Figure 32.3, which contains a battery of negligible internal resistance. This is an **RL circuit** because the elements connected to the battery are a resistor and an inductor. Suppose that the switch S is open for $t < 0$ and then closed at $t = 0$. The current in the circuit begins to increase, and a back emf (Eq. 32.1) that opposes the increasing current is induced in the inductor. Because the current is increasing, dI/dt in Equation 32.1 is positive; thus, $\mathcal{E}_L$ is negative. This negative value reflects the decrease in electric potential that occurs in going from a to b across the inductor, as indicated by the positive and negative signs in Figure 32.3.

With this in mind, we can apply Kirchhoff's loop rule to this circuit, traversing the circuit in the clockwise direction:

$$\mathcal{E} - IR - L\frac{dI}{dt} = 0 \tag{32.6}$$

where IR is the voltage drop across the resistor. (We developed Kirchhoff's rules for circuits with steady currents, but they can also be applied to a circuit in which the current is changing if we imagine them to represent the circuit at one *instant* of time.) We must now look for a solution to this differential equation, which is similar to that for the RC circuit. (See Section 28.4.)

A mathematical solution of Equation 32.6 represents the current in the circuit as a function of time. To find this solution, we change variables for convenience, letting $x = (\mathcal{E}/R) - I$, so that $dx = -dI$. With these substitutions, we can write Equation 32.6 as

$$x + \frac{L}{R}\frac{dx}{dt} = 0$$

$$\frac{dx}{x} = -\frac{R}{L}dt$$

Integrating this last expression, we have

$$\int_{x_0}^{x}\frac{dx}{x} = -\frac{R}{L}\int_{0}^{t}dt$$

$$\ln\frac{x}{x_0} = -\frac{R}{L}t$$

where x_0 is the value of x at time $t = 0$. Taking the antilogarithm of this result, we obtain

$$x = x_0 e^{-Rt/L}$$

Because $I = 0$ at $t = 0$, we note from the definition of x that $x_0 = \mathcal{E}/R$. Hence, this last expression is equivalent to

$$\frac{\mathcal{E}}{R} - I = \frac{\mathcal{E}}{R}e^{-Rt/L}$$

$$I = \frac{\mathcal{E}}{R}(1 - e^{-Rt/L})$$

This expression shows how the inductor effects the current. The current does not increase instantly to its final equilibrium value when the switch is closed but instead increases according to an exponential function. If we remove the inductance in the circuit, which we can do by letting L approach zero, the exponential term becomes zero and we see that there is no time dependence of the current in this case—the current increases instantaneously to its final equilibrium value in the absence of the inductance.

We can also write this expression as

$$I = \frac{\mathcal{E}}{R}(1 - e^{-t/\tau}) \tag{32.7}$$

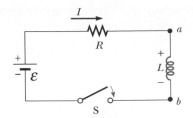

Active Figure 32.3 A series RL circuit. As the current increases toward its maximum value, an emf that opposes the increasing current is induced in the inductor.

At the Active Figures link at http://www.pse6.com, you can adjust the values of R and L to see the effect on the current. A graphical display as in Figure 32.4 is available.

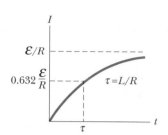

$\tau = L/R$

Active Figure 32.4 Plot of the current versus time for the RL circuit shown in Figure 32.3. The switch is open for $t < 0$ and then closed at $t = 0$, and the current increases toward its maximum value $\mathcal{E}/R$. The time constant τ is the time interval required for I to reach 63.2% of its maximum value.

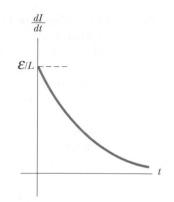

Figure 32.5 Plot of dI/dt versus time for the RL circuit shown in Figure 32.3. The time rate of change of current is a maximum at $t = 0$, which is the instant at which the switch is closed. The rate decreases exponentially with time as I increases toward its maximum value.

At the Active Figures link at http://www.pse6.com, *you can observe this graph develop after the switch in Figure 32.3 is closed.*

where the constant τ is the **time constant** of the RL circuit:

Time constant of an RL circuit

$$\tau = \frac{L}{R} \tag{32.8}$$

Physically, τ is the time interval required for the current in the circuit to reach $(1 - e^{-1}) = 0.632 = 63.2\%$ of its final value $\mathcal{E}/R$. The time constant is a useful parameter for comparing the time responses of various circuits.

Figure 32.4 shows a graph of the current versus time in the RL circuit. Note that the equilibrium value of the current, which occurs as t approaches infinity, is $\mathcal{E}/R$. We can see this by setting dI/dt equal to zero in Equation 32.6 and solving for the current I. (At equilibrium, the change in the current is zero.) Thus, we see that the current initially increases very rapidly and then gradually approaches the equilibrium value $\mathcal{E}/R$ as t approaches infinity.

Let us also investigate the time rate of change of the current. Taking the first time derivative of Equation 32.7, we have

$$\frac{dI}{dt} = \frac{\mathcal{E}}{L} e^{-t/\tau} \tag{32.9}$$

From this result, we see that the time rate of change of the current is a maximum (equal to $\mathcal{E}/L$) at $t = 0$ and falls off exponentially to zero as t approaches infinity (Fig. 32.5).

Now let us consider the RL circuit shown in Figure 32.6. The curved lines on the switch S represent a switch that is connected either to a or b at all times. (If the switch is connected to neither a nor b, the current in the circuit suddenly stops.) Suppose that the switch has been set at position a long enough to allow the current to reach its equilibrium value $\mathcal{E}/R$. In this situation, the circuit is described by the outer loop in Figure 32.6. If the switch is thrown from a to b, the circuit is now described by just the right hand loop in Figure 32.6. Thus, we have a circuit with no battery ($\mathcal{E} = 0$). Applying Kirchhoff's loop rule to the right-hand loop at the instant the switch is thrown from a to b, we obtain

$$IR + L \frac{dI}{dt} = 0$$

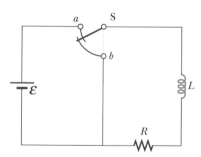

Active Figure 32.6 An RL circuit. When the switch S is in position a, the battery is in the circuit. When the switch is thrown to position b, the battery is no longer part of the circuit. The switch is designed so that it is never open, which would cause the current to stop.

At the Active Figures link at http://www.pse6.com, *you can adjust the values of R and L to see the effect on the current. A graphical display as in Figure 32.7 is available.*

It is left as a problem (Problem 16) to show that the solution of this differential equation is

$$I = \frac{\mathcal{E}}{R} e^{-t/\tau} = I_0 e^{-t/\tau} \tag{32.10}$$

where $\mathcal{E}$ is the emf of the battery and $I_0 = \mathcal{E}/R$ is the current at the instant at which the switch is thrown to b.

If the circuit did not contain an inductor, the current would immediately decrease to zero when the battery is removed. When the inductor is present, it opposes the decrease in the current and causes the current to decrease exponentially. A graph of the current in the circuit versus time (Fig. 32.7) shows that the current is continuously decreasing with time. Note that the slope dI/dt is always negative and has its maximum value at $t = 0$. The negative slope signifies that $\mathcal{E}_L = -L\,(dI/dt)$ is now positive.

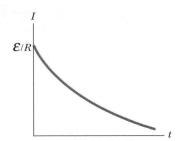

Active Figure 32.7 Current versus time for the right-hand loop of the circuit shown in Figure 32.6. For $t < 0$, the switch S is at position a. At $t = 0$, the switch is thrown to position b, and the current has its maximum value $\mathcal{E}/R$.

At the Active Figures link at http://www.pse6.com, you can observe this graph develop after the switch in Figure 32.6 is thrown to position b.

Quick Quiz 32.2 The circuit in Figure 32.8 consists of a resistor, an inductor, and an ideal battery with no internal resistance. At the instant just after the switch is closed, across which circuit element is the voltage equal to the emf of the battery? (a) the resistor (b) the inductor (c) both the inductor and resistor. After a very long time, across which circuit element is the voltage equal to the emf of the battery? (d) the resistor (e) the inductor (f) both the inductor and resistor.

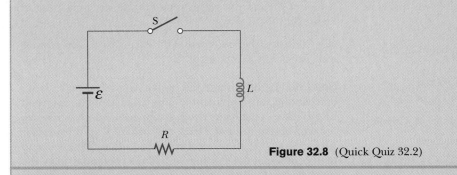

Figure 32.8 (Quick Quiz 32.2)

Quick Quiz 32.3 The circuit in Figure 32.9 includes a power source that provides a sinusoidal voltage. Thus, the magnetic field in the inductor is constantly changing. The inductor is a simple air-core solenoid. The switch in the circuit is closed and the lightbulb glows steadily. An iron rod is inserted into the interior of the solenoid, which increases the magnitude of the magnetic field in the solenoid. As this happens, the brightness of the lightbulb (a) increases, (b) decreases, (c) is unaffected.

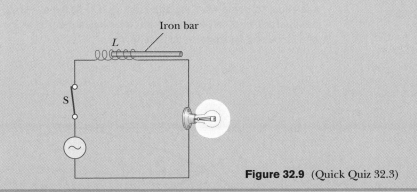

Figure 32.9 (Quick Quiz 32.3)

Quick Quiz 32.4 Two circuits like the one shown in Figure 32.6 are identical except for the value of L. In circuit A the inductance of the inductor is L_A, and in circuit B it is L_B. Switch S is thrown to position a at $t = 0$. At $t = 10$ s, the switch is thrown to position b. The resulting currents for the two circuits are as graphed in Figure 32.10.

If we assume that the time constant of each circuit is much less than 10 s, which of the following is true? (a) $L_A > L_B$; (b) $L_A < L_B$; (c) not enough information to tell.

Figure 32.10 (Quick Quiz 32.4)

Example 32.3 Time Constant of an *RL* Circuit   Interactive

(A) Find the time constant of the circuit shown in Figure 32.11a.

Solution The time constant is given by Equation 32.8:

$$\tau = \frac{L}{R} = \frac{30.0 \times 10^{-3}\,H}{6.00\,\Omega} = \boxed{5.00\ ms}$$

(B) The switch in Figure 32.11a is closed at $t = 0$. Calculate the current in the circuit at $t = 2.00$ ms.

Solution Using Equation 32.7 for the current as a function of time (with t and τ in milliseconds), we find that at $t = 2.00$ ms,

$$I = \frac{\mathcal{E}}{R}(1 - e^{-t/\tau}) = \frac{12.0\,V}{6.00\,\Omega}(1 - e^{-0.400}) = \boxed{0.659\ A}$$

A plot of the current versus time for this circuit is given in Figure 32.11b.

(C) Compare the potential difference across the resistor with that across the inductor.

Solution At the instant the switch is closed, there is no current and thus no potential difference across the resistor. At this instant, the battery voltage appears entirely across the inductor in the form of a back emf of 12.0 V as the inductor tries to maintain the zero-current condition. (The left end of the inductor is at a higher electric potential than the right end.) As time passes, the emf across the inductor decreases and the current in the resistor (and hence the potential difference across it) increases, as shown in Figure 32.12. The sum of the two potential differences at all times is 12.0 V.

What If? In Figure 32.12, we see that the voltages across the resistor and inductor are equal at a time just before 4.00 ms. What if we wanted to delay the condition in which the voltages are equal to some later instant, such as $t = 10.0$ ms? Which parameter, *L* or *R*, would require the least adjustment, in terms of a percentage change, to achieve this?

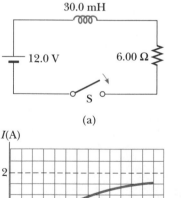

(a)

(b)

Figure 32.11 (Example 32.3) (a) The switch in this *RL* circuit is open for $t < 0$ and then closed at $t = 0$. (b) A graph of the current versus time for the circuit in part (a).

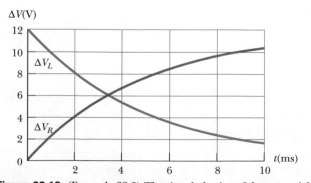

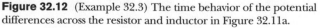

Figure 32.12 (Example 32.3) The time behavior of the potential differences across the resistor and inductor in Figure 32.11a.

Answer From Figure 32.12, we see that the voltages are equal when the voltage across the inductor has fallen to half of its original value. Thus, the time interval required for the voltages to become equal is the *half-life* $t_{1/2}$ of the decay. We introduced the half-life in the **What If?** section of Example 28.13, in describing the exponential decay in *RC* circuits, where we found that $t_{1/2} = 0.693\tau$. If we want the half-life of our *RL* circuit to be 10.0 ms, then the time constant must be

$$\tau = \frac{t_{1/2}}{0.693} = \frac{10.0 \text{ ms}}{0.693} = 14.4 \text{ ms}$$

We can achieve this time constant by holding *L* fixed and adjusting *R*; in this case,

$$\tau = \frac{L}{R} = \frac{30.0 \times 10^{-3} \text{ H}}{R} = 14.4 \text{ ms}$$

$$R = \frac{30.0 \times 10^{-3} \text{ H}}{14.4 \text{ ms}} = 2.08 \text{ }\Omega$$

This corresponds to a 65% decrease compared to the initial resistance. Now hold *R* fixed and adjust *L*:

$$\tau = \frac{L}{R} = \frac{L}{6.00 \text{ }\Omega} = 14.4 \text{ ms}$$

$$L = (6.00 \text{ }\Omega)(14.4 \text{ ms}) = 86.4 \times 10^{-3} \text{ H}$$

This represents a 188% increase in inductance! Thus, a much smaller percentage adjustment in *R* can achieve the desired effect than in *L*.

🌐 **At the Interactive Worked Example link at http://www.pse6.com, you can explore the decay of current in an RL circuit.**

32.3 Energy in a Magnetic Field

Because the emf induced in an inductor prevents a battery from establishing an instantaneous current, the battery must provide more energy than in a circuit without the inductor. Part of the energy supplied by the battery appears as internal energy in the resistor, while the remaining energy is stored in the magnetic field of the inductor. If we multiply each term in Equation 32.6 by *I* and rearrange the expression, we have

$$I\mathcal{E} = I^2 R + LI \frac{dI}{dt} \qquad (32.11)$$

Recognizing $I\mathcal{E}$ as the rate at which energy is supplied by the battery and $I^2 R$ as the rate at which energy is delivered to the resistor, we see that $LI(dI/dt)$ must represent the rate at which energy is being stored in the inductor. If we let *U* denote the energy stored in the inductor at any time, then we can write the rate dU/dt at which energy is stored as

$$\frac{dU}{dt} = LI \frac{dI}{dt}$$

To find the total energy stored in the inductor, we can rewrite this expression as $dU = LI \, dI$ and integrate:

$$U = \int dU = \int_0^I LI \, dI = L \int_0^I I \, dI$$

$$U = \tfrac{1}{2} LI^2 \qquad (32.12)$$

where *L* is constant and has been removed from the integral. This expression represents the energy stored in the magnetic field of the inductor when the current is *I*. Note that this equation is similar in form to Equation 26.11 for the energy stored in the electric field of a capacitor, $U = \tfrac{1}{2}C(\Delta V)^2$. In either case, we see that energy is required to establish a field.

We can also determine the energy density of a magnetic field. For simplicity, consider a solenoid whose inductance is given by Equation 32.5:

$$L = \mu_0 n^2 A\ell$$

The magnetic field of a solenoid is given by Equation 30.17:

$$B = \mu_0 nI$$

⚠ **PITFALL PREVENTION**

32.1 Compare Energy in a Capacitor, Resistor, and Inductor

Different energy-storage mechanisms are at work in capacitors, inductors, and resistors. A capacitor stores a given amount of energy for a fixed charge on its plates; as more charge is delivered, more energy is delivered. An inductor stores a given amount of energy for constant current; as the current increases, more energy is delivered. Energy delivered to a resistor is transformed to internal energy.

Energy stored in an inductor

Substituting the expression for L and $I = B/\mu_0 n$ into Equation 32.12 gives

$$U = \tfrac{1}{2} LI^2 = \tfrac{1}{2} \mu_0 n^2 A\ell \left(\frac{B}{\mu_0 n}\right)^2 = \frac{B^2}{2\mu_0} A\ell \qquad (32.13)$$

Because $A\ell$ is the volume of the solenoid, the magnetic energy density, or the energy stored per unit volume in the magnetic field of the inductor is

Magnetic energy density

$$u_B = \frac{U}{A\ell} = \frac{B^2}{2\mu_0} \qquad (32.14)$$

Although this expression was derived for the special case of a solenoid, it is valid for any region of space in which a magnetic field exists. Note that Equation 32.14 is similar in form to Equation 26.13 for the energy per unit volume stored in an electric field, $u_E = \tfrac{1}{2}\epsilon_0 E^2$. In both cases, the energy density is proportional to the square of the field magnitude.

Quick Quiz 32.5 You are performing an experiment that requires the highest possible energy density in the interior of a very long solenoid. Which of the following increases the energy density? (More than one choice may be correct.) (a) increasing the number of turns per unit length on the solenoid (b) increasing the cross-sectional area of the solenoid (c) increasing only the length of the solenoid while keeping the number of turns per unit length fixed (d) increasing the current in the solenoid.

Example 32.4 What Happens to the Energy in the Inductor?

Consider once again the RL circuit shown in Figure 32.6. Recall that the current in the right-hand loop decays exponentially with time according to the expression $I = I_0 e^{-t/\tau}$, where $I_0 = \mathcal{E}/R$ is the initial current in the circuit and $\tau = L/R$ is the time constant. Show that all the energy initially stored in the magnetic field of the inductor appears as internal energy in the resistor as the current decays to zero.

Solution The rate dU/dt at which energy is delivered to the resistor (which is the power) is equal to I^2R, where I is the instantaneous current:

$$\frac{dU}{dt} = I^2 R = (I_0 e^{-Rt/L})^2 R = I_0^2 R e^{-2Rt/L}$$

To find the total energy delivered to the resistor, we solve for dU and integrate this expression over the limits $t = 0$ to $t \to \infty$. (The upper limit is infinity because it takes an infinite amount of time for the current to reach zero.)

$$(1) \qquad U = \int_0^\infty I_0^2 R e^{-2Rt/L} dt = I_0^2 R \int_0^\infty e^{-2Rt/L} dt$$

The value of the definite integral can be shown to be $L/2R$ (see Problem 34) and so U becomes

$$U = I_0^2 R \left(\frac{L}{2R}\right) = \tfrac{1}{2} L I_0^2$$

Note that this is equal to the initial energy stored in the magnetic field of the inductor, given by Equation 32.12, as we set out to prove.

Example 32.5 The Coaxial Cable

Coaxial cables are often used to connect electrical devices, such as your stereo system, and in receiving signals in TV cable systems. Model a long coaxial cable as consisting of two thin concentric cylindrical conducting shells of radii a and b and length ℓ, as in Figure 32.13. The conducting shells carry the same current I in opposite directions. Imagine that the inner conductor carries current to a device and that the outer

one acts as a return path carrying the current back to the source.

(A) Calculate the self-inductance L of this cable.

Solution Conceptualize the situation with the help of Figure 32.13. While we do not have a visible coil in this geometry,

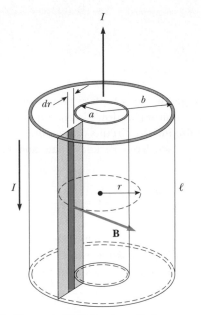

Figure 32.13 (Example 32.5) Section of a long coaxial cable. The inner and outer conductors carry equal currents in opposite directions.

imagine a thin radial slice of the coaxial cable, such as the light blue rectangle in Figure 32.13. If we consider the inner and outer conductors to be connected at the ends of the cable (above and below the figure), this slice represents one large conducting loop. The current in the loop sets up a magnetic field between the inner and outer conductors that passes through this loop. If the current changes, the magnetic field changes and the induced emf opposes the original change in the current in the conductors. We categorize this situation as one in which we can calculate an inductance, but we must return to the fundamental definition of inductance, Equation 32.2. To analyze the problem and obtain L, we must find the magnetic flux through the light blue rectangle in Figure 32.13. Ampère's law (see Section 30.3) tells us that the magnetic field in the region between the shells is due to the inner conductor and its magnitude is $B = \mu_0 I/2\pi r$, where r is

measured from the common center of the shells. The magnetic field is zero outside the outer shell ($r > b$) because the net current passing through the area enclosed by a circular path surrounding the cable is zero, and hence from Ampère's law, $\oint \mathbf{B} \cdot d\mathbf{s} = 0$. The magnetic field is zero inside the inner shell because the shell is hollow and no current is present within a radius $r < a$.

The magnetic field is perpendicular to the light blue rectangle of length ℓ and width $b - a$, the cross section of interest. Because the magnetic field varies with radial position across this rectangle, we must use calculus to find the total magnetic flux. Dividing this rectangle into strips of width dr, such as the dark blue strip in Figure 32.13, we see that the area of each strip is $\ell \, dr$ and that the flux through each strip is $B \, dA = B\ell \, dr$. Hence, we find the total flux through the entire cross section by integrating:

$$\Phi_B = \int B \, dA = \int_a^b \frac{\mu_0 I}{2\pi r} \ell \, dr = \frac{\mu_0 I \ell}{2\pi} \int_a^b \frac{dr}{r} = \frac{\mu_0 I \ell}{2\pi} \ln\left(\frac{b}{a}\right)$$

Using this result, we find that the self-inductance of the cable is

$$L = \frac{\Phi_B}{I} = \frac{\mu_0 \ell}{2\pi} \ln\left(\frac{b}{a}\right)$$

(B) Calculate the total energy stored in the magnetic field of the cable.

Solution Using Equation 32.12 and the results to part (A) gives

$$U = \tfrac{1}{2} L I^2 = \frac{\mu_0 \ell I^2}{4\pi} \ln\left(\frac{b}{a}\right)$$

To finalize the problem, note that the inductance increases if ℓ increases, if b increases, or if a decreases. This is consistent with our conceptualization—any of these changes increases the size of the loop represented by our radial slice and through which the magnetic field passes; this increases the inductance.

32.4 Mutual Inductance

Very often, the magnetic flux through the area enclosed by a circuit varies with time because of time-varying currents in nearby circuits. This condition induces an emf through a process known as *mutual induction*, so called because it depends on the interaction of two circuits.

Consider the two closely wound coils of wire shown in cross-sectional view in Figure 32.14. The current I_1 in coil 1, which has N_1 turns, creates a magnetic field. Some of the magnetic field lines pass through coil 2, which has N_2 turns. The magnetic flux caused by the current in coil 1 and passing through coil 2 is represented by Φ_{12}. In analogy to Equation 32.2, we define the **mutual inductance** M_{12} of coil 2 with

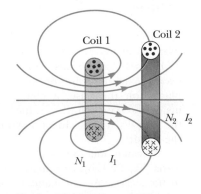

Figure 32.14 A cross-sectional view of two adjacent coils. A current in coil 1 sets up a magnetic field and some of the magnetic field lines pass through coil 2.

respect to coil 1:

Definition of mutual inductance

$$M_{12} \equiv \frac{N_2 \Phi_{12}}{I_1} \qquad (32.15)$$

Mutual inductance depends on the geometry of both circuits and on their orientation with respect to each other. As the circuit separation distance increases, the mutual inductance decreases because the flux linking the circuits decreases.

If the current I_1 varies with time, we see from Faraday's law and Equation 32.15 that the emf induced by coil 1 in coil 2 is

$$\mathcal{E}_2 = -N_2 \frac{d\Phi_{12}}{dt} = -N_2 \frac{d}{dt}\left(\frac{M_{12} I_1}{N_2}\right) = -M_{12} \frac{dI_1}{dt} \qquad (32.16)$$

In the preceding discussion, we assumed that the current is in coil 1. We can also imagine a current I_2 in coil 2. The preceding discussion can be repeated to show that there is a mutual inductance M_{21}. If the current I_2 varies with time, the emf induced by coil 2 in coil 1 is

$$\mathcal{E}_1 = -M_{21} \frac{dI_2}{dt} \qquad (32.17)$$

In mutual induction, the emf induced in one coil is always proportional to the rate at which the current in the other coil is changing. Although the proportionality constants M_{12} and M_{21} have been treated separately, it can be shown that they are equal. Thus, with $M_{12} = M_{21} = M$, Equations 32.16 and 32.17 become

$$\mathcal{E}_2 = -M \frac{dI_1}{dt} \qquad \text{and} \qquad \mathcal{E}_1 = -M \frac{dI_2}{dt}$$

These two equations are similar in form to Equation 32.1 for the self-induced emf $\mathcal{E} = -L(dI/dt)$. The unit of mutual inductance is the henry.

Quick Quiz 32.6 In Figure 32.14, coil 1 is moved closer to coil 2, with the orientation of both coils remaining fixed. Because of this movement, the mutual induction of the two coils (a) increases (b) decreases (c) is unaffected.

Example 32.6 "Wireless" Battery Charger

An electric toothbrush has a base designed to hold the toothbrush handle when not in use. As shown in Figure 32.15a, the handle has a cylindrical hole that fits loosely over a matching cylinder on the base. When the handle is placed on the base, a changing current in a solenoid inside the base cylinder induces a current in a coil inside the handle. This induced current charges the battery in the handle.

We can model the base as a solenoid of length ℓ with N_B turns (Fig. 32.15b), carrying a current I, and having a cross-sectional area A. The handle coil contains N_H turns and completely surrounds the base coil. Find the mutual inductance of the system.

Solution Because the base solenoid carries a current I, the magnetic field in its interior is

$$B = \frac{\mu_0 N_B I}{\ell}$$

Because the magnetic flux Φ_{BH} through the handle's coil caused by the magnetic field of the base coil is BA, the mutual inductance is

$$M = \frac{N_H \Phi_{BH}}{I} = \frac{N_H BA}{I} = \mu_0 \frac{N_B N_H A}{\ell}$$

Wireless charging is used in a number of other "cordless" devices. One significant example is the inductive charging that is used by some electric car manufacturers that avoids direct metal-to-metal contact between the car and the charging apparatus.

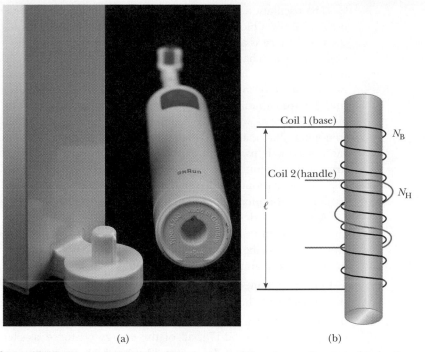

(a)   (b)

Figure 32.15 (Example 32.6) (a) This electric toothbrush uses the mutual induction of solenoids as part of its battery-charging system. (b) A coil of N_H turns wrapped around the center of a solenoid of N_B turns.

32.5 Oscillations in an *LC* Circuit

When a capacitor is connected to an inductor as illustrated in Figure 32.16, the combination is an **LC circuit.** If the capacitor is initially charged and the switch is then closed, we find that both the current in the circuit and the charge on the capacitor oscillate between maximum positive and negative values. If the resistance of the circuit is zero, no energy is transformed to internal energy. In the following analysis, we neglect the resistance in the circuit. We also assume an idealized situation in which energy is not radiated away from the circuit. We shall discuss this radiation in Chapter 34, but we neglect it for now. With these idealizations—zero resistance and no radiation—the oscillations in the circuit persist indefinitely.

Assume that the capacitor has an initial charge Q_{max} (the maximum charge) and that the switch is open for $t < 0$ and then closed at $t = 0$. Let us investigate what happens from an energy viewpoint.

When the capacitor is fully charged, the energy U in the circuit is stored in the electric field of the capacitor and is equal to $Q_{max}^2/2C$ (Eq. 26.11). At this time, the current in the circuit is zero, and therefore no energy is stored in the inductor. After the switch is closed, the rate at which charges leave or enter the capacitor plates (which is also the rate at which the charge on the capacitor changes) is equal to the current in the circuit. As the capacitor begins to discharge after the switch is closed, the energy stored in its electric field decreases. The discharge of the capacitor represents a current in the circuit, and hence some energy is now stored in the magnetic field of the inductor. Thus, energy is transferred from the electric field of the capacitor to the magnetic field of the inductor. When the capacitor is fully discharged, it stores no energy. At this time, the current reaches its maximum value, and all of the energy is stored in the inductor. The current continues in the same direction, decreasing in magnitude, with the capacitor eventually becoming fully charged again but with the polarity of its plates now opposite the initial polarity. This is followed by another discharge until the circuit returns to its original state of maximum charge Q_{max} and the plate polarity shown in Figure 32.16. The energy continues to oscillate between inductor and capacitor.

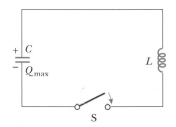

Figure 32.16 A simple *LC* circuit. The capacitor has an initial charge Q_{max}, and the switch is open for $t < 0$ and then closed at $t = 0$.

The oscillations of the *LC* circuit are an electromagnetic analog to the mechanical oscillations of a block–spring system, which we studied in Chapter 15. Much of what is discussed there is applicable to *LC* oscillations. For example, we investigated the effect of driving a mechanical oscillator with an external force, which leads to the phenomenon of *resonance*. The same phenomenon is observed in the *LC* circuit. For example, a radio tuner has an *LC* circuit with a natural frequency. When the circuit is driven by the electromagnetic oscillations of a radio signal detected by the antenna, the tuner circuit responds with a large amplitude of electrical oscillation only for the station frequency that matches the natural frequency. Therefore, only the signal from one radio station is passed on to the amplifier, even though signals from all stations are driving the circuit at the same time. When you turn the knob on the radio tuner to change the station, you are changing the natural frequency of the circuit so that it will exhibit a resonance response to a different driving frequency.

A graphical description of the fields in the inductor and the capacitor in an *LC* circuit is shown in Figure 32.17. The right side of the figure shows the analogous oscillating block–spring system studied in Chapter 15. In each case, the situation is shown at intervals of one-fourth the period of oscillation *T*. The potential energy $\frac{1}{2}kx^2$ stored in a stretched spring is analogous to the electric potential energy $\frac{1}{2}C(\Delta V_{max})^2$ stored in the capacitor. The kinetic energy $\frac{1}{2}mv^2$ of the moving block is analogous to the magnetic energy $\frac{1}{2}LI^2$ stored in the inductor, which requires the presence of moving charges. In Figure 32.17a, all of the energy is stored as electric potential energy in the capacitor at $t = 0$. In Figure 32.17b, which is one fourth of a period later, all of the energy is stored as magnetic energy $\frac{1}{2}LI_{max}^2$ in the inductor, where I_{max} is the maximum current in the circuit. In Figure 32.17c, the energy in the *LC* circuit is stored completely in the capacitor, with the polarity of the plates now opposite what it was in Figure 32.17a. In parts d and e, the system returns to the initial configuration over the second half of the cycle. At times other than those shown in the figure, part of the energy is stored in the electric field of the capacitor and part is stored in the magnetic field of the inductor. In the analogous mechanical oscillation, part of the energy is potential energy in the spring and part is kinetic energy of the block.

Let us consider some arbitrary time *t* after the switch is closed, so that the capacitor has a charge $Q < Q_{max}$ and the current is $I < I_{max}$. At this time, both circuit elements store energy, but the sum of the two energies must equal the total initial energy *U* stored in the fully charged capacitor at $t = 0$:

Total energy stored in an *LC* circuit

$$U = U_C + U_L = \frac{Q^2}{2C} + \tfrac{1}{2}LI^2 \qquad (32.18)$$

Because we have assumed the circuit resistance to be zero and we ignore electromagnetic radiation, no energy is transformed to internal energy and none is transferred out of the system of the circuit. Therefore, *the total energy of the system must remain constant in time.* This means that $dU/dt = 0$. Therefore, by differentiating Equation 32.18 with respect to time while noting that *Q* and *I* vary with time, we obtain

$$\frac{dU}{dt} = \frac{d}{dt}\left(\frac{Q^2}{2C} + \tfrac{1}{2}LI^2\right) = \frac{Q}{C}\frac{dQ}{dt} + LI\frac{dI}{dt} = 0 \qquad (32.19)$$

We can reduce this to a differential equation in one variable by remembering that the current in the circuit is equal to the rate at which the charge on the capacitor changes: $I = dQ/dt$. From this, it follows that $dI/dt = d^2Q/dt^2$. Substitution of these relationships into Equation 32.19 gives

$$\frac{Q}{C} + L\frac{d^2Q}{dt^2} = 0$$

$$\frac{d^2Q}{dt^2} = -\frac{1}{LC}Q \qquad (32.20)$$

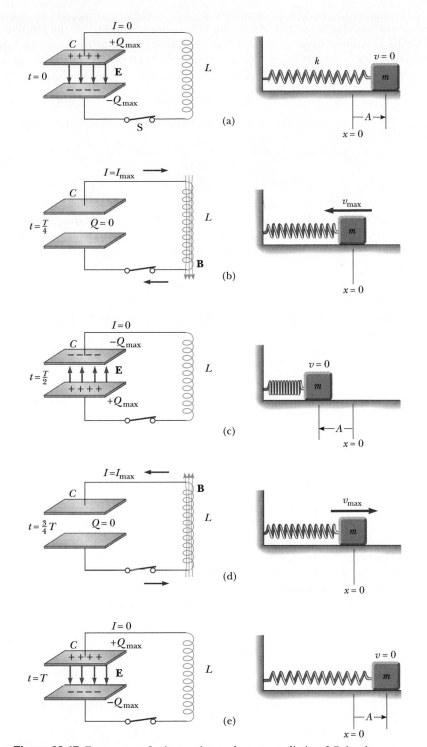

Active Figure 32.17 Energy transfer in a resistanceless, nonradiating *LC* circuit. The capacitor has a charge Q_{max} at $t = 0$, the instant at which the switch is closed. The mechanical analog of this circuit is a block–spring system.

At the Active Figures link at http://www.pse6.com, you can adjust the values of C and L to see the effect on the oscillating current. The block on the spring oscillates in a mechanical analog of the electrical oscillations. A graphical display as in Figure 32.18 is available, as is an energy bar graph.

We can solve for Q by noting that this expression is of the same form as the analogous Equations 15.3 and 15.5 for a block-spring system:

$$\frac{d^2x}{dt^2} = -\frac{k}{m}x = -\omega^2 x$$

where k is the spring constant, m is the mass of the block, and $\omega = \sqrt{k/m}$. The solution of this equation has the general form (Eq. 15.6),

$$x = A\cos(\omega t + \phi)$$

where ω is the angular frequency of the simple harmonic motion, A is the amplitude of motion (the maximum value of x), and ϕ is the phase constant; the values of A and ϕ depend on the initial conditions. Because Equation 32.20 is of the same form as the differential equation of the simple harmonic oscillator, we see that it has the solution

Charge as a function of time for an ideal *LC* circuit

$$Q = Q_{max} \cos(\omega t + \phi) \tag{32.21}$$

where Q_{max} is the maximum charge of the capacitor and the angular frequency ω is

Angular frequency of oscillation in an *LC* circuit

$$\omega = \frac{1}{\sqrt{LC}} \tag{32.22}$$

Note that the angular frequency of the oscillations depends solely on the inductance and capacitance of the circuit. This is the *natural frequency* of oscillation of the *LC* circuit.

Because Q varies sinusoidally with time, the current in the circuit also varies sinusoidally. We can easily show this by differentiating Equation 32.21 with respect to time:

Current as a function of time for an ideal *LC* current

$$I = \frac{dQ}{dt} = -\omega Q_{max} \sin(\omega t + \phi) \tag{32.23}$$

To determine the value of the phase angle ϕ, we examine the initial conditions, which in our situation require that at $t = 0$, $I = 0$ and $Q = Q_{max}$. Setting $I = 0$ at $t = 0$ in Equation 32.23, we have

$$0 = -\omega Q_{max} \sin \phi$$

which shows that $\phi = 0$. This value for ϕ also is consistent with Equation 32.21 and with the condition that $Q = Q_{max}$ at $t = 0$. Therefore, in our case, the expressions for Q and I are

$$Q = Q_{max} \cos \omega t \tag{32.24}$$

$$I = -\omega Q_{max} \sin \omega t = -I_{max} \sin \omega t \tag{32.25}$$

Graphs of Q versus t and I versus t are shown in Figure 32.18. Note that the charge on the capacitor oscillates between the extreme values Q_{max} and $-Q_{max}$, and that the current oscillates between I_{max} and $-I_{max}$. Furthermore, the current is 90° out of phase with the charge. That is, when the charge is a maximum, the current is zero, and when the charge is zero, the current has its maximum value.

Let us return to the energy discussion of the *LC* circuit. Substituting Equations 32.24 and 32.25 in Equation 32.18, we find that the total energy is

$$U = U_C + U_L = \frac{Q_{max}^2}{2C} \cos^2 \omega t + \frac{1}{2} L I_{max}^2 \sin^2 \omega t \tag{32.26}$$

This expression contains all of the features described qualitatively at the beginning of this section. It shows that the energy of the *LC* circuit continuously oscillates between energy stored in the electric field of the capacitor and energy stored in the magnetic

At the Active Figures link at http://www.pse6.com, you can observe this graph develop for the LC circuit in Figure 32.17.

Active Figure 32.18 Graphs of charge versus time and current versus time for a resistanceless, nonradiating *LC* circuit. Note that Q and I are 90° out of phase with each other.

field of the inductor. When the energy stored in the capacitor has its maximum value $Q^2_{max}/2C$, the energy stored in the inductor is zero. When the energy stored in the inductor has its maximum value $\frac{1}{2}LI^2_{max}$, the energy stored in the capacitor is zero.

Plots of the time variations of U_C and U_L are shown in Figure 32.19. The sum $U_C + U_L$ is a constant and equal to the total energy $Q^2_{max}/2C$, or $\frac{1}{2}LI^2_{max}$. Analytical verification of this is straightforward. The amplitudes of the two graphs in Figure 32.19 must be equal because the maximum energy stored in the capacitor (when $I = 0$) must equal the maximum energy stored in the inductor (when $Q = 0$). This is mathematically expressed as

$$\frac{Q^2_{max}}{2C} = \frac{LI^2_{max}}{2}$$

Using this expression in Equation 32.26 for the total energy gives

$$U = \frac{Q^2_{max}}{2C}(\cos^2 \omega t + \sin^2 \omega t) = \frac{Q^2_{max}}{2C} \qquad (32.27)$$

because $\cos^2 \omega t + \sin^2 \omega t = 1$.

In our idealized situation, the oscillations in the circuit persist indefinitely; however, remember that the total energy U of the circuit remains constant only if energy transfers and transformations are neglected. In actual circuits, there is always some resistance, and hence some energy is transformed to internal energy. We mentioned at the beginning of this section that we are also ignoring radiation from the circuit. In reality, radiation is inevitable in this type of circuit, and the total energy in the circuit continuously decreases as a result of this process.

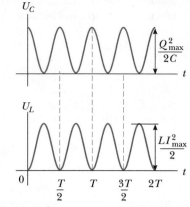

Figure 32.19 Plots of U_C versus t and U_L versus t for a resistanceless, nonradiating *LC* circuit. The sum of the two curves is a constant and equal to the total energy stored in the circuit.

Quick Quiz 32.7 At an instant of time during the oscillations of an *LC* circuit, the current is at its maximum value. At this instant, the voltage across the capacitor (a) is different from that across the inductor (b) is zero (c) has its maximum value (d) is impossible to determine

Quick Quiz 32.8 At an instant of time during the oscillations of an *LC* circuit, the current is momentarily zero. At this instant, the voltage across the capacitor (a) is different from that across the inductor (b) is zero (c) has its maximum value (d) is impossible to determine

Example 32.7 Oscillations in an *LC* Circuit   *Interactive*

In Figure 32.20, the capacitor is initially charged when switch S_1 is open and S_2 is closed. Switch S_2 is then opened, removing the battery from the circuit, and the capacitor remains charged. Switch S_1 is then closed, so that the capacitor is connected directly across the inductor.

(A) Find the frequency of oscillation of the circuit.

Solution Using Equation 32.22 gives for the frequency

$$f = \frac{\omega}{2\pi} = \frac{1}{2\pi\sqrt{LC}}$$

$$= \frac{1}{2\pi[(2.81 \times 10^{-3}\,\text{H})(9.00 \times 10^{-12}\,\text{F})]^{1/2}}$$

$$= \boxed{1.00 \times 10^6\,\text{Hz}}$$

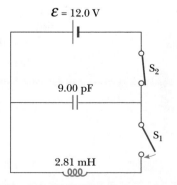
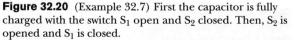

Figure 32.20 (Example 32.7) First the capacitor is fully charged with the switch S_1 open and S_2 closed. Then, S_2 is opened and S_1 is closed.

(B) What are the maximum values of charge on the capacitor and current in the circuit?

Solution The initial charge on the capacitor equals the maximum charge, and because $C = Q/\Delta V$, we have

$$Q_{max} = C\,\Delta V = (9.00 \times 10^{-12}\text{ F})(12.0\text{ V})$$

$$= \boxed{1.08 \times 10^{-10}\text{ C}}$$

From Equation 32.25, we can see how the maximum current is related to the maximum charge:

$$I_{max} = \omega Q_{max} = 2\pi f Q_{max}$$
$$= (2\pi \times 10^6\text{ s}^{-1})(1.08 \times 10^{-10}\text{ C})$$

$$I_{max} = \boxed{6.79 \times 10^{-4}\text{ A}}$$

(C) Determine the charge and current as functions of time.

Solution Equations 32.24 and 32.25 give the following expressions for the time variation of Q and I:

$$Q = Q_{max}\cos \omega t$$

$$= \boxed{(1.08 \times 10^{-10}\text{ C})\cos[(2\pi \times 10^6\text{ s}^{-1})t]}$$

$$I = -I_{max}\sin \omega t$$

$$= \boxed{(-6.79 \times 10^{-4}\text{ A})\sin[(2\pi \times 10^6\text{ s}^{-1})t]}$$

> **At the Interactive Worked Example link at http://www.pse6.com,** *you can study the oscillations in an LC circuit.*

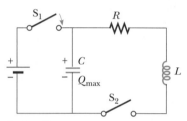

Active Figure 32.21 A series RLC circuit. Switch S_1 is closed and the capacitor is charged. S_1 is then opened and, at $t = 0$, switch S_2 is closed.

At the Active Figures link at http://www.pse6.com, you can adjust the values of R, L, and C to see the effect on the decaying charge on the capacitor. A graphical display as in Figure 32.23a is available, as is an energy bar graph.

Figure 32.22 A block–spring system moving in a viscous medium with damped harmonic motion is analogous to an RLC circuit.

32.6 The *RLC* Circuit

We now turn our attention to a more realistic circuit consisting of a resistor, an inductor, and a capacitor connected in series, as shown in Figure 32.21. Let us assume that the resistance of the resistor represents all of the resistance in the circuit. Now imagine that switch S_1 is closed and S_2 is open, so that the capacitor has an initial charge Q_{max}. Next, S_1 is opened and S_2 is closed. Once S_2 is closed and a current is established, the total energy stored in the capacitor and inductor at any time is given by Equation 32.18. However, this total energy is no longer constant, as it was in the *LC* circuit, because the resistor causes transformation to internal energy. (We continue to ignore electromagnetic radiation from the circuit in this discussion.) Because the rate of energy transformation to internal energy within a resistor is I^2R, we have

$$\frac{dU}{dt} = -I^2R$$

where the negative sign signifies that the energy U of the circuit is decreasing in time. Substituting this result into Equation 32.19 gives

$$LI\frac{dI}{dt} + \frac{Q}{C}\frac{dQ}{dt} = -I^2R \qquad (32.28)$$

To convert this equation into a form that allows us to compare the electrical oscillations with their mechanical analog, we first use the fact that $I = dQ/dt$ and move all terms to the left-hand side to obtain

$$LI\frac{d^2Q}{dt^2} + I^2R + \frac{Q}{C}I = 0$$

Now we divide through by I:

$$L\frac{d^2Q}{dt^2} + IR + \frac{Q}{C} = 0$$

$$L\frac{d^2Q}{dt^2} + R\frac{dQ}{dt} + \frac{Q}{C} = 0 \qquad (32.29)$$

The *RLC* circuit is analogous to the damped harmonic oscillator discussed in Section 15.6 and illustrated in Figure 32.22. The equation of motion for a damped

Table 32.1

Analogies Between Electrical and Mechanical Systems

Electric Circuit		One-Dimensional Mechanical System
Charge	$Q \leftrightarrow x$	Position
Current	$I \leftrightarrow v_x$	Velocity
Potential difference	$\Delta V \leftrightarrow F_x$	Force
Resistance	$R \leftrightarrow b$	Viscous damping coefficient
Capacitance	$C \leftrightarrow 1/k$	(k = spring constant)
Inductance	$L \leftrightarrow m$	Mass
Current = time derivative of charge	$I = \dfrac{dQ}{dt} \leftrightarrow v_x = \dfrac{dx}{dt}$	Velocity = time derivative of position
Rate of change of current = second time derivative of charge	$\dfrac{dI}{dt} = \dfrac{d^2Q}{dt^2} \leftrightarrow a_x = \dfrac{dv_x}{dt} = \dfrac{d^2x}{dt^2}$	Acceleration = second time derivative of position
Energy in inductor	$U_L = \frac{1}{2}LI^2 \leftrightarrow K = \frac{1}{2}mv^2$	Kinetic energy of moving object
Energy in capacitor	$U_C = \frac{1}{2}\dfrac{Q^2}{C} \leftrightarrow U = \frac{1}{2}kx^2$	Potential energy stored in a spring
Rate of energy loss due to resistance	$I^2R \leftrightarrow bv^2$	Rate of energy loss due to friction
RLC circuit	$L\dfrac{d^2Q}{dt^2} + R\dfrac{dQ}{dt} + \dfrac{Q}{C} = 0 \leftrightarrow m\dfrac{d^2x}{dt^2} + b\dfrac{dx}{dt} + kx = 0$	Damped object on a spring

block–spring system is, from Equation 15.31,

$$m\,\frac{d^2x}{dt^2} + b\,\frac{dx}{dt} + kx = 0 \tag{32.30}$$

Comparing Equations 32.29 and 32.30, we see that Q corresponds to the position x of the block at any instant, L to the mass m of the block, R to the damping coefficient b, and C to $1/k$, where k is the force constant of the spring. These and other relationships are listed in Table 32.1.

Because the analytical solution of Equation 32.29 is cumbersome, we give only a qualitative description of the circuit behavior. In the simplest case, when $R = 0$, Equation 32.29 reduces to that of a simple *LC* circuit, as expected, and the charge and the current oscillate sinusoidally in time. This is equivalent to removal of all damping in the mechanical oscillator.

When R is small, a situation analogous to light damping in the mechanical oscillator, the solution of Equation 32.29 is

$$Q = Q_{\max}\, e^{-Rt/2L} \cos \omega_d t \tag{32.31}$$

where ω_d, the angular frequency at which the circuit oscillates, is given by

$$\omega_d = \left[\frac{1}{LC} - \left(\frac{R}{2L}\right)^2\right]^{1/2} \tag{32.32}$$

That is, the value of the charge on the capacitor undergoes a damped harmonic oscillation in analogy with a block–spring system moving in a viscous medium. From Equation 32.32, we see that, when $R \ll \sqrt{4L/C}$ (so that the second term in the brackets is much smaller than the first), the frequency ω_d of the damped oscillator is close to that of the undamped oscillator, $1/\sqrt{LC}$. Because $I = dQ/dt$, it follows that the current also

At the Active Figures link at http://www.pse6.com, you can observe this graph develop for the damped RLC circuit in Figure 32.21.

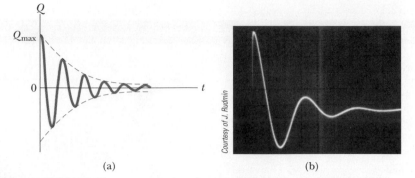

(a)   (b)

Active Figure 32.23 (a) Charge versus time for a damped *RLC* circuit. The charge decays in this way when $R > \sqrt{4L/C}$. The *Q*-versus-*t* curve represents a plot of Equation 32.31. (b) Oscilloscope pattern showing the decay in the oscillations of an *RLC* circuit.

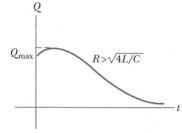

Figure 32.24 Plot of *Q* versus *t* for an overdamped *RLC* circuit, which occurs for values of $R > \sqrt{4L/C}$.

undergoes damped harmonic oscillation. A plot of the charge versus time for the damped oscillator is shown in Figure 32.23a. Note that the maximum value of *Q* decreases after each oscillation, just as the amplitude of a damped block–spring system decreases in time.

When we consider larger values of *R*, we find that the oscillations damp out more rapidly; in fact, there exists a critical resistance value $R_c = \sqrt{4L/C}$ above which no oscillations occur. A system with $R = R_c$ is said to be *critically damped*. When *R* exceeds R_c, the system is said to be *overdamped* (Fig. 32.24).

SUMMARY

Take a practice test for this chapter by clicking on the Practice Test link at http://www.pse6.com.

When the current in a coil changes with time, an emf is induced in the coil according to Faraday's law. The **self-induced emf** is

$$\mathcal{E}_L = -L \frac{dI}{dt} \tag{32.1}$$

where *L* is the **inductance** of the coil. Inductance is a measure of how much opposition a coil offers to a change in the current in the coil. Inductance has the SI unit of **henry** (H), where $1 \text{ H} = 1 \text{ V} \cdot \text{s}/\text{A}$.

The inductance of any coil is

$$L = \frac{N\Phi_B}{I} \tag{32.2}$$

where Φ_B is the magnetic flux through the coil and *N* is the total number of turns. The inductance of a device depends on its geometry. For example, the inductance of an air-core solenoid is

$$L = \frac{\mu_0 N^2 A}{\ell} \tag{32.4}$$

where *A* is the cross-sectional area, and ℓ is the length of the solenoid.

If a resistor and inductor are connected in series to a battery of emf $\mathcal{E}$, and if a switch in the circuit is open for $t < 0$ and then closed at $t = 0$, the current in the circuit varies in time according to the expression

$$I = \frac{\mathcal{E}}{R} (1 - e^{-t/\tau}) \tag{32.7}$$

where $\tau = L/R$ is the **time constant** of the RL circuit. That is, the current increases to an equilibrium value of $\mathcal{E}/R$ after a time interval that is long compared with τ. If the battery in the circuit is replaced by a resistanceless wire, the current decays exponentially with time according to the expression

$$I = \frac{\mathcal{E}}{R} e^{-t/\tau} \tag{32.10}$$

where $\mathcal{E}/R$ is the initial current in the circuit.

The energy stored in the magnetic field of an inductor carrying a current I is

$$U = \tfrac{1}{2} L I^2 \tag{32.12}$$

This energy is the magnetic counterpart to the energy stored in the electric field of a charged capacitor.

The energy density at a point where the magnetic field is B is

$$u_B = \frac{B^2}{2\mu_0} \tag{32.14}$$

The **mutual inductance** of a system of two coils is given by

$$M_{12} = \frac{N_2 \Phi_{12}}{I_1} = M_{21} = \frac{N_1 \Phi_{21}}{I_2} = M \tag{32.15}$$

This mutual inductance allows us to relate the induced emf in a coil to the changing source current in a nearby coil using the relationships

$$\mathcal{E}_2 = -M \frac{dI_1}{dt} \quad \text{and} \quad \mathcal{E}_1 = -M \frac{dI_2}{dt} \tag{32.16, 32.17}$$

In an LC circuit that has zero resistance and does not radiate electromagnetically (an idealization), the values of the charge on the capacitor and the current in the circuit vary in time according to the expressions

$$Q = Q_{\max} \cos(\omega t + \phi) \tag{32.21}$$

$$I = \frac{dQ}{dt} = -\omega Q_{\max} \sin(\omega t + \phi) \tag{32.23}$$

where $Q_{\max}$ is the maximum charge on the capacitor, ϕ is a phase constant, and ω is the angular frequency of oscillation:

$$\omega = \frac{1}{\sqrt{LC}} \tag{32.22}$$

The energy in an LC circuit continuously transfers between energy stored in the capacitor and energy stored in the inductor. The total energy of the LC circuit at any time t is

$$U = U_C + U_L = \frac{Q_{\max}^2}{2C} \cos^2 \omega t + \frac{L I_{\max}^2}{2} \sin^2 \omega t \tag{32.26}$$

At $t = 0$, all of the energy is stored in the electric field of the capacitor ($U = Q_{\max}^2/2C$). Eventually, all of this energy is transferred to the inductor ($U = L I_{\max}^2/2$). However, the total energy remains constant because energy transformations are neglected in the ideal LC circuit.

In an RLC circuit with small resistance, the charge on the capacitor varies with time according to

$$Q = Q_{\max} e^{-Rt/2L} \cos \omega_d t \tag{32.31}$$

where

$$\omega_d = \left[\frac{1}{LC} - \left(\frac{R}{2L} \right)^2 \right]^{1/2} \tag{32.32}$$

QUESTIONS

1. Why is the induced emf that appears in an inductor called a "counter" or "back" emf?

2. The current in a circuit containing a coil, resistor, and battery has reached a constant value. Does the coil have an inductance? Does the coil affect the value of the current?

3. What parameters affect the inductance of a coil? Does the inductance of a coil depend on the current in the coil?

4. How can a long piece of wire be wound on a spool so that the wire has a negligible self-inductance?

5. For the series RL circuit shown in Figure Q32.5, can the back emf ever be greater than the battery emf? Explain.

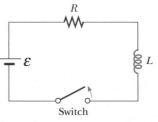

Figure Q32.5   Questions 5 and 6.

6. Suppose the switch in Figure Q32.5 has been closed for a long time and is suddenly opened. Does the current instantaneously drop to zero? Why does a spark appear at the switch contacts at the moment the switch is opened?

7. A switch controls the current in a circuit that has a large inductance. Is a spark (see Figure Q32.7) more likely to be produced at the switch when the switch is being closed or when it is being opened, or doesn't it matter? The electric arc can melt and oxidize the contact surfaces, resulting in high resistivity of the contacts and eventual destruction of the switch. Before electronic ignitions were invented, distributor contact points in automobiles had to be replaced regularly. Switches in power distribution networks and switches controlling large motors, generators, and electromagnets can suffer from arcing and can be very dangerous to operate.

8. Consider this thesis: "Joseph Henry, America's first professional physicist, caused the most recent basic change in the human view of the Universe when he discovered self-induction during a school vacation at the Albany Academy about 1830. Before that time, one could think of the Universe as composed of just one thing: matter. The energy that temporarily maintains the current after a battery is removed from a coil, on the other hand, is not energy that belongs to any chunk of matter. It is energy in the massless magnetic field surrounding the coil. With Henry's discovery, Nature forced us to admit that the Universe consists of fields as well as matter." Argue for or against the statement. What in your view comprises the Universe?

9. If the current in an inductor is doubled, by what factor does the stored energy change?

10. Discuss the similarities between the energy stored in the electric field of a charged capacitor and the energy stored in the magnetic field of a current-carrying coil.

11. What is the inductance of two inductors connected in series? Does it matter if they are solenoids or toroids?

12. The centers of two circular loops are separated by a fixed distance. For what relative orientation of the loops is their mutual inductance a maximum? a minimum? Explain.

13. Two solenoids are connected in series so that each carries the same current at any instant. Is mutual induction present? Explain.

14. In the LC circuit shown in Figure 32.16, the charge on the capacitor is sometimes zero, but at such instants the current in the circuit is not zero. How is this possible?

15. If the resistance of the wires in an LC circuit were not zero, would the oscillations persist? Explain.

16. How can you tell whether an RLC circuit is overdamped or underdamped?

17. What is the significance of critical damping in an RLC circuit?

18. Can an object exert a force on itself? When a coil induces an emf in itself, does it exert a force on itself?

Figure Q32.7

PROBLEMS

1, 2, 3 = straightforward, intermediate, challenging ☐ = full solution available in the *Student Solutions Manual and Study Guide*

🌀 = coached solution with hints available at http://www.pse6.com 💻 = computer useful in solving problem

▨ = paired numerical and symbolic problems

Section 32.1 Self-Inductance

1. A coil has an inductance of 3.00 mH, and the current in it changes from 0.200 A to 1.50 A in a time of 0.200 s. Find the magnitude of the average induced emf in the coil during this time.

2. A coiled telephone cord forms a spiral with 70 turns, a diameter of 1.30 cm, and an unstretched length of 60.0 cm. Determine the self-inductance of one conductor in the unstretched cord.

3. A 2.00-H inductor carries a steady current of 0.500 A. When the switch in the circuit is opened, the current is effectively zero after 10.0 ms. What is the average induced emf in the inductor during this time?

4. Calculate the magnetic flux through the area enclosed by a 300-turn, 7.20-mH coil when the current in the coil is 10.0 mA.

5. 🌀 A 10.0-mH inductor carries a current $I = I_{max} \sin \omega t$, with $I_{max} = 5.00$ A and $\omega/2\pi = 60.0$ Hz. What is the back emf as a function of time?

6. An emf of 24.0 mV is induced in a 500-turn coil at an instant when the current is 4.00 A and is changing at the rate of 10.0 A/s. What is the magnetic flux through each turn of the coil?

7. An inductor in the form of a solenoid contains 420 turns, is 16.0 cm in length, and has a cross-sectional area of 3.00 cm². What uniform rate of decrease of current through the inductor induces an emf of 175 μV?

8. The current in a 90.0-mH inductor changes with time as $I = 1.00t^2 - 6.00t$ (in SI units). Find the magnitude of the induced emf at (a) $t = 1.00$ s and (b) $t = 4.00$ s. (c) At what time is the emf zero?

9. A 40.0-mA current is carried by a uniformly wound air-core solenoid with 450 turns, a 15.0-mm diameter, and 12.0-cm length. Compute (a) the magnetic field inside the solenoid, (b) the magnetic flux through each turn, and (c) the inductance of the solenoid. (d) **What If?** If the current were different, which of these quantities would change?

10. A solenoid has 120 turns uniformly wrapped around a wooden core, which has a diameter of 10.0 mm and a length of 9.00 cm. (a) Calculate the inductance of the solenoid. (b) **What If?** The wooden core is replaced with a soft iron rod that has the same dimensions, but a magnetic permeability $\mu_m = 800\mu_0$. What is the new inductance?

11. A piece of copper wire with thin insulation, 200 m long and 1.00 mm in diameter, is wound onto a plastic tube to form a long solenoid. This coil has a circular cross section and consists of tightly wound turns in one layer. If the current in the solenoid drops linearly from 1.80 A to zero in 0.120 seconds, an emf of 80.0 mV is induced in the coil. What is the length of the solenoid, measured along its axis?

12. A toroid has a major radius R and a minor radius r, and is tightly wound with N turns of wire, as shown in Figure P32.12. If $R \gg r$, the magnetic field in the region enclosed by the wire of the torus, of cross-sectional area $A = \pi r^2$, is essentially the same as the magnetic field of a solenoid that has been bent into a large circle of radius R. Modeling the field as the uniform field of a long solenoid, show that the self-inductance of such a toroid is approximately

$$L \approx \frac{\mu_0 N^2 A}{2\pi R}$$

(An exact expression of the inductance of a toroid with a rectangular cross section is derived in Problem 64.)

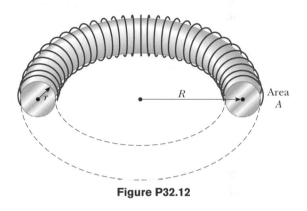

Figure P32.12

13. A self-induced emf in a solenoid of inductance L changes in time as $\mathcal{E} = \mathcal{E}_0 e^{-kt}$. Find the total charge that passes through the solenoid, assuming the charge is finite.

Section 32.2 RL Circuits

14. Calculate the resistance in an *RL* circuit in which $L = 2.50$ H and the current increases to 90.0% of its final value in 3.00 s.

15. A 12.0-V battery is connected into a series circuit containing a 10.0-Ω resistor and a 2.00-H inductor. How long will it take the current to reach (a) 50.0% and (b) 90.0% of its final value?

16. Show that $I = I_0 e^{-t/\tau}$ is a solution of the differential equation

$$IR + L\frac{dI}{dt} = 0$$

where $\tau = L/R$ and I_0 is the current at $t = 0$.

17. Consider the circuit in Figure P32.17, taking $\mathcal{E} = 6.00$ V, $L = 8.00$ mH, and $R = 4.00$ Ω. (a) What is the inductive time constant of the circuit? (b) Calculate the current in

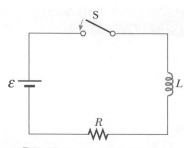

Figure P32.17 Problems 17, 18, 19, and 22.

the circuit 250 μs after the switch is closed. (c) What is the value of the final steady-state current? (d) How long does it take the current to reach 80.0% of its maximum value?

18. In the circuit shown in Figure P32.17, let $L = 7.00$ H, $R = 9.00$ Ω, and $\mathcal{E} = 120$ V. What is the self-induced emf 0.200 s after the switch is closed?

19. For the *RL* circuit shown in Figure P32.17, let the inductance be 3.00 H, the resistance 8.00 Ω, and the battery emf 36.0 V. (a) Calculate the ratio of the potential difference across the resistor to that across the inductor when the current is 2.00 A. (b) Calculate the voltage across the inductor when the current is 4.50 A.

20. A 12.0-V battery is connected in series with a resistor and an inductor. The circuit has a time constant of 500 μs, and the maximum current is 200 mA. What is the value of the inductance?

21. An inductor that has an inductance of 15.0 H and a resistance of 30.0 Ω is connected across a 100-V battery. What is the rate of increase of the current (a) at $t = 0$ and (b) at $t = 1.50$ s?

22. When the switch in Figure P32.17 is closed, the current takes 3.00 ms to reach 98.0% of its final value. If $R = 10.0$ Ω, what is the inductance?

23. The switch in Figure P32.23 is open for $t < 0$ and then closed at time $t = 0$. Find the current in the inductor and the current in the switch as functions of time thereafter.

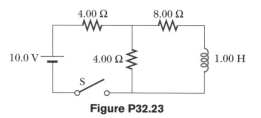

Figure P32.23

24. A series *RL* circuit with $L = 3.00$ H and a series *RC* circuit with $C = 3.00$ μF have equal time constants. If the two circuits contain the same resistance R, (a) what is the value of R and (b) what is the time constant?

25. A current pulse is fed to the partial circuit shown in Figure P32.25. The current begins at zero, then becomes 10.0 A between $t = 0$ and $t = 200$ μs, and then is zero once again. Determine the current in the inductor as a function of time.

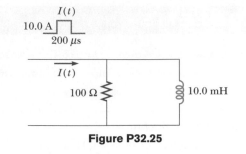

Figure P32.25

26. One application of an *RL* circuit is the generation of time-varying high voltage from a low-voltage source, as shown in Figure P32.26. (a) What is the current in the circuit a long time after the switch has been in position *a*? (b) Now the switch is thrown quickly from *a* to *b*. Compute the initial voltage across each resistor and across the inductor. (c) How much time elapses before the voltage across the inductor drops to 12.0 V?

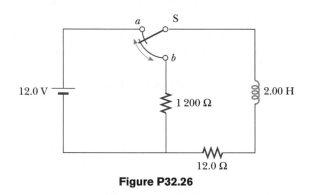

Figure P32.26

27. A 140-mH inductor and a 4.90-Ω resistor are connected with a switch to a 6.00-V battery as shown in Figure P32.27. (a) If the switch is thrown to the left (connecting the battery), how much time elapses before the current reaches 220 mA? (b) What is the current in the inductor 10.0 s after the switch is closed? (c) Now the switch is quickly thrown from *a* to *b*. How much time elapses before the current falls to 160 mA?

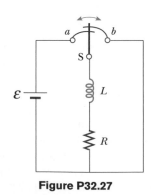

Figure P32.27

28. Consider two ideal inductors L_1 and L_2 that have *zero* internal resistance and are far apart, so that their magnetic fields do not influence each other. (a) Assuming these inductors

are connected in series, show that they are equivalent to a single ideal inductor having $L_{eq} = L_1 + L_2$. (b) Assuming these same two inductors are connected in parallel, show that they are equivalent to a single ideal inductor having $1/L_{eq} = 1/L_1 + 1/L_2$. (c) **What If?** Now consider two inductors L_1 and L_2 that have *nonzero* internal resistances R_1 and R_2, respectively. Assume they are still far apart so that their mutual inductance is zero. Assuming these inductors are connected in series, show that they are equivalent to a single inductor having $L_{eq} = L_1 + L_2$ and $R_{eq} = R_1 + R_2$. (d) If these same inductors are now connected in parallel, is it necessarily true that they are equivalent to a single ideal inductor having $1/L_{eq} = 1/L_1 + 1/L_2$ and $1/R_{eq} = 1/R_1 + 1/R_2$? Explain your answer.

Section 32.3 Energy in a Magnetic Field

29. Calculate the energy associated with the magnetic field of a 200-turn solenoid in which a current of 1.75 A produces a flux of 3.70×10^{-4} Wb in each turn.

30. The magnetic field inside a superconducting solenoid is 4.50 T. The solenoid has an inner diameter of 6.20 cm and a length of 26.0 cm. Determine (a) the magnetic energy density in the field and (b) the energy stored in the magnetic field within the solenoid.

31. An air-core solenoid with 68 turns is 8.00 cm long and has a diameter of 1.20 cm. How much energy is stored in its magnetic field when it carries a current of 0.770 A?

32. At $t = 0$, an emf of 500 V is applied to a coil that has an inductance of 0.800 H and a resistance of 30.0 Ω. (a) Find the energy stored in the magnetic field when the current reaches half its maximum value. (b) After the emf is connected, how long does it take the current to reach this value?

33. On a clear day at a certain location, a 100-V/m vertical electric field exists near the Earth's surface. At the same place, the Earth's magnetic field has a magnitude of 0.500×10^{-4} T. Compute the energy densities of the two fields.

34. Complete the calculation in Example 32.4 by proving that

$$\int_0^{\infty} e^{-2Rt/L} \, dt = \frac{L}{2R}$$

35. An RL circuit in which $L = 4.00$ H and $R = 5.00$ Ω is connected to a 22.0-V battery at $t = 0$. (a) What energy is stored in the inductor when the current is 0.500 A? (b) At what rate is energy being stored in the inductor when $I = 1.00$ A? (c) What power is being delivered to the circuit by the battery when $I = 0.500$ A?

36. A 10.0-V battery, a 5.00-Ω resistor, and a 10.0-H inductor are connected in series. After the current in the circuit has reached its maximum value, calculate (a) the power being supplied by the battery, (b) the power being delivered to the resistor, (c) the power being delivered to the inductor, and (d) the energy stored in the magnetic field of the inductor.

37. A uniform electric field of magnitude 680 kV/m throughout a cylindrical volume results in a total energy of 3.40 μJ. What magnetic field over this same region stores the same total energy?

38. Assume that the magnitude of the magnetic field outside a sphere of radius R is $B = B_0(R/r)^2$, where B_0 is a constant. Determine the total energy stored in the magnetic field outside the sphere and evaluate your result for $B_0 = 5.00 \times 10^{-5}$ T and $R = 6.00 \times 10^6$ m, values appropriate for the Earth's magnetic field.

Section 32.4 Mutual Inductance

39. Two coils are close to each other. The first coil carries a time-varying current given by $I(t) = (5.00 \text{ A}) \, e^{-0.025 \, 0t} \sin(377t)$. At $t = 0.800$ s, the emf measured across the second coil is $- 3.20$ V. What is the mutual inductance of the coils?

40. Two coils, held in fixed positions, have a mutual inductance of 100 μH. What is the peak voltage in one when a sinusoidal current given by $I(t) = (10.0 \text{ A}) \sin(1\,000t)$ is in the other coil?

41. An emf of 96.0 mV is induced in the windings of a coil when the current in a nearby coil is increasing at the rate of 1.20 A/s. What is the mutual inductance of the two coils?

42. On a printed circuit board, a relatively long straight conductor and a conducting rectangular loop lie in the same plane, as shown in Figure P31.9. Taking $h = 0.400$ mm, $w = 1.30$ mm, and $L = 2.70$ mm, find their mutual inductance.

43. Two solenoids A and B, spaced close to each other and sharing the same cylindrical axis, have 400 and 700 turns, respectively. A current of 3.50 A in coil A produces an average flux of 300 μWb through each turn of A and a flux of 90.0 μWb through each turn of B. (a) Calculate the mutual inductance of the two solenoids. (b) What is the self-inductance of A? (c) What emf is induced in B when the current in A increases at the rate of 0.500 A/s?

44. A large coil of radius R_1 and having N_1 turns is coaxial with a small coil of radius R_2 and having N_2 turns. The centers of the coils are separated by a distance x that is much larger than R_1 and R_2. What is the mutual inductance of the coils? *Suggestion:* John von Neumann proved that the same answer must result from considering the flux through the first coil of the magnetic field produced by the second coil, or from considering the flux through the second coil of the magnetic field produced by the first coil. In this problem it is easy to calculate the flux through the small coil, but it is difficult to calculate the flux through the large coil, because to do so you would have to know the magnetic field away from the axis.

45. Two inductors having self-inductances L_1 and L_2 are connected in parallel as shown in Figure P32.45a. The mutual inductance between the two inductors is M. Determine the equivalent self-inductance L_{eq} for the system (Figure P32.45b).

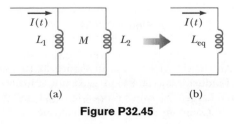

(a)   (b)

Figure P32.45

Section 32.5   Oscillations in an *LC* Circuit

46. A 1.00-μF capacitor is charged by a 40.0-V power supply. The fully charged capacitor is then discharged through a 10.0-mH inductor. Find the maximum current in the resulting oscillations.

47. An *LC* circuit consists of a 20.0-mH inductor and a 0.500-μF capacitor. If the maximum instantaneous current is 0.100 A, what is the greatest potential difference across the capacitor?

48. In the circuit of Figure P32.48, the battery emf is 50.0 V, the resistance is $250\ \Omega$, and the capacitance is $0.500\ \mu$F. The switch S is closed for a long time and no voltage is measured across the capacitor. After the switch is opened, the potential difference across the capacitor reaches a maximum value of 150 V. What is the value of the inductance?

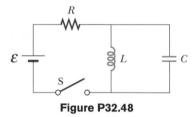

Figure P32.48

49. A fixed inductance $L = 1.05\ \mu$H is used in series with a variable capacitor in the tuning section of a radiotelephone on a ship. What capacitance tunes the circuit to the signal from a transmitter broadcasting at 6.30 MHz?

50. Calculate the inductance of an *LC* circuit that oscillates at 120 Hz when the capacitance is $8.00\ \mu$F.

51. An *LC* circuit like the one in Figure 32.16 contains an 82.0-mH inductor and a 17.0-μF capacitor that initially carries a 180-μC charge. The switch is open for $t < 0$ and then closed at $t = 0$. (a) Find the frequency (in hertz) of the resulting oscillations. At $t = 1.00$ ms, find (b) the charge on the capacitor and (c) the current in the circuit.

52. The switch in Figure P32.52 is connected to point a for a long time. After the switch is thrown to point b, what are (a) the frequency of oscillation of the *LC* circuit, (b) the maximum charge that appears on the capacitor, (c) the maximum current in the inductor, and (d) the total energy the circuit possesses at $t = 3.00$ s?

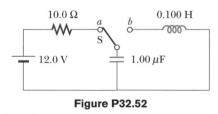

Figure P32.52

53. An *LC* circuit like that in Figure 32.16 consists of a 3.30-H inductor and an 840-pF capacitor, initially carrying a 105-μC charge. The switch is open for $t < 0$ and then closed at $t = 0$. Compute the following quantities at $t = 2.00$ ms:

(a) the energy stored in the capacitor; (b) the energy stored in the inductor; (c) the total energy in the circuit.

Section 32.6   The *RLC* Circuit

54. In Figure 32.21, let $R = 7.60\ \Omega$, $L = 2.20$ mH, and $C = 1.80\ \mu$F. (a) Calculate the frequency of the damped oscillation of the circuit. (b) What is the critical resistance?

55. Consider an *LC* circuit in which $L = 500$ mH and $C = 0.100\ \mu$F. (a) What is the resonance frequency ω_0? (b) If a resistance of $1.00\ k\Omega$ is introduced into this circuit, what is the frequency of the (damped) oscillations? (c) What is the percent difference between the two frequencies?

56. Show that Equation 32.28 in the text is Kirchhoff's loop rule as applied to the circuit in Figure 32.21.

57. The energy of an *RLC* circuit decreases by 1.00% during each oscillation when $R = 2.00\ \Omega$. If this resistance is removed, the resulting *LC* circuit oscillates at a frequency of 1.00 kHz. Find the values of the inductance and the capacitance.

58. Electrical oscillations are initiated in a series circuit containing a capacitance C, inductance L, and resistance R. (a) If $R \ll \sqrt{4L/C}$ (weak damping), how much time elapses before the amplitude of the current oscillation falls off to 50.0% of its initial value? (b) How long does it take the energy to decrease to 50.0% of its initial value?

Additional Problems

59. **Review problem.** This problem extends the reasoning of Section 26.4, Problem 26.37, Example 30.6, and Section 32.3. (a) Consider a capacitor with vacuum between its large, closely spaced, oppositely charged parallel plates. Show that the force on one plate can be accounted for by thinking of the electric field between the plates as exerting a "negative pressure" equal to the energy density of the electric field. (b) Consider two infinite plane sheets carrying electric currents in opposite directions with equal linear current densities J_s. Calculate the force per area acting on one sheet due to the magnetic field created by the other sheet. (c) Calculate the net magnetic field between the sheets and the field outside of the volume between them. (d) Calculate the energy density in the magnetic field between the sheets. (e) Show that the force on one sheet can be accounted for by thinking of the magnetic field between the sheets as exerting a positive pressure equal to its energy density. This result for magnetic pressure applies to all current configurations, not just to sheets of current.

60. Initially, the capacitor in a series *LC* circuit is charged. A switch is closed at $t = 0$, allowing the capacitor to discharge, and at time t the energy stored in the capacitor is one fourth of its initial value. Determine L, assuming C is known.

61. A 1.00-mH inductor and a 1.00-μF capacitor are connected in series. The current in the circuit is described by $I = 20.0t$, where t is in seconds and I is in amperes. The capacitor initially has no charge. Determine (a) the voltage across the inductor as a function of time, (b) the voltage across the capacitor as a function of time, and (c) the time when the energy stored in the capacitor first exceeds that in the inductor.

62. An inductor having inductance L and a capacitor having capacitance C are connected in series. The current in the circuit increases linearly in time as described by $I = Kt$, where K is a constant. The capacitor is initially uncharged. Determine (a) the voltage across the inductor as a function of time, (b) the voltage across the capacitor as a function of time, and (c) the time when the energy stored in the capacitor first exceeds that in the inductor.

63. A capacitor in a series LC circuit has an initial charge Q and is being discharged. Find, in terms of L and C, the flux through each of the N turns in the coil, when the charge on the capacitor is $Q/2$.

64. The toroid in Figure P32.64 consists of N turns and has a rectangular cross section. Its inner and outer radii are a and b, respectively. (a) Show that the inductance of the toroid is

$$L = \frac{\mu_0 N^2 h}{2\pi} \ln \frac{b}{a}$$

(b) Using this result, compute the self-inductance of a 500-turn toroid for which $a = 10.0$ cm, $b = 12.0$ cm, and $h = 1.00$ cm. (c) **What If?** In Problem 12, an approximate expression for the inductance of a toroid with $R \gg r$ was derived. To get a feel for the accuracy of that result, use the expression in Problem 12 to compute the approximate inductance of the toroid described in part (b). Compare the result with the answer to part (b).

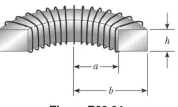

Figure P32.64

65. (a) A flat circular coil does not really produce a uniform magnetic field in the area it encloses, but estimate the self-inductance of a flat, compact circular coil, with radius R and N turns, by assuming that the field at its center is uniform over its area. (b) A circuit on a laboratory table consists of a 1.5-volt battery, a 270-Ω resistor, a switch, and three 30-cm-long patch cords connecting them. Suppose the circuit is arranged to be circular. Think of it as a flat coil with one turn. Compute the order of magnitude of its self-inductance and (c) of the time constant describing how fast the current increases when you close the switch.

66. A soft iron rod ($\mu_m = 800\mu_0$) is used as the core of a solenoid. The rod has a diameter of 24.0 mm and is 10.0 cm long. A 10.0-m piece of 22-gauge copper wire (diameter = 0.644 mm) is wrapped around the rod in a single uniform layer, except for a 10.0-cm length at each end, which is to

be used for connections. (a) How many turns of this wire can be wrapped around the rod? For an accurate answer you should add the diameter of the wire to the diameter of the rod in determining the circumference of each turn. Also note that the wire spirals diagonally along the surface of the rod. (b) What is the resistance of this inductor? (c) What is its inductance?

67. A wire of nonmagnetic material, with radius R, carries current uniformly distributed over its cross section. The total current carried by the wire is I. Show that the magnetic energy per unit length inside the wire is $\mu_0 I^2/16\pi$.

68. An 820-turn wire coil of resistance 24.0 Ω is placed around a 12 500-turn solenoid 7.00 cm long, as shown in Figure P32.68. Both coil and solenoid have cross-sectional areas of 1.00×10^{-4} m². (a) How long does it take the solenoid current to reach 63.2% of its maximum value? Determine (b) the average back emf caused by the self-inductance of the solenoid during this time interval, (c) the average rate of change in magnetic flux through the coil during this time interval, and (d) the magnitude of the average induced current in the coil.

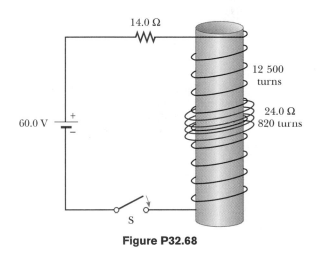

Figure P32.68

69. At $t = 0$, the open switch in Figure P32.69 is closed. By using Kirchhoff's rules for the instantaneous currents and voltages in this two-loop circuit, show that the current in the inductor at time $t > 0$ is

$$I(t) = \frac{\varepsilon}{R_1}[1 - e^{-(R'/L)t}]$$

where $R' = R_1 R_2/(R_1 + R_2)$.

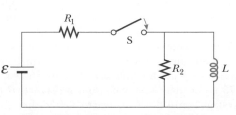

Figure P32.69 Problems 69 and 70.

70. In Figure P32.69 take $\mathcal{E} = 6.00$ V, $R_1 = 5.00 \ \Omega$, and $R_2 = 1.00 \ \Omega$. The inductor has negligible resistance. When the switch is opened after having been closed for a long time, the current in the inductor drops to 0.250 A in 0.150 s. What is the inductance of the inductor?

71. In Figure P32.71, the switch is closed for $t < 0$, and steady-state conditions are established. The switch is opened at $t = 0$. (a) Find the initial voltage $\mathcal{E}_0$ across L just after $t = 0$. Which end of the coil is at the higher potential: a or b? (b) Make freehand graphs of the currents in R_1 and in R_2 as a function of time, treating the steady-state directions as positive. Show values before and after $t = 0$. (c) How long after $t = 0$ does the current in R_2 have the value 2.00 mA?

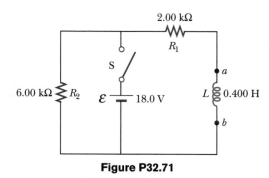

Figure P32.71

72. The open switch in Figure P32.72 is closed at $t = 0$. Before the switch is closed, the capacitor is uncharged, and all currents are zero. Determine the currents in L, C, and R and the potential differences across L, C, and R (a) at the instant after the switch is closed, and (b) long after it is closed.

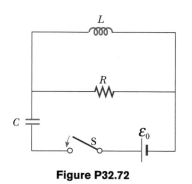

Figure P32.72

73. To prevent damage from arcing in an electric motor, a discharge resistor is sometimes placed in parallel with the armature. If the motor is suddenly unplugged while running, this resistor limits the voltage that appears across the armature coils. Consider a 12.0-V DC motor with an armature that has a resistance of 7.50 Ω and an inductance of 450 mH. Assume the back emf in the armature coils is 10.0 V when the motor is running at normal speed. (The equivalent circuit for the armature is shown in Figure P32.73.) Calculate the maximum resistance R that limits the voltage across the armature to 80.0 V when the motor is unplugged.

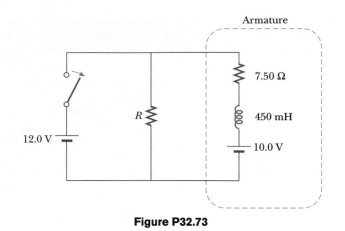

Figure P32.73

74. An air-core solenoid 0.500 m in length contains 1 000 turns and has a cross-sectional area of 1.00 cm^2. (a) Ignoring end effects, find the self-inductance. (b) A secondary winding wrapped around the center of the solenoid has 100 turns. What is the mutual inductance? (c) The secondary winding carries a constant current of 1.00 A, and the solenoid is connected to a load of 1.00 kΩ. The constant current is suddenly stopped. How much charge flows through the load resistor?

75. The lead-in wires from a television antenna are often constructed in the form of two parallel wires (Fig. P32.75). (a) Why does this configuration of conductors have an inductance? (b) What constitutes the flux loop for this configuration? (c) Ignoring any magnetic flux inside the wires, show that the inductance of a length x of this type of lead-in is

$$L = \frac{\mu_0 x}{\pi} \ln\left(\frac{w - a}{a}\right)$$

where a is the radius of the wires and w is their center-to-center separation.

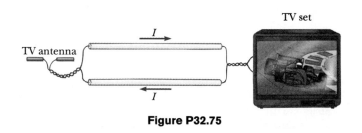

Figure P32.75

Review problems. Problems 76 through 79 apply ideas from this chapter and earlier chapters to some properties of superconductors, which were introduced in Section 27.5.

76. *The resistance of a superconductor.* In an experiment carried out by S. C. Collins between 1955 and 1958, a current was maintained in a superconducting lead ring for 2.50 yr with no observed loss. If the inductance of the ring was 3.14×10^{-8} H, and the sensitivity of the experiment was

1 part in 10^9, what was the maximum resistance of the ring? (*Suggestion:* Treat this as a decaying current in an *RL* circuit, and recall that $e^{-x} \approx 1 - x$ for small x.)

77. A novel method of storing energy has been proposed. A huge underground superconducting coil, 1.00 km in diameter, would be fabricated. It would carry a maximum current of 50.0 kA through each winding of a 150-turn Nb_3Sn solenoid. (a) If the inductance of this huge coil were 50.0 H, what would be the total energy stored? (b) What would be the compressive force per meter length acting between two adjacent windings 0.250 m apart?

78. *Superconducting power transmission.* The use of superconductors has been proposed for power transmission lines. A single coaxial cable (Fig. P32.78) could carry 1.00×10^3 MW (the output of a large power plant) at 200 kV, DC, over a distance of 1 000 km without loss. An inner wire of radius 2.00 cm, made from the superconductor Nb_3Sn, carries the current I in one direction. A surrounding superconducting cylinder, of radius 5.00 cm, would carry the return current I. In such a system, what is the magnetic field (a) at the surface of the inner conductor and (b) at the inner surface of the outer conductor? (c) How much energy would be stored in the space between the conductors in a 1 000-km superconducting line? (d) What is the pressure exerted on the outer conductor?

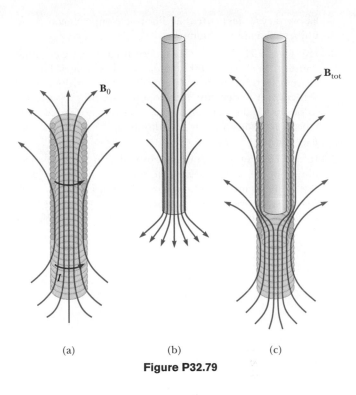

(a) (b) (c)

Figure P32.79

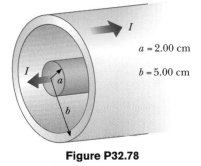

Figure P32.78

79. *The Meissner effect.* Compare this problem with Problem 65 in Chapter 26, on the force attracting a perfect dielectric into a strong electric field. A fundamental property of a Type I superconducting material is *perfect diamagnetism,* or demonstration of the *Meissner effect,* illustrated in Figure 30.35, and described as follows. The superconducting material has $\mathbf{B} = 0$ everywhere inside it. If a sample of the material is placed into an externally produced magnetic field, or if it is cooled to become superconducting while it is in a magnetic field, electric currents appear on the surface of the sample. The currents have precisely the strength and orientation required to make the total magnetic field zero throughout the interior of the sample. The following problem will help you to understand the magnetic force that can then act on the superconducting sample.

A vertical solenoid with a length of 120 cm and a diameter of 2.50 cm consists of 1 400 turns of copper wire carrying a counterclockwise current of 2.00 A, as in Figure P32.79a. (a) Find the magnetic field in the vacuum inside the solenoid. (b) Find the energy density of the magnetic

field, and note that the units J/m^3 of energy density are the same as the units N/m^2 of pressure. (c) Now a superconducting bar 2.20 cm in diameter is inserted partway into the solenoid. Its upper end is far outside the solenoid, where the magnetic field is negligible. The lower end of the bar is deep inside the solenoid. Identify the direction required for the current on the curved surface of the bar, so that the total magnetic field is zero within the bar. The field created by the supercurrents is sketched in Figure P32.79b, and the total field is sketched in Figure P32.79c. (d) The field of the solenoid exerts a force on the current in the superconductor. Identify the direction of the force on the bar. (e) Calculate the magnitude of the force by multiplying the energy density of the solenoid field times the area of the bottom end of the superconducting bar.

Answers to Quick Quizzes

32.1 (c), (f). For the constant current in (a) and (b), there is no potential difference across the resistanceless inductor. In (c), if the current increases, the emf induced in the inductor is in the opposite direction, from *b* to *a*, making *a* higher in potential than *b*. Similarly, in (f), the decreasing current induces an emf in the same direction as the current, from *b* to *a*, again making the potential higher at *a* than *b*.

32.2 (b), (d). As the switch is closed, there is no current, so there is no voltage across the resistor. After a long time, the current has reached its final value, and the inductor has no further effect on the circuit.

32.3 (b). When the iron rod is inserted into the solenoid, the inductance of the coil increases. As a result, more potential difference appears across the coil than before.

Consequently, less potential difference appears across the bulb, so the bulb is dimmer.

32.4 (b). Figure 32.10 shows that circuit B has the greater time constant because in this circuit it takes longer for the current to reach its maximum value and then longer for this current to decrease to zero after the switch is thrown to position b. Equation 32.8 indicates that, for equal resistances R_A and R_B, the condition $\tau_B > \tau_A$ means that $L_A < L_B$.

32.5 (a), (d). Because the energy density depends on the magnitude of the magnetic field, to increase the energy density, we must increase the magnetic field. For a solenoid, $B = \mu_0 nI$, where n is the number of turns per unit length. In (a), we increase n to increase the magnetic field. In

(b), the change in cross-sectional area has no effect on the magnetic field. In (c), increasing the length but keeping n fixed has no effect on the magnetic field. Increasing the current in (d) increases the magnetic field in the solenoid.

32.6 (a). M_{12} increases because the magnetic flux through coil 2 increases.

32.7 (b). If the current is at its maximum value, the charge on the capacitor is zero.

32.8 (c). If the current is zero, this is the instant at which the capacitor is fully charged and the current is about to reverse direction.

Chapter 33

Alternating Current Circuits

▲ These large transformers are used to increase the voltage at a power plant for distribution of energy by electrical transmission to the power grid. Voltages can be changed relatively easily because power is distributed by alternating current rather than direct current. (Lester Lefkowitz/Getty Images)

In this chapter we describe alternating current (AC) circuits. Every time we turn on a television set, a stereo, or any of a multitude of other electrical appliances in a home, we are calling on alternating currents to provide the power to operate them. We begin our study by investigating the characteristics of simple series circuits that contain resistors, inductors, and capacitors and that are driven by a sinusoidal voltage. We shall find that the maximum alternating current in each element is proportional to the maximum alternating voltage across the element. In addition, when the applied voltage is sinusoidal, the current in each element is also sinusoidal, but not necessarily in phase with the applied voltage. The primary aim of this chapter can be summarized as follows: if an AC source applies an alternating voltage to a series circuit containing resistors, inductors, and capacitors, we want to know the amplitude and time characteristics of the alternating current. We conclude the chapter with two sections concerning transformers, power transmission, and electrical filters.

33.1 AC Sources

An AC circuit consists of circuit elements and a power source that provides an alternating voltage Δv. This time-varying voltage is described by

$$\Delta v = \Delta V_{max} \sin \omega t$$

where ΔV_{max} is the maximum output voltage of the AC source, or the **voltage amplitude.** There are various possibilities for AC sources, including generators, as discussed in Section 31.5, and electrical oscillators. In a home, each electrical outlet serves as an AC source.

From Equation 15.12, the angular frequency of the AC voltage is

$$\omega = 2\pi f = \frac{2\pi}{T}$$

where f is the frequency of the source and T is the period. The source determines the frequency of the current in any circuit connected to it. Because the output voltage of an AC source varies sinusoidally with time, the voltage is positive during one half of the cycle and negative during the other half, as in Figure 33.1. Likewise, the current in any circuit driven by an AC source is an alternating current that also varies sinusoidally with time. Commercial electric-power plants in the United States use a frequency of 60 Hz, which corresponds to an angular frequency of 377 rad/s.

33.2 Resistors in an AC Circuit

Consider a simple AC circuit consisting of a resistor and an AC source , as shown in Figure 33.2. At any instant, the algebraic sum of the voltages around a closed loop in a circuit must be zero (Kirchhoff's loop rule). Therefore, $\Delta v + \Delta v_R = 0$, so

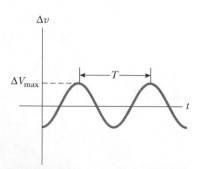

Figure 33.1 The voltage supplied by an AC source is sinusoidal with a period T.

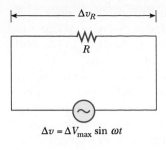

$\Delta v = \Delta V_{max} \sin \omega t$

Active Figure 33.2 A circuit consisting of a resistor of resistance R connected to an AC source, designated by the symbol ——(∿)—— .

that the magnitude of the source voltage equals the magnitude of the voltage across the resistor:

$$\Delta v = \Delta v_R = \Delta V_{max} \sin \omega t \qquad (33.1)$$

where Δv_R is the **instantaneous voltage across the resistor.** Therefore, from Equation 27.8, $R = \Delta V/I$, the instantaneous current in the resistor is

$$i_R = \frac{\Delta v_R}{R} = \frac{\Delta V_{max}}{R} \sin \omega t = I_{max} \sin \omega t \qquad (33.2)$$

where I_{max} is the maximum current:

$$I_{max} = \frac{\Delta V_{max}}{R}$$

Maximum current in a resistor

From Equations 33.1 and 33.2, we see that the instantaneous voltage across the resistor is

$$\Delta v_R = I_{max} R \sin \omega t \qquad (33.3)$$

Voltage across a resistor

A plot of voltage and current versus time for this circuit is shown in Figure 33.3a. At point a, the current has a maximum value in one direction, arbitrarily called the positive direction. Between points a and b, the current is decreasing in magnitude but is still in the positive direction. At b, the current is momentarily zero; it then begins to increase in the negative direction between points b and c. At c, the current has reached its maximum value in the negative direction.

The current and voltage are in step with each other because they vary identically with time. Because i_R and Δv_R both vary as $\sin \omega t$ and reach their maximum values at the same time, as shown in Figure 33.3a, they are said to be **in phase,** similar to the way that two waves can be in phase, as discussed in our study of wave motion in

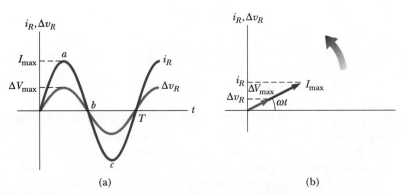

(a)   (b)

Active Figure 33.3 (a) Plots of the instantaneous current i_R and instantaneous voltage Δv_R across a resistor as functions of time. The current is in phase with the voltage, which means that the current is zero when the voltage is zero, maximum when the voltage is maximum, and minimum when the voltage is minimum. At time $t = T$, one cycle of the time-varying voltage and current has been completed. (b) Phasor diagram for the resistive circuit showing that the current is in phase with the voltage.

Chapter 18. Thus, **for a sinusoidal applied voltage, the current in a resistor is always in phase with the voltage across the resistor.** For resistors in AC circuits, there are no new concepts to learn. Resistors behave essentially the same way in both DC and AC circuits. This will not be the case for capacitors and inductors.

To simplify our analysis of circuits containing two or more elements, we use graphical constructions called *phasor diagrams*. A **phasor** is a vector whose length is proportional to the maximum value of the variable it represents (ΔV_{max} for voltage and I_{max} for current in the present discussion) and which rotates counterclockwise at an angular speed equal to the angular frequency associated with the variable. The projection of the phasor onto the vertical axis represents the instantaneous value of the quantity it represents.

Figure 33.3b shows voltage and current phasors for the circuit of Figure 33.2 at some instant of time. The projections of the phasor arrows onto the vertical axis are determined by a sine function of the angle of the phasor with respect to the horizontal axis. For example, the projection of the current phasor in Figure 33.3b is $I_{max} \sin \omega t$. Notice that this is the same expression as Equation 33.2. Thus, we can use the projections of phasors to represent current values that vary sinusoidally in time. We can do the same with time-varying voltages. The advantage of this approach is that the phase relationships among currents and voltages can be represented as vector additions of phasors, using our vector addition techniques from Chapter 3.

In the case of the single-loop resistive circuit of Figure 33.2, the current and voltage phasors lie along the same line, as in Figure 33.3b, because i_R and Δv_R are in phase. The current and voltage in circuits containing capacitors and inductors have different phase relationships.

Quick Quiz 33.1 Consider the voltage phasor in Figure 33.4, shown at three instants of time. Choose the part of the figure that represents the instant of time at which the instantaneous value of the voltage has the largest magnitude.

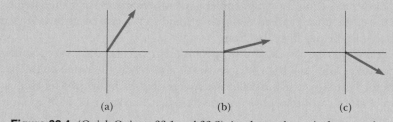

Figure 33.4 (Quick Quizzes 33.1 and 33.2) A voltage phasor is shown at three instants of time.

Quick Quiz 33.2 For the voltage phasor in Figure 33.4, choose the part of the figure that represents the instant of time at which the instantaneous value of the voltage has the smallest magnitude.

For the simple resistive circuit in Figure 33.2, note that **the average value of the current over one cycle is zero.** That is, the current is maintained in the positive direction for the same amount of time and at the same magnitude as it is maintained in the negative direction. However, the direction of the current has no effect on the behavior of the resistor. We can understand this by realizing that collisions between electrons and the fixed atoms of the resistor result in an increase in the resistor's temperature. Although this temperature increase depends on the magnitude of the current, it is independent of the direction of the current.

We can make this discussion quantitative by recalling that the rate at which energy is delivered to a resistor is the power $\mathcal{P} = i^2 R$, where i is the instantaneous current in

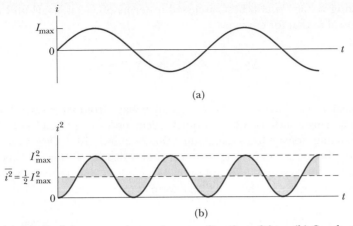

Figure 33.5 (a) Graph of the current in a resistor as a function of time. (b) Graph of the current squared in a resistor as a function of time. Notice that the gray shaded regions *under* the curve and *above* the dashed line for $I_{max}^2/2$ have the same area as the gray shaded regions *above* the curve and *below* the dashed line for $I_{max}^2/2$. Thus, the average value of i^2 is $I_{max}^2/2$.

the resistor. Because this rate is proportional to the square of the current, it makes no difference whether the current is direct or alternating—that is, whether the sign associated with the current is positive or negative. However, the temperature increase produced by an alternating current having a maximum value I_{max} is not the same as that produced by a direct current equal to I_{max}. This is because the alternating current is at this maximum value for only an instant during each cycle (Fig. 33.5a). What is of importance in an AC circuit is an average value of current, referred to as the **rms current**. As we learned in Section 21.1, the notation *rms* stands for *root-mean-square*, which in this case means the square root of the mean (average) value of the square of the current: $I_{rms} = \sqrt{\overline{i^2}}$. Because i^2 varies as $\sin^2 \omega t$ and because the average value of i^2 is $\frac{1}{2}I_{max}^2$ (see Fig. 33.5b), the rms current is[1]

$$I_{rms} = \frac{I_{max}}{\sqrt{2}} = 0.707 I_{max} \qquad (33.4)$$

rms current

This equation states that an alternating current whose maximum value is 2.00 A delivers to a resistor the same power as a direct current that has a value of $(0.707)(2.00\ \text{A}) = 1.41\ \text{A}$. Thus, the average power delivered to a resistor that carries an alternating current is

$$\mathcal{P}_{av} = I_{rms}^2 R$$

Average power delivered to a resistor

[1] That the square root of the average value of i^2 is equal to $I_{max}/\sqrt{2}$ can be shown as follows. The current in the circuit varies with time according to the expression $i = I_{max} \sin \omega t$, so $i^2 = I_{max}^2 \sin^2 \omega t$. Therefore, we can find the average value of i^2 by calculating the average value of $\sin^2 \omega t$. A graph of $\cos^2 \omega t$ versus time is identical to a graph of $\sin^2 \omega t$ versus time, except that the points are shifted on the time axis. Thus, the time average of $\sin^2 \omega t$ is equal to the time average of $\cos^2 \omega t$ when taken over one or more complete cycles. That is,

$$(\sin^2 \omega t)_{av} = (\cos^2 \omega t)_{av}$$

Using this fact and the trigonometric identity $\sin^2 \theta + \cos^2 \theta = 1$, we obtain

$$(\sin^2 \omega t)_{av} + (\cos^2 \omega t)_{av} = 2(\sin^2 \omega t)_{av} = 1$$

$$(\sin^2 \omega t)_{av} = \tfrac{1}{2}$$

When we substitute this result in the expression $i^2 = I_{max}^2 \sin^2 \omega t$, we obtain $(i^2)_{av} = \overline{i^2} = I_{rms}^2 = I_{max}^2/2$, or $I_{rms} = I_{max}/\sqrt{2}$. The factor $1/\sqrt{2}$ is valid only for sinusoidally varying currents. Other waveforms, such as sawtooth variations, have different factors.

Alternating voltage is also best discussed in terms of rms voltage, and the relationship is identical to that for current:

rms voltage

$$\Delta V_{rms} = \frac{\Delta V_{max}}{\sqrt{2}} = 0.707\,\Delta V_{max} \tag{33.5}$$

When we speak of measuring a 120-V alternating voltage from an electrical outlet, we are referring to an rms voltage of 120 V. A quick calculation using Equation 33.5 shows that such an alternating voltage has a maximum value of about 170 V. One reason we use rms values when discussing alternating currents and voltages in this chapter is that AC ammeters and voltmeters are designed to read rms values. Furthermore, with rms values, many of the equations we use have the same form as their direct current counterparts.

> **Quick Quiz 33.3** Which of the following statements might be true for a resistor connected to a sinusoidal AC source? (a) $\mathcal{P}_{av} = 0$ and $i_{av} = 0$ (b) $\mathcal{P}_{av} = 0$ and $i_{av} > 0$ (c) $\mathcal{P}_{av} > 0$ and $i_{av} = 0$ (d) $\mathcal{P}_{av} > 0$ and $i_{av} > 0$.

Example 33.1   What Is the rms Current?

The voltage output of an AC source is given by the expression $\Delta v = (200\ \text{V})\sin \omega t$. Find the rms current in the circuit when this source is connected to a 100-Ω resistor.

Solution Comparing this expression for voltage output with the general form $\Delta v = \Delta V_{max}\sin \omega t$, we see that $\Delta V_{max} = 200$ V. Thus, the rms voltage is

$$\Delta V_{rms} = \frac{\Delta V_{max}}{\sqrt{2}} = \frac{200\ \text{V}}{\sqrt{2}} = 141\ \text{V}$$

Therefore,

$$I_{rms} = \frac{\Delta V_{rms}}{R} = \frac{141\ \text{V}}{100\ \Omega} = \boxed{1.41\ \text{A}}$$

33.3 Inductors in an AC Circuit

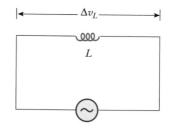

$\Delta v = \Delta V_{max}\sin \omega t$

Active Figure 33.6 A circuit consisting of an inductor of inductance L connected to an AC source.

At the Active Figures link at http://www.pse6.com, you can adjust the inductance, the frequency, and the maximum voltage. The results can be studied with the graph and phasor diagram in Figure 33.7.

Now consider an AC circuit consisting only of an inductor connected to the terminals of an AC source, as shown in Figure 33.6. If $\Delta v_L = \mathcal{E}_L = -L(di/dt)$ is the self-induced instantaneous voltage across the inductor (see Eq. 32.1), then Kirchhoff's loop rule applied to this circuit gives $\Delta v + \Delta v_L = 0$, or

$$\Delta v - L\,\frac{di}{dt} = 0$$

When we substitute $\Delta V_{max}\sin \omega t$ for Δv and rearrange, we obtain

$$\Delta v = L\,\frac{di}{dt} = \Delta V_{max}\sin \omega t \tag{33.6}$$

Solving this equation for di, we find that

$$di = \frac{\Delta V_{max}}{L}\sin \omega t\, dt$$

Integrating this expression[2] gives the instantaneous current i_L in the inductor as a function of time:

$$i_L = \frac{\Delta V_{max}}{L}\int \sin \omega t\, dt = -\frac{\Delta V_{max}}{\omega L}\cos \omega t \tag{33.7}$$

---

[2]   We neglect the constant of integration here because it depends on the initial conditions, which are not important for this situation.

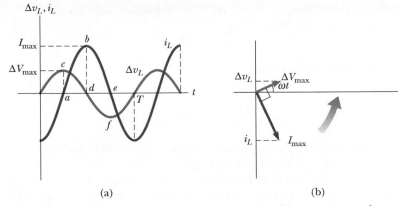

Active Figure 33.7 (a) Plots of the instantaneous current i_L and instantaneous voltage Δv_L across an inductor as functions of time. The current lags behind the voltage by 90°. (b) Phasor diagram for the inductive circuit, showing that the current lags behind the voltage by 90°.

At the Active Figures link at http://www.pse6.com, you can adjust the inductance, the frequency, and the maximum voltage of the circuit in Figure 33.6. The results can be studied with the graph and phasor diagram in this figure.

When we use the trigonometric identity $\cos \omega t = -\sin(\omega t - \pi/2)$, we can express Equation 33.7 as

$$i_L = \frac{\Delta V_{max}}{\omega L} \sin\left(\omega t - \frac{\pi}{2}\right)$$ (33.8)   **Current in an inductor**

Comparing this result with Equation 33.6, we see that the instantaneous current i_L in the inductor and the instantaneous voltage Δv_L across the inductor are *out* of phase by $(\pi/2)$ rad $= 90°$.

A plot of voltage and current versus time is provided in Figure 33.7a. In general, inductors in an AC circuit produce a current that is out of phase with the AC voltage. For example, when the current i_L in the inductor is a maximum (point b in Figure 33.7a), it is momentarily not changing, so the voltage across the inductor is zero (point d). At points like a and e, the current is zero and the rate of change of current is at a maximum. Thus, the voltage across the inductor is also at a maximum (points c and f). Note that the voltage reaches its maximum value one quarter of a period before the current reaches its maximum value. Thus, we see that

for a sinusoidal applied voltage, the current in an inductor always lags behind the voltage across the inductor by 90° (one-quarter cycle in time).

As with the relationship between current and voltage for a resistor, we can represent this relationship for an inductor with a phasor diagram as in Figure 33.7b. Notice that the phasors are at 90° to one another, representing the 90° phase difference between current and voltage.

From Equation 33.7 we see that the current in an inductive circuit reaches its maximum value when $\cos \omega t = -1$:

$$I_{max} = \frac{\Delta V_{max}}{\omega L}$$ (33.9)   **Maximum current in an inductor**

This looks similar to the relationship between current, voltage, and resistance in a DC circuit, $I = \Delta V/R$ (Eq. 27.8). In fact, because I_{max} has units of amperes and ΔV_{max} has units of volts, ωL must have units of ohms. Therefore, ωL has the same units as resistance and is related to current and voltage in the same way as resistance. It must behave in a manner similar to resistance, in the sense that it represents opposition to the flow of charge. Notice that because ωL depends on the applied frequency ω, the inductor *reacts* differently, in terms of offering resistance to current, for different frequencies. For this reason, we define ωL as the **inductive reactance:**

Inductive reactance

$$X_L \equiv \omega L \tag{33.10}$$

and we can write Equation 33.9 as

$$I_{max} = \frac{\Delta V_{max}}{X_L} \tag{33.11}$$

The expression for the rms current in an inductor is similar to Equation 33.9, with I_{max} replaced by I_{rms} and ΔV_{max} replaced by ΔV_{rms}.

Equation 33.10 indicates that, for a given applied voltage, the inductive reactance increases as the frequency increases. This is consistent with Faraday's law—the greater the rate of change of current in the inductor, the larger is the back emf. The larger back emf translates to an increase in the reactance and a decrease in the current.

Using Equations 33.6 and 33.11, we find that the instantaneous voltage across the inductor is

Voltage across an inductor

$$\Delta v_L = -L\,\frac{di}{dt} = -\Delta V_{max} \sin \omega t = -I_{max} X_L \sin \omega t \tag{33.12}$$

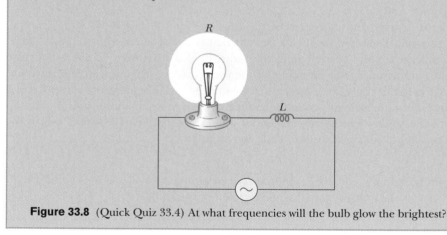

Quick Quiz 33.4 Consider the AC circuit in Figure 33.8. The frequency of the AC source is adjusted while its voltage amplitude is held constant. The lightbulb will glow the brightest at (a) high frequencies (b) low frequencies (c) The brightness will be the same at all frequencies.

Figure 33.8 (Quick Quiz 33.4) At what frequencies will the bulb glow the brightest?

Example 33.2 A Purely Inductive AC Circuit

In a purely inductive AC circuit (see Fig. 33.6), $L = 25.0$ mH and the rms voltage is 150 V. Calculate the inductive reactance and rms current in the circuit if the frequency is 60.0 Hz.

Solution Equation 33.10 gives

$$X_L = \omega L = 2\pi f L = 2\pi (60.0 \text{ Hz})(25.0 \times 10^{-3} \text{ H})$$

$$= \boxed{9.42 \ \Omega}$$

From an rms version of Equation 33.11, the rms current is

$$I_{rms} = \frac{\Delta V_{L,rms}}{X_L} = \frac{150 \text{ V}}{9.42 \ \Omega} = \boxed{15.9 \text{ A}}$$

What If? What if the frequency increases to 6.00 kHz? What happens to the rms current in the circuit?

Answer If the frequency increases, the inductive reactance increases because the current is changing at a higher rate. The increase in inductive reactance results in a lower current.

Let us calculate the new inductive reactance:

$$X_L = 2\pi (6.00 \times 10^3 \text{ Hz})(25.0 \times 10^{-3} \text{ H}) = 942 \ \Omega$$

The new current is

$$I_{rms} = \frac{150 \text{ V}}{942 \ \Omega} = 0.159 \text{ A}$$

33.4 Capacitors in an AC Circuit

Figure 33.9 shows an AC circuit consisting of a capacitor connected across the terminals of an AC source. Kirchhoff's loop rule applied to this circuit gives $\Delta v + \Delta v_C = 0$, so that the magnitude of the source voltage is equal to the magnitude of the voltage across the capacitor:

$$\Delta v = \Delta v_C = \Delta V_{max} \sin \omega t \tag{33.13}$$

where Δv_C is the instantaneous voltage across the capacitor. We know from the definition of capacitance that $C = q/\Delta v_C$; hence, Equation 33.13 gives

$$q = C \Delta V_{max} \sin \omega t \tag{33.14}$$

where q is the instantaneous charge on the capacitor. Because $i = dq/dt$, differentiating Equation 33.14 with respect to time gives the instantaneous current in the circuit:

$$i_C = \frac{dq}{dt} = \omega C \Delta V_{max} \cos \omega t \tag{33.15}$$

Using the trigonometric identity

$$\cos \omega t = \sin \left(\omega t + \frac{\pi}{2} \right)$$

we can express Equation 33.15 in the alternative form

$$i_C = \omega C \Delta V_{max} \sin \left(\omega t + \frac{\pi}{2} \right) \tag{33.16}$$

Comparing this expression with Equation 33.13, we see that the current is $\pi/2$ rad $= 90°$ out of phase with the voltage across the capacitor. A plot of current and voltage versus time (Fig. 33.10a) shows that the current reaches its maximum value one quarter of a cycle sooner than the voltage reaches its maximum value.

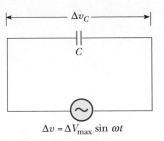

Active Figure 33.9 A circuit consisting of a capacitor of capacitance C connected to an AC source.

At the Active Figures link at http://www.pse6.com, you can adjust the capacitance, the frequency, and the maximum voltage. The results can be studied with the graph and phasor diagram in Figure 33.10.

Current in a capacitor

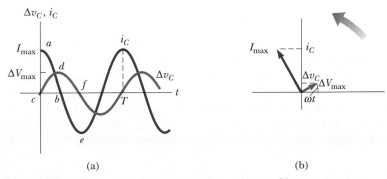

(a)   (b)

Active Figure 33.10 (a) Plots of the instantaneous current i_C and instantaneous voltage Δv_C across a capacitor as functions of time. The voltage lags behind the current by 90°. (b) Phasor diagram for the capacitive circuit, showing that the current leads the voltage by 90°.

At the Active Figures link at http://www.pse6.com, you can adjust the capacitance, the frequency, and the maximum voltage of the circuit in Figure 33.9. The results can be studied with the graph and phasor diagram in this figure.

Looking more closely, consider a point such as *b* where the current is zero. This occurs when the capacitor has just reached its maximum charge, so the voltage across the capacitor is a maximum (point *d*). At points such as *a* and *e*, the current is a maximum, which occurs at those instants at which the charge on the capacitor has just gone to zero and it begins to charge up with the opposite polarity. Because the charge is zero, the voltage across the capacitor is zero (points *c* and *f*). Thus, the current and voltage are out of phase.

As with inductors, we can represent the current and voltage for a capacitor on a phasor diagram. The phasor diagram in Figure 33.10b shows that

> for a sinusoidally applied voltage, the current always leads the voltage across a capacitor by 90°.

From Equation 33.15, we see that the current in the circuit reaches its maximum value when $\cos \omega t = 1$:

$$I_{max} = \omega C \, \Delta V_{max} = \frac{\Delta V_{max}}{(1/\omega C)} \tag{33.17}$$

As in the case with inductors, this looks like Equation 27.8, so that the denominator must play the role of resistance, with units of ohms. We give the combination $1/\omega C$ the symbol X_C, and because this function varies with frequency, we define it as the **capacitive reactance:**

$$X_C \equiv \frac{1}{\omega C} \tag{33.18}$$

and we can write Equation 33.17 as

Maximum current in a capacitor

$$I_{max} = \frac{\Delta V_{max}}{X_C} \tag{33.19}$$

The rms current is given by an expression similar to Equation 33.19, with I_{max} replaced by I_{rms} and ΔV_{max} replaced by ΔV_{rms}.

Combining Equations 33.13 and 33.19, we can express the instantaneous voltage across the capacitor as

Voltage across a capacitor

$$\Delta v_C = \Delta V_{max} \sin \omega t = I_{max} X_C \sin \omega t \tag{33.20}$$

Equations 33.18 and 33.19 indicate that as the frequency of the voltage source increases, the capacitive reactance decreases and therefore the maximum current increases. Again, note that the frequency of the current is determined by the frequency of the voltage source driving the circuit. As the frequency approaches zero, the capacitive reactance approaches infinity, and hence the current approaches zero. This makes sense because the circuit approaches direct current conditions as ω approaches zero, and the capacitor represents an open circuit.

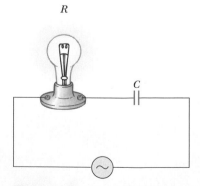

Figure 33.11 (Quick Quiz 33.5)

> **Quick Quiz 33.5** Consider the AC circuit in Figure 33.11. The frequency of the AC source is adjusted while its voltage amplitude is held constant. The lightbulb will glow the brightest at (a) high frequencies (b) low frequencies (c) The brightness will be same at all frequencies.

Quick Quiz 33.6 Consider the AC circuit in Figure 33.12. The frequency of the AC source is adjusted while its voltage amplitude is held constant. The lightbulb will glow the brightest at (a) high frequencies (b) low frequencies (c) The brightness will be same at all frequencies.

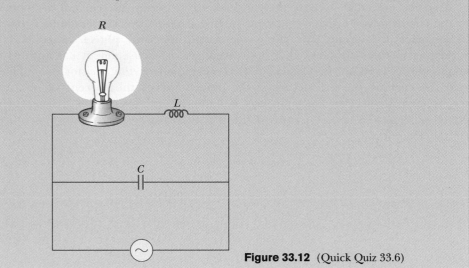

Figure 33.12 (Quick Quiz 33.6)

Example 33.3   A Purely Capacitive AC Circuit

An 8.00-μF capacitor is connected to the terminals of a 60.0-Hz AC source whose rms voltage is 150 V. Find the capacitive reactance and the rms current in the circuit.

Solution Using Equation 33.18 and the fact that $\omega = 2\pi f = 377 \text{ s}^{-1}$ gives

$$X_C = \frac{1}{\omega C} = \frac{1}{(377 \text{ s}^{-1})(8.00 \times 10^{-6} \text{ F})} = \boxed{332 \ \Omega}$$

Hence, from a modified Equation 33.19, the rms current is

$$I_{\text{rms}} = \frac{\Delta V_{\text{rms}}}{X_C} = \frac{150 \text{ V}}{332 \ \Omega} = \boxed{0.452 \text{ A}}$$

What If? What if the frequency is doubled? What happens to the rms current in the circuit?

Answer If the frequency increases, the capacitive reactance decreases—just the opposite as in the case of an inductor. The decrease in capacitive reactance results in an increase in the current.

Let us calculate the new capacitive reactance:

$$X_C = \frac{1}{\omega C} = \frac{1}{2(377 \text{ s}^{-1})(8.00 \times 10^{-6} \text{ F})} = 166 \ \Omega$$

The new current is

$$I_{\text{rms}} = \frac{150 \text{ V}}{166 \ \Omega} = 0.904 \text{ A}$$

33.5 The *RLC* Series Circuit

Figure 33.13a shows a circuit that contains a resistor, an inductor, and a capacitor connected in series across an alternating voltage source. As before, we assume that the applied voltage varies sinusoidally with time. It is convenient to assume that the instantaneous applied voltage is given by

$$\Delta v = \Delta V_{\text{max}} \sin \omega t$$

while the current varies as

$$i = I_{\text{max}} \sin(\omega t - \phi)$$

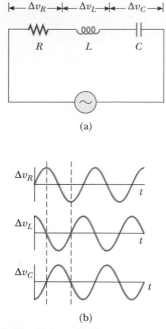

Active Figure 33.13 (a) A series circuit consisting of a resistor, an inductor, and a capacitor connected to an AC source. (b) Phase relationships for instantaneous voltages in the series *RLC* circuit.

At the Active Figures link at http://www.pse6.com, you can adjust the resistance, the inductance, and the capacitance. The results can be studied with the graph in this figure and the phasor diagram in Figure 33.15.

where ϕ is some **phase angle** between the current and the applied voltage. Based on our discussions of phase in Sections 33.3 and 33.4, we expect that the current will generally not be in phase with the voltage in an *RLC* circuit. Our aim is to determine ϕ and I_{max}. Figure 33.13b shows the voltage versus time across each element in the circuit and their phase relationships.

First, we note that because the elements are in series, the current everywhere in the circuit must be the same at any instant. That is, **the current at all points in a series AC circuit has the same amplitude and phase.** Based on the preceding sections, we know that the voltage across each element has a different amplitude and phase. In particular, the voltage across the resistor is in phase with the current, the voltage across the inductor leads the current by 90°, and the voltage across the capacitor lags behind the current by 90°. Using these phase relationships, we can express the instantaneous voltages across the three circuit elements as

$$\Delta v_R = I_{max} R \sin \omega t = \Delta V_R \sin \omega t \tag{33.21}$$

$$\Delta v_L = I_{max} X_L \sin \left(\omega t + \frac{\pi}{2} \right) = \Delta V_L \cos \omega t \tag{33.22}$$

$$\Delta v_C = I_{max} X_C \sin \left(\omega t - \frac{\pi}{2} \right) = -\Delta V_C \cos \omega t \tag{33.23}$$

where ΔV_R, ΔV_L, and ΔV_C are the maximum voltage values across the elements:

$$\Delta V_R = I_{max} R \qquad \Delta V_L = I_{max} X_L \qquad \Delta V_C = I_{max} X_C$$

At this point, we could proceed by noting that the instantaneous voltage Δv across the three elements equals the sum

$$\Delta v = \Delta v_R + \Delta v_L + \Delta v_C$$

Although this analytical approach is correct, it is simpler to obtain the sum by examining the phasor diagram, shown in Figure 33.14. Because the current at any instant is the same in all elements, we combine the three phasor pairs shown in Figure 33.14 to obtain Figure 33.15a, in which a single phasor I_{max} is used to represent the current in each element. Because phasors are rotating vectors, we can combine the three parts of Figure 33.14 by using vector addition. To obtain the vector sum of the three voltage phasors in Figure 33.15a, we redraw the phasor diagram as in Figure 33.15b. From this diagram, we see that the vector sum of the voltage amplitudes ΔV_R, ΔV_L, and ΔV_C equals a phasor whose length is the maximum applied voltage ΔV_{max}, and which makes an angle ϕ with the current phasor I_{max}. The voltage phasors ΔV_L and ΔV_C are in opposite directions along the same line, so we can construct the difference phasor $\Delta V_L - \Delta V_C$, which is perpendicular to the phasor ΔV_R. From either one of the right triangles

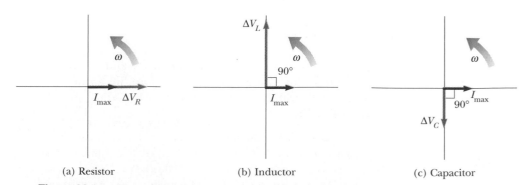

(a) Resistor   (b) Inductor   (c) Capacitor

Figure 33.14 Phase relationships between the voltage and current phasors for (a) a resistor, (b) an inductor, and (c) a capacitor connected in series.

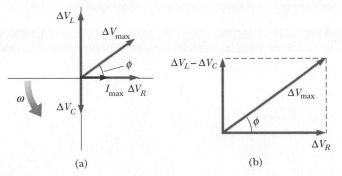

Active Figure 33.15 (a) Phasor diagram for the series *RLC* circuit shown in Figure 33.13a. The phasor ΔV_R is in phase with the current phasor I_{max}, the phasor ΔV_L leads I_{max} by 90°, and the phasor ΔV_C lags I_{max} by 90°. The total voltage ΔV_{max} makes an angle ϕ with I_{max}. (b) Simplified version of the phasor diagram shown in part (a).

At the Active Figures link at http://www.pse6.com, *you can adjust the resistance, the inductance, and the capacitance of the circuit in Figure 33.13a. The results can be studied with the graphs in Figure 33.13b and the phasor diagram in this figure.*

in Figure 33.15b, we see that

$$\Delta V_{max} = \sqrt{\Delta V_R^{\,2} + (\Delta V_L - \Delta V_C)^2} = \sqrt{(I_{max} R)^2 + (I_{max} X_L - I_{max} X_C)^2}$$

$$\Delta V_{max} = I_{max} \sqrt{R^2 + (X_L - X_C)^2} \qquad (33.24)$$

Therefore, we can express the maximum current as

$$I_{max} = \frac{\Delta V_{max}}{\sqrt{R^2 + (X_L - X_C)^2}}$$

Maximum current in an *RLC* circuit

Once again, this has the same mathematical form as Equation 27.8. The denominator of the fraction plays the role of resistance and is called the **impedance** *Z* of the circuit:

$$Z \equiv \sqrt{R^2 + (X_L - X_C)^2} \qquad (33.25)$$

Impedance

where impedance also has units of ohms. Therefore, we can write Equation 33.24 in the form

$$\Delta V_{max} = I_{max} Z \qquad (33.26)$$

We can regard Equation 33.26 as the AC equivalent of Equation 27.8. Note that the impedance and therefore the current in an AC circuit depend upon the resistance, the inductance, the capacitance, and the frequency (because the reactances are frequency-dependent).

By removing the common factor I_{max} from each phasor in Figure 33.15a, we can construct the *impedance triangle* shown in Figure 33.16. From this phasor diagram we find that the phase angle ϕ between the current and the voltage is

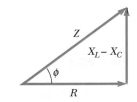

Figure 33.16 An impedance triangle for a series *RLC* circuit gives the relationship $Z = \sqrt{R^2 + (X_L - X_C)^2}$.

$$\phi = \tan^{-1}\left(\frac{X_L - X_C}{R}\right) \qquad (33.27)$$

Phase angle

Also, from Figure 33.16, we see that $\cos \phi = R/Z$. When $X_L > X_C$ (which occurs at high frequencies), the phase angle is positive, signifying that the current lags behind the applied voltage, as in Figure 33.15a. We describe this situation by saying that the circuit is *more inductive than capacitive.* When $X_L < X_C$, the phase angle is negative, signifying that the current leads the applied voltage, and the circuit is *more capacitive than inductive.* When $X_L = X_C$, the phase angle is zero and the circuit is *purely resistive.*

Table 33.1 gives impedance values and phase angles for various series circuits containing different combinations of elements.

Table 33.1

Impedance Values and Phase Angles for Various Circuit-Element Combinations[a]		
Circuit Elements	**Impedance Z**	**Phase Angle ϕ**
R	R	$0°$
C	X_C	$-90°$
L	X_L	$+90°$
R C	$\sqrt{R^2 + X_C^2}$	Negative, between $-90°$ and $0°$
R L	$\sqrt{R^2 + X_L^2}$	Positive, between $0°$ and $90°$
R L C	$\sqrt{R^2 + (X_L - X_C)^2}$	Negative if $X_C > X_L$ Positive if $X_C < X_L$

[a] In each case, an AC voltage (not shown) is applied across the elements.

Quick Quiz 33.7 Label each part of Figure 33.17 as being $X_L > X_C$, $X_L = X_C$, or $X_L < X_C$.

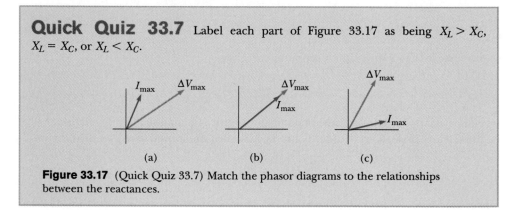

(a)   (b)   (c)

Figure 33.17 (Quick Quiz 33.7) Match the phasor diagrams to the relationships between the reactances.

Example 33.4   Finding L from a Phasor Diagram

In a series RLC circuit, the applied voltage has a maximum value of 120 V and oscillates at a frequency of 60.0 Hz. The circuit contains an inductor whose inductance can be varied, a 200-Ω resistor, and a 4.00-μF capacitor. What value of L should an engineer analyzing the circuit choose such that the voltage across the capacitor lags the applied voltage by 30.0°?

Solution The phase relationships for the voltages across the elements are shown in Figure 33.18. From the figure we see that the phase angle is $\phi = -60.0°$. (The phasors representing I_{max} and ΔV_R are in the same direction.) From Equation 33.27, we find that

$$X_L = X_C + R \tan \phi$$

Substituting Equations 33.10 and 33.18 (with $\omega = 2\pi f$) into this expression gives

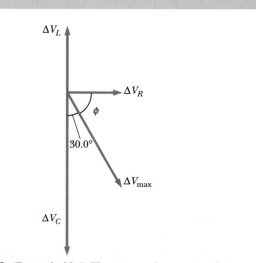

Figure 33.18 (Example 33.4) The phasor diagram for the given information.

$$2\pi f L = \frac{1}{2\pi f C} + R \tan \phi$$

$$L = \frac{1}{2\pi f}\left(\frac{1}{2\pi f C} + R \tan \phi\right)$$

Substituting the given values into the equation gives

$L = \boxed{0.84 \text{ H}}.$

Example 33.5 Analyzing a Series *RLC* Circuit **Interactive**

A series *RLC* AC circuit has $R = 425 \ \Omega$, $L = 1.25$ H, $C = 3.50 \ \mu$F, $\omega = 377$ s^{-1}, and $\Delta V_{max} = 150$ V.

(A) Determine the inductive reactance, the capacitive reactance, and the impedance of the circuit.

Solution The reactances are $X_L = \omega L = \boxed{471 \ \Omega}$ and $X_C = 1/\omega C = \boxed{758 \ \Omega}.$
The impedance is

$$Z = \sqrt{R^2 + (X_L - X_C)^2}$$
$$= \sqrt{(425 \ \Omega)^2 + (471 \ \Omega - 758 \ \Omega)^2} = \boxed{513 \ \Omega}$$

(B) Find the maximum current in the circuit.

Solution

$$I_{max} = \frac{\Delta V_{max}}{Z} = \frac{150 \text{ V}}{513 \ \Omega} = \boxed{0.292 \text{ A}}$$

(C) Find the phase angle between the current and voltage.

Solution

$$\phi = \tan^{-1}\left(\frac{X_L - X_C}{R}\right) = \tan^{-1}\left(\frac{471 \ \Omega - 758 \ \Omega}{425 \ \Omega}\right)$$
$$= \boxed{-34.0°}$$

Because the capacitive reactance is larger than the inductive reactance, the circuit is more capacitive than inductive. In this case, the phase angle ϕ is negative and the current leads the applied voltage.

(D) Find both the maximum voltage and the instantaneous voltage across each element.

Solution The maximum voltages are

$$\Delta V_R = I_{max}R = (0.292 \text{ A})(425 \ \Omega) = \boxed{124 \text{ V}}$$

$$\Delta V_L = I_{max}X_L = (0.292 \text{ A})(471 \ \Omega) = \boxed{138 \text{ V}}$$

$$\Delta V_C = I_{max}X_C = (0.292 \text{ A})(758 \ \Omega) = \boxed{221 \text{ V}}$$

Using Equations 33.21, 33.22, and 33.23, we find that we can write the instantaneous voltages across the three elements as

$$\Delta v_R = \boxed{(124 \text{ V}) \sin 377t}$$

$$\Delta v_L = \boxed{(138 \text{ V}) \cos 377t}$$

$$\Delta v_C = \boxed{(-221 \text{ V}) \cos 377t}$$

What If? What if you added up the maximum voltages across the three circuit elements? Is this a physically meaningful quantity?

Answer The sum of the maximum voltages across the elements is $\Delta V_R + \Delta V_L + \Delta V_C = 484$ V. Note that this sum is much greater than the maximum voltage of the source, 150 V. The sum of the maximum voltages is a meaningless quantity because when sinusoidally varying quantities are added, *both their amplitudes and their phases* must be taken into account. We know that the maximum voltages across the various elements occur at different times. That is, the voltages must be added in a way that takes account of the different phases.

At the Interactive Worked Example link at **http://www.pse6.com**, *you can investigate the* RLC *circuit for various values of the circuit elements.*

33.6 Power in an AC Circuit

Let us now take an energy approach to analyzing AC circuits, considering the transfer of energy from the AC source to the circuit. In Example 28.1 we found that the power delivered by a battery to a DC circuit is equal to the product of the current and the emf of the battery. Likewise, the instantaneous power delivered by an AC source to a circuit is the product of the source current and the applied voltage. For the *RLC* circuit shown in Figure 33.13a, we can express the instantaneous power $\mathcal{P}$ as

$$\mathcal{P} = i\,\Delta v = I_{max}\sin(\omega t - \phi)\,\Delta V_{max}\sin\omega t$$
$$= I_{max}\,\Delta V_{max}\sin\omega t\sin(\omega t - \phi) \tag{33.28}$$

This result is a complicated function of time and therefore is not very useful from a practical viewpoint. What is generally of interest is the average power over one or more cycles. Such an average can be computed by first using the trigonometric identity $\sin(\omega t - \phi) = \sin\omega t\cos\phi - \cos\omega t\sin\phi$. Substituting this into Equation 33.28 gives

$$\mathcal{P} = I_{max}\,\Delta V_{max}\sin^2\omega t\cos\phi - I_{max}\,\Delta V_{max}\sin\omega t\cos\omega t\sin\phi \tag{33.29}$$

We now take the time average of $\mathcal{P}$ over one or more cycles, noting that I_{max}, ΔV_{max}, ϕ, and ω are all constants. The time average of the first term on the right in Equation 33.29 involves the average value of $\sin^2\omega t$, which is $\frac{1}{2}$ (as shown in footnote 1). The time average of the second term on the right is identically zero because $\sin\omega t\cos\omega t = \frac{1}{2}\sin 2\omega t$, and the average value of $\sin 2\omega t$ is zero. Therefore, we can express the **average power** $\mathcal{P}_{av}$ as

$$\mathcal{P}_{av} = \tfrac{1}{2}I_{max}\,\Delta V_{max}\cos\phi \tag{33.30}$$

It is convenient to express the average power in terms of the rms current and rms voltage defined by Equations 33.4 and 33.5:

$$\mathcal{P}_{av} = I_{rms}\,\Delta V_{rms}\cos\phi \tag{33.31}$$

Average power delivered to an RLC circuit

where the quantity $\cos\phi$ is called the **power factor.** By inspecting Figure 33.15b, we see that the maximum voltage across the resistor is given by $\Delta V_R = \Delta V_{max}\cos\phi = I_{max}R$. Using Equation 33.5 and the fact that $\cos\phi = I_{max}R/\Delta V_{max}$, we find that we can express $\mathcal{P}_{av}$ as

$$\mathcal{P}_{av} = I_{rms}\,\Delta V_{rms}\cos\phi = I_{rms}\left(\frac{\Delta V_{max}}{\sqrt{2}}\right)\frac{I_{max}R}{\Delta V_{max}} = I_{rms}\frac{I_{max}R}{\sqrt{2}}$$

After making the substitution $I_{max} = \sqrt{2}I_{rms}$ from Equation 33.4, we have

$$\mathcal{P}_{av} = I_{rms}^2\,R \tag{33.32}$$

In words, **the average power delivered by the source is converted to internal energy in the resistor,** just as in the case of a DC circuit. When the load is purely resistive, then $\phi = 0$, $\cos\phi = 1$, and from Equation 33.31 we see that

$$\mathcal{P}_{av} = I_{rms}\,\Delta V_{rms}$$

We find that **no power losses are associated with pure capacitors and pure inductors in an AC circuit.** To see why this is true, let us first analyze the power in an AC circuit containing only a source and a capacitor. When the current begins to increase in one direction in an AC circuit, charge begins to accumulate on the capacitor, and a voltage appears across it. When this voltage reaches its maximum value, the energy stored in the capacitor is $\frac{1}{2}C(\Delta V_{max})^2$. However, this energy storage is only momentary. The capacitor is charged and discharged twice during each cycle: charge is delivered to the capacitor during two quarters of the cycle and is returned to the voltage source during the remaining two quarters. Therefore, **the average power supplied by the source is zero.** In other words, **no power losses occur in a capacitor in an AC circuit.**

Let us now consider the case of an inductor. When the current reaches its maximum value, the energy stored in the inductor is a maximum and is given by $\frac{1}{2}LI_{max}^2$. When the current begins to decrease in the circuit, this stored energy is returned to the source as the inductor attempts to maintain the current in the circuit.

Equation 33.31 shows that the power delivered by an AC source to any circuit depends on the phase—a result that has many interesting applications. For example, a factory that uses large motors in machines, generators, or transformers has a large inductive load (because of all the windings). To deliver greater power to such devices in the factory without using excessively high voltages, technicians introduce capacitance in the circuits to shift the phase.

Quick Quiz 33.8 An AC source drives an *RLC* circuit with a fixed voltage amplitude. If the driving frequency is ω_1, the circuit is more capacitive than inductive and the phase angle is $-10°$. If the driving frequency is ω_2, the circuit is more inductive than capacitive and the phase angle is $+10°$. The largest amount of power is delivered to the circuit at (a) ω_1 (b) ω_2 (c) The same amount of power is delivered at both frequencies.

Example 33.6 Average Power in an *RLC* Series Circuit

Calculate the average power delivered to the series *RLC* circuit described in Example 33.5.

Solution First, let us calculate the rms voltage and rms current, using the values of ΔV_{max} and I_{max} from Example 33.5:

$$\Delta V_{rms} = \frac{\Delta V_{max}}{\sqrt{2}} = \frac{150 \text{ V}}{\sqrt{2}} = 106 \text{ V}$$

$$I_{rms} = \frac{I_{max}}{\sqrt{2}} = \frac{0.292 \text{ A}}{\sqrt{2}} = 0.206 \text{ A}$$

Because $\phi = -34.0°$, the power factor is $\cos(-34.0°) = 0.829$; hence, the average power delivered is

$$\mathcal{P}_{av} = I_{rms} \, \Delta V_{rms} \cos\phi = (0.206 \text{ A})(106 \text{ V})(0.829)$$

$$= \boxed{18.1 \text{ W}}$$

We can obtain the same result using Equation 33.32.

33.7 Resonance in a Series *RLC* Circuit

A series *RLC* circuit is said to be **in resonance** when the current has its maximum value. In general, the rms current can be written

$$I_{rms} = \frac{\Delta V_{rms}}{Z} \tag{33.33}$$

where Z is the impedance. Substituting the expression for Z from Equation 33.25 into 33.33 gives

$$I_{rms} = \frac{\Delta V_{rms}}{\sqrt{R^2 + (X_L - X_C)^2}} \tag{33.34}$$

Because the impedance depends on the frequency of the source, the current in the *RLC* circuit also depends on the frequency. The frequency ω_0 at which $X_L - X_C = 0$ is called the **resonance frequency** of the circuit. To find ω_0, we use the condition $X_L = X_C$, from which we obtain $\omega_0 L = 1/\omega_0 C$, or

$$\omega_0 = \frac{1}{\sqrt{LC}} \tag{33.35}$$

Resonance frequency

This frequency also corresponds to the natural frequency of oscillation of an *LC* circuit (see Section 32.5). Therefore, the current in a series *RLC* circuit reaches its maximum value when the frequency of the applied voltage matches the natural oscillator frequency—which depends only on L and C. Furthermore, at this frequency the current is in phase with the applied voltage.

Quick Quiz 33.9   The impedance of a series RLC circuit at resonance is (a) larger than R (b) less than R (c) equal to R (d) impossible to determine.

A plot of rms current versus frequency for a series RLC circuit is shown in Figure 33.19a. The data assume a constant $\Delta V_{\text{rms}} = 5.0$ mV, that $L = 5.0$ μH, and that $C = 2.0$ nF. The three curves correspond to three values of R. In each case, the current reaches its maximum value at the resonance frequency ω_0. Furthermore, the curves become narrower and taller as the resistance decreases.

By inspecting Equation 33.34, we must conclude that, when $R = 0$, the current becomes infinite at resonance. However, real circuits always have some resistance, which limits the value of the current to some finite value.

It is also interesting to calculate the average power as a function of frequency for a series RLC circuit. Using Equations 33.32, 33.33, and 33.25, we find that

$$\mathcal{P}_{\text{av}} = I_{\text{rms}}^2 R = \frac{(\Delta V_{\text{rms}})^2}{Z^2} R = \frac{(\Delta V_{\text{rms}})^2 R}{R^2 + (X_L - X_C)^2} \qquad (33.36)$$

Because $X_L = \omega L$, $X_C = 1/\omega C$, and $\omega_0^2 = 1/LC$, we can express the term $(X_L - X_C)^2$ as

$$(X_L - X_C)^2 = \left(\omega L - \frac{1}{\omega C}\right)^2 = \frac{L^2}{\omega^2}(\omega^2 - \omega_0^2)^2$$

Using this result in Equation 33.36 gives

Average power as a function of frequency in an *RLC* circuit

$$\mathcal{P}_{\text{av}} = \frac{(\Delta V_{\text{rms}})^2 R\omega^2}{R^2\omega^2 + L^2(\omega^2 - \omega_0^2)^2} \qquad (33.37)$$

This expression shows that **at resonance, when $\omega = \omega_0$, the average power is a maximum** and has the value $(\Delta V_{\text{rms}})^2/R$. Figure 33.19b is a plot of average power

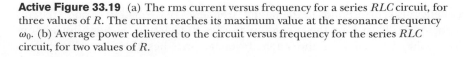

Active Figure 33.19 (a) The rms current versus frequency for a series RLC circuit, for three values of R. The current reaches its maximum value at the resonance frequency ω_0. (b) Average power delivered to the circuit versus frequency for the series RLC circuit, for two values of R.

versus frequency for two values of R in a series *RLC* circuit. As the resistance is made smaller, the curve becomes sharper in the vicinity of the resonance frequency. This curve sharpness is usually described by a dimensionless parameter known as the **quality factor,**[3] denoted by Q:

$$Q = \frac{\omega_0}{\Delta\omega}$$

where $\Delta\omega$ is the width of the curve measured between the two values of ω for which $\mathcal{P}_{av}$ has half its maximum value, called the *half-power points* (see Fig. 33.19b.) It is left as a problem (Problem 72) to show that the width at the half-power points has the value $\Delta\omega = R/L$, so

$$Q = \frac{\omega_0 L}{R} \qquad (33.38)$$

The curves plotted in Figure 33.20 show that a high-Q circuit responds to only a very narrow range of frequencies, whereas a low-Q circuit can detect a much broader range of frequencies. Typical values of Q in electronic circuits range from 10 to 100.

The receiving circuit of a radio is an important application of a resonant circuit. One tunes the radio to a particular station (which transmits an electromagnetic wave or signal of a specific frequency) by varying a capacitor, which changes the resonance frequency of the receiving circuit. When the resonance frequency of the circuit matches that of the incoming electromagnetic wave, the current in the receiving circuit increases. This signal caused by the incoming wave is then amplified and fed to a speaker. Because many signals are often present over a range of frequencies, it is important to design a high-Q circuit to eliminate unwanted signals. In this manner, stations whose frequencies are near but not equal to the resonance frequency give signals at the receiver that are negligibly small relative to the signal that matches the resonance frequency.

Quality factor

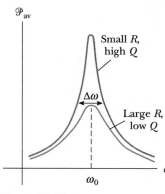

Figure 33.20 Average power versus frequency for a series *RLC* circuit. The width $\Delta\omega$ of each curve is measured between the two points where the power is half its maximum value. The power is a maximum at the resonance frequency ω_0.

Quick Quiz 33.10 An airport metal detector (see page 1003) is essentially a resonant circuit. The portal you step through is an inductor (a large loop of conducting wire) within the circuit. The frequency of the circuit is tuned to its resonance frequency when there is no metal in the inductor. Any metal on your body increases the effective inductance of the loop and changes the current in it. If you want the detector to detect a small metallic object, should the circuit have (a) a high quality factor or (b) a low quality factor?

Example 33.7   A Resonating Series *RLC* Circuit   **Interactive**

Consider a series *RLC* circuit for which $R = 150\ \Omega$, $L = 20.0$ mH, $\Delta V_{rms} = 20.0$ V, and $\omega = 5\ 000$ s^{-1}. Determine the value of the capacitance for which the current is a maximum.

Solution The current has its maximum value at the resonance frequency ω_0, which should be made to match the "driving" frequency of 5 000 s^{-1}:

$$\omega_0 = 5.00 \times 10^3\ \text{s}^{-1} = \frac{1}{\sqrt{LC}}$$

$$C = \frac{1}{\omega_0^2 L} = \frac{1}{(5.00 \times 10^3\ \text{s}^{-1})^2 (20.0 \times 10^{-3}\ \text{H})}$$

$$= 2.00\ \mu\text{F}$$

🌐 **At the Interactive Worked Example link at http://www.pse6.com,** *you can explore resonance in an RLC circuit.*

---

[3]   The quality factor is also defined as the ratio $2\pi E/\Delta E$ where E is the energy stored in the oscillating system and ΔE is the energy decrease per cycle of oscillation due to the resistance.

33.8   The Transformer and Power Transmission

As discussed in Section 27.6, when electric power is transmitted over great distances, it is economical to use a high voltage and a low current to minimize the I^2R loss in the transmission lines. Consequently, 350-kV lines are common, and in many areas even higher-voltage (765-kV) lines are used. At the receiving end of such lines, the consumer requires power at a low voltage (for safety and for efficiency in design). Therefore, a device is required that can change the alternating voltage and current without causing appreciable changes in the power delivered. The AC transformer is that device.

In its simplest form, the **AC transformer** consists of two coils of wire wound around a core of iron, as illustrated in Figure 33.21. (Compare this to Faraday's experiment in Figure 31.2.) The coil on the left, which is connected to the input alternating voltage source and has N_1 turns, is called the *primary winding* (or the *primary*). The coil on the right, consisting of N_2 turns and connected to a load resistor R, is called the *secondary winding* (or the *secondary*). The purpose of the iron core is to increase the magnetic flux through the coil and to provide a medium in which nearly all the magnetic field lines through one coil pass through the other coil. Eddy-current losses are reduced by using a laminated core. Iron is used as the core material because it is a soft ferromagnetic substance and hence reduces hysteresis losses. Transformation of energy to internal energy in the finite resistance of the coil wires is usually quite small. Typical transformers have power efficiencies from 90% to 99%. In the discussion that follows, we assume an *ideal transformer*, one in which the energy losses in the windings and core are zero.

First, let us consider what happens in the primary circuit. If we assume that the resistance of the primary is negligible relative to its inductive reactance, then the primary circuit is equivalent to a simple circuit consisting of an inductor connected to an AC source. Because the current is 90° out of phase with the voltage, the power factor cos ϕ is zero, and hence the average power delivered from the source to the primary circuit is zero. Faraday's law states that the voltage ΔV_1 across the primary is

$$\Delta V_1 = -N_1 \frac{d\Phi_B}{dt} \tag{33.39}$$

where Φ_B is the magnetic flux through each turn. If we assume that all magnetic field lines remain within the iron core, the flux through each turn of the primary equals the flux through each turn of the secondary. Hence, the voltage across the secondary is

$$\Delta V_2 = -N_2 \frac{d\Phi_B}{dt} \tag{33.40}$$

Solving Equation 33.39 for $d\Phi_B/dt$ and substituting the result into Equation 33.40, we find that

$$\Delta V_2 = \frac{N_2}{N_1} \Delta V_1 \tag{33.41}$$

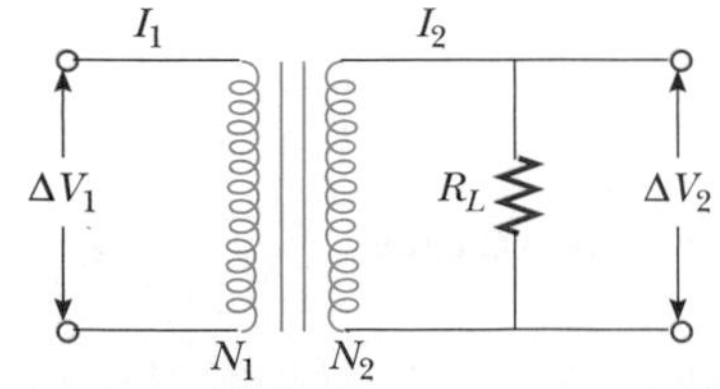

When $N_2 > N_1$, the output voltage ΔV_2 exceeds the input voltage ΔV_1. This setup is referred to as a *step-up transformer*. When $N_2 < N_1$, the output voltage is less than the input voltage, and we have a *step-down transformer*.

When the switch in the secondary circuit is closed, a current I_2 is induced in the secondary. If the load in the secondary circuit is a pure resistance, the induced current is in phase with the induced voltage. The power supplied to the secondary circuit must be provided by the AC source connected to the primary circuit, as shown in Figure 33.22. In an ideal transformer, where there are no losses, the power

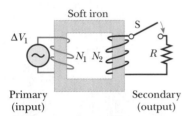

Figure 33.21 An ideal transformer consists of two coils wound on the same iron core. An alternating voltage ΔV_1 is applied to the primary coil, and the output voltage ΔV_2 is across the resistor of resistance R.

Figure 33.22 Circuit diagram for a transformer.

$I_1 \Delta V_1$ supplied by the source is equal to the power $I_2 \Delta V_2$ in the secondary circuit. That is,

$$I_1 \Delta V_1 = I_2 \Delta V_2 \qquad (33.42)$$

The value of the load resistance R_L determines the value of the secondary current because $I_2 = \Delta V_2 / R_L$. Furthermore, the current in the primary is $I_1 = \Delta V_1 / R_{eq}$, where

$$R_{eq} = \left(\frac{N_1}{N_2} \right)^2 R_L \qquad (33.43)$$

is the equivalent resistance of the load resistance when viewed from the primary side. From this analysis we see that a transformer may be used to match resistances between the primary circuit and the load. In this manner, maximum power transfer can be achieved between a given power source and the load resistance. For example, a transformer connected between the 1-kΩ output of an audio amplifier and an 8-Ω speaker ensures that as much of the audio signal as possible is transferred into the speaker. In stereo terminology, this is called *impedance matching*.

We can now also understand why transformers are useful for transmitting power over long distances. Because the generator voltage is stepped up, the current in the transmission line is reduced, and hence $I^2 R$ losses are reduced. In practice, the voltage is stepped up to around 230 000 V at the generating station, stepped down to around 20 000 V at a distributing station, then to 4 000 V for delivery to residential areas, and finally to 120–240 V at the customer's site.

There is a practical upper limit to the voltages that can be used in transmission lines. Excessive voltages could ionize the air surrounding the transmission lines, which could result in a conducting path to ground or to other objects in the vicinity. This, of course, would present a serious hazard to any living creatures. For this reason, a long string of insulators is used to keep high-voltage wires away from their supporting metal towers. Other insulators are used to maintain separation between wires.

Many common household electronic devices require low voltages to operate properly. A small transformer that plugs directly into the wall, like the one illustrated in Figure 33.23, can provide the proper voltage. The photograph shows the two windings wrapped around a common iron core that is found inside all these little "black boxes." This particular transformer converts the 120-V AC in the wall socket to 12.5-V AC. (Can you determine the ratio of the numbers of turns in the two coils?) Some black boxes also make use of diodes to convert the alternating current to direct current. (See Section 33.9.)

Nikola Tesla
American Physicist (1856–1943)

Tesla was born in Croatia but spent most of his professional life as an inventor in the United States. He was a key figure in the development of alternating current electricity, high-voltage transformers, and the transport of electrical power using AC transmission lines. Tesla's viewpoint was at odds with the ideas of Thomas Edison, who committed himself to the use of direct current in power transmission. Tesla's AC approach won out. *(UPI/CORBIS)*

Figure 33.23 The primary winding in this transformer is directly attached to the prongs of the plug. The secondary winding is connected to the power cord on the right, which runs to an electronic device. Many of these power-supply transformers also convert alternating current to direct current.

This transformer is smaller than the one in the opening photograph for this chapter. In addition, it is a step-down transformer. It drops the voltage from 4 000 V to 240 V for delivery to a group of residences.

Example 33.8 The Economics of AC Power

An electricity-generating station needs to deliver energy at a rate of 20 MW to a city 1.0 km away.

(A) If the resistance of the wires is 2.0 Ω and the energy costs about 10¢/kWh, estimate what it costs the utility company for the energy converted to internal energy in the wires during one day. A common voltage for commercial power generators is 22 kV, but a step-up transformer is used to boost the voltage to 230 kV before transmission.

Solution Conceptualize by noting that the resistance of the wires is in series with the resistance representing the load (homes and businesses). Thus, there will be a voltage drop in the wires, which means that some of the transmitted energy is converted to internal energy in the wires and never reaches the load. Because this is an estimate, let us categorize this as a problem in which the power factor is equal to 1. To analyze the problem, we begin by calculating I_{rms} from Equation 33.31:

$$I_{rms} = \frac{\mathcal{P}_{av}}{\Delta V_{rms}} = \frac{20 \times 10^6 \text{ W}}{230 \times 10^3 \text{ V}} = 87 \text{ A}$$

Now, we determine the rate at which energy is delivered to the resistance in the wires from Equation 33.32:

$$\mathcal{P}_{av} = I_{rms}^2 R = (87 \text{ A})^2 (2.0 \text{ Ω}) = 15 \text{ kW}$$

Over the course of a day, the energy loss due to the resistance of the wires is $(15 \text{ kW})(24 \text{ h}) = 360 \text{ kWh}$, at a cost of $36.

(B) Repeat the calculation for the situation in which the power plant delivers the energy at its original voltage of 22 kV.

Solution Again using Equation 33.31, we find

$$I_{rms} = \frac{\mathcal{P}_{av}}{\Delta V_{rms}} = \frac{20 \times 10^6 \text{ W}}{22 \times 10^3 \text{ V}} = 910 \text{ A}$$

and, from Equation 33.32,

$$\mathcal{P}_{av} = I_{rms}^2 R = (910 \text{ A})^2 (2.0 \text{ Ω}) = 1.7 \times 10^3 \text{ kW}$$

Cost per day = $(1.7 \times 10^3 \text{ kW})(24 \text{ h})(\$0.10/\text{kWh})$

$$= \$4\,100$$

To finalize the example, note the tremendous savings that are possible through the use of transformers and high-voltage transmission lines. This, in combination with the efficiency of using alternating current to operate motors, led to the universal adoption of alternating current instead of direct current for commercial power grids.

33.9 Rectifiers and Filters

Portable electronic devices such as radios and compact disc (CD) players are often powered by direct current supplied by batteries. Many devices come with AC–DC converters such as that in Figure 33.23. Such a converter contains a transformer that steps the voltage down from 120 V to typically 9 V and a circuit that converts alternating current to direct current. The process of converting alternating current to direct current is called **rectification,** and the converting device is called a **rectifier.**

The most important element in a rectifier circuit is a **diode,** a circuit element that conducts current in one direction but not the other. Most diodes used in modern electronics are semiconductor devices. The circuit symbol for a diode is ——▶|——, where the arrow indicates the direction of the current in the diode. A diode has low resistance to current in one direction (the direction of the arrow) and high resistance to current in the opposite direction. We can understand how a diode rectifies a current by considering Figure 33.24a, which shows a diode and a resistor connected to the secondary of a transformer. The transformer reduces the voltage from 120-V AC to the lower voltage that is needed for the device having a resistance R (the load resistance). Because the diode conducts current in only one direction, the alternating current in the load resistor is reduced to the form shown by the solid curve in Figure 33.24b. The diode conducts current only when the side of the symbol containing the arrowhead has a positive potential relative to the other side. In this situation, the diode acts as a *half-wave rectifier* because current is present in the circuit during only half of each cycle.

When a capacitor is added to the circuit, as shown by the dashed lines and the capacitor symbol in Figure 33.24a, the circuit is a simple DC power supply. The time variation in the current in the load resistor (the dashed curve in Fig. 33.24b) is close to

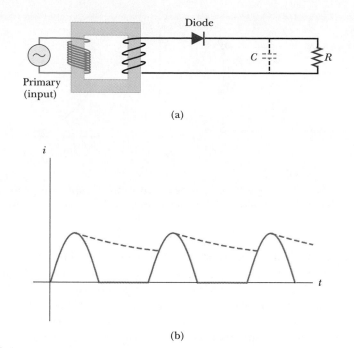

(a)

(b)

Figure 33.24 (a) A half-wave rectifier with an optional filter capacitor. (b) Current versus time in the resistor. The solid curve represents the current with no filter capacitor, and the dashed curve is the current when the circuit includes the capacitor.

being zero, as determined by the RC time constant of the circuit. As the current in the circuit begins to rise at $t = 0$ in Figure 33.24b, the capacitor charges up. When the current begins to fall, however, the capacitor discharges through the resistor, so that the current in the resistor does not fall as fast as the current from the transformer.

The RC circuit in Figure 33.24a is one example of a **filter circuit,** which is used to smooth out or eliminate a time-varying signal. For example, radios are usually powered by a 60-Hz alternating voltage. After rectification, the voltage still contains a small AC component at 60 Hz (sometimes called *ripple*), which must be filtered. By "filtered," we mean that the 60-Hz ripple must be reduced to a value much less than that of the audio signal to be amplified, because without filtering, the resulting audio signal includes an annoying hum at 60 Hz.

We can also design filters that will respond differently to different frequencies. Consider the simple series RC circuit shown in Figure 33.25a. The input voltage is across the series combination of the two elements. The output is the voltage across the resistor. A plot of the ratio of the output voltage to the input voltage as a function of the logarithm of angular frequency (see Fig. 33.25b) shows that at low frequencies ΔV_{out} is much smaller than ΔV_{in}, whereas at high frequencies the two voltages are equal. Because the circuit

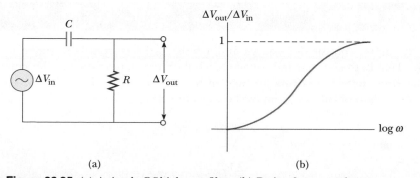

(a)   (b)

Active Figure 33.25 (a) A simple RC high-pass filter. (b) Ratio of output voltage to input voltage for an RC high-pass filter as a function of the angular frequency of the AC source.

At the Active Figures link at http://www.pse6.com, you can adjust the resistance and the capacitance of the circuit in part (a). You can then determine the output voltage for a given frequency or sweep through the frequencies to generate a curve like that in part (b).

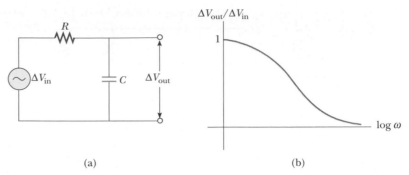

(a) (b)

Active Figure 33.26 (a) A simple *RC* low-pass filter. (b) Ratio of output voltage to input voltage for an *RC* low-pass filter as a function of the angular frequency of the AC source.

At the Active Figures link at http://www.pse6.com, you can adjust the resistance and the capacitance of the circuit in part (a). You can then determine the output voltage for a given frequency or sweep through the frequencies to generate a curve like that in part (b).

preferentially passes signals of higher frequency while blocking low-frequency signals, the circuit is called an *RC* high-pass filter. (See Problem 51 for an analysis of this filter.)

Physically, a high-pass filter works because a capacitor "blocks out" direct current and AC current at low frequencies. At low frequencies, the capacitive reactance is large and much of the applied voltage appears across the capacitor rather than across the output resistor. As the frequency increases, the capacitive reactance drops and more of the applied voltage appears across the resistor.

Now consider the circuit shown in Figure 33.26a, where we have interchanged the resistor and capacitor and the output voltage is taken across the capacitor. At low frequencies, the reactance of the capacitor and the voltage across the capacitor is high. As the frequency increases, the voltage across the capacitor drops. Thus, this is an *RC* low-pass filter. The ratio of output voltage to input voltage (see Problem 52), plotted as a function of the logarithm of ω in Figure 33.26b, shows this behavior.

You may be familiar with crossover networks, which are an important part of the speaker systems for high-fidelity audio systems. These networks use low-pass filters to direct low frequencies to a special type of speaker, the "woofer," which is designed to reproduce the low notes accurately. The high frequencies are sent to the "tweeter" speaker.

Quick Quiz 33.11 Suppose you are designing a high-fidelity system containing both large loudspeakers (woofers) and small loudspeakers (tweeters). If you wish to deliver low-frequency signals to a woofer, what device would you place in series with it? (a) an inductor (b) a capacitor (c) a resistor. If you wish to deliver high-frequency signals to a tweeter, what device would you place in series with it? (d) an inductor (e) a capacitor (f) a resistor.

SUMMARY

Take a practice test for this chapter by clicking on the Practice Test link at http://www.pse6.com.

If an AC circuit consists of a source and a resistor, the current is in phase with the voltage. That is, the current and voltage reach their maximum values at the same time.

The **rms current** and **rms voltage** in an AC circuit in which the voltages and current vary sinusoidally are given by the expressions

$$I_{rms} = \frac{I_{max}}{\sqrt{2}} = 0.707 I_{max} \tag{33.4}$$

$$\Delta V_{rms} = \frac{\Delta V_{max}}{\sqrt{2}} = 0.707\, \Delta V_{max} \tag{33.5}$$

where I_{max} and ΔV_{max} are the maximum values.

If an AC circuit consists of a source and an inductor, the current lags behind the voltage by 90°. That is, the voltage reaches its maximum value one quarter of a period before the current reaches its maximum value.

If an AC circuit consists of a source and a capacitor, the current leads the voltage by 90°. That is, the current reaches its maximum value one quarter of a period before the voltage reaches its maximum value.

In AC circuits that contain inductors and capacitors, it is useful to define the **inductive reactance** X_L and the **capacitive reactance** X_C as

$$X_L \equiv \omega L \tag{33.10}$$

$$X_C \equiv \frac{1}{\omega C} \tag{33.18}$$

where ω is the angular frequency of the AC source. The SI unit of reactance is the ohm.

The **impedance** Z of an RLC series AC circuit is

$$Z \equiv \sqrt{R^2 + (X_L - X_C)^2} \tag{33.25}$$

This expression illustrates that we cannot simply add the resistance and reactances in a circuit. We must account for the fact that the applied voltage and current are out of phase, with the **phase angle** ϕ between the current and voltage being

$$\phi = \tan^{-1}\left(\frac{X_L - X_C}{R}\right) \tag{33.27}$$

The sign of ϕ can be positive or negative, depending on whether X_L is greater or less than X_C. The phase angle is zero when $X_L = X_C$.

The **average power** delivered by the source in an RLC circuit is

$$\mathcal{P}_{av} = I_{rms}\,\Delta V_{rms}\,\cos\phi \tag{33.31}$$

An equivalent expression for the average power is

$$\mathcal{P}_{av} = I_{rms}^2\,R \tag{33.32}$$

The average power delivered by the source results in increasing internal energy in the resistor. No power loss occurs in an ideal inductor or capacitor.

The rms current in a series RLC circuit is

$$I_{rms} = \frac{\Delta V_{rms}}{\sqrt{R^2 + (X_L - X_C)^2}} \tag{33.34}$$

A series RLC circuit is in resonance when the inductive reactance equals the capacitive reactance. When this condition is met, the current given by Equation 33.34 reaches its maximum value. The **resonance frequency** ω_0 of the circuit is

$$\omega_0 = \frac{1}{\sqrt{LC}} \tag{33.35}$$

The current in a series RLC circuit reaches its maximum value when the frequency of the source equals ω_0—that is, when the "driving" frequency matches the resonance frequency.

Transformers allow for easy changes in alternating voltage. Because energy (and therefore power) are conserved, we can write

$$I_1\,\Delta V_1 = I_2\,\Delta V_2 \tag{33.42}$$

to relate the currents and voltages in the primary and secondary windings of a transformer.

QUESTIONS

1. How can the average value of a current be zero and yet the square root of the average squared current not be zero?

2. What is the time average of the "square-wave" potential shown in Figure Q33.2? What is its rms voltage?

Figure Q33.2

3. Do AC ammeters and voltmeters read maximum, rms, or average values?

4. In the clearest terms you can, explain the statement, "The voltage across an inductor leads the current by 90°."

5. Some fluorescent lights flicker on and off 120 times every second. Explain what causes this. Why can't you see it happening?

6. Why does a capacitor act as a short circuit at high frequencies? Why does it act as an open circuit at low frequencies?

7. Explain how the mnemonic "ELI the ICE man" can be used to recall whether current leads voltage or voltage leads current in *RLC* circuits. Note that E represents emf $\mathcal{E}$.

8. Why is the sum of the maximum voltages across each of the elements in a series *RLC* circuit usually greater than the maximum applied voltage? Doesn't this violate Kirchhoff's loop rule?

9. Does the phase angle depend on frequency? What is the phase angle when the inductive reactance equals the capacitive reactance?

10. In a series *RLC* circuit, what is the possible range of values for the phase angle?

11. If the frequency is doubled in a series *RLC* circuit, what happens to the resistance, the inductive reactance, and the capacitive reactance?

12. Explain why the average power delivered to an *RLC* circuit by the source depends on the phase angle between the current and applied voltage.

13. As shown in Figure 7.5a, a person pulls a vacuum cleaner at speed *v* across a horizontal floor, exerting on it a force of magnitude *F* directed upward at an angle *θ* with the horizontal. At what rate is the person doing work on the cleaner? State as completely as you can the analogy between power in this situation and in an electric circuit.

14. A particular experiment requires a beam of light of very stable intensity. Why would an AC voltage be unsuitable for powering the light source?

15. Do some research to answer these questions: Who invented the metal detector? Why? Did it work?

16. What is the advantage of transmitting power at high voltages?

17. What determines the maximum voltage that can be used on a transmission line?

18. Will a transformer operate if a battery is used for the input voltage across the primary? Explain.

19. Someone argues that high-voltage power lines actually waste more energy. He points out that the rate at which internal energy is produced in a wire is given by $(\Delta V)^2/R$, where R is the resistance of the wire. Therefore, the higher the voltage, the higher the energy waste. What if anything is wrong with his argument?

20. Explain how the quality factor is related to the response characteristics of a radio receiver. Which variable most strongly influences the quality factor?

21. Why are the primary and secondary coils of a transformer wrapped on an iron core that passes through both coils?

22. With reference to Figure Q33.22, explain why the capacitor prevents a DC signal from passing between A and B, yet allows an AC signal to pass from A to B. (The circuits are said to be capacitively coupled.)

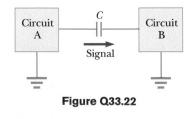

Figure Q33.22

PROBLEMS

1, 2, 3 = straightforward, intermediate, challenging   ☐ = full solution available in the *Student Solutions Manual and Study Guide*

🌐 = coached solution with hints available at http://www.pse6.com   💻 = computer useful in solving problem

▨ = paired numerical and symbolic problems

Note: Assume all AC voltages and currents are sinusoidal, unless stated otherwise.

Section 33.1 AC Sources

Section 33.2 Resistors in an AC Circuit

1. The rms output voltage of an AC source is 200 V and the operating frequency is 100 Hz. Write the equation giving the output voltage as a function of time.

2. (a) What is the resistance of a lightbulb that uses an average power of 75.0 W when connected to a 60.0-Hz power source having a maximum voltage of 170 V? (b) **What If?** What is the resistance of a 100-W bulb?

3. An AC power supply produces a maximum voltage $\Delta V_{max} = 100$ V. This power supply is connected to a 24.0-Ω resistor, and the current and resistor voltage are measured with an ideal AC ammeter and voltmeter, as shown in Figure P33.3. What does each meter read? Note that an ideal ammeter has zero resistance and that an ideal voltmeter has infinite resistance.

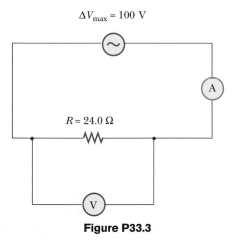

$$\Delta V_{max} = 100 \text{ V}$$

$R = 24.0 \ \Omega$

Figure P33.3

4. In the simple AC circuit shown in Figure 33.2, $R = 70.0 \ \Omega$ and $\Delta v = \Delta V_{max} \sin \omega t$. (a) If $\Delta v_R = 0.250 \ \Delta V_{max}$ for the first time at $t = 0.010 \ 0$ s, what is the angular frequency of the source? (b) What is the next value of t for which $\Delta v_R = 0.250 \ \Delta V_{max}$?

5. The current in the circuit shown in Figure 33.2 equals 60.0% of the peak current at $t = 7.00$ ms. What is the smallest frequency of the source that gives this current?

6. Figure P33.6 shows three lamps connected to a 120-V AC (rms) household supply voltage. Lamps 1 and 2 have 150-W bulbs; lamp 3 has a 100-W bulb. Find the rms current and resistance of each bulb.

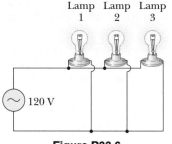

Lamp Lamp Lamp
1   2   3

120 V

Figure P33.6

7. An audio amplifier, represented by the AC source and resistor in Figure P33.7, delivers to the speaker alternating voltage at audio frequencies. If the source voltage has an amplitude of 15.0 V, $R = 8.20 \ \Omega$, and the speaker is equivalent to a resistance of 10.4 Ω, what is the time-averaged power transferred to it?

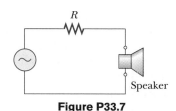

R

Speaker

Figure P33.7

Section 33.3 Inductors in an AC Circuit

8. An inductor is connected to a 20.0-Hz power supply that produces a 50.0-V rms voltage. What inductance is needed to keep the instantaneous current in the circuit below 80.0 mA?

9. In a purely inductive AC circuit, as shown in Figure 33.6, $\Delta V_{max} = 100$ V. (a) The maximum current is 7.50 A at 50.0 Hz. Calculate the inductance L. (b) **What If?** At what angular frequency ω is the maximum current 2.50 A?

10. An inductor has a 54.0-Ω reactance at 60.0 Hz. What is the maximum current if this inductor is connected to a 50.0-Hz source that produces a 100-V rms voltage?

11. 🌐 For the circuit shown in Figure 33.6, $\Delta V_{max} = 80.0$ V, $\omega = 65.0\pi$ rad/s, and $L = 70.0$ mH. Calculate the current in the inductor at $t = 15.5$ ms.

12. A 20.0-mH inductor is connected to a standard electrical outlet ($\Delta V_{rms} = 120$ V; $f = 60.0$ Hz). Determine the energy stored in the inductor at $t = (1/180)$ s, assuming that this energy is zero at $t = 0$.

13. **Review problem.** Determine the maximum magnetic flux through an inductor connected to a standard electrical outlet ($\Delta V_{rms} = 120$ V, $f = 60.0$ Hz).

Section 33.4   Capacitors in an AC Circuit

14. (a) For what frequencies does a 22.0-μF capacitor have a reactance below 175 Ω? (b) **What If?** Over this same frequency range, what is the reactance of a 44.0-μF capacitor?

15. What is the maximum current in a 2.20-μF capacitor when it is connected across (a) a North American electrical outlet having $\Delta V_{rms} = 120$ V, $f = 60.0$ Hz, and (b) **What If?** a European electrical outlet having $\Delta V_{rms} = 240$ V, $f = 50.0$ Hz?

16. A capacitor C is connected to a power supply that operates at a frequency f and produces an rms voltage ΔV. What is the maximum charge that appears on either of the capacitor plates?

17. What maximum current is delivered by an AC source with $\Delta V_{max} = 48.0$ V and $f = 90.0$ Hz when connected across a 3.70-μF capacitor?

18. A 1.00-mF capacitor is connected to a standard electrical outlet ($\Delta V_{rms} = 120$ V; $f = 60.0$ Hz). Determine the current in the capacitor at $t = (1/180)$ s, assuming that at $t = 0$, the energy stored in the capacitor is zero.

Section 33.5   The *RLC* Series Circuit

19. An inductor ($L = 400$ mH), a capacitor ($C = 4.43\ \mu$F), and a resistor ($R = 500\ \Omega$) are connected in series. A 50.0-Hz AC source produces a peak current of 250 mA in the circuit. (a) Calculate the required peak voltage ΔV_{max}. (b) Determine the phase angle by which the current leads or lags the applied voltage.

20. At what frequency does the inductive reactance of a 57.0-μH inductor equal the capacitive reactance of a 57.0-μF capacitor?

21. A series AC circuit contains the following components: $R = 150\ \Omega$, $L = 250$ mH, $C = 2.00\ \mu$F and a source with $\Delta V_{max} = 210$ V operating at 50.0 Hz. Calculate the (a) inductive reactance, (b) capacitive reactance, (c) impedance, (d) maximum current, and (e) phase angle between current and source voltage.

22. A sinusoidal voltage $\Delta v(t) = (40.0\ \text{V})\sin(100t)$ is applied to a series *RLC* circuit with $L = 160$ mH, $C = 99.0\ \mu$F, and $R = 68.0\ \Omega$. (a) What is the impedance of the circuit? (b) What is the maximum current? (c) Determine the numerical values for I_{max}, ω, and ϕ in the equation $i(t) = I_{max}\sin(\omega t - \phi)$.

23. An *RLC* circuit consists of a 150-Ω resistor, a 21.0-μF capacitor, and a 460-mH inductor, connected in series with a 120-V, 60.0-Hz power supply. (a) What is the phase angle between the current and the applied voltage? (b) Which reaches its maximum earlier, the current or the voltage?

24. Four circuit elements—a capacitor, an inductor, a resistor, and an AC source—are connected together in various ways. First the capacitor is connected to the source, and the rms current is found to be 25.1 mA. The capacitor is disconnected and discharged, and then connected in series with the resistor and the source, making the rms current 15.7 mA. The circuit is disconnected and the capacitor discharged. The capacitor is then connected in series with the inductor and the source, making the rms current 68.2 mA. After the circuit is disconnected and the capacitor discharged, all four circuit elements are connected together in a series loop. What is the rms current in the circuit?

25. A person is working near the secondary of a transformer, as shown in Figure P33.25. The primary voltage is 120 V at 60.0 Hz. The capacitance C_s, which is the stray capacitance between the hand and the secondary winding, is 20.0 pF. Assuming the person has a body resistance to ground $R_b = 50.0$ kΩ, determine the rms voltage across the body. (*Suggestion:* Redraw the circuit with the secondary of the transformer as a simple AC source.)

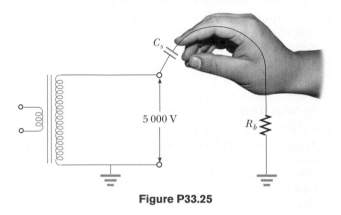

Figure P33.25

26. An AC source with $\Delta V_{max} = 150$ V and $f = 50.0$ Hz is connected between points a and d in Figure P33.26. Calculate the maximum voltages between points (a) a and b, (b) b and c, (c) c and d, and (d) b and d.

Figure P33.26 Problems 26 and 68.

27. Draw to scale a phasor diagram showing Z, X_L, X_C, and ϕ for an AC series circuit for which $R = 300\ \Omega$, $C = 11.0\ \mu$F, $L = 0.200$ H, and $f = (500/\pi)$ Hz.

28. In an *RLC* series circuit that includes a source of alternating current operating at fixed frequency and voltage, the resistance R is equal to the inductive reactance. If the plate separation of the capacitor is reduced to half of its original value, the current in the circuit doubles. Find the initial capacitive reactance in terms of R.

29. A coil of resistance 35.0 Ω and inductance 20.5 H is in series with a capacitor and a 200-V (rms), 100-Hz source. The rms current in the circuit is 4.00 A. (a) Calculate the capacitance in the circuit. (b) What is ΔV_{rms} across the coil?

Section 33.6   Power in an AC Circuit

30. The voltage source in Figure P33.30 has an output of $\Delta V_{rms} = 100$ V at an angular frequency of $\omega = 1\,000$ rad/s. Determine (a) the current in the circuit and (b) the power supplied by the source. (c) Show that the power delivered to the resistor is equal to the power supplied by the source.

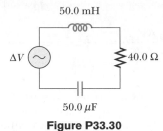

50.0 mH

ΔV 40.0 Ω

50.0 μF

Figure P33.30

31. An AC voltage of the form $\Delta v = (100 \text{ V}) \sin(1\,000t)$ is applied to a series *RLC* circuit. Assume the resistance is 400 Ω, the capacitance is 5.00 μF, and the inductance is 0.500 H. Find the average power delivered to the circuit.

32. A series *RLC* circuit has a resistance of 45.0 Ω and an impedance of 75.0 Ω. What average power is delivered to this circuit when $\Delta V_{rms} = 210$ V?

33. In a certain series *RLC* circuit, $I_{rms} = 9.00$ A, $\Delta V_{rms} = 180$ V, and the current leads the voltage by 37.0°. (a) What is the total resistance of the circuit? (b) Calculate the reactance of the circuit ($X_L - X_C$).

34. Suppose you manage a factory that uses many electric motors. The motors create a large inductive load to the electric power line, as well as a resistive load. The electric company builds an extra-heavy distribution line to supply you with a component of current that is 90° out of phase with the voltage, as well as with current in phase with the voltage. The electric company charges you an extra fee for "reactive volt-amps," in addition to the amount you pay for the energy you use. You can avoid the extra fee by installing a capacitor between the power line and your factory. The following problem models this solution.

In an *RL* circuit, a 120-V (rms), 60.0-Hz source is in series with a 25.0-mH inductor and a 20.0-Ω resistor. What are (a) the rms current and (b) the power factor? (c) What capacitor must be added in series to make the power factor 1? (d) To what value can the supply voltage be reduced, if the power supplied is to be the same as before the capacitor was installed?

35. Suppose power $\mathscr{P}$ is to be transmitted over a distance d at a voltage ΔV with only 1.00% loss. Copper wire of what diameter should be used for each of the two conductors of the transmission line? Assume the current density in the conductors is uniform.

36. A diode is a device that allows current to be carried in only one direction (the direction indicated by the arrowhead in its circuit symbol). Find in terms of ΔV and R the average power delivered to the diode circuit of Figure P33.36.

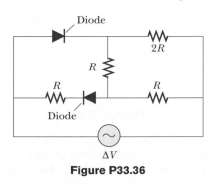

Diode

2R

R

R

R

Diode

ΔV

Figure P33.36

Section 33.7 Resonance in a Series *RLC* Circuit

37. An *RLC* circuit is used in a radio to tune into an FM station broadcasting at 99.7 MHz. The resistance in the circuit is 12.0 Ω, and the inductance is 1.40 μH. What capacitance should be used?

38. The tuning circuit of an AM radio contains an *LC* combination. The inductance is 0.200 mH, and the capacitor is variable, so that the circuit can resonate at any frequency between 550 kHz and 1 650 kHz. Find the range of values required for *C*.

39. A radar transmitter contains an *LC* circuit oscillating at 1.00×10^{10} Hz. (a) What capacitance will resonate with a one-turn loop of inductance 400 pH at this frequency? (b) If the capacitor has square parallel plates separated by 1.00 mm of air, what should the edge length of the plates be? (c) What is the common reactance of the loop and capacitor at resonance?

40. A series *RLC* circuit has components with following values: $L = 20.0$ mH, $C = 100$ nF, $R = 20.0$ Ω, and $\Delta V_{max} = 100$ V, with $\Delta v = \Delta V_{max} \sin \omega t$. Find (a) the resonant frequency, (b) the amplitude of the current at the resonant frequency, (c) the Q of the circuit, and (d) the amplitude of the voltage across the inductor at resonance.

41. A 10.0-Ω resistor, 10.0-mH inductor, and 100-μF capacitor are connected in series to a 50.0-V (rms) source having variable frequency. Find the energy that is delivered to the circuit during one period if the operating frequency is twice the resonance frequency.

42. A resistor R, inductor L, and capacitor C are connected in series to an AC source of rms voltage ΔV and variable frequency. Find the energy that is delivered to the circuit during one period if the operating frequency is twice the resonance frequency.

43. Compute the quality factor for the circuits described in Problems 22 and 23. Which circuit has the sharper resonance?

Section 33.8 The Transformer and Power Transmission

44. A step-down transformer is used for recharging the batteries of portable devices such as tape players. The turns ratio inside the transformer is 13:1 and it is used with 120-V (rms) household service. If a particular ideal transformer draws 0.350 A from the house outlet, what are (a) the voltage and (b) the current supplied to a tape player from the transformer? (c) How much power is delivered?

45. A transformer has $N_1 = 350$ turns and $N_2 = 2\,000$ turns. If the input voltage is $\Delta v(t) = (170 \text{ V}) \cos \omega t$, what rms voltage is developed across the secondary coil?

46. A step-up transformer is designed to have an output voltage of 2 200 V (rms) when the primary is connected across a 110-V (rms) source. (a) If the primary winding has 80 turns, how many turns are required on the secondary? (b) If a load resistor across the secondary draws a current of 1.50 A, what is the current in the primary, assuming ideal conditions? (c) **What If?** If the transformer actually has an efficiency of 95.0%, what is the current in the primary when the secondary current is 1.20 A?

47. In the transformer shown in Figure P33.47, the load resistor is 50.0 Ω. The turns ratio $N_1:N_2$ is 5:2, and the source voltage is 80.0 V (rms). If a voltmeter across the load measures 25.0 V (rms), what is the source resistance R_s?

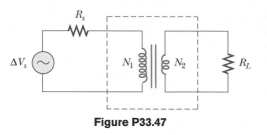

Figure P33.47

48. The secondary voltage of an ignition transformer in a furnace is 10.0 kV. When the primary operates at an rms voltage of 120 V, the primary impedance is 24.0 Ω and the transformer is 90.0% efficient. (a) What turns ratio is required? What are (b) the current in the secondary and (c) the impedance in the secondary?

49. A transmission line that has a resistance per unit length of 4.50×10^{-4} Ω/m is to be used to transmit 5.00 MW over 400 miles $(6.44 \times 10^5$ m). The output voltage of the generator is 4.50 kV. (a) What is the line loss if a transformer is used to step up the voltage to 500 kV? (b) What fraction of the input power is lost to the line under these circumstances? (c) **What If?** What difficulties would be encountered in attempting to transmit the 5.00 MW at the generator voltage of 4.50 kV?

Section 33.9 Rectifiers and Filters

50. One particular plug-in power supply for a radio looks similar to the one shown in Figure 33.23 and is marked with the following information: Input 120 V AC 8 W Output 9 V DC 300 mA. Assume that these values are accurate to two digits. (a) Find the energy efficiency of the device when the radio is operating. (b) At what rate does the device produce wasted energy when the radio is operating? (c) Suppose that the input power to the transformer is 8.0 W when the radio is switched off and that energy costs $0.135/kWh from the electric company. Find the cost of having six such transformers around the house, plugged in for thirty-one days.

51. Consider the filter circuit shown in Figure 33.25a. (a) Show that the ratio of the output voltage to the input voltage is

$$\frac{\Delta V_{out}}{\Delta V_{in}} = \frac{R}{\sqrt{R^2 + \left(\frac{1}{\omega C}\right)^2}}$$

(b) What value does this ratio approach as the frequency decreases toward zero? What value does this ratio approach as the frequency increases without limit? (c) At what frequency is the ratio equal to one half?

52. Consider the filter circuit shown in Figure 33.26a. (a) Show that the ratio of the output voltage to the input voltage is

$$\frac{\Delta V_{out}}{\Delta V_{in}} = \frac{1/\omega C}{\sqrt{R^2 + \left(\frac{1}{\omega C}\right)^2}}$$

(b) What value does this ratio approach as the frequency decreases toward zero? What value does this ratio approach as the frequency increases without limit? (c) At what frequency is the ratio equal to one half?

53. The RC high-pass filter shown in Figure 33.25 has a resistance $R = 0.500$ Ω. (a) What capacitance gives an output signal that has half the amplitude of a 300-Hz input signal? (b) What is the ratio $(\Delta V_{out}/\Delta V_{in})$ for a 600-Hz signal? You may use the result of Problem 51.

54. The RC low-pass filter shown in Figure 33.26 has a resistance $R = 90.0$ Ω and a capacitance $C = 8.00$ nF. Calculate the ratio $(\Delta V_{out}/\Delta V_{in})$ for an input frequency of (a) 600 Hz and (b) 600 kHz. You may use the result of Problem 52.

55. The resistor in Figure P33.55 represents the midrange speaker in a three-speaker system. Assume its resistance to be constant at 8.00 Ω. The source represents an audio amplifier producing signals of uniform amplitude $\Delta V_{in} = 10.0$ V at all audio frequencies. The inductor and capacitor are to function as a bandpass filter with $\Delta V_{out}/\Delta V_{in} = 1/2$ at 200 Hz and at 4 000 Hz. (a) Determine the required values of L and C. (b) Find the maximum value of the ratio $\Delta V_{out}/\Delta V_{in}$. (c) Find the frequency f_0 at which the ratio has its maximum value. (d) Find the phase shift between ΔV_{in} and ΔV_{out} at 200 Hz, at f_0, and at 4 000 Hz. (e) Find the average power transferred to the speaker at 200 Hz, at f_0, and at 4 000 Hz. (f) Treating the filter as a resonant circuit, find its quality factor.

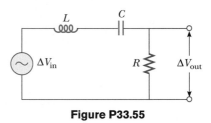

Figure P33.55

Additional Problems

56. Show that the rms value for the sawtooth voltage shown in Figure P33.56 is $\Delta V_{max}/\sqrt{3}$.

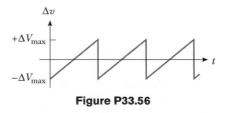

Figure P33.56

57. A series RLC circuit consists of an 8.00-Ω resistor, a 5.00-μF capacitor, and a 50.0-mH inductor. A variable

frequency source applies an emf of 400 V (rms) across the combination. Determine the power delivered to the circuit when the frequency is equal to half the resonance frequency.

58. A capacitor, a coil, and two resistors of equal resistance are arranged in an AC circuit, as shown in Figure P33.58. An AC source provides an emf of 20.0 V (rms) at a frequency of 60.0 Hz. When the double-throw switch S is open, as shown in the figure, the rms current is 183 mA. When the switch is closed in position 1, the rms current is 298 mA. When the switch is closed in position 2, the rms current is 137 mA. Determine the values of R, C, and L. Is more than one set of values possible?

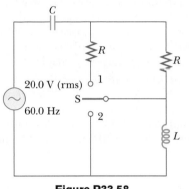

Figure P33.58

59. To determine the inductance of a coil used in a research project, a student first connects the coil to a 12.0-V battery and measures a current of 0.630 A. The student then connects the coil to a 24.0-V (rms), 60.0-Hz generator and measures an rms current of 0.570 A. What is the inductance?

60. **Review problem.** One insulated conductor from a household extension cord has mass per length 19.0 g/m. A section of this conductor is held under tension between two clamps. A subsection is located in a region of magnetic field of magnitude 15.3 mT perpendicular to the length of the cord. The wire carries an AC current of 9.00 A at 60.0 Hz. Determine some combination of values for the distance between the clamps and the tension in the cord so that the cord can vibrate in the lowest-frequency standing-wave vibrational state.

61. In Figure P33.61, find the rms current delivered by the 45.0-V (rms) power supply when (a) the frequency is very large and (b) the frequency is very small.

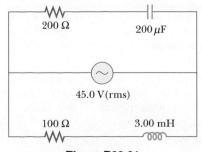

Figure P33.61

62. In the circuit shown in Figure P33.62, assume that all parameters except for C are given. (a) Find the current as a function of time. (b) Find the power delivered to the circuit. (c) Find the current as a function of time after *only* switch 1 is opened. (d) After switch 2 is *also* opened, the current and voltage are in phase. Find the capacitance C. (e) Find the impedance of the circuit when both switches are open. (f) Find the maximum energy stored in the capacitor during oscillations. (g) Find the maximum energy stored in the inductor during oscillations. (h) Now the frequency of the voltage source is doubled. Find the phase difference between the current and the voltage. (i) Find the frequency that makes the inductive reactance half the capacitive reactance.

$$\Delta v(t) = \Delta V_{max} \cos \omega t$$

Figure P33.62

63. An 80.0-Ω resistor and a 200-mH inductor are connected in *parallel* across a 100-V (rms), 60.0-Hz source. (a) What is the rms current in the resistor? (b) By what angle does the total current lead or lag behind the voltage?

64. Make an order-of-magnitude estimate of the electric current that the electric company delivers to a town (Figure P33.64) from a remote generating station. State the data you measure or estimate. If you wish, you may consider a suburban bedroom community of 20 000 people.

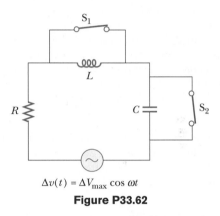

Figure P33.64

65. Consider a series RLC circuit having the following circuit parameters: $R = 200 \ \Omega$, $L = 663$ mH, and $C = 26.5 \ \mu$F. The applied voltage has an amplitude of 50.0 V and a frequency of 60.0 Hz. Find the following amplitudes: (a) The current I_{max}, including its phase constant ϕ relative to the applied voltage Δv, (b) the voltage ΔV_R

across the resistor and its phase relative to the current, (c) the voltage ΔV_C across the capacitor and its phase relative to the current, and (d) the voltage ΔV_L across the inductor and its phase relative to the current.

66. A voltage $\Delta v = (100 \text{ V}) \sin \omega t$ (in SI units) is applied across a series combination of a 2.00-H inductor, a 10.0-μF capacitor, and a 10.0-Ω resistor. (a) Determine the angular frequency ω_0 at which the power delivered to the resistor is a maximum. (b) Calculate the power delivered at that frequency. (c) Determine the two angular frequencies ω_1 and ω_2 at which the power is half the maximum value. [The Q of the circuit is $\omega_0/(\omega_2 - \omega_1)$.]

67. *Impedance matching.* Example 28.2 showed that maximum power is transferred when the internal resistance of a DC source is equal to the resistance of the load. A transformer may be used to provide maximum power transfer between two AC circuits that have different impedances Z1 and Z2, where 1 and 2 are subscripts and the Z's are italic (as in the centered equation). (a) Show that the ratio of turns N_1/N_2 needed to meet this condition is

$$\frac{N_1}{N_2} = \sqrt{\frac{Z_1}{Z_2}}$$

(b) Suppose you want to use a transformer as an impedance-matching device between an audio amplifier that has an output impedance of 8.00 kΩ and a speaker that has an input impedance of 8.00 Ω. What should your N_1/N_2 ratio be?

68. A power supply with $\Delta V_{\text{rms}} = 120$ V is connected between points a and d in Figure P33.26. At what frequency will it deliver a power of 250 W?

69. Figure P33.69a shows a parallel RLC circuit, and the corresponding phasor diagram is given in Figure P33.69b. The instantaneous voltages (and rms voltages) across each of the three circuit elements are the same, and each is in

phase with the current through the resistor. The currents in C and L lead or lag behind the current in the resistor, as shown in Figure P33.69b. (a) Show that the rms current delivered by the source is

$$I_{\text{rms}} = \Delta V_{\text{rms}} \left[\frac{1}{R^2} + \left(\omega C - \frac{1}{\omega L} \right)^2 \right]^{1/2}$$

(b) Show that the phase angle ϕ between ΔV_{rms} and I_{rms} is

$$\tan \phi = R \left(\frac{1}{X_C} - \frac{1}{X_L} \right)$$

70. An 80.0-Ω resistor, a 200-mH inductor, and a 0.150-μF capacitor are connected *in parallel* across a 120-V (rms) source operating at 374 rad/s. (a) What is the resonant frequency of the circuit? (b) Calculate the rms current in the resistor, inductor, and capacitor. (c) What rms current is delivered by the source? (d) Is the current leading or lagging behind the voltage? By what angle?

71. 💻 A series RLC circuit is operating at 2 000 Hz. At this frequency, $X_L = X_C = 1\,884\ \Omega$. The resistance of the circuit is 40.0 Ω. (a) Prepare a table showing the values of X_L, X_C, and Z for $f = 300, 600, 800, 1\,000, 1\,500, 2\,000, 3\,000, 4\,000, 6\,000$, and 10 000 Hz. (b) Plot on the same set of axes X_L, X_C, and Z as a function of $\ln f$.

72. 💻 A series RLC circuit in which $R = 1.00\ \Omega$, $L = 1.00$ mH, and $C = 1.00$ nF is connected to an AC source delivering 1.00 V (rms). Make a precise graph of the power delivered to the circuit as a function of the frequency and verify that the full width of the resonance peak at half-maximum is $R/2\pi L$.

73. 💻 Suppose the high-pass filter shown in Figure 33.25 has $R = 1\,000\ \Omega$ and $C = 0.050\,0\ \mu$F. (a) At what frequency does $\Delta V_{\text{out}}/\Delta V_{\text{in}} = \frac{1}{2}$? (b) Plot $\log_{10}(\Delta V_{\text{out}}/\Delta V_{\text{in}})$ versus $\log_{10}(f)$ over the frequency range from 1 Hz to 1 MHz. (This log–log plot of gain versus frequency is known as a *Bode plot.*)

Answers to Quick Quizzes

33.1 (a). The phasor in part (a) has the largest projection onto the vertical axis.

33.2 (b). The phasor in part (b) has the smallest-magnitude projection onto the vertical axis.

33.3 (c). The average power is proportional to the rms current, which, as Figure 33.5 shows, is nonzero even though the average current is zero. Condition (a) is valid only for an open circuit, and conditions (b) and (d) cannot be true because $i_{\text{av}} = 0$ if the source is sinusoidal.

33.4 (b). For low frequencies, the reactance of the inductor is small so that the current is large. Most of the voltage from the source is across the bulb, so the power delivered to it is large.

33.5 (a). For high frequencies, the reactance of the capacitor is small so that the current is large. Most of the voltage from the source is across the bulb, so the power delivered to it is large.

33.6 (b). For low frequencies, the reactance of the capacitor is large so that very little current exists in the capacitor

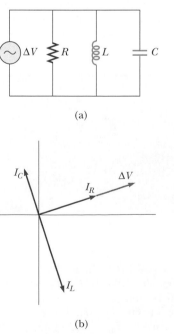

(a)

(b)

Figure P33.69

branch. The reactance of the inductor is small so that current exists in the inductor branch and the lightbulb glows. As the frequency increases, the inductive reactance increases and the capacitive reactance decreases. At high frequencies, more current exists in the capacitor branch than the inductor branch and the lightbulb glows more dimly.

33.7 (a) $X_L < X_C$. (b) $X_L = X_C$. (c) $X_L > X_C$.

33.8 (c). The cosine of $-\phi$ is the same as that of $+\phi$, so the $\cos\phi$ factor in Equation 33.31 is the same for both frequencies. The factor ΔV_{rms} is the same because the source voltage is fixed. According to Equation 33.27, changing $+\phi$ to $-\phi$ simply interchanges the values of X_L and X_C. Equation 33.25 tells us that such an interchange does not affect the impedance, so that the current I_{rms} in Equation 33.31 is the same for both frequencies.

33.9 (c). At resonance, $X_L = X_C$. According to Equation 33.25, this gives us $Z = R$.

33.10 (a). The higher the quality factor, the more sensitive the detector. As you can see from Figure 33.19, when $Q = \omega_0/\Delta\omega$ is high, a slight change in the resonance frequency (as might happen when a small piece of metal passes through the portal) causes a large change in current that can be detected easily.

33.11 (a) and (e). The current in an inductive circuit decreases with increasing frequency (see Eq. 33.9). Thus, an inductor connected in series with a woofer blocks high-frequency signals and passes low-frequency signals. The current in a capacitive circuit increases with increasing frequency (see Eq. 33.17). When a capacitor is connected in series with a tweeter, the capacitor blocks low-frequency signals and passes high-frequency signals.

Chapter 34

Electromagnetic Waves

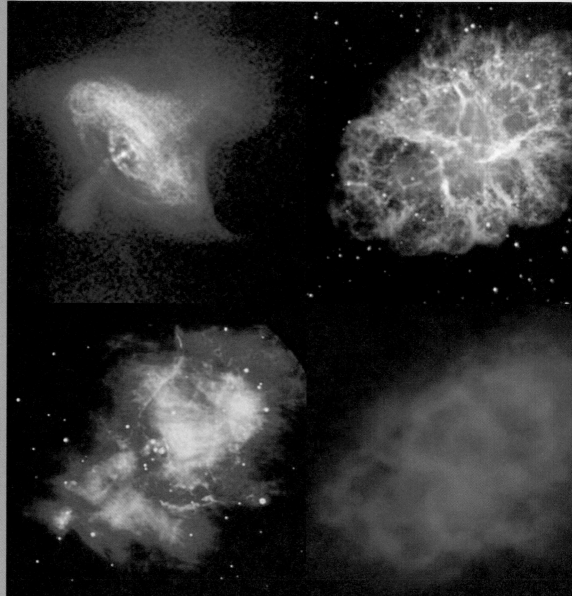

▲ Electromagnetic waves cover a broad spectrum of wavelengths, with waves in various
wavelength ranges having distinct properties. These images of the Crab Nebula show
different structure for observations made with waves of various wavelengths. The images
(clockwise starting from the upper left) were taken with x-rays, visible light, radio waves, and
infrared waves. (upper left–NASA/CXC/SAO; upper right–Palomar Observatory; lower
right–VLA/NRAO; lower left–WM Keck Observatory)

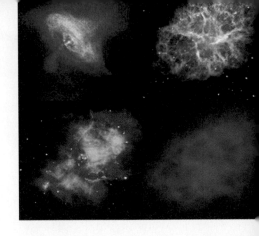

The waves described in Chapters 16, 17, and 18 are mechanical waves. By definition, the propagation of mechanical disturbances—such as sound waves, water waves, and waves on a string—requires the presence of a medium. This chapter is concerned with the properties of electromagnetic waves, which (unlike mechanical waves) can propagate through empty space.

In Section 31.7 we gave a brief description of Maxwell's equations, which form the theoretical basis of all electromagnetic phenomena. The consequences of Maxwell's equations are far-reaching and dramatic. The Ampère–Maxwell law predicts that a time-varying electric field produces a magnetic field, just as Faraday's law tells us that a time-varying magnetic field produces an electric field.

Astonishingly, Maxwell's equations also predict the existence of electromagnetic waves that propagate through space at the speed of light c. This chapter begins with a discussion of how Heinrich Hertz confirmed Maxwell's prediction when he generated and detected electromagnetic waves in 1887. That discovery has led to many practical communication systems, including radio, television, radar, and opto-electronics. On a conceptual level, Maxwell unified the subjects of light and electromagnetism by developing the idea that light is a form of electromagnetic radiation.

Next, we learn how electromagnetic waves are generated by oscillating electric charges. The waves consist of oscillating electric and magnetic fields at right angles to each other and to the direction of wave propagation. Thus, electromagnetic waves are transverse waves. The waves radiated from the oscillating charges can be detected at great distances. Furthermore, electromagnetic waves carry energy and momentum and hence can exert pressure on a surface.

The chapter concludes with a look at the wide range of frequencies covered by electromagnetic waves. For example, radio waves (frequencies of about 10^7 Hz) are electromagnetic waves produced by oscillating currents in a radio tower's transmitting antenna. Light waves are a high-frequency form of electromagnetic radiation (about 10^{14} Hz) produced by oscillating electrons in atoms.

34.1 Maxwell's Equations and Hertz's Discoveries

In his unified theory of electromagnetism, Maxwell showed that electromagnetic waves are a natural consequence of the fundamental laws expressed in the following four equations (see Section 31.7):

$$\oint \mathbf{E} \cdot d\mathbf{A} = \frac{q}{\epsilon_0} \qquad (34.1)$$

$$\oint \mathbf{B} \cdot d\mathbf{A} = 0 \qquad (34.2)$$

James Clerk Maxwell
Scottish Theoretical Physicist (1831–1879)

Maxwell developed the electromagnetic theory of light and the kinetic theory of gases, and explained the nature of Saturn's rings and color vision. Maxwell's successful interpretation of the electromagnetic field resulted in the field equations that bear his name. Formidable mathematical ability combined with great insight enabled him to lead the way in the study of electromagnetism and kinetic theory. He died of cancer before he was 50. (*North Wind Picture Archives*)

Maxwell's equations

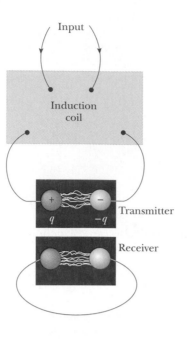

Input

Induction
coil

+ — Transmitter

q $-q$

Receiver

Figure 34.1 Schematic diagram of Hertz's apparatus for generating and detecting electromagnetic waves. The transmitter consists of two spherical electrodes connected to an induction coil, which provides short voltage surges to the spheres, setting up oscillations in the discharge between the electrodes. The receiver is a nearby loop of wire containing a second spark gap.

$$\oint \mathbf{E} \cdot d\mathbf{s} = -\frac{d\Phi_B}{dt} \tag{34.3}$$

$$\oint \mathbf{B} \cdot d\mathbf{s} = \mu_0 I + \mu_0 \epsilon_0 \frac{d\Phi_E}{dt} \tag{34.4}$$

In the next section we show that Equations 34.3 and 34.4 can be combined to obtain a wave equation for both the electric field and the magnetic field. In empty space, where $q = 0$ and $I = 0$, the solution to these two equations shows that the speed at which electromagnetic waves travel equals the measured speed of light. This result led Maxwell to predict that light waves are a form of electromagnetic radiation.

The experimental apparatus that Hertz used to generate and detect electromagnetic waves is shown schematically in Figure 34.1. An induction coil is connected to a transmitter made up of two spherical electrodes separated by a narrow gap. The coil provides short voltage surges to the electrodes, making one positive and the other negative. A spark is generated between the spheres when the electric field near either electrode surpasses the dielectric strength for air (3×10^6 V/m; see Table 26.1). In a strong electric field, the acceleration of free electrons provides them with enough energy to ionize any molecules they strike. This ionization provides more electrons, which can accelerate and cause further ionizations. As the air in the gap is ionized, it becomes a much better conductor, and the discharge between the electrodes exhibits an oscillatory behavior at a very high frequency. From an electric-circuit viewpoint, this is equivalent to an LC circuit in which the inductance is that of the coil and the capacitance is due to the spherical electrodes.

Because L and C are small in Hertz's apparatus, the frequency of oscillation is high, on the order of 100 MHz. (Recall from Eq. 32.22 that $\omega = 1/\sqrt{LC}$ for an LC circuit.) Electromagnetic waves are radiated at this frequency as a result of the oscillation (and hence acceleration) of free charges in the transmitter circuit. Hertz was able to detect these waves using a single loop of wire with its own spark gap (the receiver). Such a receiver loop, placed several meters from the transmitter, has its own effective inductance, capacitance, and natural frequency of oscillation. In Hertz's experiment, sparks were induced across the gap of the receiving electrodes when the frequency of the receiver was adjusted to match that of the transmitter. Thus, Hertz demonstrated that the oscillating current induced in the receiver was produced by electromagnetic waves radiated by the transmitter. His experiment is analogous to the mechanical phenomenon in which a tuning fork responds to acoustic vibrations from an identical tuning fork that is oscillating.

Heinrich Rudolf Hertz

German Physicist (1857–1894)

Hertz made his most important discovery of electromagnetic waves in 1887. After finding that the speed of an electromagnetic wave was the same as that of light, Hertz showed that electromagnetic waves, like light waves, could be reflected, refracted, and diffracted. Hertz died of blood poisoning at the age of 36. During his short life, he made many contributions to science. The hertz, equal to one complete vibration or cycle per second, is named after him. (*Hulton-Deutsch Collection/CORBIS*)

Additionally, Hertz showed in a series of experiments that the radiation generated by his spark-gap device exhibited the wave properties of interference, diffraction, reflection, refraction, and polarization, all of which are properties exhibited by light, as we shall see in Part 5 of the text. Thus, it became evident that the radio-frequency waves Hertz was generating had properties similar to those of light waves and differed only in frequency and wavelength. Perhaps his most convincing experiment was the measurement of the speed of this radiation. Waves of known frequency were reflected from a metal sheet and created a standing-wave interference pattern whose nodal points could be detected. The measured distance between the nodal points enabled determination of the wavelength λ. Using the relationship $v = \lambda f$ (Eq. 16.12), Hertz found that v was close to 3×10^8 m/s, the known speed c of visible light.

34.2   Plane Electromagnetic Waves

The properties of electromagnetic waves can be deduced from Maxwell's equations. One approach to deriving these properties is to solve the second-order differential equation obtained from Maxwell's third and fourth equations. A rigorous mathematical treatment of that sort is beyond the scope of this text. To circumvent this problem, we assume that the vectors for the electric field and magnetic field in an electromagnetic wave have a specific space–time behavior that is simple but consistent with Maxwell's equations.

To understand the prediction of electromagnetic waves more fully, let us focus our attention on an electromagnetic wave that travels in the x direction (the *direction of propagation*). In this wave, the electric field **E** is in the y direction, and the magnetic field **B** is in the z direction, as shown in Figure 34.2. Waves such as this one, in which the electric and magnetic fields are restricted to being parallel to a pair of perpendicular axes, are said to be **linearly polarized waves.** Furthermore, we assume that at any point in space, the magnitudes E and B of the fields depend upon x and t only, and not upon the y or z coordinate.

Let us also imagine that the source of the electromagnetic waves is such that a wave radiated from *any* position in the yz plane (not just from the origin as might be suggested by Figure 34.2) propagates in the x direction, and all such waves are emitted in phase. If we define a **ray** as the line along which the wave travels, then all rays for these waves are parallel. This entire collection of waves is often called a **plane wave.** A surface connecting points of equal phase on all waves, which we call a **wave front,** as introduced in Chapter 17, is a geometric plane. In comparison, a point source of radiation sends waves out radially in all directions. A surface connecting points of equal phase for this situation is a sphere, so this is called a **spherical wave.**

We can relate E and B to each other with Equations 34.3 and 34.4. In empty space, where $q = 0$ and $I = 0$, Equation 34.3 remains unchanged and Equation 34.4 becomes

$$\oint \mathbf{B} \cdot d\mathbf{s} = \epsilon_0 \mu_0 \frac{d\Phi_E}{dt} \tag{34.5}$$

Using Equations 34.3 and 34.5 and the plane-wave assumption, we obtain the following differential equations relating E and B. (We shall derive these equations formally later in this section.)

$$\frac{\partial E}{\partial x} = -\frac{\partial B}{\partial t} \tag{34.6}$$

$$\frac{\partial B}{\partial x} = -\mu_0 \epsilon_0 \frac{\partial E}{\partial t} \tag{34.7}$$

Note that the derivatives here are partial derivatives. For example, when we evaluate $\partial E / \partial x$, we assume that t is constant. Likewise, when we evaluate $\partial B / \partial t$, x is held constant. Taking the derivative of Equation 34.6 with respect to x and combining the

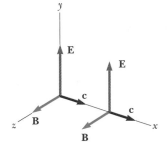

Figure 34.2 An electromagnetic wave traveling at velocity **c** in the positive x direction. The electric field is along the y direction, and the magnetic field is along the z direction. These fields depend only on x and t.

▲ **PITFALL PREVENTION**

34.1   What Is "a" Wave?

A sticky point in these types of discussions is what we mean by a *single* wave. We could define one wave as that which is emitted by a single charged particle. In practice, however, the word *wave* represents both the emission from a *single point* ("wave radiated from any position in the yz plane") and the collection of waves from *all points* on the source ("plane wave"). You should be able to use this term in both ways and to understand its meaning from the context.

result with Equation 34.7, we obtain

$$\frac{\partial^2 E}{\partial x^2} = -\frac{\partial}{\partial x}\left(\frac{\partial B}{\partial t}\right) = -\frac{\partial}{\partial t}\left(\frac{\partial B}{\partial x}\right) = -\frac{\partial}{\partial t}\left(-\mu_0 \epsilon_0 \frac{\partial E}{\partial t}\right)$$

$$\frac{\partial^2 E}{\partial x^2} = \mu_0 \epsilon_0 \frac{\partial^2 E}{\partial t^2} \qquad (34.8)$$

In the same manner, taking the derivative of Equation 34.7 with respect to x and combining it with Equation 34.6, we obtain

$$\frac{\partial^2 B}{\partial x^2} = \mu_0 \epsilon_0 \frac{\partial^2 B}{\partial t^2} \qquad (34.9)$$

Equations 34.8 and 34.9 both have the form of the general wave equation[1] with the wave speed v replaced by c, where

Speed of electromagnetic waves

$$c = \frac{1}{\sqrt{\mu_0 \epsilon_0}} \qquad (34.10)$$

Taking $\mu_0 = 4\pi \times 10^{-7}\,\text{T·m/A}$ and $\epsilon_0 = 8.854\,19 \times 10^{-12}\,\text{C}^2/\text{N·m}^2$ in Equation 34.10, we find that $c = 2.997\,92 \times 10^8$ m/s. Because this speed is precisely the same as the speed of light in empty space, we are led to believe (correctly) that light is an electromagnetic wave.

The simplest solution to Equations 34.8 and 34.9 is a sinusoidal wave, for which the field magnitudes E and B vary with x and t according to the expressions

Sinusoidal electric and magnetic fields

$$E = E_{\text{max}} \cos(kx - \omega t) \qquad (34.11)$$

$$B = B_{\text{max}} \cos(kx - \omega t) \qquad (34.12)$$

where E_{max} and B_{max} are the maximum values of the fields. The angular wave number is $k = 2\pi/\lambda$, where λ is the wavelength. The angular frequency is $\omega = 2\pi f$, where f is the wave frequency. The ratio ω/k equals the speed of an electromagnetic wave, c:

$$\frac{\omega}{k} = \frac{2\pi f}{2\pi/\lambda} = \lambda f = c$$

where we have used Equation 16.12, $v = c = \lambda f$, which relates the speed, frequency, and wavelength of any continuous wave. Thus, for electromagnetic waves, the wavelength and frequency of these waves are related by

$$\lambda = \frac{c}{f} = \frac{3.00 \times 10^8\,\text{m/s}}{f} \qquad (34.13)$$

Figure 34.3a is a pictorial representation, at one instant, of a sinusoidal, linearly polarized plane wave moving in the positive x direction. Figure 34.3b shows how the electric and magnetic field vectors at a fixed location vary with time.

Taking partial derivatives of Equations 34.11 (with respect to x) and 34.12 (with respect to t), we find that

$$\frac{\partial E}{\partial x} = -kE_{\text{max}} \sin(kx - \omega t)$$

$$\frac{\partial B}{\partial t} = \omega B_{\text{max}} \sin(kx - \omega t)$$

---

[1] The general wave equation is of the form $(\partial^2 y/\partial x^2) = (1/v^2)(\partial^2 y/\partial t^2)$ where v is the speed of the wave and y is the wave function. The general wave equation was introduced as Equation 16.27, and it would be useful for you to review Section 16.6.

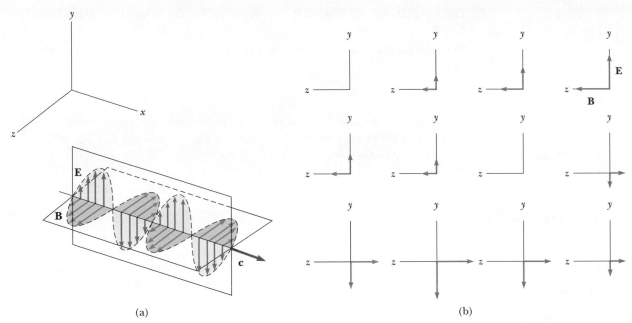

(a)   (b)

Active Figure 34.3 Representation of a sinusoidal, linearly polarized plane electromagnetic wave moving in the positive x direction with velocity **c**. (a) The wave at some instant. Note the sinusoidal variations of E and B with x. (b) A time sequence (starting at the upper left) illustrating the electric and magnetic field vectors at a fixed point in the yz plane, as seen by an observer looking in the negative x direction. The variations of E and B with t are sinusoidal.

At the Active Figures link at http://www.pse6.com, you can observe the wave in part (a) and the variation of the fields in part (b). In addition, you can take a "snapshot" of the wave at an instant of time and investigate the electric and magnetic fields at that instant.

Substituting these results into Equation 34.6, we find that at any instant

$$kE_{max} = \omega B_{max}$$

$$\frac{E_{max}}{B_{max}} = \frac{\omega}{k} = c$$

Using these results together with Equations 34.11 and 34.12, we see that

$$\frac{E_{max}}{B_{max}} = \frac{E}{B} = c \qquad (34.14)$$

That is, **at every instant the ratio of the magnitude of the electric field to the magnitude of the magnetic field in an electromagnetic wave equals the speed of light.**

Finally, note that electromagnetic waves obey the superposition principle (which we discussed in Section 18.1 with respect to mechanical waves) because the differential equations involving E and B are linear equations. For example, we can add two waves with the same frequency and polarization simply by adding the magnitudes of the two electric fields algebraically.

Let us summarize the properties of electromagnetic waves as we have described them:

- The solutions of Maxwell's third and fourth equations are wave-like, with both E and B satisfying a wave equation.

- Electromagnetic waves travel through empty space at the speed of light $c = 1/\sqrt{\epsilon_0 \mu_0}$.

- The components of the electric and magnetic fields of plane electromagnetic waves are perpendicular to each other and perpendicular to the direction of wave propagation. We can summarize the latter property by saying that electromagnetic waves are transverse waves.

▲ **PITFALL PREVENTION**

34.2 E Stronger Than B?

Because the value of c is so large, some students incorrectly interpret Equation 34.14 as meaning that the electric field is much stronger than the magnetic field. Electric and magnetic fields are measured in different units, however, so they cannot be directly compared. In Section 34.3, we find that the electric and magnetic fields contribute equally to the energy of the wave.

Properties of electromagnetic waves

- The magnitudes of **E** and **B** in empty space are related by the expression $E/B = c$.
- Electromagnetic waves obey the principle of superposition.

> **Quick Quiz 34.1** What is the phase difference between the sinusoidal oscillations of the electric and magnetic fields in Figure 34.3? (a) 180° (b) 90° (c) 0 (d) impossible to determine.

Example 34.1 An Electromagnetic Wave   Interactive

A sinusoidal electromagnetic wave of frequency 40.0 MHz travels in free space in the x direction, as in Figure 34.4.

(A) Determine the wavelength and period of the wave.

Solution Using Equation 34.13 for light waves and given that $f = 40.0$ MHz $= 4.00 \times 10^7$ s^{-1}, we have

$$\lambda = \frac{c}{f} = \frac{3.00 \times 10^8 \text{ m/s}}{4.00 \times 10^7 \text{ s}^{-1}} = \boxed{7.50 \text{ m}}$$

The period T of the wave is the inverse of the frequency:

$$T = \frac{1}{f} = \frac{1}{4.00 \times 10^7 \text{ s}^{-1}} = \boxed{2.50 \times 10^{-8} \text{ s}}$$

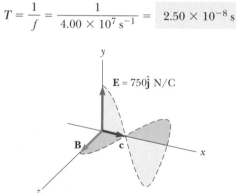

Figure 34.4 (Example 34.1) At some instant, a plane electromagnetic wave moving in the x direction has a maximum electric field of 750 N/C in the positive y direction. The corresponding magnetic field at that point has a magnitude E/c and is in the z direction.

(B) At some point and at some instant, the electric field has its maximum value of 750 N/C and is along the y axis. Calculate the magnitude and direction of the magnetic field at this position and time.

Solution From Equation 34.14 we see that

$$B_{\text{max}} = \frac{E_{\text{max}}}{c} = \frac{750 \text{ N/C}}{3.00 \times 10^8 \text{ m/s}} = \boxed{2.50 \times 10^{-6} \text{ T}}$$

Because **E** and **B** must be perpendicular to each other and perpendicular to the direction of wave propagation (x in this case), we conclude that **B** is in the z direction.

(C) Write expressions for the space–time variation of the components of the electric and magnetic fields for this wave.

Solution We can apply Equations 34.11 and 34.12 directly:

$$E = E_{\text{max}} \cos(kx - \omega t) = (750 \text{ N/C}) \cos(kx - \omega t)$$
$$B = B_{\text{max}} \cos(kx - \omega t) = (2.50 \times 10^{-6} \text{ T}) \cos(kx - \omega t)$$

where

$$\omega = 2\pi f = 2\pi (4.00 \times 10^7 \text{ s}^{-1}) = 2.51 \times 10^8 \text{ rad/s}$$
$$k = \frac{2\pi}{\lambda} = \frac{2\pi}{7.50 \text{ m}} = 0.838 \text{ rad/m}$$

Explore electromagnetic waves of different frequencies at the Interactive Worked Example link at **http://www.pse6.com.**

Derivation of Equations 34.6 and 34.7

To derive Equation 34.6, we start with Faraday's law, Equation 34.3:

$$\oint \mathbf{E} \cdot d\mathbf{s} = -\frac{d\Phi_B}{dt}$$

Let us again assume that the electromagnetic wave is traveling in the x direction, with the electric field **E** in the positive y direction and the magnetic field **B** in the positive z direction.

Consider a rectangle of width dx and height ℓ lying in the xy plane, as shown in Figure 34.5. To apply Equation 34.3, we must first evaluate the line integral of $\mathbf{E} \cdot d\mathbf{s}$ around this rectangle. The contributions from the top and bottom of the rectangle are zero because $\mathbf{E}$ is perpendicular to $d\mathbf{s}$ for these paths. We can express the electric field on the right side of the rectangle as

$$E(x + dx, t) \approx E(x, t) + \frac{dE}{dx}\bigg]_{t\,\text{constant}} dx = E(x, t) + \frac{\partial E}{\partial x}\, dx$$

while the field on the left side[2] is simply $E(x, t)$. Therefore, the line integral over this rectangle is approximately

$$\oint \mathbf{E} \cdot d\mathbf{s} = [E(x + dx, t)]\ell - [E(x, t)]\ell \approx \ell \left(\frac{\partial E}{\partial x}\right) dx \qquad (34.15)$$

Because the magnetic field is in the z direction, the magnetic flux through the rectangle of area $\ell\, dx$ is approximately $\Phi_B = B\ell\, dx$. (This assumes that dx is very small compared with the wavelength of the wave.) Taking the time derivative of the magnetic flux gives

$$\frac{d\Phi_B}{dt} = \ell\, dx\, \frac{dB}{dt}\bigg]_{x\,\text{constant}} = \ell\, dx\, \frac{\partial B}{\partial t} \qquad (34.16)$$

Substituting Equations 34.15 and 34.16 into Equation 34.3 gives

$$\ell \left(\frac{\partial E}{\partial x}\right) dx = -\ell\, dx\, \frac{\partial B}{\partial t}$$

$$\frac{\partial E}{\partial x} = -\frac{\partial B}{\partial t}$$

This expression is Equation 34.6.

In a similar manner, we can verify Equation 34.7 by starting with Maxwell's fourth equation in empty space (Eq. 34.5). In this case, the line integral of $\mathbf{B} \cdot d\mathbf{s}$ is evaluated around a rectangle lying in the xz plane and having width dx and length ℓ, as in Figure 34.6. Noting that the magnitude of the magnetic field changes from $B(x, t)$ to $B(x + dx, t)$ over the width dx and that the direction in which we take the line integral is as shown in Figure 34.6, the line integral over this rectangle is found to be approximately

$$\oint \mathbf{B} \cdot d\mathbf{s} = [B(x, t)]\ell - [B(x + dx, t)]\ell \approx -\ell \left(\frac{\partial B}{\partial x}\right) dx \qquad (34.17)$$

The electric flux through the rectangle is $\Phi_E = E\ell\, dx$, which, when differentiated with respect to time, gives

$$\frac{\partial \Phi_E}{\partial t} = \ell\, dx\, \frac{\partial E}{\partial t} \qquad (34.18)$$

Substituting Equations 34.17 and 34.18 into Equation 34.5 gives

$$-\ell \left(\frac{\partial B}{\partial x}\right) dx = \mu_0 \epsilon_0 \ell\, dx \left(\frac{\partial E}{\partial t}\right)$$

$$\frac{\partial B}{\partial x} = -\mu_0 \epsilon_0 \frac{\partial E}{\partial t}$$

which is Equation 34.7.

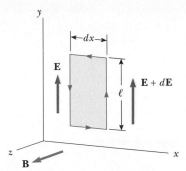

Figure 34.5 At an instant when a plane wave moving in the $+x$ direction passes through a rectangular path of width dx lying in the xy plane, the electric field in the y direction varies from $\mathbf{E}$ to $\mathbf{E} + d\mathbf{E}$. This spatial variation in $\mathbf{E}$ gives rise to a time-varying magnetic field along the z direction, according to Equation 34.6.

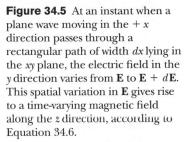
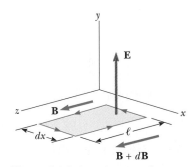

Figure 34.6 At an instant when a plane wave passes through a rectangular path of width dx lying in the xz plane, the magnetic field in the z direction varies from $\mathbf{B}$ to $\mathbf{B} + d\mathbf{B}$. This spatial variation in $\mathbf{B}$ gives rise to a time-varying electric field along the y direction, according to Equation 34.7.

---

[2]   Because dE/dx in this equation is expressed as the change in E with x at a given instant t, dE/dx is equivalent to the partial derivative $\partial E/\partial x$. Likewise, dB/dt means the change in B with time at a particular position x, so in Equation 34.16 we can replace dB/dt with $\partial B/\partial t$.

34.3   Energy Carried by Electromagnetic Waves

Electromagnetic waves carry energy, and as they propagate through space they can transfer energy to objects placed in their path. The rate of flow of energy in an electromagnetic wave is described by a vector **S**, called the **Poynting vector,** which is defined by the expression

Poynting vector

$$\mathbf{S} \equiv \frac{1}{\mu_0} \mathbf{E} \times \mathbf{B} \tag{34.19}$$

The magnitude of the Poynting vector represents the rate at which energy flows through a unit surface area perpendicular to the direction of wave propagation. Thus, the magnitude of the Poynting vector represents *power per unit area*. The direction of the vector is along the direction of wave propagation (Fig. 34.7). The SI units of the Poynting vector are $\text{J/s} \cdot \text{m}^2 = \text{W/m}^2$.

As an example, let us evaluate the magnitude of **S** for a plane electromagnetic wave where $|\mathbf{E} \times \mathbf{B}| = EB$. In this case,

$$S = \frac{EB}{\mu_0} \tag{34.20}$$

Because $B = E/c$, we can also express this as

$$S = \frac{E^2}{\mu_0 c} = \frac{c}{\mu_0} B^2$$

These equations for S apply at any instant of time and represent the *instantaneous* rate at which energy is passing through a unit area.

What is of greater interest for a sinusoidal plane electromagnetic wave is the time average of S over one or more cycles, which is called the *wave intensity I*. (We discussed the intensity of sound waves in Chapter 17.) When this average is taken, we obtain an expression involving the time average of $\cos^2(kx - \omega t)$, which equals $\frac{1}{2}$. Hence, the average value of S (in other words, the intensity of the wave) is

Wave intensity

$$I = S_{\text{av}} = \frac{E_{\max} B_{\max}}{2\mu_0} = \frac{E_{\max}^2}{2\mu_0 c} = \frac{c}{2\mu_0} B_{\max}^2 \tag{34.21}$$

Recall that the energy per unit volume, which is the instantaneous energy density u_E associated with an electric field, is given by Equation 26.13,

$$u_E = \tfrac{1}{2} \epsilon_0 E^2$$

and that the instantaneous energy density u_B associated with a magnetic field is given by Equation 32.14:

$$u_B = \frac{B^2}{2\mu_0}$$

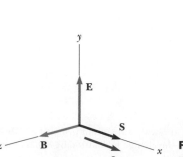

Figure 34.7 The Poynting vector **S** for a plane electromagnetic wave is along the direction of wave propagation.

Because E and B vary with time for an electromagnetic wave, the energy densities also vary with time. When we use the relationships $B = E/c$ and $c = 1/\sqrt{\epsilon_0\mu_0}$, the expression for u_B becomes

$$u_B = \frac{(E/c)^2}{2\mu_0} = \frac{\epsilon_0\mu_0}{2\mu_0}E^2 = \tfrac{1}{2}\epsilon_0 E^2$$

Comparing this result with the expression for u_E, we see that

$$u_B = u_E = \tfrac{1}{2}\epsilon_0 E^2 = \frac{B^2}{2\mu_0}$$

That is, **the instantaneous energy density associated with the magnetic field of an electromagnetic wave equals the instantaneous energy density associated with the electric field.** Hence, in a given volume the energy is equally shared by the two fields.

The **total instantaneous energy density** u is equal to the sum of the energy densities associated with the electric and magnetic fields:

$$u = u_E + u_B = \epsilon_0 E^2 = \frac{B^2}{\mu_0}$$

◀ Total instantaneous energy density of an electromagnetic wave

When this total instantaneous energy density is averaged over one or more cycles of an electromagnetic wave, we again obtain a factor of $\tfrac{1}{2}$. Hence, for any electromagnetic wave, the total average energy per unit volume is

$$u_{av} = \epsilon_0 (E^2)_{av} = \tfrac{1}{2}\epsilon_0 E_{max}^2 = \frac{B_{max}^2}{2\mu_0} \qquad (34.22)$$

◀ Average energy density of an electromagnetic wave

Comparing this result with Equation 34.21 for the average value of S, we see that

$$I = S_{av} = cu_{av} \qquad (34.23)$$

In other words, **the intensity of an electromagnetic wave equals the average energy density multiplied by the speed of light.**

Quick Quiz 34.2 An electromagnetic wave propagates in the $-y$ direction. The electric field at a point in space is momentarily oriented in the $+x$ direction. The magnetic field at that point is momentarily oriented in the (a) $-x$ direction (b) $+y$ direction (c) $+z$ direction (d) $-z$ direction.

Quick Quiz 34.3 Which of the following is constant for a plane electromagnetic wave? (a) magnitude of the Poynting vector (b) energy density u_E (c) energy density u_B (d) wave intensity.

Example 34.2   Fields on the Page

Estimate the maximum magnitudes of the electric and magnetic fields of the light that is incident on this page because of the visible light coming from your desk lamp. Treat the bulb as a point source of electromagnetic radiation that is 5% efficient at transforming energy coming in by electrical transmission to energy leaving by visible light.

Solution Recall from Equation 17.7 that the wave intensity I a distance r from a point source is $I = \mathscr{P}_{av}/4\pi r^2$, where $\mathscr{P}_{av}$ is the average power output of the source and $4\pi r^2$ is the area of a sphere of radius r centered on the source. Because

the intensity of an electromagnetic wave is also given by Equation 34.21, we have

$$I = \frac{\mathscr{P}_{av}}{4\pi r^2} = \frac{E_{max}^2}{2\mu_0 c}$$

We must now make some assumptions about numbers to enter in this equation. If we have a 60-W lightbulb, its output at 5% efficiency is approximately 3.0 W by visible light. (The remaining energy transfers out of the bulb by conduction and invisible radiation.) A reasonable distance from the bulb to the page might be 0.30 m. Thus, we have

$$E_{max} = \sqrt{\frac{\mu_0 c \mathcal{P}_{av}}{2\pi r^2}}$$

$$= \sqrt{\frac{(4\pi \times 10^{-7} \, \text{T} \cdot \text{m/A})(3.00 \times 10^8 \, \text{m/s})(3.0 \, \text{W})}{2\pi(0.30 \, \text{m})^2}}$$

$$= \boxed{45 \, \text{V/m}}$$

From Equation 34.14,

$$B_{max} = \frac{E_{max}}{c} = \frac{45 \, \text{V/m}}{3.00 \times 10^8 \, \text{m/s}} = \boxed{1.5 \times 10^{-7} \, \text{T}}$$

This value is two orders of magnitude smaller than the Earth's magnetic field, which, unlike the magnetic field in the light wave from your desk lamp, is not oscillating.

34.4 Momentum and Radiation Pressure

Electromagnetic waves transport linear momentum as well as energy. It follows that, as this momentum is absorbed by some surface, pressure is exerted on the surface. We shall assume in this discussion that the electromagnetic wave strikes the surface at normal incidence and transports a total energy U to the surface in a time interval Δt. Maxwell showed that, if the surface absorbs all the incident energy U in this time interval (as does a black body, introduced in Section 20.7), the total momentum $\mathbf{p}$ transported to the surface has a magnitude

Momentum transported to a perfectly absorbing surface

$$p = \frac{U}{c} \qquad \text{(complete absorption)} \qquad (34.24)$$

The pressure exerted on the surface is defined as force per unit area F/A. Let us combine this with Newton's second law:

$$P = \frac{F}{A} = \frac{1}{A}\frac{dp}{dt}$$

⚠ PITFALL PREVENTION

34.5 So Many p's

We have p for momentum and P for pressure, and these are both related to $\mathcal{P}$ for power! Be sure you keep these all straight.

If we now replace p, the momentum transported to the surface by radiation, from Equation 34.24, we have

$$P = \frac{1}{A}\frac{dp}{dt} = \frac{1}{A}\frac{d}{dt}\left(\frac{U}{c}\right) = \frac{1}{c}\frac{(dU/dt)}{A}$$

We recognize $(dU/dt)/A$ as the rate at which energy is arriving at the surface per unit area, which is the magnitude of the Poynting vector. Thus, the radiation pressure P exerted on the perfectly absorbing surface is

Radiation pressure exerted on a perfectly absorbing surface

$$P = \frac{S}{c} \qquad (34.25)$$

If the surface is a perfect reflector (such as a mirror) and incidence is normal, then the momentum transported to the surface in a time interval Δt is twice that given by Equation 34.24. That is, the momentum transferred to the surface by the incoming light is $p = U/c$, and that transferred by the reflected light also is $p = U/c$. Therefore,

$$p = \frac{2U}{c} \qquad \text{(complete reflection)} \qquad (34.26)$$

The momentum delivered to a surface having a reflectivity somewhere between these two extremes has a value between U/c and $2U/c$, depending on the properties of the surface. Finally, the radiation pressure exerted on a perfectly reflecting surface for normal incidence of the wave is[3]

Radiation pressure exerted on a perfectly reflecting surface

$$P = \frac{2S}{c} \qquad (34.27)$$

---

[3] For oblique incidence on a perfectly reflecting surface, the momentum transferred is $(2U \cos\theta)/c$ and the pressure is $P = (2S \cos^2\theta)/c$ where θ is the angle between the normal to the surface and the direction of wave propagation.

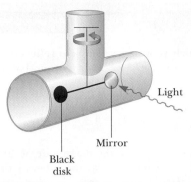

Figure 34.8 An apparatus for measuring the pressure exerted by light. In practice, the system is contained in a high vacuum.

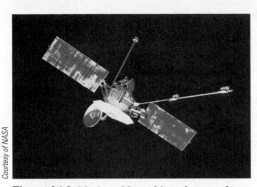

Figure 34.9 Mariner 10 used its solar panels to "sail on sunlight."

Although radiation pressures are very small (about $5 \times 10^{-6} \, \text{N/m}^2$ for direct sunlight), they have been measured with torsion balances such as the one shown in Figure 34.8. A mirror (a perfect reflector) and a black disk (a perfect absorber) are connected by a horizontal rod suspended from a fine fiber. Normal-incidence light striking the black disk is completely absorbed, so all of the momentum of the light is transferred to the disk. Normal-incidence light striking the mirror is totally reflected, and hence the momentum transferred to the mirror is twice as great as that transferred to the disk. The radiation pressure is determined by measuring the angle through which the horizontal connecting rod rotates. The apparatus must be placed in a high vacuum to eliminate the effects of air currents.

NASA is exploring the possibility of *solar sailing* as a low-cost means of sending spacecraft to the planets. Large sheets would experience radiation pressure from sunlight and would be used in much the way canvas sheets are used on earthbound sailboats. In 1973 NASA engineers took advantage of the momentum of the sunlight striking the solar panels of Mariner 10 (Fig. 34.9) to make small course corrections when the spacecraft's fuel supply was running low. (This procedure was carried out when the spacecraft was in the vicinity of the planet Mercury. Would it have worked as well near Pluto?)

Quick Quiz 34.4 To maximize the radiation pressure on the sails of a spacecraft using solar sailing, should the sheets be (a) very black to absorb as much sunlight as possible or (b) very shiny, to reflect as much sunlight as possible?

Quick Quiz 34.5 In an apparatus such as that in Figure 34.8, the disks are illuminated uniformly over their areas. Suppose the black disk is replaced by one with half the radius. Which of the following are different after the disk is replaced? (a) radiation pressure on the disk, (b) radiation force on the disk, (c) radiation momentum delivered to the disk in a given time interval.

Conceptual Example 34.3   Sweeping the Solar System

A great amount of dust exists in interplanetary space. Although in theory these dust particles can vary in size from molecular size to much larger, very little of the dust in our solar system is smaller than about 0.2 μm. Why?

Solution The dust particles are subject to two significant forces—the gravitational force that draws them toward the Sun and the radiation-pressure force that pushes them away from the Sun. The gravitational force is proportional to the cube of the radius of a spherical dust particle because it is proportional to the mass and therefore to the volume $4\pi r^3/3$ of the particle. The radiation pressure is proportional to the square of the radius because it depends on the planar cross section of the particle. For large particles, the gravitational force is greater than the force from radiation pressure. For particles having radii less than about 0.2 μm, the radiation-pressure force is greater than the gravitational force, and as a result these particles are swept out of the Solar System.

Example 34.4   Pressure from a Laser Pointer   `Interactive`

Many people giving presentations use a laser pointer to direct the attention of the audience to information on a screen. If a 3.0-mW pointer creates a spot on a screen that is 2.0 mm in diameter, determine the radiation pressure on a screen that reflects 70% of the light that strikes it. The power 3.0 mW is a time-averaged value.

Solution In conceptualizing this situation, we do not expect the pressure to be very large. We categorize this as a calculation of radiation pressure using something like Equation 34.25 or Equation 34.27, but complicated by the 70% reflection. To analyze the problem, we begin by determining the magnitude of the beam's Poynting vector. We divide the time-averaged power delivered via the electromagnetic wave by the cross-sectional area of the beam:

$$S_{av} = \frac{\mathcal{P}_{av}}{A} = \frac{\mathcal{P}_{av}}{\pi r^2} = \frac{3.0 \times 10^{-3}\,\text{W}}{\pi \left(\dfrac{2.0 \times 10^{-3}\,\text{m}}{2}\right)^2} = 955\,\text{W/m}^2$$

Now we can determine the radiation pressure from the laser beam. Equation 34.27 indicates that a completely reflected beam would apply an average pressure of $P_{av} = 2S_{av}/c$. We can model the actual reflection as follows. Imagine that the surface absorbs the beam, resulting in pressure $P_{av} = S_{av}/c$. Then the surface emits the beam, resulting in additional pressure $P_{av} = S_{av}/c$. If the surface emits only a fraction f of the beam (so that f is the amount of the incident beam reflected), then the pressure due to the emitted beam is $P_{av} = f\,S_{av}/c$. Thus, the total pressure on the surface due to absorption and re-emission (reflection) is

$$P_{av} = \frac{S_{av}}{c} + f\,\frac{S_{av}}{c} = (1 + f)\,\frac{S_{av}}{c}$$

Notice that if $f = 1$, which represents complete reflection, this equation reduces to Equation 34.27. For a beam that is 70% reflected, the pressure is

$$P_{av} = (1 + 0.70)\,\frac{955\,\text{W/m}^2}{3.0 \times 10^8\,\text{m/s}} = \boxed{5.4 \times 10^{-6}\,\text{N/m}^2}$$

To finalize the example, consider first the magnitude of the Poynting vector. This is about the same as the intensity of sunlight at the Earth's surface. (For this reason, it is not safe to shine the beam of a laser pointer into a person's eyes; that may be more dangerous than looking directly at the Sun.) Note also that the pressure has an extremely small value, as expected. (Recall from Section 14.2 that atmospheric pressure is approximately $10^5\,\text{N/m}^2$.)

What If? What if the laser pointer is moved twice as far away from the screen? Does this affect the radiation pressure on the screen?

Answer Because a laser beam is popularly represented as a beam of light with constant cross section, one might be tempted to claim that the intensity of radiation, and therefore the radiation pressure, would be independent of distance from the screen. However, a laser beam does not have a constant cross section at all distances from the source—there is a small but measurable divergence of the beam. If the laser is moved farther away from the screen, the area of illumination on the screen will increase, decreasing the intensity. In turn, this will reduce the radiation pressure.

In addition, the doubled distance from the screen will result in more loss of energy from the beam due to scattering from air molecules and dust particles as the light travels from the laser to the screen. This will further reduce the radiation pressure.

At the Interactive Worked Example link at **http://www.pse6.com,** *you can investigate the pressure on the screen for various laser and screen parameters.*

Example 34.5   Solar Energy

As noted in the preceding example, the Sun delivers about $10^3\,\text{W/m}^2$ of energy to the Earth's surface via electromagnetic radiation.

(A) Calculate the total power that is incident on a roof of dimensions 8.00 m × 20.0 m.

Solution We assume that the average magnitude of the Poynting vector for solar radiation at the surface of the Earth is $S_{av} = 1\,000\,\text{W/m}^2$; this represents the power per unit area, or the light intensity. Assuming that the radiation is incident normal to the roof, we obtain

$$\mathcal{P}_{av} = S_{av}A = (1\,000\,\text{W/m}^2)(8.00 \times 20.0\,\text{m}^2)$$

$$= \boxed{1.60 \times 10^5\,\text{W}}$$

(B) Determine the radiation pressure and the radiation force exerted on the roof, assuming that the roof covering is a perfect absorber.

Solution Using Equation 34.25 with $S_{av} = 1\,000\,\text{W/m}^2$, we find that the radiation pressure is

$$P_{av} = \frac{S_{av}}{c} = \frac{1\,000\,\text{W/m}^2}{3.00 \times 10^8\,\text{m/s}} = \boxed{3.33 \times 10^{-6}\,\text{N/m}^2}$$

Because pressure equals force per unit area, this corresponds to a radiation force of

$$F = P_{av}A = (3.33 \times 10^{-6}\,\text{N/m}^2)(160\,\text{m}^2)$$

$$= \boxed{5.33 \times 10^{-4}\,\text{N}}$$

34.5 Production of Electromagnetic Waves by an Antenna

Neither stationary charges nor steady currents can produce electromagnetic waves. Whenever the current in a wire changes with time, however, the wire emits electromagnetic radiation. **The fundamental mechanism responsible for this radiation is the acceleration of a charged particle. Whenever a charged particle accelerates, it must radiate energy.**

Let us consider the production of electromagnetic waves by a *half-wave antenna*. In this arrangement, two conducting rods are connected to a source of alternating voltage (such as an *LC* oscillator), as shown in Figure 34.10. The length of each rod is equal to one quarter of the wavelength of the radiation that will be emitted when the oscillator operates at frequency *f*. The oscillator forces charges to accelerate back and forth between the two rods. Figure 34.10 shows the configuration of the electric and magnetic fields at some instant when the current is upward. The electric field lines, due to the separation of charges in the upper and lower portions of the antenna, resemble those of an electric dipole. (As a result, this type of antenna is sometimes called a *dipole antenna*.) Because these charges are continuously oscillating between the two rods, the antenna can be approximated by an oscillating electric dipole. The magnetic field lines, due to the current representing the movement of charges between the ends of the antenna, form concentric circles around the antenna and are perpendicular to the electric field lines at all points. The magnetic field is zero at all points along the axis of the antenna. Furthermore, **E** and **B** are 90° out of phase in time—for example, the current is zero when the charges at the outer ends of the rods are at a maximum.

At the two points where the magnetic field is shown in Figure 34.10, the Poynting vector **S** is directed radially outward. This indicates that energy is flowing away from the antenna at this instant. At later times, the fields and the Poynting vector reverse direction as the current alternates. Because **E** and **B** are 90° out of phase at points near the dipole, the net energy flow is zero. From this, we might conclude (incorrectly) that no energy is radiated by the dipole.

However, we find that energy is indeed radiated. Because the dipole fields fall off as $1/r^3$ (as shown in Example 23.6 for the electric field of a static dipole), they are negligible at great distances from the antenna. At these great distances, something else causes a type of radiation different from that close to the antenna. The source of this radiation is the continuous induction of an electric field by the time-varying magnetic field and the induction of a magnetic field by the time-varying electric field, predicted by Equations 34.3 and 34.4. The electric and magnetic fields produced in this manner are in phase with each other and vary as $1/r$. The result is an outward flow of energy at all times.

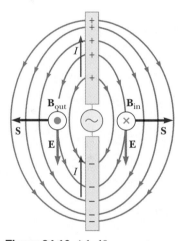

Figure 34.10 A half-wave antenna consists of two metal rods connected to an alternating voltage source. This diagram shows **E** and **B** at an arbitrary instant when the current is upward. Note that the electric field lines resemble those of a dipole (shown in Fig. 23.22).

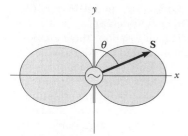

Figure 34.11 Angular dependence of the intensity of radiation produced by an oscillating electric dipole. The distance from the origin to a point on the edge of the gray shape is proportional to the intensity of radiation.

The angular dependence of the radiation intensity produced by a dipole antenna is shown in Figure 34.11. Note that the intensity and the power radiated are a maximum in a plane that is perpendicular to the antenna and passing through its midpoint. Furthermore, the power radiated is zero along the antenna's axis. A mathematical solution to Maxwell's equations for the dipole antenna shows that the intensity of the radiation varies as $(\sin^2 \theta)/r^2$, where θ is measured from the axis of the antenna.

Electromagnetic waves can also induce currents in a receiving antenna. The response of a dipole receiving antenna at a given position is a maximum when the antenna axis is parallel to the electric field at that point and zero when the axis is perpendicular to the electric field.

Quick Quiz 34.6 If the antenna in Figure 34.10 represents the source of a distant radio station, rank the following points in terms of the intensity of the radiation, from greatest to least: (a) a distance d to the right of the antenna (b) a distance $2d$ to the left of the antenna (c) a distance $2d$ in front of the antenna (out of the page) (d) a distance d above the antenna (toward the top of the page).

Quick Quiz 34.7 If the antenna in Figure 34.10 represents the source of a distant radio station, what would be the best orientation for your portable radio antenna located to the right of the figure—(a) up–down along the page, (b) left–right along the page, or (c) perpendicular to the page?

34.6 The Spectrum of Electromagnetic Waves

The various types of electromagnetic waves are listed in Figure 34.12, which shows the **electromagnetic spectrum.** Note the wide ranges of frequencies and wavelengths. No sharp dividing point exists between one type of wave and the next. Remember that **all forms of the various types of radiation are produced by the same phenomenon—accelerating charges.** The names given to the types of waves are simply for convenience in describing the region of the spectrum in which they lie.

Radio waves, whose wavelengths range from more than 10^4 m to about 0.1 m, are the result of charges accelerating through conducting wires. They are generated by such electronic devices as LC oscillators and are used in radio and television communication systems.

Microwaves have wavelengths ranging from approximately 0.3 m to 10^{-4} m and are also generated by electronic devices. Because of their short wavelengths, they are well suited for radar systems and for studying the atomic and molecular properties of matter. Microwave ovens are an interesting domestic application of these waves. It has been suggested that solar energy could be harnessed by beaming microwaves to the Earth from a solar collector in space.

Infrared waves have wavelengths ranging from approximately 10^{-3} m to the longest wavelength of visible light, 7×10^{-7} m. These waves, produced by molecules and room-temperature objects, are readily absorbed by most materials. The infrared (IR) energy absorbed by a substance appears as internal energy because the energy agitates the atoms of the object, increasing their vibrational or translational motion, which results in a temperature increase. Infrared radiation has practical and scientific applications in many areas, including physical therapy, IR photography, and vibrational spectroscopy.

Visible light, the most familiar form of electromagnetic waves, is the part of the electromagnetic spectrum that the human eye can detect. Light is produced by the rearrangement of electrons in atoms and molecules. The various wavelengths of visible

▲ **PITFALL PREVENTION**

34.6 "Heat Rays"

Infrared rays are often called "heat rays." This is a misnomer. While infrared radiation is used to raise or maintain temperature, as in the case of keeping food warm with "heat lamps" at a fast-food restaurant, all wavelengths of electromagnetic radiation carry energy that can cause the temperature of a system to increase. As an example, consider a potato baking in your microwave oven.

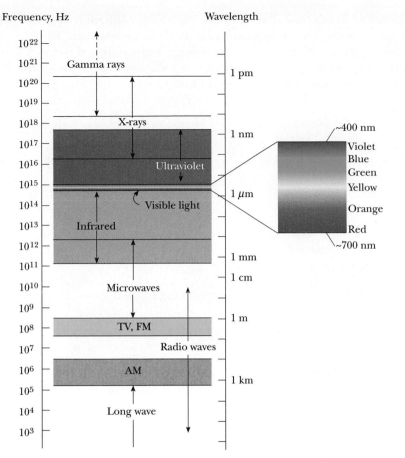

Wearing sunglasses that do not block ultraviolet (UV) light is worse for your eyes than wearing no sunglasses. The lenses of any sunglasses absorb some visible light, thus causing the wearer's pupils to dilate. If the glasses do not also block UV light, then more damage may be done to the lens of the eye because of the dilated pupils. If you wear no sunglasses at all, your pupils are contracted, you squint, and much less UV light enters your eyes. High-quality sunglasses block nearly all the eye-damaging UV light.

Figure 34.12 The electromagnetic spectrum. Note the overlap between adjacent wave types. The expanded view to the right shows details of the visible spectrum.

light, which correspond to different colors, range from red ($\lambda \approx 7 \times 10^{-7}$ m) to violet ($\lambda \approx 4 \times 10^{-7}$ m). The sensitivity of the human eye is a function of wavelength, being a maximum at a wavelength of about 5.5×10^{-7} m. With this in mind, why do you suppose tennis balls often have a yellow-green color?

Ultraviolet waves cover wavelengths ranging from approximately 4×10^{-7} m to 6×10^{-10} m. The Sun is an important source of ultraviolet (UV) light, which is the main cause of sunburn. Sunscreen lotions are transparent to visible light but absorb most UV light. The higher a sunscreen's solar protection factor (SPF), the greater the percentage of UV light absorbed. Ultraviolet rays have also been implicated in the formation of cataracts, a clouding of the lens inside the eye.

Most of the UV light from the Sun is absorbed by ozone (O_3) molecules in the Earth's upper atmosphere, in a layer called the stratosphere. This ozone shield converts lethal high-energy UV radiation to infrared radiation, which in turn warms the stratosphere. Recently, a great deal of controversy has arisen concerning the possible depletion of the protective ozone layer as a result of the chemicals emitted from aerosol spray cans and used as refrigerants.

X-rays have wavelengths in the range from approximately 10^{-8} m to 10^{-12} m. The most common source of x-rays is the stopping of high-energy electrons upon bombarding a metal target. X-rays are used as a diagnostic tool in medicine and as a treatment for certain forms of cancer. Because x-rays damage or destroy living tissues and organisms, care must be taken to avoid unnecessary exposure or overexposure. X-rays are also used in the study of crystal structure because x-ray wavelengths are comparable to the atomic separation distances in solids (about 0.1 nm).

Gamma rays are electromagnetic waves emitted by radioactive nuclei (such as ^{60}Co and ^{137}Cs) and during certain nuclear reactions. High-energy gamma rays are a component of cosmic rays that enter the Earth's atmosphere from space. They have wavelengths ranging from approximately 10^{-10} m to less than 10^{-14} m. They are highly penetrating and produce serious damage when absorbed by living tissues. Consequently, those working near such dangerous radiation must be protected with heavily absorbing materials, such as thick layers of lead.

Quick Quiz 34.8 In many kitchens, a microwave oven is used to cook food. The frequency of the microwaves is on the order of 10^{10} Hz. The wavelengths of these microwaves are on the order of (a) kilometers (b) meters (c) centimeters (d) micrometers.

Quick Quiz 34.9 A radio wave of frequency on the order of 10^5 Hz is used to carry a sound wave with a frequency on the order of 10^3 Hz. The wavelength of this radio wave is on the order of (a) kilometers (b) meters (c) centimeters (d) micrometers.

Example 34.6 A Half-Wave Antenna

A half-wave antenna works on the principle that the optimum length of the antenna is half the wavelength of the radiation being received. What is the optimum length of a car antenna when it receives a signal of frequency 94.7 MHz?

Solution Equation 34.13 tells us that the wavelength of the signal is

$$\lambda = \frac{3.00 \times 10^8 \text{ m/s}}{9.47 \times 10^7 \text{ Hz}} = \boxed{3.16 \text{ m}}$$

Thus, to operate most efficiently, the antenna should have a length of $(3.16 \text{ m})/2 = 1.58$ m. For practical reasons, car antennas are usually one-quarter wavelength in size.

SUMMARY

Take a practice test for this chapter by clicking on the Practice Test link at http://www.pse6.com.

Electromagnetic waves, which are predicted by Maxwell's equations, have the following properties:

• The electric field and the magnetic field each satisfy a wave equation. These two wave equations, which can be obtained from Maxwell's third and fourth equations, are

$$\frac{\partial^2 E}{\partial x^2} = \mu_0 \epsilon_0 \frac{\partial^2 E}{\partial t^2} \qquad (34.8)$$

$$\frac{\partial^2 B}{\partial x^2} = \mu_0 \epsilon_0 \frac{\partial^2 B}{\partial t^2} \qquad (34.9)$$

• The waves travel through a vacuum with the speed of light c, where

$$c = \frac{1}{\sqrt{\mu_0 \epsilon_0}} = 3.00 \times 10^8 \text{ m/s} \qquad (34.10)$$

• The electric and magnetic fields are perpendicular to each other and perpendicular to the direction of wave propagation. (Hence, electromagnetic waves are transverse waves.)

• The instantaneous magnitudes of **E** and **B** in an electromagnetic wave are related by the expression

$$\frac{E}{B} = c \qquad (34.14)$$

- The waves carry energy. The rate of flow of energy crossing a unit area is described by the Poynting vector **S**, where

$$\mathbf{S} \equiv \frac{1}{\mu_0} \mathbf{E} \times \mathbf{B} \tag{34.19}$$

- Electromagnetic waves carry momentum and hence exert pressure on surfaces. If an electromagnetic wave whose Poynting vector is **S** is completely absorbed by a surface upon which it is normally incident, the radiation pressure on that surface is

$$P = \frac{S}{c} \quad \text{(complete absorption)} \tag{34.25}$$

If the surface totally reflects a normally incident wave, the pressure is doubled.

The electric and magnetic fields of a sinusoidal plane electromagnetic wave propagating in the positive x direction can be written

$$E = E_{max} \cos(kx - \omega t) \tag{34.11}$$

$$B = B_{max} \cos(kx - \omega t) \tag{34.12}$$

where ω is the angular frequency of the wave and k is the angular wave number. These equations represent special solutions to the wave equations for E and B. The wavelength and frequency of electromagnetic waves are related by

$$\lambda = \frac{c}{f} = \frac{3.00 \times 10^8 \text{ m/s}}{f} \tag{34.13}$$

The average value of the Poynting vector for a plane electromagnetic wave has a magnitude

$$S_{av} = \frac{E_{max} B_{max}}{2\mu_0} = \frac{E_{max}^2}{2\mu_0 c} = \frac{c}{2\mu_0} B_{max}^2 \tag{34.21}$$

The intensity of a sinusoidal plane electromagnetic wave equals the average value of the Poynting vector taken over one or more cycles.

The electromagnetic spectrum includes waves covering a broad range of wavelengths, from long radio waves at more than 10^4 m to gamma rays at less than 10^{-14} m.

QUESTIONS

1. Radio stations often advertise "instant news." If they mean that you can hear the news the instant they speak it, is their claim true? About how long would it take for a message to travel across this country by radio waves, assuming that the waves could be detected at this range?

2. Light from the Sun takes approximately 8.3 min to reach the Earth. During this time interval the Earth has continued to rotate on its axis. How far is the actual direction of the Sun from its image in the sky?

3. When light (or other electromagnetic radiation) travels across a given region, what is it that oscillates? What is it that is transported?

4. Do all current-carrying conductors emit electromagnetic waves? Explain.

5. What is the fundamental source of electromagnetic radiation?

6. If a high-frequency current is passed through a solenoid containing a metallic core, the core becomes warm due to induction. Explain why the material rises in temperature in this situation.

7. Does a wire connected to the terminals of a battery emit electromagnetic waves? Explain.

8. If you charge a comb by running it through your hair and then hold the comb next to a bar magnet, do the electric and magnetic fields produced constitute an electromagnetic wave?

9. List as many similarities and differences between sound waves and light waves as you can.

10. Describe the physical significance of the Poynting vector.

11. For a given incident energy of an electromagnetic wave, why is the radiation pressure on a perfectly reflecting surface twice as great as that on a perfect absorbing surface?

12. Before the advent of cable television and satellite dishes, city dwellers often used "rabbit ears" atop their sets (Fig. Q34.12). Certain orientations of the receiving antenna on a television set give better reception than others. Furthermore, the best orientation varies from station to station. Explain.

George Semple

Figure Q34.12 Questions 12, 14, 15, and 16, and Problem 49. The V-shaped pair of long rods is the VHF antenna and the loop is the UHF antenna.

13. Often when you touch the indoor antenna on a radio or television receiver, the reception instantly improves. Why?

14. Explain how the (dipole) VHF antenna of a television set works. (See Fig. Q34.12.)

15. Explain how the UHF (loop) antenna of a television set works. (See Fig. Q34.12.)

16. Explain why the voltage induced in a UHF (loop) antenna depends on the frequency of the signal, while the voltage in a VHF (dipole) antenna does not. (See Fig. Q34.12.)

17. Electrical engineers often speak of the radiation resistance of an antenna. What do you suppose they mean by this phrase?

18. What does a radio wave do to the charges in the receiving antenna to provide a signal for your car radio?

19. An empty plastic or glass dish being removed from a microwave oven is cool to the touch. How can this be possible? (Assume that your electric bill has been paid.)

20. Why should an infrared photograph of a person look different from a photograph taken with visible light?

21. Suppose that a creature from another planet had eyes that were sensitive to infrared radiation. Describe what the alien would see if it looked around the room you are now in. In particular, what would be bright and what would be dim?

22. A welder must wear protective glasses and clothing to prevent eye damage and sunburn. What does this imply about the nature of the light produced by the welding?

23. A home microwave oven uses electromagnetic waves with a wavelength of about 12.2 cm. Some 2.4-GHz cordless telephones suffer noisy interference when a microwave oven is used nearby. Locate the waves used by both devices on the electromagnetic spectrum. Do you expect them to interfere with each other?

PROBLEMS

1, 2, 3 = straightforward, intermediate, challenging ☐ = full solution available in the *Student Solutions Manual and Study Guide*

🚀 = coached solution with hints available at http://www.pse6.com 🖥 = computer useful in solving problem

▨ = paired numerical and symbolic problems

Section 34.1 Maxwell's Equations and Hertz's Discoveries

Note: Assume that the medium is vacuum unless specified otherwise.

1. A very long, thin rod carries electric charge with the linear density 35.0 nC/m. It lies along the x axis and moves in the x direction at a speed of 15.0 Mm/s. (a) Find the electric field the rod creates at the point (0, 20.0 cm, 0). (b) Find the magnetic field it creates at the same point.

(c) Find the force exerted on an electron at this point, moving with a velocity of $(240\hat{\mathbf{i}})$ Mm/s.

Section 34.2 Plane Electromagnetic Waves

2. (a) The distance to the North Star, Polaris, is approximately 6.44×10^{18} m. If Polaris were to burn out today, in what year would we see it disappear? (b) How long does it take for sunlight to reach the Earth? (c) How long does it take for a microwave radar signal to travel from the Earth to the Moon and back? (d) How long does it take for a radio wave to travel once around the Earth in a great circle, close to the planet's surface? (e) How long

does it take for light to reach you from a lightning stroke 10.0 km away?

3. The speed of an electromagnetic wave traveling in a transparent nonmagnetic substance is $v = 1/\sqrt{\kappa\mu_0\epsilon_0}$, where κ is the dielectric constant of the substance. Determine the speed of light in water, which has a dielectric constant at optical frequencies of 1.78.

4. An electromagnetic wave in vacuum has an electric field amplitude of 220 V/m. Calculate the amplitude of the corresponding magnetic field.

5. Figure 34.3 shows a plane electromagnetic sinusoidal wave propagating in the x direction. Suppose that the wavelength is 50.0 m, and the electric field vibrates in the xy plane with an amplitude of 22.0 V/m. Calculate (a) the frequency of the wave and (b) the magnitude and direction of **B** when the electric field has its maximum value in the negative y direction. (c) Write an expression for **B** with the correct unit vector, with numerical values for B_{max}, k, and ω, and with its magnitude in the form

$$B = B_{max} \cos(kx - \omega t)$$

6. Write down expressions for the electric and magnetic fields of a sinusoidal plane electromagnetic wave having a frequency of 3.00 GHz and traveling in the positive x direction. The amplitude of the electric field is 300 V/m.

7. In SI units, the electric field in an electromagnetic wave is described by

$$E_y = 100 \sin(1.00 \times 10^7 x - \omega t)$$

Find (a) the amplitude of the corresponding magnetic field oscillations, (b) the wavelength λ, and (c) the frequency f.

8. Verify by substitution that the following equations are solutions to Equations 34.8 and 34.9, respectively:

$$E = E_{max} \cos(kx - \omega t)$$
$$B = B_{max} \cos(kx - \omega t)$$

9. **Review problem.** A standing-wave interference pattern is set up by radio waves between two metal sheets 2.00 m apart. This is the shortest distance between the plates that will produce a standing-wave pattern. What is the fundamental frequency?

10. A microwave oven is powered by an electron tube called a magnetron, which generates electromagnetic waves of frequency 2.45 GHz. The microwaves enter the oven and are reflected by the walls. The standing-wave pattern produced in the oven can cook food unevenly, with hot spots in the food at antinodes and cool spots at nodes, so a turntable is often used to rotate the food and distribute the energy. If a microwave oven intended for use with a turntable is instead used with a cooking dish in a fixed position, the antinodes can appear as burn marks on foods such as carrot strips or cheese. The separation distance between the burns is measured to be 6 cm $\pm$ 5%. From these data, calculate the speed of the microwaves.

Section 34.3   Energy Carried by Electromagnetic Waves

11. How much electromagnetic energy per cubic meter is contained in sunlight, if the intensity of sunlight at the Earth's surface under a fairly clear sky is 1 000 W/m²?

12. An AM radio station broadcasts isotropically (equally in all directions) with an average power of 4.00 kW. A dipole receiving antenna 65.0 cm long is at a location 4.00 miles from the transmitter. Compute the amplitude of the emf that is induced by this signal between the ends of the receiving antenna.

13. What is the average magnitude of the Poynting vector 5.00 miles from a radio transmitter broadcasting isotropically with an average power of 250 kW?

14. A monochromatic light source emits 100 W of electromagnetic power uniformly in all directions. (a) Calculate the average electric-field energy density 1.00 m from the source. (b) Calculate the average magnetic-field energy density at the same distance from the source. (c) Find the wave intensity at this location.

15. A community plans to build a facility to convert solar radiation to electrical power. They require 1.00 MW of power, and the system to be installed has an efficiency of 30.0% (that is, 30.0% of the solar energy incident on the surface is converted to useful energy that can power the community). What must be the effective area of a perfectly absorbing surface used in such an installation, assuming sunlight has a constant intensity of 1 000 W/m²?

16. Assuming that the antenna of a 10.0-kW radio station radiates spherical electromagnetic waves, compute the maximum value of the magnetic field 5.00 km from the antenna, and compare this value with the surface magnetic field of the Earth.

17. The filament of an incandescent lamp has a 150-Ω resistance and carries a direct current of 1.00 A. The filament is 8.00 cm long and 0.900 mm in radius. (a) Calculate the Poynting vector at the surface of the filament, associated with the static electric field producing the current and the current's static magnetic field. (b) Find the magnitude of the static electric and magnetic fields at the surface of the filament.

18. One of the weapons being considered for the "Star Wars" antimissile system is a laser that could destroy ballistic missiles. When a high-power laser is used in the Earth's atmosphere, the electric field can ionize the air, turning it into a conducting plasma that reflects the laser light. In dry air at 0°C and 1 atm, electric breakdown occurs for fields with amplitudes above about 3.00 MV/m. (a) What laser beam intensity will produce such a field? (b) At this maximum intensity, what power can be delivered in a cylindrical beam of diameter 5.00 mm?

19. In a region of free space the electric field at an instant of time is $\mathbf{E} = (80.0\hat{\mathbf{i}} + 32.0\hat{\mathbf{j}} - 64.0\hat{\mathbf{k}})$ N/C and the magnetic field is $\mathbf{B} = (0.200\hat{\mathbf{i}} + 0.080\,0\hat{\mathbf{j}} + 0.290\hat{\mathbf{k}})$ μT. (a) Show that the two fields are perpendicular to each other. (b) Determine the Poynting vector for these fields.

20. Let us model the electromagnetic wave in a microwave oven as a plane traveling wave moving to the left, with an intensity of 25.0 kW/m². An oven contains two cubical

containers of small mass, each full of water. One has an edge length of 6.00 cm and the other, 12.0 cm. Energy falls perpendicularly on one face of each container. The water in the smaller container absorbs 70.0% of the energy that falls on it. The water in the larger container absorbs 91.0%. (That is, the fraction 0.3 of the incoming microwave energy passes through a 6-cm thickness of water, and the fraction $(0.3)(0.3) = 0.09$ passes through a 12-cm thickness.) Find the temperature change of the water in each container over a time interval of 480 s. Assume that a negligible amount of energy leaves either container by heat.

21. A lightbulb filament has a resistance of 110 Ω. The bulb is plugged into a standard 120-V (rms) outlet, and emits 1.00% of the electric power delivered to it by electromagnetic radiation of frequency f. Assuming that the bulb is covered with a filter that absorbs all other frequencies, find the amplitude of the magnetic field 1.00 m from the bulb.

22. A certain microwave oven contains a magnetron that has an output of 700 W of microwave power for an electrical input power of 1.40 kW. The microwaves are entirely transferred from the magnetron into the oven chamber through a waveguide, which is a metal tube of rectangular cross section with width 6.83 cm and height 3.81 cm. (a) What is the efficiency of the magnetron? (b) Assuming that the food is absorbing all the microwaves produced by the magnetron and that no energy is reflected back into the waveguide, find the direction and magnitude of the Poynting vector, averaged over time, in the waveguide near the entrance to the oven chamber. (c) What is the maximum electric field at this point?

23. High-power lasers in factories are used to cut through cloth and metal (Fig. P34.23). One such laser has a beam diameter of 1.00 mm and generates an electric field

Figure P34.23 A laser cutting device mounted on a robot arm is being used to cut through a metallic plate.

having an amplitude of 0.700 MV/m at the target. Find (a) the amplitude of the magnetic field produced, (b) the intensity of the laser, and (c) the power delivered by the laser.

24. A 10.0-mW laser has a beam diameter of 1.60 mm. (a) What is the intensity of the light, assuming it is uniform across the circular beam? (b) What is the average energy density of the beam?

25. At one location on the Earth, the rms value of the magnetic field caused by solar radiation is 1.80 μT. From this value calculate (a) the rms electric field due to solar radiation, (b) the average energy density of the solar component of electromagnetic radiation at this location, and (c) the average magnitude of the Poynting vector for the Sun's radiation. (d) Compare the value found in part (c) to the value of the solar intensity given in Example 34.5.

Section 34.4   Momentum and Radiation Pressure

26. A 100-mW laser beam is reflected back upon itself by a mirror. Calculate the force on the mirror.

27. A radio wave transmits 25.0 W/m^2 of power per unit area. A flat surface of area A is perpendicular to the direction of propagation of the wave. Calculate the radiation pressure on it, assuming the surface is a perfect absorber.

28. A possible means of space flight is to place a perfectly reflecting aluminized sheet into orbit around the Earth and then use the light from the Sun to push this "solar sail." Suppose a sail of area 6.00×10^5 m^2 and mass 6 000 kg is placed in orbit facing the Sun. (a) What force is exerted on the sail? (b) What is the sail's acceleration? (c) How long does it take the sail to reach the Moon, 3.84×10^8 m away? Ignore all gravitational effects, assume that the acceleration calculated in part (b) remains constant, and assume a solar intensity of 1 340 W/m^2.

29. A 15.0-mW helium–neon laser ($\lambda = 632.8$ nm) emits a beam of circular cross section with a diameter of 2.00 mm. (a) Find the maximum electric field in the beam. (b) What total energy is contained in a 1.00-m length of the beam? (c) Find the momentum carried by a 1.00-m length of the beam.

30. Given that the intensity of solar radiation incident on the upper atmosphere of the Earth is 1 340 W/m^2, determine (a) the intensity of solar radiation incident on Mars, (b) the total power incident on Mars, and (c) the radiation force that acts on the planet if it absorbs nearly all of the light. (d) Compare this force to the gravitational attraction between Mars and the Sun. (See Table 13.2.)

31. A plane electromagnetic wave has an intensity of 750 W/m^2. A flat, rectangular surface of dimensions 50.0 cm $\times$ 100 cm is placed perpendicular to the direction of the wave. The surface absorbs half of the energy and reflects half. Calculate (a) the total energy absorbed by the surface in 1.00 min and (b) the momentum absorbed in this time.

32. A uniform circular disk of mass 24.0 g and radius 40.0 cm hangs vertically from a fixed, frictionless, horizontal hinge at a point on its circumference. A horizontal beam of electromagnetic radiation with intensity 10.0 MW/m² is incident on the disk in a direction perpendicular to its surface. The disk is perfectly absorbing, and the resulting radiation pressure makes the disk rotate. Find the angle through which the disk rotates as it reaches its new equilibrium position. (Assume that the radiation is *always* perpendicular to the surface of the disk.)

Section 34.5 Production of Electromagnetic Waves by an Antenna

33. Figure 34.10 shows a Hertz antenna (also known as a half-wave antenna, because its length is $\lambda/2$). The antenna is located far enough from the ground that reflections do not significantly affect its radiation pattern. Most AM radio stations, however, use a Marconi antenna, which consists of the top half of a Hertz antenna. The lower end of this (quarter-wave) antenna is connected to Earth ground, and the ground itself serves as the missing lower half. What are the heights of the Marconi antennas for radio stations broadcasting at (a) 560 kHz and (b) 1 600 kHz?

34. Two hand-held radio transceivers with dipole antennas are separated by a large fixed distance. If the transmitting antenna is vertical, what fraction of the maximum received power will appear in the receiving antenna when it is inclined from the vertical by (a) 15.0°? (b) 45.0°? (c) 90.0°?

35. Two radio-transmitting antennas are separated by half the broadcast wavelength and are driven in phase with each other. In which directions are (a) the strongest and (b) the weakest signals radiated?

36. Review problem. Accelerating charges radiate electromagnetic waves. Calculate the wavelength of radiation produced by a proton moving in a circle of radius R perpendicular to a magnetic field of magnitude B.

37. A very large flat sheet carries a uniformly distributed electric current with current per unit width J_s. Example 30.6 demonstrated that the current creates a magnetic field on both sides of the sheet, parallel to the sheet and perpendicular to the current, with magnitude $B = \frac{1}{2}\mu_0 J_s$. If the current oscillates in time according to

$$\mathbf{J}_s = J_{max}(\cos \omega t)\hat{\mathbf{j}} = J_{max}[\cos(-\omega t)]\hat{\mathbf{j}},$$

the sheet radiates an electromagnetic wave as shown in Figure P34.37. The magnetic field of the wave is described by the wave function $\mathbf{B} = \frac{1}{2}\mu_0 J_{max}[\cos(kx - \omega t)]\hat{\mathbf{k}}$. (a) Find the wave function for the electric field in the wave. (b) Find the Poynting vector as a function of x and t. (c) Find the intensity of the wave. (d) **What If?** If the sheet is to emit radiation in each direction (normal to the plane of the sheet) with intensity 570 W/m², what maximum value of sinusoidal current density is required?

Section 34.6 The Spectrum of Electromagnetic Waves

38. Classify waves with frequencies of 2 Hz, 2 kHz, 2 MHz, 2 GHz, 2 THz, 2 PHz, 2 EHz, 2 ZHz, and 2 YHz on the electromagnetic spectrum. Classify waves with wavelengths of 2 km, 2 m, 2 mm, 2 μm, 2 nm, 2 pm, 2 fm, and 2 am.

39. The human eye is most sensitive to light having a wavelength of 5.50×10^{-7} m, which is in the green-yellow region of the visible electromagnetic spectrum. What is the frequency of this light?

40. Compute an order-of-magnitude estimate for the frequency of an electromagnetic wave with wavelength equal to (a) your height; (b) the thickness of this sheet of paper. How is each wave classified on the electromagnetic spectrum?

41. What are the wavelengths of electromagnetic waves in free space that have frequencies of (a) 5.00×10^{19} Hz and (b) 4.00×10^9 Hz?

42. Suppose you are located 180 m from a radio transmitter. (a) How many wavelengths are you from the transmitter if the station calls itself 1 150 AM? (The AM band frequencies are in kilohertz.) (b) **What If?** What if this station is 98.1 FM? (The FM band frequencies are in megahertz.)

43. A radar pulse returns to the receiver after a total travel time of 4.00×10^{-4} s. How far away is the object that reflected the wave?

44. *This just in!* An important news announcement is transmitted by radio waves to people sitting next to their radios 100 km from the station, and by sound waves to people sitting across the newsroom, 3.00 m from the newscaster. Who receives the news first? Explain. Take the speed of sound in air to be 343 m/s.

45. The United States Navy has long proposed the construction of extremely low-frequency (ELF) communication systems. Such waves could penetrate the oceans to reach distant submarines. Calculate the length of a quarter-

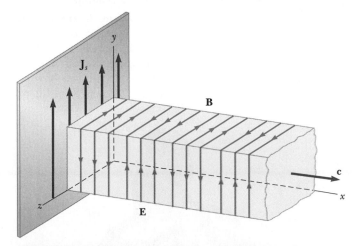

Figure P34.37 Representation of the plane electromagnetic wave radiated by an infinite current sheet lying in the yz plane. The vector **B** is in the z direction, the vector **E** is in the y direction, and the direction of wave motion is along x. Both vectors have magnitudes proportional to $\cos(kx - \omega t)$.

wavelength antenna for a transmitter generating ELF waves of frequency 75.0 Hz. How practical is this?

46. What are the wavelength ranges in (a) the AM radio band (540–1 600 kHz), and (b) the FM radio band (88.0–108 MHz)?

Additional Problems

47. Assume that the intensity of solar radiation incident on the cloudtops of the Earth is 1 340 W/m². (a) Calculate the total power radiated by the Sun, taking the average Earth–Sun separation to be 1.496×10^{11} m. (b) Determine the maximum values of the electric and magnetic fields in the sunlight at the Earth's location.

48. The intensity of solar radiation at the top of the Earth's atmosphere is 1 340 W/m². Assuming that 60% of the incoming solar energy reaches the Earth's surface and assuming that you absorb 50% of the incident energy, make an order-of-magnitude estimate of the amount of solar energy you absorb in a 60-min sunbath.

49. **Review problem.** In the absence of cable input or a satellite dish, a television set can use a dipole-receiving antenna for VHF channels and a loop antenna for UHF channels (Fig. Q34.12). The UHF antenna produces an emf from the changing magnetic flux through the loop. The TV station broadcasts a signal with a frequency f, and the signal has an electric-field amplitude E_{max} and a magnetic-field amplitude B_{max} at the location of the receiving antenna. (a) Using Faraday's law, derive an expression for the amplitude of the emf that appears in a single-turn circular loop antenna with a radius r, which is small compared with the wavelength of the wave. (b) If the electric field in the signal points vertically, what orientation of the loop gives the best reception?

50. Consider a small, spherical particle of radius r located in space a distance R from the Sun. (a) Show that the ratio F_{rad}/F_{grav} is proportional to $1/r$, where F_{rad} is the force exerted by solar radiation and F_{grav} is the force of gravitational attraction. (b) The result of part (a) means that, for a sufficiently small value of r, the force exerted on the particle by solar radiation exceeds the force of gravitational attraction. Calculate the value of r for which the particle is in equilibrium under the two forces. (Assume that the particle has a perfectly absorbing surface and a mass density of 1.50 g/cm³. Let the particle be located 3.75×10^{11} m from the Sun, and use 214 W/m² as the value of the solar intensity at that point.)

51. A dish antenna having a diameter of 20.0 m receives (at normal incidence) a radio signal from a distant source, as shown in Figure P34.51. The radio signal is a continuous sinusoidal wave with amplitude $E_{max} = 0.200 \ \mu\text{V/m}$. Assume the antenna absorbs all the radiation that falls on the dish. (a) What is the amplitude of the magnetic field in this wave? (b) What is the intensity of the radiation received by this antenna? (c) What is the power received by the antenna? (d) What force is exerted by the radio waves on the antenna?

Figure P34.51

52. One goal of the Russian space program is to illuminate dark northern cities with sunlight reflected to Earth from a 200-m diameter mirrored surface in orbit. Several smaller prototypes have already been constructed and put into orbit. (a) Assume that sunlight with intensity 1 340 W/m² falls on the mirror nearly perpendicularly and that the atmosphere of the Earth allows 74.6% of the energy of sunlight to pass through it in clear weather. What is the power received by a city when the space mirror is reflecting light to it? (b) The plan is for the reflected sunlight to cover a circle of diameter 8.00 km. What is the intensity of light (the average magnitude of the Poynting vector) received by the city? (c) This intensity is what percentage of the vertical component of sunlight at Saint Petersburg in January, when the sun reaches an angle of 7.00° above the horizon at noon?

53. In 1965, Arno Penzias and Robert Wilson discovered the cosmic microwave radiation left over from the Big Bang expansion of the Universe. Suppose the energy density of this background radiation is 4.00×10^{-14} J/m³. Determine the corresponding electric field amplitude.

54. A hand-held cellular telephone operates in the 860- to 900-MHz band and has a power output of 0.600 W from an antenna 10.0 cm long (Fig. P34.54). (a) Find the average magnitude of the Poynting vector 4.00 cm from the antenna, at the location of a typical person's

Amos Morgan/Getty Images

Figure P34.54

head. Assume that the antenna emits energy with cylindrical wave fronts. (The actual radiation from antennas follows a more complicated pattern.) (b) The ANSI/IEEE C95.1-1991 maximum exposure standard is 0.57 mW/cm^2 for persons living near cellular telephone base stations, who would be continuously exposed to the radiation. Compare the answer to part (a) with this standard.

55. A linearly polarized microwave of wavelength 1.50 cm is directed along the positive x axis. The electric field vector has a maximum value of 175 V/m and vibrates in the xy plane. (a) Assume that the magnetic field component of the wave can be written in the form $B = B_{\max} \sin(kx - \omega t)$ and give values for $B_{\max}$, k, and ω. Also, determine in which plane the magnetic field vector vibrates. (b) Calculate the average value of the Poynting vector for this wave. (c) What radiation pressure would this wave exert if it were directed at normal incidence onto a perfectly reflecting sheet? (d) What acceleration would be imparted to a 500-g sheet (perfectly reflecting and at normal incidence) with dimensions of 1.00 m × 0.750 m?

56. The Earth reflects approximately 38.0% of the incident sunlight from its clouds and surface. (a) Given that the intensity of solar radiation is 1 340 W/m^2, what is the radiation pressure on the Earth, in pascals, at the location where the Sun is straight overhead? (b) Compare this to normal atmospheric pressure at the Earth's surface, which is 101 kPa.

57. An astronaut, stranded in space 10.0 m from his spacecraft and at rest relative to it, has a mass (including equipment) of 110 kg. Because he has a 100-W light source that forms a directed beam, he considers using the beam as a photon rocket to propel himself continuously toward the spacecraft. (a) Calculate how long it takes him to reach the spacecraft by this method. (b) **What If?** Suppose, instead, that he decides to throw the light source away in a direction opposite the spacecraft. If the mass of the light source is 3.00 kg and, after being thrown, it moves at 12.0 m/s relative to the recoiling astronaut, how long does it take for the astronaut to reach the spacecraft?

58. **Review problem.** A 1.00-m-diameter mirror focuses the Sun's rays onto an absorbing plate 2.00 cm in radius, which holds a can containing 1.00 L of water at 20.0°C. (a) If the solar intensity is 1.00 kW/m^2, what is the intensity on the absorbing plate? (b) What are the maximum magnitudes of the fields **E** and **B**? (c) If 40.0% of the energy is absorbed, how long does it take to bring the water to its boiling point?

59. Lasers have been used to suspend spherical glass beads in the Earth's gravitational field. (a) A black bead has a mass of 1.00 μg and a density of 0.200 g/cm^3. Determine the radiation intensity needed to support the bead. (b) If the beam has a radius of 0.200 cm, what is the power required for this laser?

60. Lasers have been used to suspend spherical glass beads in the Earth's gravitational field. (a) A black bead has a mass

m and a density ρ. Determine the radiation intensity needed to support the bead. (b) If the beam has a radius r, what is the power required for this laser?

61. A microwave source produces pulses of 20.0-GHz radiation, with each pulse lasting 1.00 ns. A parabolic reflector with a face area of radius 6.00 cm is used to focus the microwaves into a parallel beam of radiation, as shown in Figure P34.61. The average power during each pulse is 25.0 kW. (a) What is the wavelength of these microwaves? (b) What is the total energy contained in each pulse? (c) Compute the average energy density inside each pulse. (d) Determine the amplitude of the electric and magnetic fields in these microwaves. (e) Assuming this pulsed beam strikes an absorbing surface, compute the force exerted on the surface during the 1.00-ns duration of each pulse.

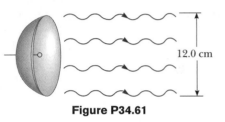

Figure P34.61

62. The electromagnetic power radiated by a nonrelativistic moving point charge q having an acceleration a is

$$\mathcal{P} = \frac{q^2 a^2}{6\pi\epsilon_0 c^3}$$

where ϵ_0 is the permittivity of free space and c is the speed of light in vacuum. (a) Show that the right side of this equation has units of watts. (b) An electron is placed in a constant electric field of magnitude 100 N/C. Determine the acceleration of the electron and the electromagnetic power radiated by this electron. (c) **What If?** If a proton is placed in a cyclotron with a radius of 0.500 m and a magnetic field of magnitude 0.350 T, what electromagnetic power does this proton radiate?

63. A thin tungsten filament of length 1.00 m radiates 60.0 W of power in the form of electromagnetic waves. A perfectly absorbing surface in the form of a hollow cylinder of radius 5.00 cm and length 1.00 m is placed concentrically with the filament. Calculate the radiation pressure acting on the cylinder. (Assume that the radiation is emitted in the radial direction, and ignore end effects.)

64. The torsion balance shown in Figure 34.8 is used in an experiment to measure radiation pressure. The suspension fiber exerts an elastic restoring torque. Its torque constant is 1.00×10^{-11} N·m/degree, and the length of the horizontal rod is 6.00 cm. The beam from a 3.00-mW helium–neon laser is incident on the black disk, and the mirror disk is completely shielded.

Calculate the angle between the equilibrium positions of the horizontal bar when the beam is switched from "off" to "on."

65. A "laser cannon" of a spacecraft has a beam of cross-sectional area A. The maximum electric field in the beam is E. The beam is aimed at an asteroid that is initially moving in the direction of the spacecraft. What is the acceleration of the asteroid relative to the spacecraft if the laser beam strikes the asteroid perpendicular to its surface, and the surface is nonreflecting? The mass of the asteroid is m. Ignore the acceleration of the spacecraft.

66. A plane electromagnetic wave varies sinusoidally at 90.0 MHz as it travels along the $+x$ direction. The peak value of the electric field is 2.00 mV/m, and it is directed along the $\pm y$ direction. (a) Find the wavelength, the period, and the maximum value of the magnetic field. (b) Write expressions in SI units for the space and time variations of the electric field and of the magnetic field. Include numerical values and include subscripts to indicate coordinate directions. (c) Find the average power per unit area that this wave carries through space. (d) Find the average energy density in the radiation (in joules per cubic meter). (e) What radiation pressure would this wave exert upon a perfectly reflecting surface at normal incidence?

Note: Section 20.7 introduced electromagnetic radiation as a mode of energy transfer. The following three problems use ideas introduced both there and in the current chapter.

67. Eliza is a black cat with four black kittens: Penelope, Rosalita, Sasha, and Timothy. Eliza's mass is 5.50 kg, and each kitten has mass 0.800 kg. One cool night all five sleep snuggled together on a mat, with their bodies forming one hemisphere. (a) Assuming that the purring heap has uniform density 990 kg/m³, find the radius of the hemisphere. (b) Find the area of its curved surface. (c) Assume the surface temperature is uniformly 31.0°C and the emissivity is 0.970. Find the intensity of radiation emitted by the cats at their curved surface, and (d) the radiated power from this surface. (e) You may think of the emitted electromagnetic wave as having a single predominant frequency (of 31.2 THz). Find the amplitude of the electric field just outside the surface of the cozy pile, and (f) the amplitude of the magnetic field. (g) Are the sleeping cats charged? Are they current-carrying? Are they magnetic? Are they a radiation source? Do they glow in the dark? Give an explanation for your answers so that they do not seem contradictory. (h) **What If?** The next night the kittens all sleep alone, curling up into separate hemispheres like their mother. Find the total radiated power of the family. (For simplicity, we ignore throughout the cats' absorption of radiation from the environment.)

68. **Review problem.** (a) An elderly couple has a solar water heater installed on the roof of their house (Fig. P34.68). The heater consists of a flat closed box with

Figure P34.68

extraordinarily good thermal insulation. Its interior is painted black, and its front face is made of insulating glass. Assume that its emissivity for visible light is 0.900 and its emissivity for infrared light is 0.700. Assume that light from the noon Sun is incident perpendicular to the glass with an intensity of 1 000 W/m², and that no water enters or leaves the box. Find the steady-state temperature of the interior of the box. (b) **What If?** The couple builds an identical box with no water tubes. It lies flat on the ground in front of the house. They use it as a cold frame, where they plant seeds in early spring. Assuming the same noon Sun is at an elevation angle of 50.0°, find the steady-state temperature of the interior of this box when its ventilation slots are tightly closed.

69. **Review problem.** The study of Creation suggests a Creator with an inordinate fondness for beetles and for small red stars. A small red star radiates electromagnetic waves with power 6.00×10^{23} W, which is only 0.159% of the luminosity of the Sun. Consider a spherical planet in a circular orbit around this star. Assume the emissivity of the planet is equal for infrared and for visible light. Assume the planet has a uniform surface temperature. Identify the projected area over which the planet absorbs starlight and the radiating area of the planet. If beetles thrive at a temperature of 310 K, what should be the radius of the planet's orbit?

Answers to Quick Quizzes

34.1 (c). Figure 34.3b shows that the **B** and **E** vectors reach their maximum and minimum values at the same time.

34.2 (c). The **B** field must be in the $+z$ direction in order that the Poynting vector be directed along the $-y$ direction.

34.3 (d). The first three choices are instantaneous values and vary in time. The wave intensity is an average over a full cycle.

34.4 (b). To maximize the pressure on the sails, they should be perfectly reflective, so that the pressure is given by Equation 34.27.

34.5 (b), (c). The radiation pressure (a) does not change because pressure is force per unit area. In (b), the smaller disk absorbs less radiation, resulting in a smaller force. For the same reason, the momentum in (c) is reduced.

34.6 (a), (b) = (c), (d). The closest point along the x axis in Figure 34.11 (choice a) will represent the highest intensity. Choices (b) and (c) correspond to points equidistant in different directions. Choice (d) is along the axis of the antenna and the intensity is zero.

34.7 (a). The best orientation is parallel to the transmitting antenna because that is the orientation of the electric field. The electric field moves electrons in the receiving antenna, thus inducing a current that is detected and amplified.

34.8 (c). Either Equation 34.13 or Figure 34.12 can be used to find the order of magnitude of the wavelengths.

34.9 (a). Either Equation 34.13 or Figure 34.12 can be used to find the order of magnitude of the wavelength.

Some Physical Constants[a]

Quantity	Symbol	Value[b]
Atomic mass unit	u	$1.660\ 538\ 73\ (13) \times 10^{-27}\,\mathrm{kg}$ $931.494\ 013\ (37)\ \mathrm{MeV}/c^2$
Avogadro's number	N_A	$6.022\ 141\ 99\ (47) \times 10^{23}\ \mathrm{particles/mol}$
Bohr magneton	$\mu_B = \dfrac{e\hbar}{2m_e}$	$9.274\ 008\ 99\ (37) \times 10^{-24}\,\mathrm{J/T}$
Bohr radius	$a_0 = \dfrac{\hbar^2}{m_e e^2 k_e}$	$5.291\ 772\ 083\ (19) \times 10^{-11}\,\mathrm{m}$
Boltzmann's constant	$k_B = \dfrac{R}{N_A}$	$1.380\ 650\ 3\ (24) \times 10^{-23}\,\mathrm{J/K}$
Compton wavelength	$\lambda_C = \dfrac{h}{m_e c}$	$2.426\ 310\ 215\ (18) \times 10^{-12}\,\mathrm{m}$
Coulomb constant	$k_e = \dfrac{1}{4\pi\epsilon_0}$	$8.987\ 551\ 788\ \ldots \times 10^9\ \mathrm{N\cdot m^2/C^2}$ (exact)
Deuteron mass	m_d	$3.343\ 583\ 09\ (26) \times 10^{-27}\,\mathrm{kg}$ $2.013\ 553\ 212\ 71\ (35)\ \mathrm{u}$
Electron mass	m_e	$9.109\ 381\ 88\ (72) \times 10^{-31}\,\mathrm{kg}$ $5.485\ 799\ 110\ (12) \times 10^{-4}\ \mathrm{u}$ $0.510\ 998\ 902\ (21)\ \mathrm{MeV}/c^2$
Electron volt	eV	$1.602\ 176\ 462\ (63) \times 10^{-19}\,\mathrm{J}$
Elementary charge	e	$1.602\ 176\ 462\ (63) \times 10^{-19}\,\mathrm{C}$
Gas constant	R	$8.314\ 472\ (15)\ \mathrm{J/K\cdot mol}$
Gravitational constant	G	$6.673\ (10) \times 10^{-11}\ \mathrm{N\cdot m^2/kg^2}$
Josephson frequency–voltage ratio	$\dfrac{2e}{h}$	$4.835\ 978\ 98\ (19) \times 10^{14}\ \mathrm{Hz/V}$
Magnetic flux quantum	$\Phi_0 = \dfrac{h}{2e}$	$2.067\ 833\ 636\ (81) \times 10^{-15}\ \mathrm{T\cdot m^2}$
Neutron mass	m_n	$1.674\ 927\ 16\ (13) \times 10^{-27}\,\mathrm{kg}$ $1.008\ 664\ 915\ 78\ (55)\ \mathrm{u}$ $939.565\ 330\ (38)\ \mathrm{MeV}/c^2$
Nuclear magneton	$\mu_n = \dfrac{e\hbar}{2m_p}$	$5.050\ 783\ 17\ (20) \times 10^{-27}\,\mathrm{J/T}$
Permeability of free space	μ_0	$4\pi \times 10^{-7}\ \mathrm{T\cdot m/A}$ (exact)
Permittivity of free space	$\epsilon_0 = \dfrac{1}{\mu_0 c^2}$	$8.854\ 187\ 817 \ldots \times 10^{-12}\ \mathrm{C^2/N\cdot m^2}$ (exact)
Planck's constant	h	$6.626\ 068\ 76\ (52) \times 10^{-34}\,\mathrm{J\cdot s}$
	$\hbar = \dfrac{h}{2\pi}$	$1.054\ 571\ 596\ (82) \times 10^{-34}\,\mathrm{J\cdot s}$
Proton mass	m_p	$1.672\ 621\ 58\ (13) \times 10^{-27}\,\mathrm{kg}$ $1.007\ 276\ 466\ 88\ (13)\ \mathrm{u}$ $938.271\ 998\ (38)\ \mathrm{MeV}/c^2$
Rydberg constant	R_H	$1.097\ 373\ 156\ 854\ 9\ (83) \times 10^7\ \mathrm{m^{-1}}$
Speed of light in vacuum	c	$2.997\ 924\ 58 \times 10^8\ \mathrm{m/s}$ (exact)

[a] These constants are the values recommended in 1998 by CODATA, based on a least-squares adjustment of data from different measurements. For a more complete list, see P. J. Mohr and B. N. Taylor, *Rev. Mod. Phys.* 72:351, 2000.

[b] The numbers in parentheses for the values above represent the uncertainties of the last two digits.

Solar System Data

Body	Mass (kg)	Mean Radius (m)	Period (s)	Distance from the Sun (m)
Mercury	3.18×10^{23}	2.43×10^6	7.60×10^6	5.79×10^{10}
Venus	4.88×10^{24}	6.06×10^6	1.94×10^7	1.08×10^{11}
Earth	5.98×10^{24}	6.37×10^6	3.156×10^7	1.496×10^{11}
Mars	6.42×10^{23}	3.37×10^6	5.94×10^7	2.28×10^{11}
Jupiter	1.90×10^{27}	6.99×10^7	3.74×10^8	7.78×10^{11}
Saturn	5.68×10^{26}	5.85×10^7	9.35×10^8	1.43×10^{12}
Uranus	8.68×10^{25}	2.33×10^7	2.64×10^9	2.87×10^{12}
Neptune	1.03×10^{26}	2.21×10^7	5.22×10^9	4.50×10^{12}
Pluto	$\approx 1.4 \times 10^{22}$	$\approx 1.5 \times 10^6$	7.82×10^9	5.91×10^{12}
Moon	7.36×10^{22}	1.74×10^6	—	—
Sun	1.991×10^{30}	6.96×10^8	—	—

Physical Data Often Used[a]

Average Earth–Moon distance	3.84×10^8 m
Average Earth–Sun distance	1.496×10^{11} m
Average radius of the Earth	6.37×10^6 m
Density of air (20°C and 1 atm)	1.20 kg/m^3
Density of water (20°C and 1 atm)	1.00×10^3 kg/m^3
Free-fall acceleration	9.80 m/s^2
Mass of the Earth	5.98×10^{24} kg
Mass of the Moon	7.36×10^{22} kg
Mass of the Sun	1.99×10^{30} kg
Standard atmospheric pressure	1.013×10^5 Pa

[a] These are the values of the constants as used in the text.

Some Prefixes for Powers of Ten

Power	Prefix	Abbreviation	Power	Prefix	Abbreviation
10^{-24}	yocto	y	10^1	deka	da
10^{-21}	zepto	z	10^2	hecto	h
10^{-18}	atto	a	10^3	kilo	k
10^{-15}	femto	f	10^6	mega	M
10^{-12}	pico	p	10^9	giga	G
10^{-9}	nano	n	10^{12}	tera	T
10^{-6}	micro	μ	10^{15}	peta	P
10^{-3}	milli	m	10^{18}	exa	E
10^{-2}	centi	c	10^{21}	zetta	Z
10^{-1}	deci	d	10^{24}	yotta	Y

Standard Abbreviations and Symbols for Units

Symbol	Unit	Symbol	Unit
A	ampere	K	kelvin
u	atomic mass unit	kg	kilogram
atm	atmosphere	kmol	kilomole
Btu	British thermal unit	L	liter
C	coulomb	lb	pound
°C	degree Celsius	ly	lightyear
cal	calorie	m	meter
d	day	min	minute
eV	electron volt	mol	mole
°F	degree Fahrenheit	N	newton
F	farad	Pa	pascal
ft	foot	rad	radian
G	gauss	rev	revolution
g	gram	s	second
H	henry	T	tesla
h	hour	V	volt
hp	horsepower	W	watt
Hz	hertz	Wb	weber
in.	inch	yr	year
J	joule	Ω	ohm

Mathematical Symbols Used in the Text and Their Meaning

Symbol	Meaning
$=$	is equal to
$\equiv$	is defined as
$\neq$	is not equal to
$\propto$	is proportional to
$\sim$	is on the order of
$>$	is greater than
$<$	is less than
$\gg (\ll)$	is much greater (less) than
$\approx$	is approximately equal to
Δx	the change in x
$\sum_{i=1}^{N} x_i$	the sum of all quantities x_i from $i = 1$ to $i = N$
$\lvert x \rvert$	the magnitude of x (always a nonnegative quantity)
$\Delta x \rightarrow 0$	Δx approaches zero
$\dfrac{dx}{dt}$	the derivative of x with respect to t
$\dfrac{\partial x}{\partial t}$	the partial derivative of x with respect to t
$\displaystyle\int$	integral

Conversions[a]

Length

1 in. = 2.54 cm (exact)

1 m = 39.37 in. = 3.281 ft

1 ft = 0.304 8 m

12 in. = 1 ft

3 ft = 1 yd

1 yd = 0.914 4 m

1 km = 0.621 mi

1 mi = 1.609 km

1 mi = 5 280 ft

$1\ \mu\text{m} = 10^{-6}\ \text{m} = 10^{3}\ \text{nm}$

$1\ \text{lightyear} = 9.461 \times 10^{15}\ \text{m}$

Area

$1\ \text{m}^2 = 10^4\ \text{cm}^2 = 10.76\ \text{ft}^2$

$1\ \text{ft}^2 = 0.092\ 9\ \text{m}^2 = 144\ \text{in.}^2$

$1\ \text{in.}^2 = 6.452\ \text{cm}^2$

Volume

$1\ \text{m}^3 = 10^6\ \text{cm}^3 = 6.102 \times 10^4\ \text{in.}^3$

$1\ \text{ft}^3 = 1\ 728\ \text{in.}^3 = 2.83 \times 10^{-2}\ \text{m}^3$

$1\ \text{L} = 1\ 000\ \text{cm}^3 = 1.057\ 6\ \text{qt} = 0.035\ 3\ \text{ft}^3$

$1\ \text{ft}^3 = 7.481\ \text{gal} = 28.32\ \text{L} = 2.832 \times 10^{-2}\ \text{m}^3$

$1\ \text{gal} = 3.786\ \text{L} = 231\ \text{in.}^3$

Mass

1 000 kg = 1 t (metric ton)

1 slug = 14.59 kg

$1\ \text{u} = 1.66 \times 10^{-27}\ \text{kg} = 931.5\ \text{MeV}/c^2$

Some Approximations Useful for Estimation Problems

1 m ≈ 1 yd

1 kg ≈ 2 lb

$1\ \text{N} \approx \frac{1}{4}\ \text{lb}$

$1\ \text{L} \approx \frac{1}{4}\ \text{gal}$

Force

1 N = 0.224 8 lb

1 lb = 4.448 N

Velocity

1 mi/h = 1.47 ft/s = 0.447 m/s = 1.61 km/h

1 m/s = 100 cm/s = 3.281 ft/s

1 mi/min = 60 mi/h = 88 ft/s

Acceleration

$1\ \text{m/s}^2 = 3.28\ \text{ft/s}^2 = 100\ \text{cm/s}^2$

$1\ \text{ft/s}^2 = 0.304\ 8\ \text{m/s}^2 = 30.48\ \text{cm/s}^2$

Pressure

$1\ \text{bar} = 10^5\ \text{N/m}^2 = 14.50\ \text{lb/in.}^2$

1 atm = 760 mm Hg = 76.0 cm Hg

$1\ \text{atm} = 14.7\ \text{lb/in.}^2 = 1.013 \times 10^5\ \text{N/m}^2$

$1\ \text{Pa} = 1\ \text{N/m}^2 = 1.45 \times 10^{-4}\ \text{lb/in.}^2$

Time

$1\ \text{yr} = 365\ \text{days} = 3.16 \times 10^7\ \text{s}$

$1\ \text{day} = 24\ \text{h} = 1.44 \times 10^3\ \text{min} = 8.64 \times 10^4\ \text{s}$

Energy

1 J = 0.738 ft·lb

1 cal = 4.186 J

$1\ \text{Btu} = 252\ \text{cal} = 1.054 \times 10^3\ \text{J}$

$1\ \text{eV} = 1.6 \times 10^{-19}\ \text{J}$

$1\ \text{kWh} = 3.60 \times 10^6\ \text{J}$

Power

1 hp = 550 ft·lb/s = 0.746 kW

1 W = 1 J/s = 0.738 ft·lb/s

1 Btu/h = 0.293 W

1 m/s ≈ 2 mi/h

$1\ \text{yr} \approx \pi \times 10^7\ \text{s}$

60 mi/h ≈ 100 ft/s

$1\ \text{km} \approx \frac{1}{2}\ \text{mi}$

[a] See Table A.1 of Appendix A for a more complete list.

The Greek Alphabet

Alpha	A	α	Iota	I	ι	Rho	P	ρ
Beta	B	β	Kappa	K	κ	Sigma	Σ	σ
Gamma	Γ	γ	Lambda	Λ	λ	Tau	T	τ
Delta	Δ	δ	Mu	M	μ	Upsilon	Y	υ
Epsilon	E	ϵ	Nu	N	ν	Phi	Φ	ϕ
Zeta	Z	ζ	Xi	Ξ	ξ	Chi	X	χ
Eta	H	η	Omicron	O	o	Psi	Ψ	ψ
Theta	Θ	θ	Pi	Π	π	Omega	Ω	ω

About the cover

It takes a vast amount of energy, as illustrated by the bow wave, to move this ship through the water. This ship, as indicated by the white symbol just above the red area, has a bulbous bow that extends beneath the water. Bulbous bows have been used on ships since the 1950's and have been found to reduce the fuel requirements for traveling through water at typical cruising speeds by up to 25%. While there is still debate over the exact principles upon which the bulbous bow depends, the theoretical explanations involve physical concepts that are discussed in this textbook.

Accompanied by FREE learning resources!

PhysicsNow

This Web-based collection of dynamic technology resources assesses your unique study needs, giving you a personalized learning plan that will enhance your conceptual and computational skills. **PhysicsNow** helps you succeed by focusing your study time on the concepts you need to master to maximize your time investment. As you work through text chapters you'll see notes in the margins that direct you to the media-enhanced activities on **PhysicsNow**. And best of all, you can easily access **PhysicsNow** by using the FREE PIN CODE packaged with this text! Log on to **www.pse6.com** now!

Physics for Scientists and Engineers, Sixth Edition
Companion Web Site www.pse6.com

The text-specific Companion Web Site offers a wealth of chapter-by-chapter learning tools. For each chapter of the text you will find objectives, an outline, a summary, **InfoTrac® College Edition** exercises, Internet exercises, practice problems, a tutorial quiz, and Web links. Through this site, you will also gain access to **PhysicsNow**'s diverse range of resources.

InfoTrac® College Edition

When you purchase a new copy of **Physics for Scientists and Engineers, Sixth Edition**, you automatically receive a FREE four-month subscription to **InfoTrac College Edition**! This extensive online library opens the door to the full text (not just abstracts) of countless articles from thousands of publications including *American Scientist, Physics Review, Science, Science Weekly*, and more! *Journals subject to change.*

Also available to enhance your study sessions:

Student Solutions Manual with Study Guide
Volume I: 0-534-40855-9 (Volume 1-22) • Volume II: 0-534-40856-7 (Volume 23-46)
by John R. Gordon, Ralph McGrew, and Raymond Serway. This two-volume manual features detailed solutions to 20% of the end-of-chapter problems from the text. The manual also features a list of important equations, concepts, and answers to selected end-of-chapter questions.

THOMSON
BROOKS/COLE

Visit Brooks/Cole online at **www.brookscole.com**

For your learning solutions: **www.thomsonlearning.com**

ISBN 0-534-40850-8

9 780534 408503